Horizons

Pre-Algebra
Teachers Guide

Author:

Shelly Chittam, M.S.

Managing Editor:

Alan Christopherson, M.S.

Editors:

Laura Messner, B.A.
Rachelle Wiersma, M.A.

Graphic Design & Illustration:

Ron A. Hartmann, B.A.

Alpha Omega Publications, Inc. • Rock Rapids, IA

©MMX by Alpha Omega Publications, Inc.®

804 N. 2nd Ave. E.

Rock Rapids, IA 51246-1759

Printed in the United States of America

ISBN 978-0-7403-2243-3

Pre-Algebra

Teachers Guide

Contents

Course Introduction

Purpose

This pre-algebra course has a two-fold purpose. First, students have a thorough review of math concepts taught in elementary school that are vital for success in upper-level math courses. These concepts include basic math operations with whole numbers, decimals, fractions, percents, roots, and exponents. Emphasis is placed on practical application of the concepts.

The second purpose of the course is to introduce the students to concepts of algebra, trigonometry, and geometry in preparation for upper-level math courses. After completing this course of study, students should be well prepared for a high school level course in Algebra I.

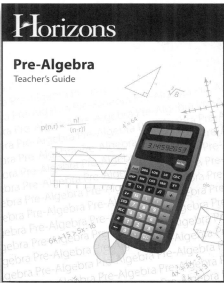

Materials

Materials available for this course include the Teacher's Guide, the Student Book, and the Tests and Resources Book. The students will have to supply notebook paper, as well as a scientific calculator, colored pencils, a ruler, and graph paper. Often the Student Workbook will not have sufficient space for working out all of the steps to the problems. Notebook paper should be used for these situations. Graph paper should have no more than five squares per inch, although quad-rule paper is recommended. The Student Workbook and the Tests and Resources Book were designed to be consumables. Both have perforated pages for easy tear out but it is recommended that the Student Workbook remain intact to serve as a resource when students wish to review previously covered concepts.

Horizons Pre-Algebra, Teacher's Guide

Layout

Each Lesson in the Student Text has a teaching box in the upper left side of the first page and a Classwork section in the upper right side of the first page. The teaching box is intended for use by both the teacher and the students as an aid to understanding the lesson. New concepts are presented here in detail so students who miss a lesson in class should be able to catch up any missed work with minimal outside help. The Classwork section is intended for the class to do together, with individual students explaining the problems for the class.

Teaching Box — 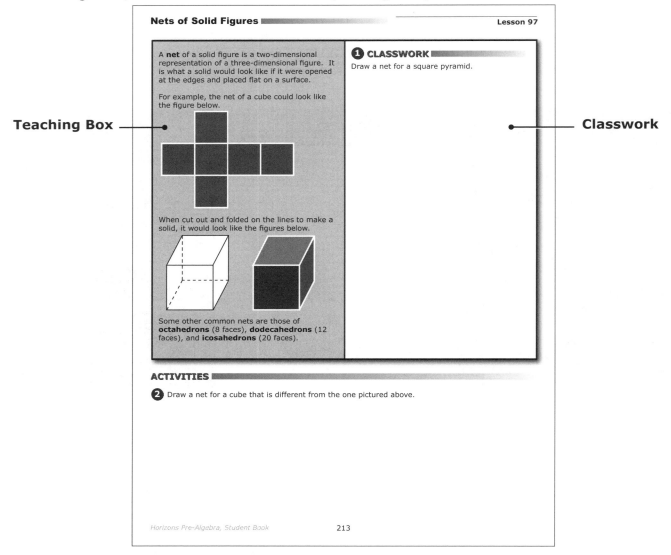 — **Classwork**

Layout continued:

Following the Classwork section is the Activities section. The first problem set in each Activities section is for reinforcement of the concept taught in that lesson. The remaining Activities sections are for review of previously taught concepts. The Activities sections are part of the assignment for each lesson.

Activities ———•

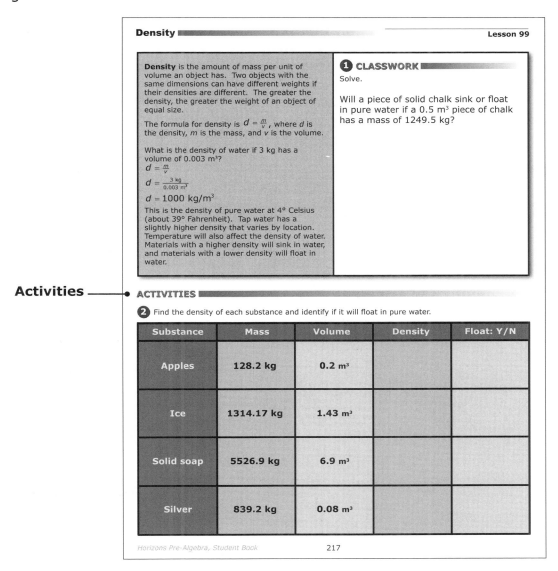

Density Lesson 99

Density is the amount of mass per unit of volume an object has. Two objects with the same dimensions can have different weights if their densities are different. The greater the density, the greater the weight of an object of equal size.

The formula for density is $d = \frac{m}{v}$, where d is the density, m is the mass, and v is the volume.

What is the density of water if 3 kg has a volume of 0.003 m³?
$d = \frac{m}{v}$
$d = \frac{3 \text{ kg}}{0.003 \text{ m}^3}$
$d = 1000$ kg/m³

This is the density of pure water at 4° Celsius (about 39° Fahrenheit). Tap water has a slightly higher density that varies by location. Temperature will also affect the density of water. Materials with a higher density will sink in water, and materials with a lower density will float in water.

❶ CLASSWORK
Solve.

Will a piece of solid chalk sink or float in pure water if a 0.5 m³ piece of chalk has a mass of 1249.5 kg?

ACTIVITIES

❷ Find the density of each substance and identify if it will float in pure water.

Substance	Mass	Volume	Density	Float: Y/N
Apples	128.2 kg	0.2 m³		
Ice	1314.17 kg	1.43 m³		
Solid soap	5526.9 kg	6.9 m³		
Silver	839.2 kg	0.08 m³		

Horizons Pre-Algebra, Student Book   217

Lesson Plans

Each Lesson Plan lists all concepts taught and reviewed for that individual lesson. The Learning Objectives always relate to the new material taught in that lesson. Each Lesson Plan contains Teaching Tips to aid the teacher in presenting the new material. As often as possible, new material is introduced following a review of related, previously-taught material. The Lesson Plans give detailed helps for the teacher, including sample problems, illustrations, and visual aids. The solution keys for the student activities are also part of each lesson plan.

Concepts ———

Learning Objectives ———

Materials Needed ———

Teaching Tips ———

Solution Keys ———

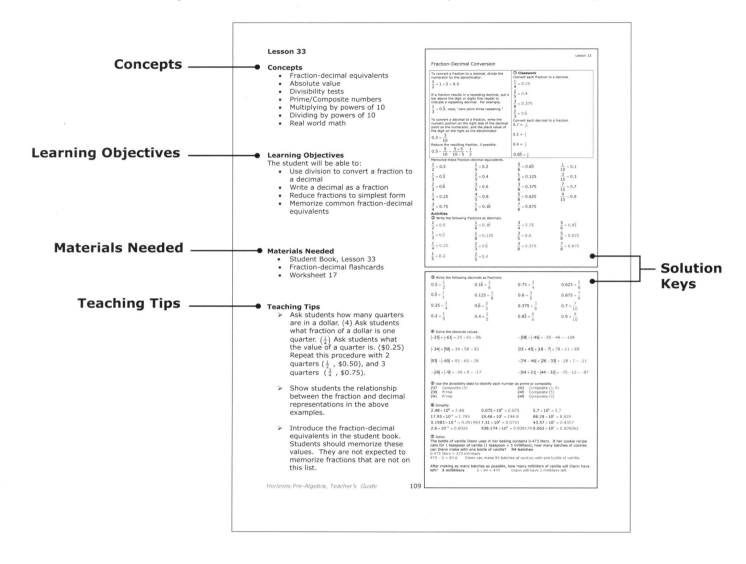

Lesson Plans continued:

Some Lesson Plans will include a Worksheet. These are found in the Tests and Resources Book. Some Worksheets are for additional practice of a new concept while others are for review or a quiz grade. The Lesson Plan will indicate which case applies for each Worksheet. Those intended for additional practice will appear in the Assignments section at the end of the Lesson Plan.

Worksheet
(In *Tests & Resources*)

Worksheet Solution
(In *Teacher's Guide*)

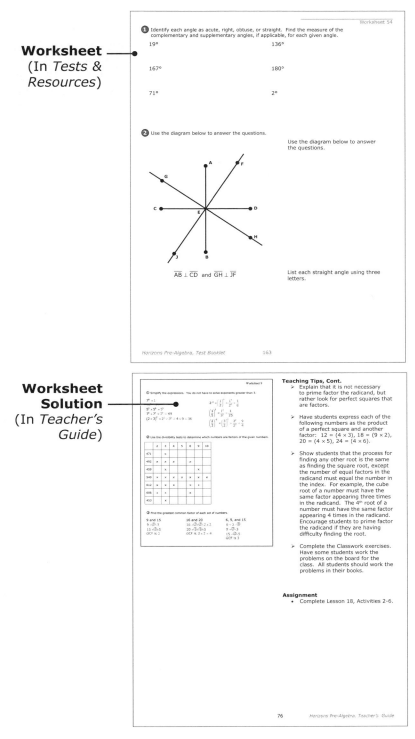

Learning Styles

Students learn in different ways. Some students can master a concept by listening to instructions or watching someone else do it while others are very "hand-on" and must physically do something to learn a new concept. This book addresses the various learning styles by using a lecture-demonstration method to teach new concepts and review old concepts, and manipulatives are used where appropriate to aid in the understanding of new concepts.

Algebra Tiles

Algebra tiles are located in the Tests and Resources Book. Students should cut these out the first time the Lesson Plan calls for them, and store them in a zip-top bag for future use. These manipulatives will assist both visual and kinesthetic learners in mastering algebraic concepts. Details on their use are given in the Lesson Plans where needed.

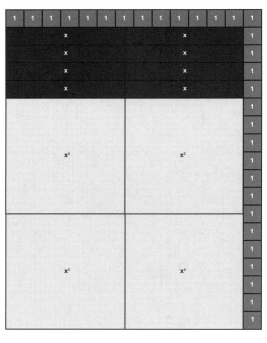

A Math Minute with . . .

At the beginning of each set of 10 lessons the students will read an interview from a Christian who is using pre-algebra in his or her daily life. The word problems that appear in the section will be based on the career of the individual that has been interviewed. Each of the 16 sections of material in this course utilizes a different individual and career. None of these people were college math majors and some of them have successful careers without earning a college degree.

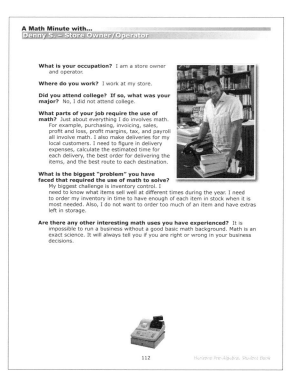

College Test Prep

As your students progress through their high school years, they will take a number of standardized tests that measure their skills in math, grammar, writing, vocabulary, and reading comprehension. Most colleges use the scores on these tests to determine whether or not to grant students admission to their colleges. Many scholarships are also based on the test scores, so it is important that students do as well as they can.

At the close of each set of 10 lessons, the students will be given a section of multiple choice questions. These questions are the same style and format as questions that are likely to appear on the math sections of standardized tests. They are also the same difficulty level as the pre-algebra questions that appear on the tests.

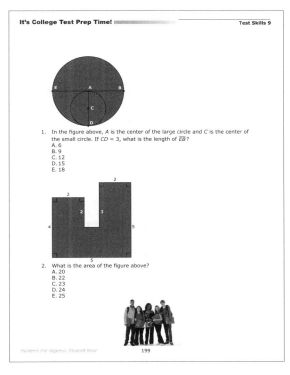

Evaluation

This course has 16 tests, 4 exams, and 80 worksheets. One test follows each set of 10 lessons, and one exam follows every 40 lessons. Exam 4 is also a final exam. You have the option of administering the first two pages as a fourth quarter exam, or all six pages as a cumulative final exam. Many of the worksheets are used as quizzes at the teacher's discretion. Worksheets that are appropriate for quizzes are identified in the corresponding Lesson Plans.

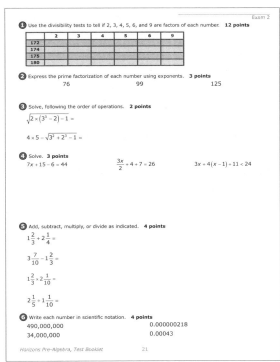

Readiness Evaluation

Why Evaluate Readiness?

Teaching could be defined as the process of starting with what a student knows and guiding him to added knowledge with new material. While this may not be a dictionary definition of teaching, it is descriptive of the processes involved. Determining a student's readiness for Pre-Algebra is the first step to successful teaching.

Types of Readiness

True readiness has little to do with chronological age. Emotional maturity and mental preparation are the main components of academic readiness. The teacher who is dealing directly with the student is best able to determine a child's emotional maturity. All emotionally immature students may need special student training in their problem areas. A child's mental *preparation* can be more easily discerned with a simple diagnostic evaluation. Observing the child's attitude of confidence or insecurity while taking the evaluation may help determine emotional readiness.

Determining Readiness

The pre-algebra *Readiness Evaluation* on the following pages helps the teacher to determine if student(s) are ready to begin studying math at the pre-algebra level. Complete this evaluation the first or second day of school.

The evaluation should take 45-60 minutes. It would be helpful to evaluate all of the students to determine what each student knows. However, you may want to evaluate only those student(s) who you sense have not had a thorough preparation for this course. It is especially important to evaluate any student who is using this curriculum for the first time. The student(s) should be able to complete the test on their own with the teacher making sure they understand the directions for each individual activity.

The answer key follows the test. Count each individual answer as a separate point. The total for the test is 61 points. The student(s) should achieve a score of 43 or more points to be ready to begin pre-algebra. Be sure to note the areas of weakness of each student, even those who have scored over 43 points. If the student(s) scored under 43 points, they may need to repeat a previous math level or do some refresher work in their areas of weakness. For possible review of the identified areas of weakness, refer to the chart *Appearance of Concepts* in the *Horizons Math 6 Teacher's Guide*. It will locate lessons where the concepts were taught.

Horizons Pre-Algebra Readiness Evaluation

① Solve. **20 Points**

49319 +72165	62145 +14906	87881 +98373	19.67 +65.34	457.09 +256.8

28473 −10662	67294 −34154	86476 −75093	39.974 −16.237	567.23 −92.3745

233 ×92	437 ×65	812 ×96	7.3 ×6.1	7.8 ×.66

$96\overline{)768}$ $47\overline{)423}$ $66\overline{)264}$ $.15\overline{)1.35}$ $.16\overline{)20.8}$

② Estimate the sum by rounding to the nearest thousand. **4 Points**

2903 +1102 ≈   7987 +2019 ≈   4176 +8885 ≈   3997 +4009 ≈

③ Estimate each product by rounding to the nearest ten. **4 Points**

21 x 128 ≈
67 x 32 ≈
58 x 61 ≈
52 x 48 ≈

④ Find all of the factors for each of the following numbers. **4 Points**

12   18

15   21

⑤ Identify each number as prime or composite. **9 Points**

2	5	13
3	7	15
4	11	19

⑥ Solve. **6 Points**

$x + 6 + 5 = 18$ $\qquad$ $x + 3x + 3 + 7 = 26$ $\qquad$ $2x + 3x + 6 - 1 = 20$

$3x + x - 9 + 4 = 31$ $\qquad$ $5x - 2x + 11 - 4 - 1 = 24$ $\qquad$ $6x + 2x - x - 8 - 4 + 1 = 38$

⑦ Add, subtract, multiply, or divide as indicated. **8 Points**

$\dfrac{1}{7} + \dfrac{4}{7} =$ $\qquad\qquad\qquad\qquad$ $\dfrac{2}{5} \times \dfrac{1}{5} =$

$\dfrac{1}{3} + \dfrac{1}{6} =$ $\qquad\qquad\qquad\qquad$ $\dfrac{5}{8} \times \dfrac{4}{5} =$

$\dfrac{4}{5} - \dfrac{3}{5} =$ $\qquad\qquad\qquad\qquad$ $\dfrac{3}{8} \div \dfrac{1}{8} =$

$\dfrac{9}{10} - \dfrac{3}{4} =$ $\qquad\qquad\qquad\qquad$ $\dfrac{5}{8} \div \dfrac{3}{4} =$

⑧ Solve. **2 Points**

What is 45% of 80? $\qquad\qquad\qquad$ What is 0.36% of 600?

⑨ Identify each shape. **4 Points**

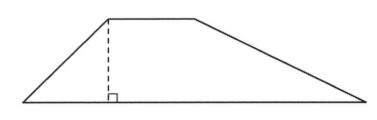

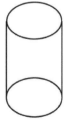

_____

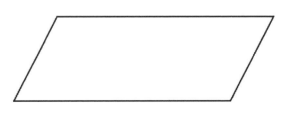

_____ _____61 points total

① Solve.   **20 Points**

49319	62145	87881	19.67	457.09
+72165	+14906	+98373	+65.34	+256.8
121,484	77,051	186,254	85.01	713.89

28473	67294	86476	39.974	567.23
−10662	−34154	−75093	−16.237	−92.3745
17,811	33,140	11,383	23.737	474.8555

233	437	812	7.3	7.8
×92	×65	×96	×6.1	×.66
466	2185	4872	73	468
+20970	+26220	+73080	+4380	+4680
21,436	28,405	77,952	44.53	5.148

$$96\overline{)768} = 8$$
768
000

$$47\overline{)423} = 9$$
423
000

$$66\overline{)264} = 4$$
264
000

$$.15\overline{)1.35} = 9$$
135

$$.16\overline{)20.80} = 130$$
16
48
48

② Estimate the sum by rounding to the nearest thousand.   **4 Points**

2903	≈	3000	7987	≈	8000	4176	≈	4000	3997	≈	4000
+1102		+1000	+2019		+2000	+8885		+9000	+4009		+4000
		4,000			10,000			13,000			8,000

③ Estimate each product by rounding to the nearest ten.   **4 Points**

21 x 128 ≈ 20 x 130 = 2,600
67 x 32 ≈ 70 x 30 = 2,100
58 x 61 ≈ 60 x 60 = 3,600
52 x 48 ≈ 50 x 50 = 2,500

④ Find all of the factors for each of the following numbers.   **4 Points**

12	1, 2, 3, 4, 6, 12		18	1, 2, 3, 6, 9, 18
15	1, 3, 5, 15		21	1, 3, 7, 21

⑤ Identify each number as prime or composite.   **9 Points**

2	Prime	5	Prime	13	Prime
3	Prime	7	Prime	15	Composite
4	Composite	11	Prime	19	Prime

⑥ Solve.

6 Points

$$x + 6 + 5 = 18$$
$$x + 11 = 18$$
$$x = 7$$

$$x + 3x + 3 + 7 = 26$$
$$4x + 10 = 26$$
$$4x = 16$$
$$x = 4$$

$$2x + 3x + 6 - 1 = 20$$
$$5x + 5 = 20$$
$$5x = 15$$
$$x = 3$$

$$3x + x - 9 + 4 = 31$$
$$4x - 5 = 31$$
$$4x = 36$$
$$x = 9$$

$$5x - 2x + 11 - 4 - 1 = 24$$
$$3x + 6 = 24$$
$$3x = 18$$
$$x = 6$$

$$6x + 2x - x - 8 - 4 + 1 = 38$$
$$7x - 11 = 38$$
$$7x = 49$$
$$x = 7$$

⑦ Add, subtract, multiply, or divide as indicated.

8 Points

$$\frac{1}{7} + \frac{4}{7} = \frac{1+4}{7} = \frac{5}{7}$$

$$\frac{1}{3} + \frac{1}{6} = \frac{1 \times 2}{3 \times 2} + \frac{1}{6} = \frac{2}{6} + \frac{1}{6} = \frac{3}{6} = \frac{1}{2}$$

$$\frac{4}{5} - \frac{3}{5} = \frac{4-3}{5} = \frac{1}{5}$$

$$\frac{9}{10} - \frac{3}{4} = \frac{9 \times 2}{10 \times 2} - \frac{3 \times 5}{4 \times 5} = \frac{18}{20} - \frac{15}{20} = \frac{3}{20}$$

$$\frac{2}{5} \times \frac{1}{5} = \frac{2 \times 1}{5 \times 5} = \frac{2}{25}$$

$$\frac{\overset{1}{\cancel{5}}}{\underset{2}{\cancel{8}}} \times \frac{\overset{1}{\cancel{4}}}{\underset{1}{\cancel{5}}} = \frac{1}{2}$$

$$\frac{3}{8} \div \frac{1}{8} = \frac{3}{\underset{1}{\cancel{8}}} \times \frac{\overset{1}{\cancel{8}}}{1} = \frac{3}{1} = 3$$

$$\frac{5}{8} \div \frac{3}{4} = \frac{5}{\underset{2}{\cancel{8}}} \times \frac{\overset{1}{\cancel{4}}}{3} = \frac{5 \times 1}{2 \times 3} = \frac{5}{6}$$

⑧ Solve.

2 Points

What is 45% of 80?

$$x = 0.45(80)$$

$$x = 36$$

What is 0.36% of 600?

$$x = 0.0036(600)$$

$$x = 2.16$$

⑨ Identify each shape.

4 Points

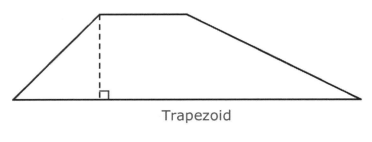

Trapezoid

Parallelogram

Cylinder

Pyramid

61 points total

Preparing a Lesson

GENERAL INFORMATION

There is some room on the teacher lessons for you to write your own notes. The more you personalize your teacher's guide in this way, the more useful it will be to you. You will notice that there are 160 student lessons in the curriculum. This allows for the inevitable interruptions to the school year like holidays, test days, inclement weather days, and those unexpected interruptions. It also allows the teacher the opportunity to spend more time teaching any concept that the student(s) may have difficulty with. Or, you might wish to spend a day doing some of the fun activities mentioned in the Teaching Tips. If you find that the student(s) need extra drill, use the worksheets.

STUDENT'S LESSONS
Organization

The lessons are designed to be completed in forty-five to sixty minutes a day. If extra manipulatives or worksheets are utilized, you will need to allow more time for teaching. Each lesson consists of a major concept and practice of previously taught concepts. If the student(s) find the presence of four or five different activities in one lesson a little overwhelming at the beginning, start guiding the student(s) through each activity. By the end of two weeks, they should be able to work more independently as they adjust to the format. Mastery of a new concept is not necessary the first time it is presented. Complete understanding of a new concept will come as the concept is approached from different views using different methods at different intervals.

Tests

Tests are in the *Tests and Resources* book. The test structure is such that the student(s) will have had sufficient practice with a concept to have learned it before being tested. Therefore, no concept is tested until the initial presentation has been completed. For example, Test 2 covers concepts completed in Lessons 8-17. Lessons 18-20 may include the introduction of some new material which will not be covered in Test 2. The Lesson Plans state which Lessons are covered on each Test in the Assignment section of every tenth Lesson. Tests may be administered after every tenth lesson as a separate class day or as part of the following lesson. For example, Test 1 may be administered at the beginning of the class period for Lesson 11 or as a separate day if you wish to give students the entire class period to complete the test. Lessons 149-160 are review for Exam 4 with no new material introduced, so you have the option of combining review lessons to allow enough days in the school year to complete the full curriculum and still allow a full class period for tests. There are a total of 180 Lessons, Tests, and Exams.

TEACHER'S LESSONS
Organization

Each lesson is organized into the following sections: **Concepts**, **Learning Objectives**, **Materials Needed**, and **Teaching Tips**. To be a master teacher you will need to prepare each lesson well in advance.

Concepts

Concepts are listed at the beginning of each lesson. New concepts are listed first followed by concepts that are practiced from previous lessons. The concepts are developed in a progression that is designed to give the student(s) a solid foundation in the math skills while providing enough variety to hold the student's interest.

Learning Objectives

The Learning Objectives list criteria for the student's performance. They state what the student should be able to do at the completion of the lesson. You will find objectives helpful in determining the student's progress, the need for remedial work, and readiness for more advanced information. Objectives are stated in terms of measurable student performance. The teacher then has a fixed level of performance to be attained before the student(s) are ready to progress to the next level.

Materials Needed

Materials Needed lists the things you'll need to find before you teach each lesson. Sometimes you will also find instructions on how to make your own materials. This section also lists the worksheets. There is approximately one worksheet for every two lessons. If worksheets are suggested in a particular lesson you will find them listed. Each worksheet has a worksheet number. The *Teacher's Guide* identifies where these resource worksheets are essential to the lessons. The worksheets will be handy for many purposes. You might use them for extra work for student(s) who demonstrate extra aptitude or ability or as remedial work for the student(s) who demonstrate a lack of aptitude or ability. You may also make your own worksheets and note where you would use them in the materials section on the teacher's lesson.

Teaching Tips

The teaching tips are related to the Activities in the lesson. Some Teaching Tips require the teacher to make a manipulative needed to complete the activity. Teaching Tips are activities that the teacher can do to enhance the teaching process. You will find them useful for helping the student who needs additional practice to master the concepts or for the student who needs to be challenged by extra work.

In the Teaching Tips the teacher will find directions for teaching each lesson. All activities are designed to be teacher directed both in the student lesson and in the teacher's guide. You will need to use your own judgment concerning how much time is necessary to carry out the activities. Each activity is important to the overall scope of the lesson and must be completed.

Please do not put off looking at the activities in the lesson until you are actually teaching. Taking time to preview what you will be teaching is essential. Choose the manipulatives that fit your program best.

Each lesson in the Student Book starts with a **Teaching Box** that discusses the new material being introduced in the lesson. Sample problems are often included in this section. Some students will be able to read and comprehend the information on their own. Other students need to be guided through this section for complete understanding. Next to the Teaching Box is the **Classwork** section. The Classwork section gives the student(s) an opportunity to perform guided practice on the new concept. Following the Teaching Box and Classwork of each lesson are the numbered **Activities** problems for the lesson. Number 2 of the **Activities** section always applies the skills learned in the Teaching Box. The remaining activities review previously taught concepts.

ANSWER KEYS

The reduced page answer keys in the *Teacher's Guide* provide solutions to the activities. It is suggested that you give the student(s) a grade for tests and quizzes only. Daily work is to be a learning experience for the student, so do not put unnecessary pressure on them. You should correct every paper. At the beginning of each class period, the teacher should quickly check for completion of each student paper, without checking each problem for accuracy. The teacher may then either give the answers to the Activities, or have individual students work the problems on the board. Students should check their own papers and make corrections as needed. It is important to allow students the opportunity to ask questions about the previous day's assignment. This will save much time over the teacher grading all of the homework, and allow the students to have immediate follow-up and reinforcement of concepts missed.

WORKSHEETS

Worksheets are in the *Tests and Resources* book. These worksheets have been developed for reinforcement and drill. There is a complete listing of worksheets and where they might best be used on pages of the introduction. Answer keys to the worksheets are provided in the same manner as for the student lessons.

Pre-Algebra Scope and Sequence

1. **Number Theory**
   *Number terminology
   Prime and composite
   Prime factorization
   Finding all factors of a number
   Factor trees
   Exponents
   Scientific notation
   Order of operations
   Square roots
   *Absolute value

2. **Integers**
   >, <, =
   Comparing integers
   Inverses
   Adding integers
   Subtracting integers
   Multiplying integers
   Dividing integers

3. **Addition and Subtraction**
   Addition properties and terms
   Subtraction properties and terms
   Addition with 4, 5, and 6 digits
   Subtraction with 4, 5, and 6 digits
   Adding and subtracting equations
   Solving for missing addends
   Estimation

4. **Multiplication**
   Properties, terms, and facts
   Multiples
   Two digit times two digit
   Three digit times three digit
   Four digit times four digit
   Five digit times five digit
   Solving for missing factors
   *Exponents: meaning of a negative exponent, powers of negative numbers, product of powers, power of a power, power of a product

5. **Division**
   Properties and terms
   One, two, three, and four digit divisors
   Divisibility tests

Horizons Pre-Algebra, Teacher's Guide

6. **Geometry**
   Perimeter
   *Circumference of circle
   Area of parallelogram, triangle, and circle
   *Area of trapezoid
   Volume of cube and cylinder
   *Volume of pyramid, cone, and sphere
   *Nets of 3-D shapes
   *Surface area of prism, cylinder, sphere, and pyramid
   Shapes and solids
   Symmetry
   Congruent polygons
   *Congruent triangles
   Points, lines, planes, rays, line segments
   Parallel, intersecting, perpendicular lines
   *Transversals
   Angles: acute, right, obtuse
   *Angles: adjacent, complementary, supplementary
   Angles: ray, vertex
   Circles: radius, diameter, chord, central angle
   *Circles: tangent
   Triangles: scalene, isosceles, equilateral
   Triangles: right, equiangular, acute, obtuse
   Polygons: sides, vertices, diagonals
   *Pythagorean formula
   *Informal Transformations: flips, turns, slides, scaling
   *Transformations: reflection, rotation, translation, dilation

7. **Fractions**
   Equivalent fractions
   Greatest common factor
   Least common multiple
   Reducing fractions
   Comparing fractions
   Adding fractions and mixed numbers
   Subtracting fractions and mixed numbers
   Multiplying fractions and mixed numbers
   Dividing fractions and mixed numbers
   Improper fractions
   Reciprocals

8. **Decimals**
   Decimal-fraction equivalents
   Decimal-percent equivalents
   Word numbers to hundred thousandths
   Comparing decimals
   Adding decimals
   Subtracting decimals
   Multiplying decimals
   Dividing decimals
   Powers of 10
   Repeating decimals

9. **Ratio and proportion**
   Writing simple ratios
   Finding equal ratios
   *Writing proportions
   Cross multiplying
   Solving proportions
   Ratio as a percent
   *Scale drawings

10. **Measurement**
    English-metric linear equivalents
    English-metric liquid equivalents
    English-metric weight equivalents
    Fahrenheit-Celsius conversions
    Celsius-Fahrenheit conversions
    *Mass
    *Density
    *Velocity
    Time

11. **Graphs**
    Bar
    Line
    Pictograph
    Circle
    Coordinate graphs
    *Using graphs to solve equations

12. **Percent**
    Finding the percent of a number
    Percent-decimal equivalents
    Discount
    *Mark-up
    *Percent increase
    *Percent decrease
    *Percents less than 1
    *Percents more than 100

13. **Applications**
    Simple interest
    *Compound interest
    *Commission

14. **Problem solving**
    Choosing an operation
    Multiple step problems
    Writing equations
    Reasonable and unreasonable answers

15. **Probability and statistics**
    Measures of center: mean, median, mode
    Measures of dispersion (spread): range
    *Frequency distribution
    *Histogram
    *Stem-and-leaf plots
    *Box-and-whisker plots
    *Probability and odds
    *Odds in favor
    *Odds against
    *Multiplication principle of counting
    *Combined probabilities
    *Permutations
    *Combinations
    *Mutually exclusive events
    *Independent and dependent events
    *Expected value

16. **Algebra**
    *Like terms
    Writing expressions with one variable
    Equations with one variable
    *Inequalities with one variable
    *Two variable equations
    *Slope and y-intercept
    *Graphs of equations
    *Graphing inequalities
    *Functions
    *Graphs of functions
    *Systems of equations
    *Using algebra tiles
    *Polynomial expressions
    *Adding polynomials
    *Subtracting polynomials
    *Multiplying monomials
    *Dividing monomials
    *Multiplying polynomials by monomials
    *Dividing polynomials by monomials
    *Multiplying polynomials
    *Dividing polynomials
    *FOIL method
    *Simplifying expressions

17. **Trigonometry**
    *Trigonometric ratios: sine, cosine, tangent
    *Trigonometric relationships in right triangles

    *New concepts

Where To Use *Pre-Algebra Worksheets*

In the *Tests and Resources* book you will find eighty worksheets.
This chart shows where worksheets may be used for *Horizons Pre-Algebra*.

No.	Concept	Lessons Where Worksheets Are Used
1	5-digit Addition and Subtraction	2
2	2-digit Multiplication, 3-digit by 2-digit Division	3
3	Identify Numbers, Estimate Sums and Products	5
4	Signed Numbers, Absolute Value	8
5	Factors and Multiples	9
6	Exponential Form	12
7	Squares, Order of Operations	13
8	Order of Operations	15
9	Exponents, Divisibility Tests, GCF	18
10	LCM, GCF, Radical Expressions	20
11	Radicals, Writing Mathematical Expressions	22
12	Addition and Subtraction of Decimals	23
13	Combining Like Terms	25
14	Solving Inequalities, Operations with Decimals.	28
15	Powers of Ten	30
16	Operations with Powers of Ten	32
17	Decimal–Fraction Conversions	33
18	Metric Conversions	35
19	Decimal to Fraction Equivalents	38
20	English to Metric Conversions	40
21	Addition of Mixed Numbers	42
22	Subtraction of Mixed Numbers	43
23	English to Metric Length Conversion	45
24	Proportions	48
25	Percents	50
26	Fraction to Percent Conversions, Percent Decrease	52
27	Mark-up and Discount	53
28	Discount and Mark-up	55
29	Simple Interest	58
30	Pictographs	60
31	Compound Interest	62
32	Mean, Median	63
33	Pictographs, Circle Graphs	65
34	Frequency Distribution	68
35	Probabilities	70
36	Stem-and-Leaf Plot, Histogram	72
37	Probability, Odds	73
38	Probability, Odds	75
39	Probabilities	78
40	Expected Values	80

Where To Use Pre-Algebra Worksheets, continued:

Horizons Pre-Algebra Appearance of Concepts

Lesson 1
Number terminology
Properties of addition
Addition
Subtraction

Lesson 2
Rounding
Estimation
Multiplication
Division
Number terminology

Lesson 3
Signed numbers
Rounding
Estimation
Addition
Subtraction
Multiplication
Division

Lesson 4
Signed numbers
Properties of multiplication
Multiplication
Division
Rounding
Estimation
Word problems

Lesson 5
Absolute value
Inverse operations
Signed numbers
Addition
Subtraction
Math puzzles

Lesson 6
Factors
Signed numbers
Absolute value
Word problems

Lesson 7
Multiples
Factors
Signed numbers
Addition
Subtraction
Word problems

Lesson 8
Prime/composite numbers
Factors
Multiples
Multiplication
Division

Lesson 9
Prime factorization
Multiples
Absolute value
Addition
Subtraction

Lesson 10
Exponents
Prime factorization
Signed numbers
Multiplication

Lesson 11
Powers of numbers
Square numbers
Cubed numbers
Prime factorization
Absolute value
Multiples
Word problems

Lesson 12
Order of operations
Prime factorization
Signed numbers
Square numbers
Number puzzles

Lesson 13
Distributive property
Prime factorization
Prime/composite numbers
Factors
Word problems

Lesson 14
Exponents
Order of operations
Prime factorization
Square numbers
Number puzzles

Lesson 15
Divisibility tests
Prime/composite numbers
Order of operations
Prime factorization
Exponents
Word problems

Lesson 16
Greatest common factor
Divisibility tests
Prime/composite numbers
Order of operations
Word problems

Lesson 17
Least common multiple
Prime factorization
Order of operations
Greatest common factor
Word problems

Lesson 18
Square roots
Cube roots
Root terminology
Divisibility tests
Prime/composite numbers
Greatest common factor
Least common multiple

Horizons Pre-Algebra, Teacher's Guide

Horizons Pre-Algebra Appearance of Concepts, continued:

Lesson 19
Writing expressions with
    one variable
Like terms
Signed numbers
Least common multiple
Roots
Word problems

Lesson 20
Equations with one variable
Simplifying expressions
Signed numbers
Divisibility tests
Prime/composite numbers
Greatest common factor
Least common multiple
Word problems

Lesson 21
Word problems
Absolute value
Divisibility tests
Prime/composite numbers
Greatest common factor
Roots

Lesson 22
Inequalities with one
    variable
Absolute value
Factors
Roots
Math puzzles
Word problems

Lesson 23
Decimal system
Addition
Subtraction
Multiples
Least common multiple
Equations with one variable
Inequalities with one
    variable
Word problems

Lesson 24
Comparing decimals
Rounding
Addition
Factors
Roots
Equations with one variable
Inequalities with one
    variable
Word problems

Lesson 25
Multiplying decimals
Roots
Equations with one variable
Inequalities with one
    variable
Word problems

Lesson 26
Dividing decimals
Divisibility tests
Prime/composite numbers
Equations with one variable
Inequalities with one
    variable
Multiplying decimals

Lesson 27
Powers of 10
Prime factorization
Exponents
Equations with one variable
Multiplying decimals
Dividing decimals
Word problems

Lesson 28
Multiplying by powers of 10
Divisibility tests
Prime/composite numbers
Order of operations
Multiplying decimals
Dividing decimals
Word problems

Lesson 29
Dividing by powers of 10
Prime factorization
Inequalities with one
    variable
Multiplying decimals
Dividing decimals

Lesson 30
Metric system: Kilo-
Like terms
Order of operations
Inequalities with one
    variable
Powers of 10
Dividing decimals

Lesson 31
Metric System: Centi-,
    Milli-
Metric system conversions
Order of operations
Greatest common factor
Powers of 10
Word problems

Lesson 32
Equivalent fractions
Signed numbers
Powers of 10
Metric conversions
Adding decimals
Subtracting decimals

Lesson 33
Fraction-decimal
    equivalents
Absolute value
Divisibility tests
Prime/composite numbers
Powers of 10
Word problems

Horizons Pre-Algebra Appearance of Concepts, continued:

Lesson 34
Adding fractions
Greatest common factor
Metric system conversion
Powers of 10
Least common multiple
Absolute value
Word problems

Lesson 35
Subtracting fractions
Divisibility tests
Prime/composite numbers
Roots
Fraction-decimal
    equivalents
Word problems

Lesson 36
Multiplying fractions
Fraction-decimal
    equivalents
Powers of 10
Metric system conversion
Word problems

Lesson 37
Dividing fractions
Roots
Divisibility tests
Factors
Powers of 10
Metric system conversion
Word problems

Lesson 38
Improper Fractions
Equations with one variable
Divisibility tests
Multiples
Word problems

Lesson 39
Mixed numbers
Adding and subtracting
    mixed numbers
Equations with one
    variable
Word problems

Lesson 40
English-metric length
    conversions
English length equivalents
Prime factorization
Dividing decimals
Adding and subtracting
    mixed numbers

Lesson 41
Multiplying mixed numbers
Divisibility tests
Prime/composite numbers
Multiplying decimals
Dividing fractions
Mixed numbers and
    improper fractions
Word problems

Lesson 42
Dividing mixed numbers
Prime factorization
Exponents
Order of operations
Distributive property
Equations with one
    variable
Inequalities with one
    variable
Dividing decimals
Adding mixed numbers

Lesson 43
Ratios
Inequalities with one
    variable
Multiplying fractions
Dividing fractions
Multiplying mixed numbers
Dividing mixed numbers
Subtracting mixed numbers

Lesson 44
Proportions
Metric system conversion
Powers of 10
Order of operations
Equations with one variable
Word problems

Lesson 45
Scale drawings
Ratios and proportions
Word problems
Greatest common factor
Multiplying and dividing
    mixed numbers
Absolute value

Lesson 46
Scientific notation
Multiplying mixed numbers
Dividing mixed numbers
Divisibility tests
Prime/composite numbers
Word problems

Lesson 47
Percent
Percent-decimal conversion
Least common multiple
Fraction-decimal
    equivalents
Solving proportions
Scale drawings

Horizons Pre-Algebra Appearance of Concepts, continued:

Lesson 48
Finding the percent of a
  number
Prime factorization
Roots
Scientific notation
Word problems

Lesson 49
Fraction-percent conversion
Least common multiple
Prime factorization
Roots
Finding percents
Scientific notation

Lesson 50
Percent decrease
Word problems
Greatest common factor
Fraction-decimal-percent
  equivalents
English-metric conversions
English length equivalents

Lesson 51
Discounts and sale prices
Equations with one variable
Multiplying fractions
Multiplying mixed numbers
Scale drawings
Word problems

Lesson 52
Percent increase
Scientific notation
Equations with one variable
Multiplying decimals
Adding and subtracting
  mixed numbers
Word problems

Lesson 53
Calculating mark-up
Prime factorization
Exponents
Dividing decimals
Multiplying fractions
Multiplying mixed numbers
Roots
Word problems

Lesson 54
Simple interest
Inequalities with one
  variable
Divisibility tests
Prime/composite numbers
Multiplying decimals
Word problems

Lesson 55
Commission
Prime factorization
Exponents
Equations with one variable
Dividing fractions
Dividing mixed numbers
Simple interest
Word problems

Lesson 56
Percents less than 1
Inequalities with one
  variable
Multiplying and dividing
  fractions
Multiplying and dividing
  mixed numbers
Percents
Word problems

Lesson 57
Profits and royalties
Fraction-decimal-percent
  conversion
Simple interest
Powers of 10
Metric conversions
Word problems

Lesson 58
Compound interest
Adding and subtracting
  mixed numbers
Divisibility tests
Prime/composite numbers
Word problems

Lesson 59
Percents greater than 100
Greatest common factor
Powers of 10
Metric conversions
Simple interest
Compound interest
Proportions
Word problems

Lesson 60
Pictographs
Divisibility tests
Prime/composite numbers
Roots
Compound interest
Multiplying and dividing
  fractions
Multiplying and dividing
  mixed numbers

Lesson 61
Circle graphs
Natural numbers
Factors
Greatest common factor
English measurement
  conversion
Proportions
Word problems

Horizons Pre-Algebra Appearance of Concepts, continued:

Lesson 62
Mean
Least common multiple
Roots
Compound interest
Scale drawings
Ratios

Lesson 63
Median
Mean
Equations with one variable
Least common multiple
Powers of 10
Metric system
Circle graphs
Word problems

Lesson 64
Frequency distribution
Pictographs
Adding and subtracting
    mixed numbers
Word problems

Lesson 65
Mode
Equations with one variable
Multiplying decimals
Multiplying and dividing
    mixed numbers
Roots
Scientific notation
Word problems

Lesson 66
Range
Mean
Median
Mode
Equations with one variable
Inequalities with one
    variable
Dividing decimals
Word problems

Lesson 67
Stem-and-leaf plots
Median
Mode
Prime factorization
Exponents
Inequalities with one
    variable
Ratios
Word problems

Lesson 68
Histograms
Stem-and-leaf plots
Percents
Percents less than 1
Percents greater than 100
Word problems

Lesson 69
Box-and-whisker plots
5-number summary
Prime factorization
Exponents
Mean
Median
Mode
Range

Lesson 70
Probability
Powers of 10
Metric system
Fraction-decimal-percent
    conversion
Simple interest
Word problems

Lesson 71
Bar graphs
Divisibility tests
Prime/composite numbers
Measurement conversions
Dividing fractions
Roots
Word problems

Lesson 72
Line graphs
Divisibility tests
Prime/composite numbers
Greatest common factor
Simple interest
Word problems

Lesson 73
Probability
Odds in favor
Odds against
Roots
Word problems

Lesson 74
Multiplication principle of
    counting
Measurement conversions
Proportions
Improper fractions
Compound interest
Word problems

Lesson 75
Combined probabilities
Greatest common factor
Roots
Simple interest
Compound interest
Scale drawings
Ratios

Lesson 76
Permutations
Least common multiple
Equations with one variable
Powers of 10
Metric conversions
Line graphs
Word problems

Horizons Pre-Algebra Appearance of Concepts, continued:

Lesson 77
Combinations
Divisibility tests
Prime/composite numbers
Equations with one variable
Mean, median, and mode
Range
Histogram
Box-and-whisker plot
Word problems

Lesson 78
Mutually exclusive events
Least common multiple
Scientific notation
Permutations
Combinations
Word problems

Lesson 79
Independent events
Dependent events
Inequalities with one
    variable
Probability
Odds
Permutations
Combinations
Word problems

Lesson 80
Expected value
Percent
Simple interest
Compound interest
Probability
Word problems

Lesson 81
Plane geometry terms
Order of operations
Absolute value
Mean, median, and mode
Range
Dividing fractions
Dividing mixed numbers

Lesson 82
Perimeter and area of
    parallelograms
Perimeter and area of
    rhombuses
Order of operations
Absolute value
Multiplying fractions
Multiplying mixed numbers

Lesson 83
Perimeter and area of
    rectangles
Perimeter and area of
    squares
Simple interest
Probability and odds
Word problems

Lesson 84
Perimeter and area of
    triangles
Perimeter and area of
    parallelograms
Area of rectangles
Probability
Expected outcome
Word problems

Lesson 85
Perimeter and area of
    trapezoids
Isosceles trapezoids
Perimeter and area of
    rectangles
English-metric conversions
Scale drawings
Word problems

Lesson 86
Circumference and area of
    circles
Area of rectangles
Word problems

Lesson 87
Congruent polygons
Area of circles
Area of rectangles
Percent
Word problems

Lesson 88
Symmetry
Compound interest
Scale drawings
Area of trapezoids
Word problems

Lesson 89
Congruent triangles
Perimeter and area of
    squares
Perimeter and area of
    rectangles
Area of triangles
Circumference and area of
    circles

Lesson 90
Solid geometry terms
Faces, edges, and vertices
Prisms
Pyramids
Divisibility tests
Prime/composite numbers
Prime factorization
Exponents
Permutations
Combinations
Area of trapezoids

Lesson 91
Volume of prisms
Volume of cubes
Area of polygons
Word problems

Horizons Pre-Algebra Appearance of Concepts, continued:

Lesson 92
Surface area of prisms
Lateral area of prisms
Divisibility tests
Prime/composite numbers
Word problems

Lesson 93
Pyramids
Volume of a pyramid
Lateral area of a pyramid
Surface area of a pyramid

Lesson 94
Cylinders
Volume of a cylinder
Lateral area of a cylinder
Surface area of a cylinder
Word problems

Lesson 95
Cones
Volume of a cone
Lateral area of a cone
Surface area of a cone
Word problems

Lesson 96
Spheres
Volume of a sphere
Surface area of a sphere
Divisibility tests
Prime/composite numbers
Prime factorization
Faces, edges, and vertices
Word problems

Lesson 97
Nets of solid figures
Octahedrons
Dodecahedrons
Icosahedrons

Lesson 98
Mass
Weight
Volume of solid figures
Surface area of spheres

Lesson 99
Density
Mass
Word problems

Lesson 100
Time
Velocity
Simple interest
Compound interest
Word problems

Lesson 101
Points, lines, and planes
Proportions
Bar graphs
Word problems

Lesson 102
Line segments
Rays
Intersecting lines
Parallel lines
Skew lines
Word problems

Lesson 103
Parts of a circle
Divisibility tests
Prime/composite numbers
Parallel and skew lines
Word problems

Lesson 104
Acute, right, and obtuse
    angles
Adjacent angles
Complementary angles
Supplementary angles
Straight angles
Prime factorization
Exponents
Word problems

Lesson 105
Perpendicular lines
Complementary angles
Straight angles
Divisibility tests
Prime/composite numbers
Sum of interior angles of a
    polygon

Lesson 106
Parallel lines
Perpendicular lines
Interior angles
Exterior angles
Regular polygons

Lesson 107
Transversals
Interior angles
Exterior angles
Vertical angles
Corresponding angles
Mean, median, and mode
5-number summary
Box-and-whisker plot

Lesson 108
Coordinate plane
Quadrants
Graphing points
Area of triangles
Area of polygons

Lesson 109
Two-variable equations
Independent variables
Dependent variables
Solving two-variable
    equations
Solving one-variable
    equations and
    inequalities

Lesson 110
Graphing equations
Area of polygons
Percent

Lesson 111
Graphing inequalities
Area of polygons
Volume of prisms

Lesson 112
Functions
Graphs of functions
Graphing two-variables
    equations

Lesson 113
Slope
Graphing two-variables
    equations
Word problems

Lesson 114
y-intercept
Slope-intercept form
Slope
Graphing two-variables
    equations
Writing two-variables
    equations
Word problems

Lesson 115
Systems of equations
Slope-intercept form
Coordinate points
Word problems

Lesson 116
Systems of equations
Adding equations
Simple interest
Compound interest
Word problems

Lesson 117
Systems of equations
Subtracting equations
Divisibility tests
Prime/composite numbers
Angles
Word problems

Lesson 118
Fahrenheit – Celsius
    conversion
Sum of interior angles of a
    polygon
Regular polygons
Word problems

Lesson 119
Celsius – Fahrenheit
    conversion
Volume
Surface area
Word problems

Lesson 120
English-metric conversions
Ounces
Quarts
Gallons
Milliliters
Liters
Word problems

Lesson 121
English-metric conversions
Weight
Mass
Temperature
Word problems

Lesson 122
Pythagorean formula
Hypotenuse
Right triangles
Word problems

Lesson 123
30-60-90 triangles
Pythagorean formula
Word problems

Lesson 124
45-45-90 triangles
Pythagorean formula
Word problems

Lesson 125
Sine
Right triangles
Divisibility tests
Prime/composite numbers
Greatest common factor
Least common multiple
Word problems

Lesson 126
Cosine
Right triangles
Sine
Word problems

Lesson 127
Tangent
30-60-90 triangles
45-45-90 triangles
Area of triangles
Pythagorean formula

Horizons Pre-Algebra Appearance of Concepts, continued:

Lesson 128
Trigonometric ratios
Sine
Cosine
Tangent
Pythagorean formula
30-60-90 triangles
45-45-90 triangles

Lesson 129
Algebra tiles
Multiplying binomial by
  monomials
Word problems

Lesson 130
Polynomial expressions
Constants
Coefficients
Monomials
Binomials
Trinomials
Simple interest
Compound interest
Word problems

Lesson 131
Adding polynomials
Algebra tiles
Pythagorean formula
Word problems

Lesson 132
Subtracting polynomials
Algebra tiles
30-60-90 triangles
Area of rectangles
Percent
Word problems

Lesson 133
Multiplying monomials
Exponents
Adding polynomials
Subtracting polynomials
Word problems

Lesson 134
Dividing monomials
Simple interest
Compound interest
Word problems

Lesson 135
Multiplying polynomials by
  monomials
Algebra tiles
Greatest common factor
Divisibility tests
Prime/composite numbers
Least common multiple
Temperature conversion
Word problems

Lesson 136
Dividing polynomials by
  monomials
Algebra tiles
Word problems

Lesson 137
Multiplying polynomials
Algebra tiles
Word problems

Lesson 138
The FOIL method
Multiplying polynomials
Adding polynomials
Subtracting polynomials
Multiplying polynomials by
  monomials
Dividing polynomials by
  monomials

Lesson 139
Dividing polynomials
Area of plane figures
Percent
Word problems

Lesson 140
Flips
Graphing points
Scale drawings
Word problems

Lesson 141
Turns
Divisibility tests
Prime/composite numbers
Volume of prisms
Word problems

Lesson 142
Slides
Greatest common factor
Least common multiple
Simple interest
Compound interest
Temperature conversion

Lesson 143
Scaling
Enlargements
Reductions
Word problems

Lesson 144
Reflections
Flips
Adding polynomials
Subtracting polynomials
Multiplying polynomials by
  monomials
Dividing polynomials by
  monomials

Lesson 145
Rotations
Turns
Word problems

Horizons Pre-Algebra Appearance of Concepts, continued:

Lesson 146
Translations
Slides
Slope
y-intercept
Graphing linear equations
Systems of equations

Lesson 147
Dilations
Compressions
Scaling
Graphing inequalities
Word problems

Lesson 148
Area of regular polygons
Apothem
Perimeter
Word problems

Lesson 149
Terms and definitions
Number terminology
Order of operations
Divisibility tests
Prime/composite numbers
Absolute value
Exponents

Lesson 150
Divisibility tests
Factors
Greatest common factor
Least common multiple
Roots
Inequalities
Powers of 10
Metric conversions

Lesson 151
Adding mixed numbers
Subtracting mixed numbers
Multiplying mixed numbers
Dividing mixed numbers
English-metric conversions
English length conversions
Word problems

Lesson 152
Proportions
Percents
Fraction-percent equivalents
Simple interest
Compound interest

Lesson 153
Pictograph
Circle graph
Bar graph
Probability
Stem-and-leaf plots
Mean, median, and mode
Range
Box-and-whisker plots
Histogram
Word problems

Lesson 154
Probability and odds
Permutations
Combinations
Angles
Lines
Points
Rays
Segments

Lesson 155
Terms and definitions
Volume of cylinders
Surface area of cylinders
Surface area of pyramids
Volume of spheres
Surface area of spheres
Velocity
Distance
Time

Lesson 156
Area of plane figures
Volume of prisms
Volume of cones
Surface area of cones
Parts of a circle
Types of angles
Parallel lines

Lesson 157
Terms and definitions
Graphing inequalities
Graphing functions
Regular polygons

Lesson 158
Slope
y-intercept
Graphing linear equations
Systems of equations
Coordinate points
Pythagorean formula
Sine
Cosine
Tangent

Lesson 159
Terms and definitions
English-metric conversions
Weight
Mass
Reflections

Lesson 160
Temperature conversion
Multiplying polynomials by
   monomials
Dividing polynomials by
   binomials
Adding polynomials
Subtracting polynomials
The FOIL method
Dividing polynomials by
   monomials

Lesson 1

Concepts
- Number terminology
- Properties of addition
- Addition with regrouping
- Subtraction with regrouping

Learning Objectives
The student will be able to:
- Define terms related to numbers
- Identify numbers as *natural*, *whole*, *integer*, *rational*, *irrational*, and *real*
- Apply the properties of addition
- Add sets of 4-digit addends
- Subtract two 4-digit numbers

Materials Needed
- Student Book, Lesson 1
- A Math Minute with Dan D.

Teaching Tips
➢ Administer the Readiness Test. This test is not to be graded as part of the course grade, but rather as an aid in determining individual student readiness for pre-algebra. Worksheets may be assigned as necessary to assist students who need further help.

➢ Emphasize that math is necessary for life, not just for those who pursue a career in a math-related field. Introduce Math Minutes. These features will appear throughout the book at the beginning of every 10-lesson segment. Each word problem in the 10 lessons following a Math Minute will relate to the individual featured in the Math Minute. Introduce Dan D. – Missionary Radio, Orphanage.

Introduction to A Math Minute with……

Often students ask:

Who uses this stuff anyway?

I will NEVER be a math major. Why do I have to learn all this?

Will I ever have to use pre-algebra in the real world?

Math is a school subject that is used daily by people in their work, homes and play. Many people use math in their jobs, even if those jobs do not require a college degree in mathematics. There is a very good chance you will have to use math on at least a pre-algebra level when you get a job.

While you may find some of the topics in pre-algebra challenging, they will help you learn more about math and God's carefully designed world. You do not know what plans God has for your life. You may be surprised in the directions God leads you and find that you use math in ways you never expected.

Throughout this book, you will read interviews with several Christians who are using pre-algebra in their daily lives. None of these people were college math majors. Some of them have successful careers without earning a college degree. Whether or not God's plan for your life includes college, math will play a role in your future.

"For I know the plans I have for you," declares the LORD, "plans to prosper you and not to harm you, plans to give you hope and a future."
Jeremiah 29:11 NIV

A Math Minute with . . .

Dan D. – Missionary Radio, Orphanage

What is your occupation? Missionary in Uganda

Where do you work? I work in Soroti, Uganda in a church, Bible institute, and orphanage. I also manage a radio station.

Did you attend college? If so, what was your major? B.A. in Communications with an emphasis on Advertising/Public Relations

What parts of your job require the use of math? I frequently use math when converting from US dollars to Uganda shillings. I also use geometry and math when constructing buildings and furnishings at the orphanage and radio station.

What is the biggest "problem" you have faced that required the use of math to solve? I frequently used math when we were designing our solar power system. I needed to estimate the electricity load of the broadcast equipment. Some of the equipment ran all day while other pieces only ran for a few hours. I then had to calculate the loss on energy conversions (to/from battery.) I also had to determine the total power to be produced by the solar panels divided by the number of hours of sunlight per day. This was then divided by the wattage of the panels to determine how many panels were needed. I used those numbers to determine what gauge of wire to install, the capacity of the inverter, etc. The battery room also needed to be constructed along with a concrete slab for solar panels. This meant estimating the number of bricks needed, the truck loads of sand and stone delivered, the bags of cement purchased, and the sheets of metal mesh bought. The entire project has been one large math problem!

Are there any other interesting math uses you have experienced? Every month our money is worth something different. It often changes several times a day. Buying groceries is a constant calculation as to what the value of the U.S. dollar is for that day.

Number Terminology

Natural numbers are counting numbers. (1, 2, 3, . . .)

Whole numbers are the natural numbers and zero. (0, 1, 2, . . .)

Integers are the positive and negative whole numbers. (-1, 0, 1, . . .)

Rational numbers are numbers that can be written as a fraction. $(\frac{1}{2}, \frac{4}{3}, \frac{7}{1}, 10.5)$

Irrational numbers are numbers that CANNOT be written as a fraction. $(\sqrt{2}, \pi)$

Real numbers are numbers in any of the above categories.

① Classwork

Identify each number as *natural, whole, integer, rational, irrational,* or *real*. Some numbers may have more than one answer.

	3	-8	$\sqrt{3}$	0	$2\frac{1}{3}$	$\frac{5}{6}$	π	6.2
Natural	x							
Whole	x			x				
Integer	x	x		x				
Rational	x	x		x	x	x		x
Irrational			x				x	
Real	x	x	x	x	x	x	x	x

Something to Think About...

Associative Property of Addition: You can group the addends in different ways and still get the same sum. 1 + (2 + 3) = 1 + 5 = 6 (1 + 2) + 3 = 3 + 3 = 6

Commutative Property of Addition: You can change the order of the addends and still get the same sum. 2 + 3 = 5   3 + 2 = 5

Identity Property of Addition: You can add zero to any number and it won't change the value of the number. 4 + 0 = 4   0 + 4 = 4

Activities

② Identify each number as *natural, whole, integer, rational, irrational,* or *real*. Some numbers may have more than one answer.

	14	$-\sqrt{2}$	$5\frac{7}{8}$	-4	0	13.47	π	$\frac{3}{4}$	-0.01
Natural	x								
Whole	x				x				
Integer	x			x	x				
Rational	x		x	x	x	x		x	x
Irrational		x					x		
Real	x	x	x	x	x	x	x	x	x

③ Add or subtract as indicated.

2547	2990	6377	6358	7893	4774
5321	5047	4676	9395	4792	4428
+4876	+4221	+1881	+1881	+9610	+9536
12,744	12,258	12,934	17,634	22,295	18,738

7737	5325	8365	4297	4874	2393
6967	5433	6778	6676	6805	4121
+6513	+4960	+8286	+2930	+2126	+4314
21,217	15,718	23,429	13,903	13,805	10,828

3311	8235	1458	4548	3173	3552
9654	9791	1838	3683	9999	2792
+1830	+4133	+4185	+6039	+6450	+4512
14,795	22,159	7,481	14,270	19,622	10,856

5782	9322	3325	1815	7548	7697
−2455	−9110	−2091	−1468	−4855	−1165
3,327	212	1,234	347	2,693	6,532

6798	2394	8151	8624	6365	9667
−4739	−1389	−2918	−5261	−6052	−3382
2,059	1,005	5,233	3,363	313	6,285

5232	6112	8145	4103	4981	3372
−3853	−5584	−5885	−3474	−2219	−1703
1,379	528	2,260	629	2,762	1,669

Teaching Tips, Cont.

➤ Define the terms in the teaching box of Lesson 1. Ask students to give other examples of each type of number. They may find it difficult to think of other examples of irrational numbers. That is fine at this point in time. Some students may give the square root of other numbers. This is a correct answer UNLESS the student gives the square root of a perfect square. This concept will be discussed further in Lesson 18.

➤ Complete the Classwork exercises orally with the students supplying the answers. Have students mark the correct answers in their books. Explain that the value of π is a decimal that never ends and never repeats. In math, it is acceptable to use the value 3.14 or $\frac{22}{7}$ for π when an exact answer is not required.

➤ The first 100 digits of pi: 3.14159265358979323846264338327950288419716939937510582097494459230781640628620899862803482534211706.... (Neither you nor the students are expected to know or memorize this. Often, students will ask, just to see if you know!)

➤ Review addition and subtraction based on student performance on the Readiness Test.

Assignment

• Complete Lesson 1, Activities 2-3.

Lesson 2

Concepts
- Rounding
- Estimating sums and differences
- Estimating products
- Multiplication
- Division
- Number terminology

Learning Objectives
The student will be able to:
- Round numbers to the nearest ten or hundred
- Estimate sums by rounding
- Estimate differences by rounding
- Estimate products by rounding
- Multiply two 2-digit numbers
- Divide a 3-digit number by a 2-digit number

Materials Needed
- Student Book, Lesson 2
- Worksheet 1

Teaching Tips
➢ Define the terms in the teaching box of Lesson 2. Review place value as necessary. Ask students to round 4-digit numbers to the nearest 10 and 100. (You may choose to use the 4-digit numbers from the addends in Lesson 1 Activity 3.)

➢ Remind students that the only digit they should consider in deciding whether or not to round up is the digit immediately to the right of the place value they are rounding. It is a common mistake for students to begin at the ones place and round each digit, working up to the digit they are asked to round. For example, 4849 rounded to the nearest hundred is 4800. If a student begins at the ones place, he will round to 4850 and then to 4900, producing a wrong answer.

Rounding and Estimation

Rounding is a method of approximating a given number. Look at the digit to the immediate right of the place value you want to round to. Round down if that number is a 0, 1, 2, 3, or 4. Round up if that number is a 5, 6, 7, 8, or 9.

7846 rounds to 8000, 7800, or 7850, depending on which place value you choose.

Estimation is a method of quickly arriving at an approximate answer. Estimation is useful when an exact answer is not needed. To estimate an answer, round each term and then perform the required mathematical operation.

To estimate the sum of 5232 + 3853, round each to the nearest thousand and add:
5000 + 4000 = 9000

To estimate the product of 19 x 21, round each to the nearest ten and multiply: 20 x 20 = 400

① **Classwork**

Estimate the sum.

172 + 329 ≈ 200 + 300 = 500
416 + 792 ≈ 400 + 800 = 1200
6017 + 2949 ≈ 6000 + 3000 = 9000

Estimate the product.

41 x 39 ≈ 40 x 40 = 1600
(round both to the nearest 10)
103 x 298 ≈ 100 x 300 = 30,000
(round both to the nearest 100)
699 x 11 ≈ 700 x 10 = 7000
(round both to the nearest 10)

Activities

② Estimate the sum by rounding to the nearest hundred. Use the symbol ≈ to show two values are approximately equal.

107 +298 ≈	100 +300 400	392 +204 ≈	400 +200 600

209 +188 ≈ 200 +200 / 400

587 +312 ≈ 600 +300 / 900

219 +970 ≈ 200 +1000 / 1200

437 +972 ≈ 400 +1000 / 1400

687 +123 ≈ 700 +100 / 800

708 +297 ≈ 700 +300 / 1000

③ Estimate each product by rounding to the nearest ten.

11 x 129 ≈ 10 x 130 = 1300   26 x 33 ≈ 30 x 30 = 900

87 x 22 ≈ 90 x 20 = 1800   99 x 251 ≈ 100 x 250 = 25,000

47 x 72 ≈ 50 x 70 = 3500   78 x 81 ≈ 80 x 80 = 6400

53 x 68 ≈ 50 x 70 = 3500   31 x 48 ≈ 30 x 50 = 1500

④ Identify each number as *natural, whole, integer, rational, irrational,* or *real.*
Some numbers may have more than one answer.

	$2\sqrt{3}$	-4	π	0	$5\frac{2}{3}$	$\frac{7}{4}$	13	$-\frac{1}{2}$	26.3
Natural							x		
Whole				x			x		
Integer		x		x			x		
Rational		x		x	x	x	x	x	x
Irrational	x		x						
Real	x	x	x	x	x	x	x	x	x

⑤ Multiply or divide as indicated.

32 ×58 256 +1600 1,856	87 ×23 261 +1740 2,001	50 ×45 250 +2000 2,250	13 ×24 52 +260 312	85 ×53 245 +4250 4,505	83 ×56 498 +4250 4,648

13 ×71 13 +910 923	11 ×57 77 +550 627	66 ×80 00 +5280 5,280	24 ×45 120 +960 1,080	20 ×84 80 +1600 1,680	68 ×55 340 +3400 3,740

```
      18              16              17               2
48)864          57)912          38)646          91)182
   48              57              38              182
  384             342             266             000
  384             342             266
  000             000             000
```

```
       8               9              11              19
27)216          33)297          84)924          42)798
   216             297             84              42
   000             000            844             378
                                   844             378
                                   000             000
```

① Add.

1454	7213	8353	2492
+8036	+3885	+7667	+4698
9490	11,098	16,020	7190

34268	68096	65345	24888
+21327	+41483	+34572	+24587
55,595	109,579	99,917	49,475

353110	949269	319269	136653
+128277	+654698	+847185	+345702
481,387	1,603,967	1,166,454	482,355

② Subtract.

3357	9940	7897	8023
−1738	−2116	−6268	−6651
1619	7824	1629	1372

41940	81242	91661	77985
−22782	−74580	−36877	−75573
19,158	6662	54,784	2412

520852	507669	452478	702928
−497823	−304727	−251972	−653841
23,029	202,942	200,506	49,087

Teaching Tips, Cont.

➢ Ask students to give examples of times that an estimated answer would be desirable. (travel times, guessing number of beans in a jar, etc.)

➢ Explain that estimated amounts are easily calculated by rounding the exact number to the nearest 10 or 100 before doing the calculations.

➢ Complete the Classwork exercises. Have some students work the problems on the board for the class and explain their answers. All students should work the problems in their books.

➢ Review multiplication and division as necessary, based on student performance on the readiness test.

Assignments

- Complete Lesson 2, Activities 2-5.
- Worksheet 1 (Optional.)

Lesson 3

Concepts
- Adding signed numbers
- Subtracting signed numbers
- Rounding
- Estimation
- Addition, subtraction, multiplication, and division

Learning Objectives
The student will be able to:
- Apply the rules of adding and subtracting signed numbers
- Add numbers with like signs
- Add numbers with opposite signs
- Subtract numbers with like signs
- Subtract numbers with opposite signs

Materials Needed
- Student Book, Lesson 3
- Worksheet 2.

Teaching Tips
➤ Teach the rules for adding and subtracting signed numbers in the teaching box of Lesson 3. Use a number line to illustrate the directions signed numbers move. Positive numbers move in the positive, or right, direction on the number line, and negative numbers move in the negative, or left, direction on the number line. This will help students "see" what is happening when they are adding a negative.

➤ Write the following sentences on the board:
The game will begin in one <u>minute</u>. It is important to pay attention to <u>minute</u> details.

Signed Numbers   Lesson 3

Signed Number Rules:	① Classwork

Signed Number Rules:

When adding two numbers with the same sign, add the numbers like normal, and keep the same sign in the answer. $(+2) + (+5) = (+7)$
$(-2) + (-5) = (-7)$

When adding two numbers with opposite signs, ignore the signs (use the absolute values) and subtract the smaller number from the larger number. Keep the sign of the larger number as the sign in the answer.

$(+5) + (-2) = (5 - 2) = 3$. 5 is larger than 2 and 5 is positive in the problem, so the answer is positive. $(+5) + (-2) = (+3)$.

$(-5) + (+2) = -(5 - 2) = 3$. 5 is larger than 2 and 5 is negative in the problem, so the answer is negative. $(-5) + (+2) = (-3)$

When subtracting signed numbers, change the sign of the second number and add.
$(+5) - (-2) = (+5) + (+2) = 5 + 2 = 7$

① Classwork

Solve, using the rules for signed numbers.

$(+9) + (+5) = 9 + 5 = 14$

$(+9) + (-5) = 9 - 5 = 4$

$(-9) + (+5) = -(9 - 5) = -4$

$(-9) + (-5) = -(9 + 5) = -14$

$(+9) - (-5) = (+9) + (+5) = 9 + 5 = 14$

$(-9) - (-5) = (-9) + (+5) = -(9 - 5) = -4$

$(+9) - (+5) = (+9) + (-5) = 9 - 5 = 4$

$(-9) - (+5) = (-9) + (-5) = -14$

$4 + (-3) + 7 - (-2) = 4 - 3 + 7 + 2 = 10$

Activities

② Solve, using the rules for signed numbers. Write the problem vertically, if necessary.

$(+7) + (+9) = 7 + 9 = 16$

$(-7) + (+9) = 9 - 7 = 2$

$(-7) + (-9) = -(7 + 9) = -16$

$(+7) + (-9) = -(9 - 7) = -2$

$(+53) + (+77) = 53 + 77 = 130$

$(+53) + (-77) = -(77 - 53) = -24$

$(+7) - (-9) = 7 + 9 = 16$

$(-7) - (-9) = (-7) + (+9) = 9 - 7 = 2$

$(-53) + (+77) = 77 - 53 = 24$

$(-53) + (-77) = -(53 + 77) = -130$

$(+242) - (+397) = (+242) + (-397) = -(397 - 242) = -155$
$(+242) + (-397) = -(397 - 242) = -155$
$(-242) + (+397) = 397 - 242 = 155$

$(-242) - (-397) = (-242) + (+397) = 397 - 242 = 155$

---

③ Estimate the sum by rounding to the nearest hundred.

619 $\approx$ 600	198 $\approx$ 200	217 $\approx$ 200	389 $\approx$ 400
$+884$ $+900$	$+707$ $+700$	$+585$ $+600$	$+901$ $+900$
$1,500$	900	800	$1,300$

④ Solve.

8159	7324	3672	9233	7364	2543	2807
4393	3495	9297	8655	3902	9696	4060
+7353	+9641	+7748	+8753	+9387	+5734	+6334
19,905	20,460	20,717	26,641	20,653	17,973	13,201

3041	5546	8659	2055	4284	6715	5269
−1617	−1409	−8372	−1011	−4079	−4337	−3176
1,424	4,137	287	1,044	205	2,378	2,093

28	24	70	38	57	85	45
×56	×34	×84	×53	×30	×28	×24
168	96	280	114	00	680	180
+1400	+720	+5600	+1900	+1710	+1700	+900
1,568	816	5,880	2,014	1,710	2,380	1,080

22	18	4	3	2	42	12
29)638	45)810	71)284	35)105	76)152	23)966	72)864
58	45	284	105	152	92	72
58	360	000	000	000	46	144
58	360				46	144
00	000				00	000

5-digit Multiplication, 3-digit by 2-digit Division — Worksheet 2

① Multiply.

46	23	55	32
×32	×65	×41	×68
92	115	55	256
+1380	+1380	+2200	+1920
1472	1495	2255	2176

238	415	714	465
×32	×93	×22	×39
476	1245	1428	4185
+7140	+37350	+14280	+13950
7616	38,595	15,708	18,135

808	753	379	835
×893	×627	×759	×146
2424	5271	3411	5010
72720	15060	18950	33400
+646400	+451800	+265300	+83500
721,544	472,131	287,661	121,910

② Divide.

9	8	9	7
16)144	18)144	17)153	19)133
144	144	153	133

15	29	17	18
13)195	14)406	16)272	19)342
13	28	16	19
65	126	112	152
65	126	112	152

37	19	25	28
16)592	24)456	23)575	27)756
48	24	46	54
112	216	115	216
112	216	115	216

Teaching Tips, Cont.

➤ Ask a student to read the sentences out loud and have him explain how he knew how to pronounce the underlined words. (Context, meaning) The underlined words are called heteronyms because they look the same but have different meanings and pronunciations.

➤ Explain that the dash is the mathematical equivalent of a heteronym. Although subtraction and negative numbers use the same symbol, the symbol has different meanings, depending on its context.

➤ Subtracting does not mean to move left on the number line, but rather to move in the opposite direction of the sign. Thus, subtracting a negative number moves right that number of spaces.

Assignments

- Complete Lesson 3, Activities 2-4.
- Worksheet 2 (Optional.)

Lesson 4

Concepts
- Multiplying signed numbers
- Properties of multiplication
- Multiplication and division
- Math in the real world

Learning Objectives
The student will be able to:
- Apply the rules of multiplying signed numbers
- Multiply numbers with like signs
- Multiply numbers with opposite signs
- Recognize parentheses as a multiplication symbol
- Use multiplication to solve real-world problems

Materials Needed
- Student Book, Lesson 4

Teaching Tips
➢ Teach the rules for multiplying signed numbers. Point out to the students that the same rules apply for dividing signed numbers.

➢ Use a number line to illustrate the principle of skip counting as multiplication. When you have a positive number of negatives, you keep moving in the negative direction, or left on the number line. When you are multiplying by a negative, that is the same as subtracting that many negatives in skip counting.

➢ Remind students that subtracting a negative moves in the positive direction, and multiplying a negative by a negative also moves in the positive direction.

Properties of Multiplication

Signed Number Rules

When multiplying two numbers with the same sign, the answer is ALWAYS positive.

$(+5) \times (+4) = 20 \qquad (-5) \times (-4) = 20$

When multiplying two numbers with different signs, the answer is ALWAYS negative.

$(+5) \times (-4) = -20 \qquad (-5) \times (+4) = -20$

When multiplying more than two numbers, count the number of negatives. If there is an even number of negative terms, the answer is positive. If there is an odd number of negative terms, the answer is negative.

① Classwork
Solve, using the rules for multiplying signed numbers.

$(+9) \times (+5) = 45$
$(+9) \times (-5) = -45$
$(-9) \times (+5) = -45$
$(-9) \times (-5) = 45$
$(-3)(5)(-2) = (-15)(-2) = 30$
$(3)(5)(2) = (15)(2) = 30$
$(-3)(-5)(-2) = (15)(-2) = -30$
$(3)(5)(-2) = (15)(-2) = -30$

Something to Think About...
Two parentheses next to each other with no symbol between them means multiply.
$(5)(4) = 20 \qquad (-5)(4) = -20$

Commutative Property of Multiplication: You can change the order of the terms and still get the same product.
$2 \times 3 = 6$ and $3 \times 2 = 6$

Associative Property of Multiplication: You can group the terms in different ways and still get the same product.
$2 \times (3 \times 4) = 2 \times 12 = 24$ and $(2 \times 3) \times 4 = 6 \times 4 = 24$

Identity Property of Multiplication: You can multiply zero by any number and the product is always zero.
$0 \times 4 = 0$ and $4 \times 0 = 0$

Activities
② Solve, using the rules for multiplying signed numbers.

$(7)(9) = 63$	$(-2)(11) = -22$
$(7)(-9) = -63$	$(3)(7)(-2) = (21)(-2) = -42$
$(-7)(9) = -63$	$(6)(-7)(1) = (-42)(1) = -42$
$(-7)(-9) = 63$	$(-9)(-9)(-1) = (81)(-1) = -81$
$(12)(-3) = -36$	$(-3)(8)(2) = (-24)(2) = -48$
$(-12)(3) = -36$	$(-4)(-9)(1) = (36)(1) = 36$
$(10)(-6) = -60$	$(12)(10)(-1) = (120)(-1) = -120$
$(4)(7) = 28$	$(-11)(8)(-1) = (-88)(-1) = 88$
$(-8)(-5) = 40$	$(-9)(-12)(-1) = (108)(-1) = -108$

③ Solve.

32	50	36	48	15	88
×45	×82	×99	×45	×98	×18
160	100	324	240	120	704
+1280	+4000	+3240	+1920	+1350	+880
1,440	4,100	3,564	2,160	1,470	1,584

696	359	628	867	963	589
×98	×18	×97	×90	×49	×77
5568	2872	4396	000	8667	4123
+62640	+3590	+56520	+78030	+38520	+41230
68,208	6,462	60,916	78,030	47,187	45,353

```
      15          8          9          3          3          3
 36)540     34)272     53)477     92)276     58)174     69)207
    36         272        477        276        174        207
   180         000        000        000        000        000
   180
   000
```

```
      12         30          9          6         29         48
 66)792     17)510     73)657     57)342     34)986     18)864
    66         51         657        342        68         72
   132         00        000        000        306        144
   132         00                              306        144
   000         00                              000        000
```

④ Estimate the sum by rounding to the nearest thousand.

1907	2000		3972	4000		2169	2000		5987	6000
+3118	+3000	≈	+2024	+2000	≈	+1880	+2000	≈	+3012	+3000
	5,000			6,000			4,000			9,000

⑤ Solve the word problem.
Dan has budgeted $175 for groceries and supplies on his next trip to Kampala, the capital city of Uganda. One U.S. dollar is worth 2090 Ugandan shillings. How many shillings has Dan budgeted for groceries and supplies?
175 x 2090 = 365,750 Ugandan shillings

Teaching Tips, Cont.

➤ Write the following problems on the board:
2 × 3 =, (2)(3)=, 2(3)=, 2·3 =
Explain to the students that all four problems mean "2 times 3."

➤ Teach the properties of multiplication. At this point, it is not necessary for the students to memorize the names of the properties, but it is important that they understand and can apply the concept. Specifically mention the usefulness of the commutative property. Encourage students to look for factors that will multiply together to make the problem easier.

➤ Write the problem 2 × 8 × 5 on the board. Ask a student to explain how to solve that problem. After the student has given his explanation, point out that most people would not be able to multiply 16 × 5 in their heads, but that 10 × 8 is easy to calculate.

➤ Complete the Classwork exercises. Have some students work the problems on the board for the class and explain their answers. All students should work the problems in their books.

Assignment
• Complete Lesson 4, Activities 2-5.

Lesson 5

Concepts
- Absolute value
- Inverse operations
- Adding signed numbers
- Subtracting signed numbers
- Addition with 5-digit numbers
- Subtraction with 5-digit numbers

Learning Objectives
The student will be able to:
- Define *absolute value*
- Find the absolute value of positive and negative numbers
- Find the absolute value of mathematical expressions
- Define *inverse operations*

Materials Needed
- Student Book, Lesson 5
- Worksheet 3

Teaching Tips
➢ Have students complete Worksheet 3 in class. This may be for added practice of earlier topics or graded as a quiz.

➢ Define the terms in the teaching box of Lesson 5. Emphasize that absolute value is a number's distance from zero on the number line. Distance is always positive.

➢ Define *inverse operations*. Explain that inverse operations are mathematical opposites. Addition is the opposite of subtraction, and multiplication is the opposite of division.

Lesson 5

Absolute Value

The **absolute value** of a number is the number's distance from zero on a number line. The absolute value of 5, written as $|5|$, is 5, because the number 5 is 5 units away from zero. The absolute value of −5, written as $|-5|$, is also 5, because −5 is 5 units away from zero.

① Classwork
Solve the following absolute value problems.

$|23| = 23$ $-|6| = -6$

$|-11| = 11$ $-|-37| = -37$

Something to Think About...

How can you "undo" a mathematical operation? **Inverse operations** are the solution!

Addition and subtraction are inverse operations. Subtraction will undo addition, and addition will undo subtraction.

Multiplication and division are also inverse operations. One will undo the other.

Activities

② Solve, using the rules of absolute values.

$|6| = 6$
$|42| = 42$
$|-27| = 27$
$|-69| = 69$
$-|91| = -91$
$-|-87| = -87$
$-|29| = -29$
$-|-34| = -34$
$|13 + 9| = 22$

$-|21 + 12| = -33$
$|5 + 8| = 13$
$|1 - 2| = 1$
$-|7 - 10| = -3$
$-|12 + 7| = -19$
$-|3 - 5| = -2$
$|6| + |14| = 6 + 14 = 20$
$-|9| + |15| = 9 + 15 = 24$
$|-7| + |-23| =$
7 + 23 = 30

$|-9| + |26| = 9 + 26 = 35$
$|25| - |-4| = 25 - 4 = 21$
$-|19| + |-3| =$
-19 + 3 = -16
$-|21| - |-8| =$
-21 - 8 = -29
$|36| - |25| = 36 - 25 = 11$
$-|-15| - |-12| =$
-15 - 12 = -27
$|9 + 8| + |13 - 7| =$
17 + 6 = 23
$-|14 - 6| + |5 - 7| =$
-8 + 2 = -6
$-|16 + 4| - |32 - 8| =$
-20 - 24 = -44

③ Solve, using the rules for signed numbers. Write the problem vertically, if necessary.

$(+17) + (+5) = 17 + 5 = 22$
$(-3) + (+14) = 14 - 3 = 11$
$(-8) - (-16) = (-8) + (+16) = 16 - 8 = 8$
$(+67) + (-15) = 67 - 15 = 52$
$(+25) + (+15) = 25 + 15 = 40$
$(+36) - (-14) =$
$(+36) + (+14) = 36 + 14 = 50$

$(-7) + (+28) = 28 - 7 = 21$
$(-13) + (-42) = -(13 + 42) = -55$
$(+44) - (+11) = 44 - 11 = 33$
$(+16) + (-9) = 16 - 9 = 7$
$(-17) + (+26) = 26 - 17 = 9$
$(-8) - (-27) =$
$(-8) + (+27) = 27 - 8 = 19$

---

④ Solve.

13181	36449	33338	54882	12254	78877	49771
61753	27774	66365	24016	20332	44737	89601
+39105	+90028	+16534	+11533	+93153	+10569	+19007
114,039	154,251	116,237	90,431	125,739	134,183	158,379

54383	75352	36346	59566	98891	38232	85419
80359	93241	57772	87940	60338	29253	13602
+45430	+25387	+97115	+82159	+59681	+30753	+64106
180,172	193,980	191,233	229,665	218,910	98,238	163,127

37009	77128	63248	23956	23058	43628	44825
−34370	−23370	−12294	−12523	−15455	−30301	−22323
2,639	53,758	50,954	11,433	7,603	13,327	22,502

31141	69004	24152	93487	59707	14557	45065
−25706	−13952	−21021	−34960	−56588	−10411	−13389
5,435	55,052	3,131	58,527	3,119	4,146	31,676

⑤ Follow the directions. Do your work on another piece of paper, if necessary.

Write the first three digits of your phone number (not the area code). _____
                                                                    X 80

= _____
  +1

= _____
  X 250

= _____

Add the last four digits of your phone number + _____

= _____

Add the last four digits of your phone number again + _____

Answers will vary. The answer will be the student's 7-digit phone number. = _____
                                                                          - 250
The first three digits will be the numbers in the first blank.
The last four digits will be the numbers in the 5ᵗʰ or 7ᵗʰ blanks. = _____
                                                                     ÷ 2

= _____

① Identify each number as *natural*, *whole*, *integer*, *rational*, *irrational*, or *real*. Some numbers may have more than one answer.

	$3\sqrt{7}$	-8	π	0	$3\frac{2}{5}$	$\frac{9}{8}$	21	$-\frac{1}{3}$	37.1
Natural							x		
Whole				x			x		
Integer		x		x			x		
Rational		x		x	x	x	x	x	x
Irrational	x		x						
Real	x	x	x	x	x	x	x	x	x

② Estimate the sum by rounding to the nearest hundred.

$\begin{array}{r} 205 \\ +197 \\ \hline \end{array} \approx \begin{array}{r} 200 \\ +200 \\ \hline 400 \end{array}$ $\begin{array}{r} 494 \\ +303 \\ \hline \end{array} \approx \begin{array}{r} 500 \\ +300 \\ \hline 800 \end{array}$ $\begin{array}{r} 406 \\ +296 \\ \hline \end{array} \approx \begin{array}{r} 400 \\ +300 \\ \hline 700 \end{array}$ $\begin{array}{r} 688 \\ +213 \\ \hline \end{array} \approx \begin{array}{r} 700 \\ +200 \\ \hline 900 \end{array}$

$\begin{array}{r} 318 \\ +774 \\ \hline \end{array} \approx \begin{array}{r} 300 \\ +800 \\ \hline 1100 \end{array}$ $\begin{array}{r} 328 \\ +981 \\ \hline \end{array} \approx \begin{array}{r} 300 \\ +1000 \\ \hline 1300 \end{array}$ $\begin{array}{r} 886 \\ +219 \\ \hline \end{array} \approx \begin{array}{r} 900 \\ +200 \\ \hline 1100 \end{array}$ $\begin{array}{r} 301 \\ +597 \\ \hline \end{array} \approx \begin{array}{r} 300 \\ +600 \\ \hline 900 \end{array}$

③ Estimate each product by rounding to the nearest ten.

12 x 127 = 10 x 130 = 1300
88 x 21 = 90 x 20 = 1800
49 x 71 = 50 x 70 = 3500
51 x 69 = 50 x 70 = 3500
28 x 32 = 30 x 30 = 900
99 x 252 = 100 x 250 = 25,000
77 x 82 = 80 x 80 = 6400
32 x 47 = 30 x 50 = 1500

Teaching Tips, Cont.

➤ Explain that absolute value gives a number's distance from zero. Inverse operations get a number back to its starting point, no matter what that starting point is. Inverse operations are the foundation of math fact families.

➤ To illustrate absolute value and inverse operations, ask the students the following questions: If John jogs 1 mile east, turns around, and jogs 1 mile west, how many miles has John jogged? (2) Changing direction does not affect the sign of the answer. Traveling east is like moving in the positive direction on the number line. Traveling west is like moving in the negative direction on the number line. If John starts at mile marker 8 and bicycles for 6 miles, at what mile marker will he end? (14) How many miles must he bicycle to return to mile marker 8? (6) This is using inverse operations. 8 + 6 = 14 and 14 − 6 = 8

➤ When working absolute value problems, always solve inside the absolute value sign first (the answer inside the absolute value sign is always positive), then apply any signs and operations outside the absolute value sign.

➤ Complete the Classwork exercises. Have some students work the problems on the board for the class. All students should work the problems in their books.

Assignment
- Complete Lesson 5, Activities 2-5.

Lesson 6

Concepts
- Factors
- Signed numbers
- Absolute value
- Math in the real world

Learning Objectives
The student will be able to:
- Define *factor*
- Find all natural number factors of a given number
- Solve real-world problems using addition, multiplication, and division

Materials Needed
- Student Book, Lesson 6
- Algebra tiles (cut from the *Tests and Resources* book)
- Zip-top sandwich bags – 1 per student

Teaching Tips
➢ Define *factor* from the teaching box. Ask a student to define *natural number*. (Refer to Lesson 1, if necessary.)

➢ Have students take out 12 of the single unit squares from the algebra tiles. Ask them to arrange the squares to form a rectangle. The dimensions of the rectangle are factors. A 3 x 4 rectangle shows that 3 and 4 are factors of 12.

➢ This activity also works to arrange the squares in equal-sized groups. They should try groups of 1, 2, 3, etc. all the way up to 12. Which group sizes work? Which ones don't? The group sizes that work are the factors of 12.

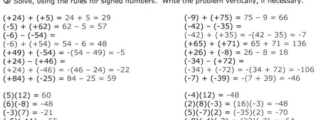

Factors

A **factor** is a natural number that divides into another number with no remainder.
4 is a factor of 12 because $12 \div 4 = 3$.
From this example, we can see that 3 is also a factor of 12.
All the factors of 12 are 1, 2, 3, 4, 6, and 12.

① **Classwork**
Find all the factors of the following numbers:
6   1, 2, 3, 6
15   1, 3, 5, 15
16   1, 2, 4, 8, 16

Activities
② Find all of the factors for each of the following numbers.

2   1, 2
3   1, 3
4   1, 2, 4
5   1, 5
6   1, 2, 3, 6
7   1, 7
8   1, 2, 4, 8
9   1, 3, 9
10   1, 2, 5, 10

③ Solve, using the rules for signed numbers. Write the problem vertically, if necessary.

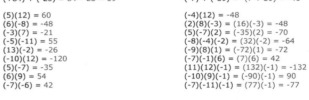

(+24) + (+5) = 24 + 5 = 29
(-5) + (+62) = 62 − 5 = 57
(-6) − (-54) =
(-6) + (+54) = 54 − 6 = 48
(+49) + (-54) = -(54 − 49) = -5
(+24) − (+46) =
(+24) + (-46) = -(46 − 24) = -22
(+84) + (-25) = 84 − 25 = 59

(-9) + (+75) = 75 − 9 = 66
(-42) − (-35) =
(-42) + (+35) = -(42 − 35) = -7
(+65) + (+71) = 65 + 71 = 136
(+26) + (-8) = 26 − 8 = 18
(-34) − (+72) =
(-34) + (-72) = -(34 + 72) = -106
(-7) + (-39) = -(7 + 39) = -46

(5)(12) = 60
(6)(-8) = -48
(-3)(7) = -21
(-5)(-11) = 55
(13)(-2) = -26
(-10)(12) = -120
(5)(-7) = -35
(6)(9) = 54
(-7)(-6) = 42

(-4)(12) = -48
(2)(8)(-3) = (16)(-3) = -48
(5)(-7)(2) = (-35)(2) = -70
(-8)(-4)(-2) = (32)(-2) = -64
(-9)(8)(1) = (-72)(1) = -72
(-7)(-1)(6) = (7)(6) = 42
(11)(12)(-1) = (132)(-1) = -132
(-10)(9)(-1) = (-90)(-1) = 90
(-7)(-11)(-1) = (77)(-1) = -77

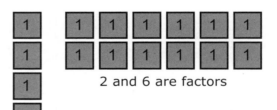

2 and 6 are factors

3 and 4 are factors

1 and 12 are factors

④ Solve, using the rules of absolute values.

$|-7| + |-23| = 7 + 23 = 30$

$|-9| + |26| = 9 + 26 = 35$

$|25| - |-4| = 25 - 4 = 21$

$-|19| + |-3| = -19 + 3 = -(19 - 3) = -16$

$-|21| - |-8| = -21 - (+8) = -21 + (-8) = -$
$(21 + 8) = -29$

$|36| - |25| = 36 - 25 = 11$

$-|-15| - |-12| = -15 - (+12) =$
-15 + (-12) = -(15 + 12) = -27

$|9 + 8| + |13 - 7| = 17 + 6 = 23$

$-|14 - 6| + |5 - 7| =$
-8 + 2 = -(8 - 2) = -6

$-|16 + 4| - |32 - 8| =$
-20 - 26 = -20 + (-26) =
-(20 + 26) = -46

⑤ Solve the word problems.
At Dan's radio station in Soroti, Uganda, each solar panel can generate 80 watts of power per hour of sunshine each day. If Soroti averages 5 hours of sunshine per day, how much power is generated by one solar panel each day?
80 watts x 5 = 400 watts of power

Each day, the radio station uses the following items: radio transmitter: 5400 watts, computer: 420 watts, broadcast equipment: 900 watts, energy-efficient light bulbs: 180 watts, battery charging: 1380 watts. What is the total number of watts needed to operate the radio station for one day?
5400 watts + 420 watts + 900 watts + 180 watts + 1380 watts = 8280 watts

Based on the above information, how many solar panels does Dan need to install to operate the radio station? Because 20 panels will not be enough (there is a remainder of 280), Dan must install at least 21 panels to generate enough power.

```
        20
400)8280
     800
     280
     000
     280
```

Assignment
• Complete Lesson 6, Activities 2-5.

2 and 6 are factors

3 and 4 are factors

5 is not a factor

Lesson 7

Concepts
- Multiples
- Factors
- Signed numbers
- Addition
- Subtraction
- Math in the real world

Learning Objectives
The student will be able to:
- Define *multiple*
- Calculate 5 multiples of a given natural number
- Find all natural number factors of a given natural number
- Apply multiplication and division to real world problems

Materials Needed
- Student Book, Lesson 7

Teaching Tips
➢ Have students count to 60 by 3's, 4's, and 5's.

➢ Define *multiple* from the teaching box, showing students that they have just listed multiples of 3, 4, and 5.

➢ Students who are having difficulty with multiples may want to use the algebra tiles at first. Have the students arrange the individual squares of the algebra tiles into groups of the given number. For example, for multiples of five, they should make several groups of five squares. They can then count the squares to find the multiples. Encourage the students to skip count rather than count every individual square. This will reinforce the idea that multiples are the result of skip counting.

Multiples

Multiples	
A **multiple** is the result of skip counting. It is also the product of two factors. 12 is a multiple of 4 because $4+4+4=12$ and $4 \times 3 = 12$. 12 is also a multiple of 1, 2, 3, 6, and 12. A number is the multiple of each of its factors.	① **Classwork** List 5 multiples of each of the following numbers: 2 2, 4, 6, 8, 10, etc. 5 5, 10, 15, 20, 25, etc. 7 7, 14, 21, 28, 35, etc.

Activities

② Write 5 multiples of each of the following numbers.

2 2, 4, 6, 8, 10, etc.

3 3, 6, 9, 12, 15, etc.

4 4, 8, 12, 16, 20, etc.

5 5, 10, 15, 20, 25, etc.

6 6, 12, 18, 24, 30, etc.

7 7, 14, 21, 28, 35, etc.

8 8, 16, 24, 32, 40, etc.

9 9, 18, 27, 36, 45, etc.

10 10, 20, 30, 40, 50, etc.

③ Find all of the factors for each of the following numbers.

11 1, 11

12 1, 2, 3, 4, 6, 12

13 1, 13

14 1, 2, 7, 14

15 1, 3, 5, 15

16 1, 2, 4, 8, 16

17 1, 17

18 1, 2, 3, 6, 9, 18

19 1, 19

20 1, 2, 4, 5, 10, 20

---

④ Solve, using the rules for signed numbers. Write the problem vertically, if necessary.

$(-18) + (+73) = 73 - 18 = 55$

$(+57) + (-2) = 57 - 2 = 55$

$(-57) - (-48) =$
$(-57) + (+48) = -(57 - 48) = -9$

$(-61) - (+81) =$
$(-61) + (-81) = -(61 + 81) = -142$

$(+45) + (+35) = 45 + 35 = 80$

$(-5) + (-37) = -(5 + 37) = -42$

$(11)(5) = 55$

$(3)(9)(-3) = (27)(-3) = -81$

$(-6)(-7) = 42$

$(4)(-2)(9) = (-8)(9) = -72$

$(-3)(8) = -24$

$(-2)(-7)(-10) = (14)(-10) = -140$

⑤ Solve.

24506	57576	62347	39065	71208	21132	91618
+50531	+92835	+21132	+13199	+23228	+47480	+44019
75,037	150,411	83,479	52,264	94,436	68,612	135,637

36072	82616	45960	16651	78161	91664	46423
−13620	−57297	−29773	−11290	−29382	−74450	−24520
22,452	25,319	16,187	5,361	48,779	17,214	21,903

⑦ Solve the word problems.

Dan's radio station uses 8280 watts of power each day. If one rechargeable 12-volt battery can supply 720 watts of useable power, how many batteries does Dan need to connect to his solar power system?
$8280 \div 720 = 11.5$ batteries. There is no such thing as connecting part of a battery, so Dan must connect 12 batteries to his solar power system.

If each battery costs $410, how much does it cost for all the batteries for the radio station?
$410 x 12 = $4920

The batteries must be replaced every 60 months. At this rate, how much should Dan save each month to have enough money saved to buy new batteries at the end of the 60 months? (Assume the price doesn't change.)
$4920 ÷ 60 = $82 each month for the next 5 years

Teaching Tips, Cont.
> Complete the Classwork exercises. Have some students work the problems on the board for the class. All students should work the problems in their books.

Assignment
• Complete Lesson 7, Activities 2-5.

Lesson 8

Concepts
- Prime numbers
- Composite numbers
- Factors
- Multiples
- Multiplication
- Division

Learning Objectives
The student will be able to:
- Define *prime numbers*
- Define *composite numbers*
- Identify each natural number 1-100 as prime or composite
- Find prime factors of a given natural number

Materials Needed
- Student Book, Lesson 8
- Worksheet 4

Teaching Tips
➢ Have students complete Worksheet 4 in class. This may be for added practice of earlier topics, or graded as a quiz, if desired.

➢ Define *prime* and *composite* from the teaching box. Emphasize that 0 and 1 are neither prime nor composite, and that 2 is the only even prime number. Point out the phrase *greater than 1* in the definition of composite. This explains why 0 and 1 are not included as composite numbers.

Prime and Composite Numbers

Prime numbers are natural numbers whose only factors are 1 and itself. 3 is a prime number because its only factors are 1 and 3.

Composite numbers are all numbers greater than 1 that are not prime.

The numbers 0 and 1 are neither prime nor composite, and 2 is the only even prime number.

① **Classwork**
Find all the factors of each number. Use this information to identify each as either *prime* or *composite*.

3 1, 3, prime
4 1, 2, 4, composite
5 1, 5, prime
6 1, 2, 3, 6, composite
7 1, 7, prime

Activities

② Find the prime numbers in the list below by following the directions.
1. Cross out the number 1.
2. Circle the number 2. Cross out every other number after two (the multiples of 2).
3. Circle the number 3. Cross out every third number after three (the multiples of 3).
4. Circle the number 5. Cross out every fifth number after five (the multiples of 5).
5. Circle the number 7. Cross out every seventh number after seven (the multiples of 7).
6. Circle all remaining numbers. The circled numbers are the prime numbers less than 100.
7. This is called the sieve of Eratosthenes.

1	2	3	4	5	6	7	8	9	10
11	12	13	14	15	16	17	18	19	20
21	22	23	24	25	26	27	28	29	30
31	32	33	34	35	36	37	38	39	40
41	42	43	44	45	46	47	48	49	50
51	52	53	54	55	56	57	58	59	60
61	62	63	64	65	66	67	68	69	70
71	72	73	74	75	76	77	78	79	80
81	82	83	84	85	86	87	88	89	90
91	92	93	94	95	96	97	98	99	100

Write the prime numbers less than 100.

__2__ __3__ __5__ __7__ __11__ __13__ __17__ __19__ __23__ __29__ __31__ __37__ __41__
__43__ __47__ __53__ __59__ __61__ __67__ __71__ __73__ __79__ __83__ __89__ __97__

---

③ Find all of the natural number factors for each of the following numbers. Circle the factors that are prime numbers.

12   1, ②, ③, 4, 6, 12

14   1, ②, ⑦, 14

15   1, ③, ⑤, 15

16   1, ②, 4, 8, 16

18   1, ②, ③, 6, 9, 18

20   1, ②, 4, ⑤, 10, 20

21   1, ③, ⑦, 21

④ List 5 multiples of each of the following numbers.

21   21, 42, 63, 84, 105, etc.
22   22, 44, 66, 88, 110, etc.
23   23, 46, 69, 92, 115, etc.
24   24, 48, 72, 96, 120, etc.
25   25, 50, 75, 100, 125, etc.
30   30, 60, 90, 120, 150, etc.
40   40, 80, 120, 160, 200, etc.

⑤ Solve.

	689	276	648	659	527	374
	×21	×75	×79	×85	×34	×20
	689	1380	5832	3295	2108	000
	+13780	+19320	+45360	+52720	+15810	+7480
	14,469	20,700	51,192	56,015	17,918	7,480

	12	5	4	19	26	32
	77)924	37)185	72)288	18)342	37)962	26)832
	77	185	288	18	74	78
	154	000	000	162	222	52
	154			162	222	52
	000			000	000	00

① Solve, using the rules for signed numbers.

$(+8) + (+5) = 8 + 5 = 13$

$(-8) + (+5) = -(8 - 5) = -3$

$(-8) + (-5) = -(8 + 5) = -13$

$(+8) + (-5) = 8 - 5 = 3$

$(+8) - (-5) = 8 + 5 = 13$

$(-8) - (-5) = (-8) + (+5) = -(8 - 5) = -3$

$(8)(5) = 40$

$(8)(-5) = -40$

$(-8)(5) = -40$

$(-8)(-5) = 40$

② Solve, using the rules of absolute values.

$|14| = 14$

$|-31| = 31$

$-|27| = -27$

$-|29| = -29$

$-|-18| = -18$

$|26 + 10| = 36$

$-|22 + 11| = -33$

$|-2 + 15| = 13$

Teaching Tips, Cont.

➤ Tell students that another definition of *prime* is a number that has exactly two unique natural number factors. The number 1 does not have two *unique* factors and is not prime. (This concept is critical in the next lesson when the prime factorization of numbers is found. Because 1 is not a prime number, it is not listed as part of the prime factorization of any number. This allows for a single correct prime factorization for each natural number.)

➤ Complete the Classwork exercises. Have some students work the problems on the board for the class. All students should work the problems in their books.

Assignment

• Complete Lesson 8, Activities 2-5.

Lesson 9

Concepts
- Prime factorization
- Multiples
- Absolute value
- Addition
- Subtraction

Learning Objectives
The student will be able to:
- Define *prime factor*
- Explain the process for finding prime factors
- Use repeated division or factor trees to find the prime factorization of a natural number

Materials Needed
- Student Book, Lesson 9
- Worksheet 5

Teaching Tips
➤ Review the definitions of *prime* and *composite* from Lesson 8. Remind students that 1 is neither prime nor composite.

➤ Review the definition of *factor* from Lesson 6. Have the students list all factors of 24.
(1, 2, 3, 4, 6, 8, 12, 24)

➤ Ask the students to identify each factor as prime or composite. Emphasize again that 1 is neither prime nor composite. (Primes are 2 and 3; Composites are 4, 6, 8, 12, and 24.) Have the students list factors of the composites until they have no more composite factors.

➤ Define *prime factor* and *prime factorization* from the teaching box.

Prime Factorization

Prime factors of a number are the prime numbers that divide into the number with no remainder.
Prime factorization is the process of finding all the prime numbers that multiply together to get the original number.

There are two ways to find the prime factorization of a number. One is to continually divide by prime numbers until you get a quotient that is prime.
$24 \div 2 = 12$
$12 \div 2 = 6$
$6 \div 2 = 3$
The prime factors of 24 are 2, 2, 2, and 3.

The second way is to make a factor tree. Write the original number as the product of any two factors you think of. Continue factoring these factors until all factors are prime.

① **Classwork**
Find the prime factorization of each number.

Activities
② Find the prime factorization of each number. Use the method of your choice.

15	20	27	30
15 = 3 x 5	20 = 2 x 2 x 5	27 = 3 x 3 x 3	30 = 2 x 3 x 5

35	39	48	52
35 = 5 x 7	39 = 3 x 13	48 = 2 x 2 x 2 x 2 x 3	52 = 2 x 2 x 13

---

③ List 5 multiples of each of the following numbers.
50   50, 100, 150, 200, 250, etc.
60   60, 120, 180, 240, 300, etc.
70   70, 140, 210, 280, 350, etc.
80   80, 160, 240, 320, 400, etc.
90   90, 180, 270, 360, 450, etc.

④ Solve, using the rules of absolute values.

$|-9| + |-32| = 9 + 32 = 41$

$|47| - |18| = 47 - 18 = 29$

$|-7| + |46| = 7 + 46 = 53$

$-|-31| - |-22| = -31 - (+22) = -31 + (-22) = -(31 + 22) = -53$

$|31| - |-6| = 31 - 6 = 25$

$|3 + 14| + |10 - 8| = 17 + 2 = 19$

$-|27| + |-10| = -27 + 10 = -(27 - 10) = -17$

$-|21 - 9| + |14 - 6| = -12 + 8 = -(12 - 8) = -4$

$-|11| - |-3| = -11 - (+3) = -11 + (-3) = -(11 + 3) = -14$

$-|27 + 5| - |12 - 7| = -32 - (+5) = -32 + (-5) = -(32 + 5) = -37$

⑤ Solve.

47772 +83715	43241 +60406	93541 +70907	50848 +16315	46474 +48824	77942 +56827	87039 +90504
131,487	103,647	164,448	67,163	95,298	134,769	177,543

22101 +97119	21621 +65211	88840 +40655	55346 +58971	50521 +64222	94289 +18375	40942 +14131
119,220	86,832	129,495	114,317	114,743	112,664	55,073

32892 −31714	90361 −42879	58636 −40797	83186 −73376	80195 −38420	71750 −35717	36607 −11328
1,178	47,482	17,839	9,810	41,775	36,033	25,279

89147 −46005	56692 −31829	23747 −13485	36763 −33654	79400 −52411	87794 −39276	37623 −23831
43,142	24,863	10,262	3,109	26,989	48,518	13,792

① Find all of the factors for each of the following numbers and identify as prime or composite.

11 1, 11   Prime
12 1, 2, 3, 4, 6, 12   Composite
13 1, 13   Prime
14 1, 2, 7, 14   Composite
15 1, 3, 5, 15   Composite
16 1, 2, 4, 8, 16   Composite
17 1, 17   Prime
18 1, 2, 3, 6, 9, 18   Composite
19 1, 19   Prime
20 1, 2, 4, 5, 10, 20   Composite

② Write 5 multiples of each of the following numbers.

5   5, 10, 15, 20, 25, etc.
6   6, 12, 18, 24, 30, etc.
7   7, 14, 21, 28, 35, etc.
8   8, 16, 24, 32, 40, etc.
9   9, 18, 27, 36, 45, etc.
11 11, 22, 33, 44, 55, etc.
12 12, 24, 36, 48, 60, etc.
13 13, 26, 39, 52, 65, etc.
15 15, 30, 45, 60, 75, etc.

① Find the prime factorization of each of the following numbers.

12	25	32
$12 = 2 \times 2 \times 3$	$25 = 5 \times 5$	$32 = 2 \times 2 \times 2 \times 2 \times 2$

Teaching Tips, Cont.

➢ Demonstrate the procedures for finding the prime factorization of 24, emphasizing that prime numbers must be used as the divisors when doing repeated division, but any factor may be used in a factor tree.

➢ Complete the Classwork exercises. Have some students work the problems on the board for the class. All students should work the problems in their books.

Assignments

- Complete Lesson 9, Activities 2-5
- Worksheet 5 (Optional).

Note: Factorization by division can be done by dividing upside-down:

Step 1:   ② | 24
                  ‾‾‾
                   12

Step 2:   ② | 24
                  ‾‾‾
               ② | 12
                  ‾‾‾
                    6

Step 3:   ② | 24
                  ‾‾‾
               ② | 12
                  ‾‾‾
               ② |_6
                  ‾‾‾
                  ③

Continue dividing the quotient by prime numbers until the quotient is prime. This method makes it easy to identify all of the prime factors.

Lesson 10

Concepts
- Exponents
- Prime factorization
- Signed numbers
- Multiplication

Learning Objectives
The student will be able to:
- Define *exponent* and *base*
- Use exponents to express products
- Write exponential notations in expanded form
- Solve exponential expressions

Materials Needed
- Student Book, Lesson 10
- Calculator

Teaching Tips
➢ Many older calculators will calculate exponential numbers when you repeatedly press the [=] key. Try this on your calculator before class to make sure it works! Have a student press [2] [x] [2] [=] [=] [=] . . . and read the numbers as they appear. The students should get 4, 8, 16, 32, etc. Note: This will not work on the new scientific calculators or those with multiple display lines.

➢ Define *exponent* and *base* from the teaching box. Tell students that the base is the number on the bottom. (This concept will carry over in later years when they are learning logarithms with different bases.) It will also help to remember that the exponent is elevated.

Exponents

Exponents tell how many times a number is multiplied by itself. The number being multiplied is called the **base**. The exponent is written as a small number on the upper right side of the base. In the expression 4^3, the number 4 is the base and the number 3 is the exponent. $4^3 = 4 \times 4 \times 4 = 64$ The answer to an exponential expression is always a multiple of the base.	① **Classwork** Expand and solve the following exponential expressions. $2^3 = 2 \times 2 \times 2 = 8$ $3^2 = 3 \times 3 = 9$ $2^5 = 2 \times 2 \times 2 \times 2 \times 2 = 32$ $3^3 = 3 \times 3 \times 3 = 27$

Activities

② Write the expanded form expressions in exponential form. Do not solve them.

$3 \times 3 \times 3 \times 3 \times 3 = 3^5$ $\qquad\qquad$ $7 \times 7 \times 7 \times 7 \times 7 \times 7 = 7^6$

$5 \times 5 \times 5 = 5^3$ $\qquad\qquad$ $12 \times 12 \times 12 \times 12 = 12^4$

$4 \times 4 \times 4 \times 4 \times 4 \times 4 \times 4 \times 4 = 4^8$ $\qquad\qquad$ $8 \times 8 \times 8 \times 8 \times 8 \times 8 \times 8 = 8^7$

③ Write the following exponential expressions in expanded form and solve.

$2^2 = 2 \times 2 = 4$

$3^2 = 3 \times 3 = 9$

$2^3 = 2 \times 2 \times 2 = 8$

$4^2 = 4 \times 4 = 16$

$2^4 = 2 \times 2 \times 2 \times 2 = 16$

$3^3 = 3 \times 3 \times 3 = 27$

$2^5 = 2 \times 2 \times 2 \times 2 \times 2 = 32$

$4^3 = 4 \times 4 \times 4 = 64$

Exponents

④ Find the prime factorization of each number. Use the method of your choice.

8	24	44
8 = 2 x 2 x 2	24 = 2 x 2 x 2 x 3	44 = 2 x 2 x 11

33	14	28
33 = 3 x 11	14 = 2 x 7	28 = 2 x 2 x 7

46	40	18
46 = 2 x 23	40 = 2 x 2 x 2 x 5	18 = 2 x 3 x 3

50	21	42
50 = 2 x 5 x 5	21 = 3 x 7	42 = 2 x 3 x 7

⑤ Complete the multiplication chart, following the rules of signed numbers.

x	2	-3	4	-5	6	-7	8	-9	10
3	6	-9	12	-15	18	-21	24	-27	30
-4	-8	12	-16	20	-24	28	-32	36	-40
5	10	-15	20	-25	30	-35	40	-45	50
-6	-12	18	-24	30	-36	42	-48	54	-60
7	14	-21	28	-35	42	-49	56	-63	70
-8	-16	24	-32	40	-48	56	-64	72	-80
9	18	-27	36	-45	54	-63	72	-81	90

Teaching Tips, Cont.

➢ Demonstrate the proper form for writing numbers with exponents, using the numbers from the calculator as an example.

➢ Complete the Classwork exercises. Have some students work the problems on the board for the class. All students should work the problems in their books.

➢ Review for Test 1 using worksheets 1-5. These worksheets were all assigned in previous lessons.

Assignments

• Complete Lesson 10, Activities 2-5.
• Study for test (Lessons 1-7)

Test 1

Testing Objectives

The student will be able to:

- Identify numbers as *natural*, *whole*, *integer*, *rational*, *irrational*, and *real*
- Estimate sums by rounding
- Apply the rules of adding, subtracting and multiplying signed numbers
- Solve expressions with absolute values
- Find all natural number factors of a given number
- Calculate 5 multiples of a given natural number
- Add sets of 5-digit addends
- Subtract two 5-digit numbers
- Divide a 3-digit number by a 2-digit number

Materials Needed

- Test 1
- *It's College Test Prep Time!* from Student Book
- *A Math Minute with …* Ric B. from Student Book

Teaching Tips

➢ Administer Test 1, allowing the students 30-40 minutes to complete the test.

➢ When all students are finished taking the test, introduce the College Test Prep Time from the student book. This page may be completed in class or assigned as homework.

➢ Have students read the Math Minute interview for Lessons 11-20.

---

① Identify each number as *natural, whole, integer, rational, irrational,* or *real*. Some numbers may have more than one answer.   **24 points**

	68	$-\sqrt{5}$	$2\frac{3}{8}$	-3	0	46.66	π	$\frac{5}{9}$	-0.07
Natural	x								
Whole	x				x				
Integer	x			x	x				
Rational	x		x	x	x	x		x	x
Irrational		x					x		
Real	x	x	x	x	x	x	x	x	x

② Estimate the sum by rounding to the nearest thousand.   **4 points**

$$2903 \approx 3000$$
$$+1102 \approx +1000$$
$$\overline{\quad 4,000}$$

$$7987 \approx 8000$$
$$+2019 \approx +2000$$
$$\overline{\quad 10,000}$$

$$4176 \approx 4000$$
$$+8885 \approx +9000$$
$$\overline{\quad 13,000}$$

$$3997 \approx 4000$$
$$+4009 \approx +4000$$
$$\overline{\quad 8,000}$$

③ Estimate each product by rounding to the nearest ten.   **4 points**

21 x 128 ≈ 20 x 130 = 2,600
67 x 32 ≈ 70 x 30 = 2,100
58 x 61 ≈ 60 x 60 = 3,600
52 x 48 ≈ 50 x 50 = 2,500

④ Solve, using the rules for signed numbers.   **14 points**

(+48) + (+4) = 48 + 4 = 52
(-2) + (+24) = 24 - 2 = 22
(-3) - (-34) =
(-3) + (+34) = 34 - 3 = 31

(+99) + (-72) = 99 - 72 = 27
(+35) - (+71) =
(+35) + (-71) = -(71 - 35) = -36
(-18) - (+82) = (-18) + (-82) = -100

(9)(11) = 99
(5)(-6) = -30
(-9)(4) = -36
(-3)(-20) = 60

(-6)(40) = -240
(10)(13)(-1) = (130)(-1) = -130
(-11)(8)(-1) = (-88)(-1) = 88
(-5)(-12)(-1) = (60)(-1) = -60

⑤ Solve, using the rules of absolute values.   **10 points**

$|-2| + |-75| = 2 + 75 = 77$
$|-3| + |56| = 3 + 56 = 59$
$|75| - |-9| = 75 - 9 = 66$
$-|12| + |-4| = (-12) + (+4) =$
$-(12 - 4) = -8$
$-|79| - |-1| = (-79) - (+1) =$
$(-79) + (-1) = -80$

$|97| - |93| = 97 - 93 = 4$
$-|-21| - |-18| = (-21) - (+18) =$
$(-21) + (-18) = -39$
$|8 + 2| + |23 - 6| = 10 + 17 = 27$
$-|16 - 2| + |6 - 9| = (-14) + (+3) =$
$-(14 - 3) = -11$
$-|27 + 3| - |61 - 9| = (-30) - (+52) =$
$(-30) + (-52) = -82$

---

⑥ Find all of the natural number factors for each of the following numbers.   **34 points**

12   1, 2, 3, 4, 6, 12
15   1, 3, 5, 15
18   1, 2, 3, 6, 9, 18
20   1, 2, 4, 5, 10, 20
21   1, 3, 7, 21
24   1, 2, 3, 4, 6, 8, 12, 24

⑦ Write 5 multiples of each of the following numbers.   **25 points**

7   7, 14, 21, 28, 35, etc.
10   10, 20, 30, 40, 50, etc.
11   11, 22, 33, 44, 55, etc.
15   15, 30, 45, 60, 75, etc.
20   20, 40, 60, 80, 100, etc.

⑧ Solve.   **20 points**

85419	64106	88873	72945	17811
+13602	+12925	+97381	+34994	+62835
99,021	77,031	186,254	107,939	80,646

15433	48738	86476	18754	93312
−10662	−34154	−75093	−13354	−50873
4,771	14,584	11,383	5,400	42,439

177	435	812	646	688
×92	×35	×96	×15	×55
354	2175	4872	3230	3440
+15930	+13050	+73080	+6460	+34400
16,284	15,225	77,952	9,690	37,840

$$\begin{array}{r}7\\94\overline{)658}\\\underline{658}\\000\end{array}$$

$$\begin{array}{r}3\\44\overline{)132}\\\underline{132}\\000\end{array}$$

$$\begin{array}{r}4\\66\overline{)264}\\\underline{264}\\000\end{array}$$

$$\begin{array}{r}14\\42\overline{)588}\\\underline{42}\\168\\\underline{168}\\000\end{array}$$

$$\begin{array}{r}17\\33\overline{)561}\\\underline{33}\\231\\\underline{231}\\000\end{array}$$

135 points

It's College Test Prep Time!

As you progress through your high school years, you will take a number of standardized tests that measure your skills in math, grammar, writing, vocabulary, and reading comprehension. Most colleges use your scores on these tests to determine whether or not to grant you admission to the college. Many scholarships are also based on your test scores, so it is important that you do as well as you can.

Periodically throughout this book, you will find a section of multiple choice questions. These questions are the same style and format as questions that are likely to appear on the math sections of these tests. They are also the same difficulty level as the pre-algebra questions that appear on the tests.

1. Which of the following numbers is NOT a factor of 78?
   Factors of 78 are 1, 2, 3, 6, 13, 26, 39, 78
   A. 3
   B. 6
   C. 13
   D. 36
   E. 39

2. Round 145.0792 to the nearest tenth.
   A. 145.0
   B. 145.1
   C. 145.07
   D. 145.08
   E. 145.079

3. P = the set of positive integer factors of 9 **1, 3, 9**
   Q = the set of positive integer factors of 12 **1, 2, 3, 4, 6, 12**
   R = the set of positive integer factors of 15 **1, 3, 5, 15**

   P, Q, and R represent three sets of numbers, as defined above. Which set of numbers below belongs to all three sets?
   A. {1, 3}
   B. {1, 3, 9}
   C. {1, 3, 5, 15}
   D. {1, 2, 3, 4, 6, 12}
   E. {1, 2, 3, 4, 5, 6, 9, 12, 15}

4. How many positive three-digit integers exist, such that all three digits are the same? **111, 222, 333, 444, 555, 666, 777, 888, 999**
   A. 3
   B. 5
   C. 8
   D. 9
   E. 10

A Math Minute with . . .

Ric B. – Youth Pastor

What is your occupation? Youth/Recreation Pastor

Where do you work? I work in the youth ministry of a Baptist church.

Did you attend college? If so, what was your major? Yes. My major was Religion with Youth Emphasis.

What parts of your job require the use of math? Most! I always have to give a head count for every service, so basic math is necessary to count people. I also organize retreats which involves calculating several different kinds of costs. For instance, if we take our students to Florida, we have to determine our costs months in advance. We must estimate the potential number of participants based on past attendance, trends, and, of course, FAITH. We use that number to guarantee the hotel a certain number of people we will pay for, and we will be obligated to pay whether they attend or not. We also have to determine the costs for meals, entertainment, musicians, speakers, travels costs, chaperones, and other miscellaneous items. I need to submit this estimated expenditure request to the pastor before leaving, so we know what we will be spending. Many similar mathematical problems are involved in my job.

What is the biggest "problem" you have faced that required the use of math to solve? We have to line fields for our sports program. We must use algebra to figure the rise and run of the fields, so we can ensure they are square. Math is a life saver!

Are there any other interesting math uses you have experienced? We track our attendance with percentages and also with times of the year. We use this to find the most common time of year when our attendance is high or low so that we can plan appropriately.

Lesson 11

Concepts
- Powers of numbers
- Square numbers
- Cubed numbers
- Prime factorization
- Absolute value
- Multiples
- Math in the real world

Learning Objectives
The student will be able to:
- Read exponential expressions correctly
- Calculate the square of a natural number
- Calculate the cube of a natural number
- Recognize powers of numbers as multiples of those numbers

Materials Needed
- Student Book, Lesson 11

Teaching Tips
➢ Teach the proper way to read exponential expressions from the teaching box.

➢ Review the definition of multiple from Lesson 7.

➢ Draw the chart at the right on the board, leaving out the numbers in the <u>Multiples</u> and <u>Square</u> columns.

➢ Have the students fill in the blanks for the <u>Multiples</u> column, listing the first five multiples for each number.

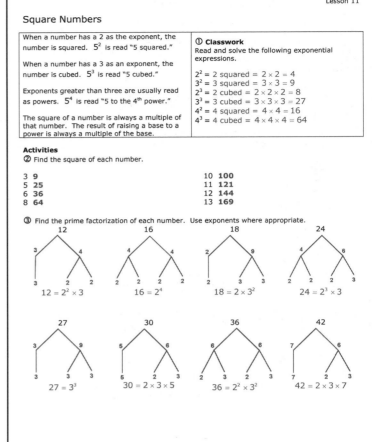

Square Numbers

When a number has a 2 as the exponent, the number is squared. 5^2 is read "5 squared."

When a number has a 3 as an exponent, the number is cubed. 5^3 is read "5 cubed."

Exponents greater than three are usually read as powers. 5^4 is read "5 to the 4th power."

The square of a number is always a multiple of that number. The result of raising a base to a power is always a multiple of the base.

① **Classwork**
Read and solve the following exponential expressions.

$2^2 = 2$ squared $= 2 \times 2 = 4$
$3^2 = 3$ squared $= 3 \times 3 = 9$
$2^3 = 2$ cubed $= 2 \times 2 \times 2 = 8$
$3^3 = 3$ cubed $= 3 \times 3 \times 3 = 27$
$4^2 = 4$ squared $= 4 \times 4 = 16$
$4^3 = 4$ cubed $= 4 \times 4 \times 4 = 64$

Activities
② Find the square of each number.

3 **9**
5 **25**
6 **36**
8 **64**

10 **100**
11 **121**
12 **144**
13 **169**

③ Find the prime factorization of each number. Use exponents where appropriate.

$12 = 2^2 \times 3$
$16 = 2^4$
$18 = 2 \times 3^2$
$24 = 2^3 \times 3$
$27 = 3^3$
$30 = 2 \times 3 \times 5$
$36 = 2^2 \times 3^2$
$42 = 2 \times 3 \times 7$

Number	Multiples	Square
2	2, 4, 6, 8, 10	4
3	3, 6, 9, 12, 15	9
4	4, 8, 12, 16, 20	16
5	5, 10, 15, 20, 25	25

④ Solve the absolute values.

$|5 + 7| = 12$ $|-5| + |13| = 5 + 13 = 18$
$|8 - 13| = |-5| = 5$ $|-14| - |-3| = 14 - 3 = 11$
$-|10 - 7| = -3$ $|7 - 10| - |6 - 2| = |-3| - |4| = 3 - 4 = -1$
$-|6 - 9| = -|-3| = -3$ $-|10 - 15| - |4 - 9| =$
                                                    $-|-5| - |-5| = -5 - 5 = -10$

⑤ List 5 multiples of each number.

5	5, 10, 15, 20, 25, etc.
10	10, 20, 30, 40, 50, etc.
15	15, 30, 45, 60, 75, etc.
20	20, 40, 60, 80, 100, etc.
25	25, 50, 75, 100, 125, etc.

⑥ Solve. Remember to label your answers.

Ric has 100 teenagers and 10 chaperones signed up to go on the summer youth retreat. Ric has calculated the following expenses per person for the retreat: Lodging – $205, Food – $135, Activities – $60. If Ric wants the teenagers to pay the expenses for the chaperones, how much does Ric need to charge each teenager for the retreat?

Total expenses for 1 person:	Total expenses for 110 people:	Total expenses for 1 teenager:
$205	$400 x 110 = $44,000	$440
135		$100\overline{)44,000}$
+60		
$400		

If Ric wants to charge each teenager $200 for the retreat and pay the difference from the church youth budget, how much is the church paying toward the youth retreat for all the teenagers?

100 teenagers pay	The church pays
100 x $200 = $20,000	$44,000 – $20,000 = $24,000

Teaching Tips, Cont.

➢ Once the Multiples column is complete, have students fill in the Square column. Ask the students if there is anything in common between the two columns of numbers. Students should notice that all square numbers are also multiples of the base number.

➢ Explain that every power of every number will always be a multiple of the base number. This is because a multiple always has the base number as a factor. In the case of powers of numbers, the base number is a unique factor, appearing the same number of times as the number in the exponent.

➢ Complete the Classwork exercises. Have some students work the problems on the board for the class and explain their answers. All students should work the problems in their books.

Assignment

• Complete Lesson 11, Activities 2-6.

Lesson 12

Concepts
- Order of operations
- Prime factorization
- Signed numbers
- Square numbers

Learning Objectives
The student will be able to:
- Memorize the correct sequence for the order of operations
- Apply the order of operations to mathematical expressions
- Calculate correctly the answer of mathematical expressions with up to 6 terms

Materials Needed
- Student Book, Lesson 12
- Worksheet 6

Teaching Tips
➤ Have students complete Worksheet 6 in class. This may be for added practice of earlier topics, or graded as a quiz, if desired.

➤ Ask students what would happen in a football game if there were no rules. How would you know how many points to give a team for a field goal, touchdown, extra point(s), safety, etc? Elicit the idea that rules are necessary for the game to be played properly. Tie this in with the fact that God is a God of order, and the Bible teaches that all things should be done decently and in order. (1 Cor. 14:40)

Order of Operations

There is a specific order you must follow in working more complex math problems to get the correct answer. This is known as the **Order of Operations**. When simplifying mathematical expressions, first look for any **parentheses** and simplify inside each set of parentheses. Second, apply any **exponents** in the problem. Next, do all **multiplication** and **division** together in the order they appear in the expression from left to right. Finally, do all **addition** and **subtraction** together in the order they appear in the expression from left to right. You can remember the proper order of operations by remembering this sentence: **P**lease **E**xcuse **M**y **D**ear **A**unt **S**ally. (**P**arentheses, **E**xponents, **M**ultiplication, **D**ivision, **A**ddition, and **S**ubtraction)

To solve the problem $6 + 2(1 + 3)^2$, first simplify the parentheses to get $6 + 2(4)^2$.

Next, take care of the exponent: $6 + 2(16)$ and then do all multiplication. (There is no division in this expression, or that would be done in this step, as well.) You should have $6 + 32$, which gives you $6 + 32 = 38$.

① Classwork
Simplify the expressions, following the proper order of operations.

$5 - 2 + 3(5 - 3)^3 =$
$5 - 2 + 3(2)^3 =$
$5 - 2 + 3(8) =$
$5 - 2 + 24 =$
$3 + 24 = 27$

$(6 - 3)^2 + 10 \div 2 =$
$(3)^2 + 10 \div 2 =$
$9 + 10 \div 2 =$
$9 + 5 = 14$

$3 + 2^3 - 2(12 \div 3) =$
$3 + 2^3 - 2(4) =$
$3 + 8 - 2(4) =$
$3 + 8 - 8 =$
$11 - 8 = 3$

Activities

② Simplify each expression, following the proper order of operations.
$4 + 10 \div 2 = 4 + 5 = 9$
$21 - 2 \times 3 = 21 - 6 = 15$
$10 - 2 \times 3 + 5 = 10 - 6 + 5 = 4 + 5 = 9$
$2 + 3 \times 3 + 7 = 2 + 9 + 7 = 11 + 7 = 18$
$10 \div 5 \times 3 + 2 - 1 \times 3 = 2 \times 3 + 2 - 1 \times 3 = 6 + 2 - 1 \times 3 = 6 + 2 - 3 = 8 - 3 = 5$
$12 \div (2 \times 3) + 3 - 1 \times 2 = 12 \div 6 + 3 - 1 \times 2 = 2 + 3 - 1 \times 2 = 2 + 3 - 2 = 5 - 2 = 3$
$(6 - 2) \times 2 - 3 = 4 \times 2 - 3 = 8 - 3 = 5$
$(7 - 4)^2 - 10 \div 2 = (3)^2 - 10 \div 2 = 9 - 10 \div 2 = 9 - 5 = 4$
$(2 + 5) - 2^2 + 3 \times 4 = 7 - 2^2 + 3 \times 4 = 7 - 4 + 3 \times 4 = 7 - 4 + 12 = 3 + 12 = 15$
$(5 - 2)^3 - 5^2 + 2 \times 7 = (3)^3 - 5^2 + 2 \times 7 = 27 - 25 + 2 \times 7 = 27 - 25 + 14 = 2 + 14 = 16$
$2^3 \times 3 \div (5 + 1) - 4 = 2^3 \times 3 \div 6 - 4 = 8 \times 3 \div 6 - 4 = 24 \div 6 - 4 = 4 - 4 = 0$
$(4^2 - (12 - 7) + 1) \div 6 = (4^2 - 5 + 1) \div 6 = (16 - 5 + 1) \div 6 = (11 + 1) \div 6 = 12 \div 6 = 2$
$((6 + 2 \times 3) \div 3)^2 = ((6 + 6) \div 3)^2 = (12 \div 3)^2 = 4^2 = 16$

③ Find the prime factorization of each number. Use exponents where appropriate.

14
$14 = 2 \times 7$

15
$15 = 3 \times 5$

20
$20 = 2^2 \times 5$

25
$25 = 5^2$

28
$28 = 2^2 \times 7$

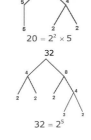

32
$32 = 2^5$

④ Solve, using the rules for signed numbers. Write the problem vertically, if necessary.

$(-53) + (+14) =$
$-(53 - 14) = -39$

$(-37) - (-85) =$
$(-37) + 85 = 85 - 37 = 48$

$(+51) + (+73) =$
$51 + 73 = 124$

$(+92) + (-7) =$
$92 - 7 = 85$

$(-42) - (+77) =$
$(-42) + (-77) = -(42 + 77) = -119$

$(-9) + (-84) =$
$-(9 + 84) = -93$

$(12)(7) = 84$

$(-4)(-9) = 36$

$(-5)(12) = -60$

$(2)(10)(-8) = (20)(-8) = -160$

$(6)(-3)(3) = (-18)(3) = -54$

$(-4)(-4)(-5) = (16)(-5) = -80$

⑤ Insert the values of 1^2, 2^2, 3^2, and 4^2 in the magic square to make the sum of each row, column, and diagonal equal. **The sum of each is 34.**

16	5	9	4
3	10	6	15
2	11	7	14
13	8	12	1

① Write the expanded form expressions in exponential form. Do not solve them.

$2 \times 2 \times 2 \times 2 \times 2 = 2^5$

$8 \times 8 \times 8 = 8^3$

$11 \times 11 \times 11 \times 11 \times 11 \times 11 \times 11 \times 11 = 11^8$

$5 \times 5 \times 5 \times 5 \times 5 \times 5 = 5^6$

$14 \times 14 \times 14 \times 14 = 14^4$

② Write the following exponential expressions in expanded form and solve.

$4^2 = 4 \times 4 = 16$

$7^2 = 7 \times 7 = 49$

$3^3 = 3 \times 3 \times 3 = 27$

$10^2 = 10 \times 10 = 100$

$2^4 = 2 \times 2 \times 2 \times 2 = 16$

③ Find the prime factorization of each number. Use exponents where appropriate.

$18 = 2 \times 3^2$ $24 = 2^3 \times 3$ $27 = 3^3$

Teaching Tips, Cont.

➢ Write the following problem on the board: 4 + 10 ÷ 2 =. Ask several students for the answer to the problem. (Students will most likely give 7 as the answer, but the real answer is 9.) For both answers, ask the student supplying the answer to tell how he/she arrived at the answer.

➢ Explain that without rules in math, we would have the same situation as a football game without rules. There would be no way to tell who was right and who was wrong when two different answers were given.

➢ Introduce the order of operations in the teaching box. Point out the mnemonic device for remembering the order of operations.

➢ Complete the Classwork exercises. Have some students work the problems on the board for the class and explain their answers. All students should work the problems in their books.

Assignment

- Complete Lesson 12, Activities 2-5.

Lesson 13

Concepts

- Distributive property
- Prime factorization
- Prime/Composite numbers
- Factors
- Math in the real world

Learning Objectives

The student will be able to:

- Explain the distributive property
- Use the distributive property to simplify expressions
- Analyze expressions to determine the best method of solving

Materials Needed

- Student Book, Lesson 13
- Worksheet 7

Teaching Tips

➢ Review the order of operations from Lesson 12.

➢ Write the following problem on the board: $7(10 + 6) =$. Have students solve it, following the order of operations.
$(7 \times 16 = 112)$.

➢ Show students that sometimes it is easier to "distribute" the 7 to each member inside the parentheses.
$7 \times 10 + 7 \times 6 = 70 + 42 = 112$.

Distributive Property

The **Distributive Property** allows another method of working with parenthetical expressions that are multiplied by a single factor.	① **Classwork** Simplify the expressions, using the distributive property.
In some cases, it is easier to multiply each term in the parentheses by the factor outside the parentheses and then simplify.	$5(12 + 7) = 5(12) + 5(7) = 60 + 35 = 95$
	$3(15 + 7) = 3(15) + 3(7) = 45 + 21 = 66$
$2(15 + 13) = 2(15) + 2(13) = 30 + 26 = 56$ rather than $2(15 + 13) = 2(28) = 56$	$9(10 + 6) = 9(10) + 9(6) = 90 + 54 = 144$

Activities

② Use the distributive property to simplify each expression.

$2(25 + 9) = 50 + 18 = 68$ $7(10 + 3) = 70 + 21 = 91$

$4(8 + 10) = 32 + 40 = 72$ $8(9 + 5) = 72 + 40 = 112$

$6(1 + 20) = 6 + 120 = 126$ $3(15 + 7 + 4) = 45 + 21 + 12 = 78$

③ Find the prime factorization of the following numbers. Use exponents where appropriate.

$34 = 2 \times 17$

$38 = 2 \times 19$

$39 = 3 \times 13$

$44 = 2^2 \times 11$

$45 = 3^2 \times 5$

$46 = 2 \times 23$

---

④ Find all of the natural number factors for each of the following numbers. Circle the prime numbers.

24   1, ②, ③, 4, 6, 8, 12, 24
25   1, ⑤, 25
26   1, ②, ⑬, 26
27   1, ③, 9, 27
28   1, ②, 4, ⑦, 14, 28
29   1, ㉙
30   1, ②, ③, ⑤, 6, 10, 15, 30

⑤ Solve. Remember to label your answers.

Ric is organizing the church's sports league. He wants to charge each child one fee that includes a uniform, an end-of-season trophy, and a meal at each game. He also must charge enough to cover the cost of fields, equipment, and maintenance. Soccer uniforms are $28 each, football uniforms are $53 each, trophies are $4 each, and meals cost $10 for the season. Fields, equipment, and maintenance cost $795 for the season. If there are 149 kids playing soccer and 116 kids playing football, how much should Ric charge each soccer player?
There are 149 + 116 = 265 kids total
Fields, equipment, and maintenance costs are $795 ÷ 265 = $3 per player.
Cost per soccer player: $28 + $4 + $10 + $3 = $45

Based on the above information, how much should Ric charge each football player?
Cost per football player: $53 + $4 + $10 + $3 = $70

Field paint costs $51 per case of 12 cans of red paint and $45 per case of 12 cans of white paint. Each week, Ric uses 9 cans of white paint and 4 cans of red paint to stripe the fields. If there are 8 weeks in the season, how many cases of each color does Ric need to buy?
White paint: 9 x 8 = 72 cans needed. 72 ÷ 12 = 6 cases of white paint needed.
Red paint: 4 x 8 = 32 cans of red paint. 32 ÷ 12 = 2 R8. 3 cases of red paint needed.

How much will Ric spend on red paint?
$51 x 3 = $153

How much will Ric spend on white paint?
$45 x 6 = $270

① Find the square of each number.

2	**4**	6	**36**
3	**9**	7	**49**
4	**16**	8	**64**
5	**25**	9	**81**

② Simplify each expression, following the proper order of operations.

$6 + 12 \div 3 =$
$6 + 4 = 10$
$27 - 5 \times 2 =$
$27 - 10 = 17$
$16 - 3 \times 4 + 9 =$
$16 - 12 + 9 = 4 + 9 = 13$
$4 + 8 \times 5 \div 4 =$
$4 + 40 \div 4 = 4 + 10 = 14$
$15 \div 3 \times 6 + 4 - 2 \times 2 =$
$5 \times 6 + 4 - 2 \times 2 = 30 + 4 - 2 \times 2 = 30 + 4 - 4 = 34 - 4 = 30$
$16 \div (2 \times 4) + 5 - 1 \times 3 =$
$16 \div 8 + 5 - 1 \times 3 = 2 + 5 - 1 \times 3 = 2 + 5 - 3 = 7 - 3 = 4$
$(11 - 3) \times 3 - 16 =$
$8 \times 3 - 16 = 24 - 16 = 8$
$(11 - 6)^2 - 18 \div 3 =$
$(5)^2 - 18 \div 3 = 25 - 18 \div 3 = 25 - 6 = 19$
$(11 + 6) - 3^2 + 2 \times 4 =$
$17 - 3^2 + 2 \times 4 = 17 - 9 + 2 \times 4 = 17 - 9 + 8 = 8 + 8 = 16$
$(8 - 5)^3 - 4^2 - 3 \times 2 =$
$(3)^3 - 4^2 - 3 \times 2 = 27 - 16 - 3 \times 2 = 27 - 16 - 6 = 11 - 6 = 5$
$2^3 \times 4 \div (9 + 7) - 3 =$
$2^3 \times 4 \div 16 - 3 = 8 \times 4 \div 16 - 3 = 32 \div 16 - 3 = 2 - 3 = -1$
$(6^2 - (12 + 13) + 7) \div 3 =$
$(6^2 - 25 + 7) \div 3 = (36 - 25 + 7) \div 3 = (11 + 7) \div 3 = 18 \div 3 = 6$
$((8 + 4 \times 3) \div 5)^2 =$
$((8 + 12) \div 5)^2 = (20 \div 5)^2 = 4^2 = 16$

Teaching Tips, Cont.

➢ Teach the distributive property in the teaching box. Emphasize that the distributive property should not be used in place of the traditional order of operations in every case. There are times when solving inside the parentheses first will produce a problem that is easier to solve than using the distributive property. Every problem must be evaluated on a case-by-case basis.

➢ Complete the Classwork exercises. Have some students work the problems on the board for the class and explain their answers. All students should work the problems in their books.

Assignments

* Complete Lesson 13, Activities 2-5.
* Worksheet 7 (Optional.)

Lesson 14

Concepts
- Exponents
- Order of operations
- Prime factorization
- Square numbers

Learning Objectives
The student will be able to:
- Apply the rules for working with exponents
- Multiply terms with equal bases
- Divide terms with equal bases
- Simplify expressions with negative exponents

Materials Needed
- Student Book, Lesson 14

Teaching Tips
➢ Ask the students to solve $2 \div 2$. (1) Now have them express the problem using exponents. ($2^1 \div 2^1$) What is the answer? (1) The format of the number does not change the answer, as long as the terms are equivalent.

➢ Teach the rules for working with exponents in the teaching box. Show students that the problem above can be written $2^{1-1} = 2^0 = 1$. Emphasize that any number raised to the zero power is equal to 1. If students are still questioning the validity of this fact, refer to the original $2^1 \div 2^1$ problem. This problem is obviously equal to 1 because anything divided by itself equals 1. Following the rules of dividing exponents, the resulting term has a zero exponent.

Exponents

Rules for working with exponents	① Classwork
Any number (except zero) raised to the 0th power equals 1. $3^0 = 1$	Simplify the expressions. You do not have to solve exponents greater than 3.
Any number raised to the 1st power equals itself. $3^1 = 3$	$7^0 = 1$
When multiplying terms with equal bases, add the exponents. $3^2\left(3^3\right) = 3^5$	$12^1 = 12$ $2^4 \times 2^3 = 2^7$
When dividing terms with equal bases, subtract the exponents. $3^3 \div 3^2 = 3^1$	$3^6 \div 3^4 = 3^2 = 9$
When the product of two or more factors has an exponent, raise each individual factor to that exponent. $\left(2 \times 3\right)^4 = 2^4 \times 3^4$ Note that this is the same as 6^4.	$\left(3 \times 5\right)^2 = 3^2 \times 5^2 = 9 \times 25 = 225$ $4^{-2} = \left(\frac{1}{4}\right)^2 = \frac{1^2}{4^2} = \frac{1}{16}$
When a number has a negative exponent, take the reciprocal of the number (the numerator and denominator switch places) and make the exponent positive. $3^{-2} = \frac{1}{3^2}$ and $\left(\frac{2}{3}\right)^{-3} = \left(\frac{3}{2}\right)^3 = \frac{3^3}{2^3}$	$\left(\frac{3}{4}\right)^2 = \frac{3^2}{4^2} = \frac{9}{16}$ $\left(\frac{2}{3}\right)^{-3} = \left(\frac{3}{2}\right)^3 = \frac{3^3}{2^3} = \frac{27}{8}$

Activities

② Simplify the expressions. You do not have to solve exponents greater than 3.

$6^0 = 1$ $\qquad$ $23^0 = 1$

$13^1 = 13$ $\qquad$ $31^1 = 31$

$3^2 \times 3^4 = 3^6$ $\qquad$ $5^3 \times 5^2 = 5^5$

$5^5 \div 5^3 = 5^2 = 25$ $\qquad$ $10^4 \div 10^1 = 10^3 = 1,000$

$\left(2 \times 4\right)^2 = 2^2 \times 4^2 = 4 \times 16 = 64$ $\qquad$ $\left(3 \times 4\right)^3 = 3^3 \times 4^3 = 27 \times 64 = 1728$

$2^{-3} = \left(\frac{1}{2}\right)^3 = \frac{1^3}{2^3} = \frac{1}{8}$ $\qquad$ $7^{-2} = \left(\frac{1}{7}\right)^2 = \frac{1^2}{7^2} = \frac{1}{49}$

$\left(\frac{1}{2}\right)^2 = \frac{1^2}{2^2} = \frac{1}{4}$ $\qquad$ $\left(\frac{2}{3}\right)^3 = \frac{2^3}{3^3} = \frac{8}{27}$

$\left(\frac{3}{4}\right)^{-2} = \left(\frac{4}{3}\right)^2 = \frac{4^2}{3^2} = \frac{16}{9}$ $\qquad$ $\left(\frac{5}{2}\right)^{-3} = \left(\frac{2}{5}\right)^3 = \frac{2^3}{5^3} = \frac{8}{125}$

③ Simplify, following the order of operations.

$(4+2)^2 - 10 \div 2 - 2^4 =$

$6^2 - 10 \div 2 - 16 = 36 - 10 \div 2 - 16 = 36 - 5 - 16 = 31 - 16 = 15$

$5 + 3 + 3^2 - 2(3+4) + 7^0 =$

$5 + 3 + 3^2 - 2(7) + 7^0 = 5 + 3 + 9 - 2(7) + 1 = 5 + 3 + 9 - 14 + 1 = 8 + 9 - 14 + 1 = 17 - 14 + 1 = 3 + 1 = 4$

$7 + 2 \times 3 + 4^0 - 2 \times 2 =$

$7 + 2 \times 3 + 1 - 2 \times 2 = 7 + 6 + 1 - 4 = 13 + 1 - 4 = 14 - 4 = 10$

$\left((3+6)^2 \div (13-4) + 15^0\right) \div 2 =$

$(9^2 \div 9 + 15^0) \div 2 = (81 \div 9 + 1) \div 2 = (9+1) \div 2 = 10 \div 2 = 5$

④ Find the prime factorization of each number. Use exponents where appropriate.

8	9	12
$8 = 2 \times 2 \times 2 = 2^3$	$9 = 3 \times 3 = 3^2$	$12 = 2 \times 2 \times 3 = 2^2 \times 3$

16	18	20
$16 = 2 \times 2 \times 2 \times 2 = 2^4$	$18 = 2 \times 3 \times 3 = 2 \times 3^2$	$20 = 2 \times 2 \times 5 = 2^2 \times 5$

24	27	28
$24 = 2 \times 2 \times 2 \times 3 = 2^3 \times 3$	$27 = 3 \times 3 \times 3 = 3^3$	$28 = 2 \times 2 \times 7 = 2^2 \times 7$

⑤ Insert the values of 1^2, 2^2, 3^2, 4^2 and 5^2 in the magic square to make the sum of each row, column, and diagonal equal. **The sum of each is 65.**

15	16	22	3	9
8	14	20	21	2
1	7	13	19	25
24	5	6	12	18
17	23	4	10	11

Teaching Tips, Cont.

➢ To show students why the negative exponent works the way it does, give the problem $2^2 \div 2^4$. According to the rules of exponents, this equals $2^{2-4} = 2^{-2}$. Written as a fraction, you have

$$\frac{1 \times \cancel{2} \times \cancel{2}}{1 \times \cancel{2} \times \cancel{2} \times 2 \times 2} = \frac{1}{2 \times 2} = \frac{1}{2^2} = \frac{1}{4}$$

➢ Complete the Classwork exercises. Have some students work the problems on the board for the class and explain their answers. All students should work the problems in their books.

Assignment

- Complete Lesson 14, Activities 2-5.

Lesson 15

Concepts
- Divisibility tests
- Prime/Composite numbers
- Order of operations
- Prime factorization
- Exponents
- Math in the real world

Learning Objectives
The student will be able to:
- Memorize the divisibility tests
- Apply the divisibility tests to natural numbers
- Identify 3-digit numbers as multiples of 2, 3, 4, 5, 6, 9, or 10.

Materials Needed
- Student Book, Lesson 15
- Worksheet 8

Teaching Tips
➢ Have students complete Worksheet 8 in class. This may be for added practice of earlier topics, or graded as a quiz, if desired.

➢ Teach the divisibility tests in the teaching box. Tell the students that there is no simple divisibility test for 7. Trying to divide a number by 7 as a test is faster and easier than the applicable divisibility test. The same is true for a divisibility test for 8, although if a number is divisible by 4, you can divide by 4 and apply the divisibility test for 2 to the quotient. (The divisibility tests for 7 and 8 are provided on the following page for your reference. Students are not expected to memorize the tests for 7 and 8.)

Divisibility Tests

Use the following **divisibility tests** to determine whether or not a number is divisible by another number.

Divisible by 2: any number ending in a 0, 2, 4, 6, or 8.

Divisible by 3: any number whose digits have a sum that is a multiple of 3. For example, 15 is divisible by 3 because $1 + 5 = 6$ and 6 is a multiple of 3.

Divisible by 4: any number ending in 00, and any number whose final two digits form a number that is a multiple of 4. For example, 128 is divisible by 4 because 28 is a multiple of 4. $4 \times 7 = 28$.

Divisible by 5: any number ending in a 0 or 5.

Divisible by 6: any even number whose digits have a sum that is a multiple of 3.

Divisible by 9: any number whose digits have a sum that is a multiple of 9. For example, 387 is divisible by 9 because $3 + 8 + 7 = 18$ and 18 is a multiple of 9.

Divisible by 10: any number ending in a 0.

① **Classwork**
Use the divisibility tests to determine which numbers are factors of the given numbers.

	2	3	4	5	6	9	10
627		x					
564	x	x	x		x		
747		x				x	
900	x	x	x	x	x	x	x
432	x	x	x		x	x	
822	x	x			x		
537		x					

Activities

② Use the divisibility tests to identify each number as prime or composite.

125 Composite (5)
127 Prime
129 Composite (3)
131 Prime
135 Composite (3, 5, 9)
137 Prime
139 Prime
141 Composite (3)

③ Simplify the following expressions, following the proper order of operations.

$12 - 3 \times 4 + 2 \times 5 + 4 = 12 - 12 + 10 + 4 = 0 + 10 + 4 = 10 + 4 = 14$

$(13 - 2 + 7) \div (8 - 5) = (11 + 7) \div 3 = 18 \div 3 = 6$

$3^2 + 2^3 - 6 \div 3 = 9 + 8 - 6 \div 3 = 9 + 8 - 2 = 17 - 2 = 15$

$(3 + 7)^2 \div 4 \div 5 + 2 \times 3 =$

$10^2 \div 4 \div 5 + 2 \times 3 = 100 \div 4 \div 5 + 2 \times 3 = 25 \div 5 + 2 \times 3 = 5 + 2 \times 3 = 5 + 6 = 11$

$(5 + 10 \div 2 - 7)^3 \div 9 + 2 = (5 + 5 - 7)^3 \div 9 + 2 = 3^3 \div 9 + 2 = 27 \div 9 + 2 = 3 + 2 = 5$

$1^3 + 2^2 - 3 \times 4^0 + 8 \div 4 = 1 + 4 - 3 \times 1 + 8 \div 4 = 1 + 4 - 3 + 2 = 5 - 3 + 2 = 2 + 2 = 4$

④ Find the prime factorization of each number. Use exponents where appropriate.

30
$30 = 2 \times 3 \times 5$

32
$32 = 2 \times 2 \times 2 \times 2 \times 2 = 2^5$

33
$33 = 3 \times 11$

34
$34 = 2 \times 17$

35
$35 = 5 \times 7$

36
$36 = 2 \times 2 \times 3 \times 3 = 2^2 \times 3^2$

38
$38 = 2 \times 19$

39
$39 = 3 \times 13$

40
$40 = 2 \times 2 \times 2 \times 5 = 2^3 \times 5$

⑤ Solve. Remember to label your answers.

Ric has the following activities planned for the school year: Back-to-school party – $5, discipleship training class – $30, flag football – $5, Christmas party – $10, winter ski retreat – $120, basketball game – $16, dodge ball tournament – $5, spring break race around town – $30, baseball game – $11, summer retreat – $200. If he wants to give parents the option of paying for activities in twelve equal monthly payments, how much is due each month?
Total due: $5 + $30 + $5 + $10 + $120 + $16 + $5 + $30 + $11 + $200 = $432
Total due each month: $432 ÷ 12 = $36

Ric gives the teenagers the option of doing odd jobs around the church in the evenings and on Saturdays. He gives them a $5 discount on their activity fees for every hour they work. If a teenager volunteers at the church for 2 hours each weekend for 4 weekends each month, will the discount be enough to cover the teen's activity expenses?   YES
Discount each week: $5 x 2 = $10
Discount each month: $10 x 4 = $40
The $40 discount each month will be enough to cover the $36 per month for activities.

Horizons Pre-Algebra, Teacher's Guide   68

Teaching Tips, Cont.

➢ Explain that the divisibility tests should be memorized so the students can apply them when needed. They will be used extensively beginning in Lesson 18.

➢ Complete the Classwork exercises. Have some students work the problems on the board for the class. All students should work the problems in their books.

Assignment

• Complete Lesson 15, Activities 2-5.

Notes on Divisibility Tests

Divisibility test for 7:
Multiply the digit in the ones place by two. Subtract this number from the remaining digits in the original number. If the difference is divisible by 7 (or equal to 0), then the original number is also divisible by 7. If the number is still too big to tell, repeat the above steps until you get a number that you know is or is not a multiple of 7.
For example, is 392 divisible by 7?
$2 \times 2 = 4$
$39 - 4 = 35$
35 is divisible by 7; (7×5), so 392 is also divisible by 7; (7×56)

Divisibility test for 8:
If the last three digits of a number are divisible by 8, then the number is divisible by 8. This is because 1000 is divisible by 8, so you only have to check the last three digits.

Lesson 16

Concepts
- Greatest common factor
- Divisibility tests
- Prime/Composite numbers
- Order of operations
- Math in the real world

Learning Objectives
The student will be able to:
- Define *greatest common factor*
- Find the prime factorization of natural numbers
- Identify common factors of a given set of natural numbers
- Calculate the greatest common factor of a set of 2 or 3 natural numbers

Materials Needed
- Student Book, Lesson 16

Teaching Tips
➢ Review prime factoring from Lesson 9.

➢ Have students find the prime factorization of 8 and 12. ($2 \times 2 \times 2$ and $2 \times 2 \times 3$) Ask them to identify factors that appear in both sets (2×2).

➢ Define *greatest common factor* from the teaching box.

➢ Teach the procedure for finding the greatest common factor. Remind students to always circle the prime factors that appear as a factor in every number in the set. If a prime number appears more than once in every number in the set, circle it the same number of times that it appears in every number.

Greatest Common Factor

The **greatest common factor** of two or more numbers is the largest factor that is common to all the given numbers.	① **Classwork** Find the greatest common factor of each set of numbers.
To find the greatest common factor, begin by finding the prime factorization of each number. For example, to find the greatest common factor of 12 and 18, find the prime factorization of each number. $12 = 2 \times 2 \times 3$ $18 = 2 \times 3 \times 3$	9 and 12 $9 = 3 \times ③$ $12 = 2 \times 2 \times ③$ The GCF of 9 and 12 is 3.
Then, circle all prime number factors that are common to both numbers. $12 = ② \times 2 \times ③$ $18 = ② \times 3 \times ③$	15 and 35 $15 = 3 \times ⑤$ $35 = ⑤ \times 7$ The GCF of 15 and 35 is 5
Finally, multiply the circled prime factors to find the greatest common factor. $2 \times 3 = 6$ The greatest common factor of 12 and 18 is 6.	16, 24, and 32 $16 = ② \times ② \times ② \times 2$ $24 = ② \times ② \times ② \times 3$ $32 = ② \times ② \times ② \times 2 \times 2$ The GCF of 16, 24, and 32 is $2 \times 2 \times 2 = 8$

Activities

② Find the greatest common factor of each set of numbers.

9 and 15	12 and 16	15 and 24
$9 = ③ \times 3$	$12 = ② \times ② \times 3$	$15 = ③ \times 5$
$15 = ③ \times 5$	$16 = ② \times ② \times 2 \times 2$	$24 = 2 \times 2 \times 2 \times ③$
GCF is 3	GCF is $2 \times 2 = 4$	CFG is 3

16 and 18	16 and 20	20 and 24
$16 = ② \times 2 \times 2 \times 2$	$16 = ② \times ② \times 2 \times 2$	$20 = ② \times ② \times 5$
$18 = ② \times 3 \times 3$	$20 = ② \times ② \times 5$	$24 = ② \times ② \times 2 \times 3$
GCF is 2	GCF is $2 \times 2 = 4$	GCF is $2 \times 2 = 4$

12, 15, and 18	6, 9, and 15	10, 18, and 30
$12 = 2 \times 2 \times ③$	$6 = 2 \times ③$	$10 = ② \times 5$
$15 = ③ \times 5$	$9 = ③ \times 3$	$18 = ② \times 3 \times 3$
$18 = 2 \times ③ \times 3$	$15 = ③ \times 5$	$30 = ② \times 3 \times 5$
GCF is 3	GCF is 3	GCF is 2

③ Use the divisibility tests to identify each number as prime or composite.

145	Composite (5)	153	Composite (3, 9)
147	Composite (3)	155	Composite (5)
149	Prime	157	Prime
151	Prime	159	Composite (3)

④ Simplify the following expressions, following the proper order of operations.

$6 + 5 - 3 \times 2 + 10 \div 2 + 3^2 - 7^0 = 6 + 5 - 3 \times 2 + 10 \div 2 + 9 - 1 = 6 + 5 - 6 + 5 + 9 - 1 =$
$\qquad 11 - 6 + 5 + 9 - 1 = 5 + 5 + 9 - 1 = 10 + 9 - 1 = 19 - 1 = 18$

$\left(3(6-4)^2 + 4\right) \div 2 = \left(3\left(2^2\right) + 4\right) \div 2 = \left(3(4) + 4\right) \div 2 = (12 + 4) \div 2 = 16 \div 2 = 8$

$\left(3 \times 4 \div (8 - 2)\right)^3 = \left(3 \times 4 \div 6\right)^3 = \left(12 \div 6\right)^3 = 2^3 = 8$

$\left(1^0 + 2^1 + 3^2\left(4^2 - 2 \times 3\right) - 3\right) \div 9 =$

$\left(1^0 + 2^1 + 3^2(16 - 2 \times 3) - 3\right) \div 9 = \left(1^0 + 2^1 + 3^2(16 - 6) - 3\right) \div 9 =$

$\left(1^0 + 2^1 + 3^2(10) - 3\right) \div 9 = \left(1 + 2 + 9(10) - 3\right) \div 9 = (1 + 2 + 90 - 3) \div 9 =$

$(3 + 90 - 3) \div 9 = (93 - 3) \div 9 = 90 \div 9 = 10$

⑤ Solve. Remember to label your answers.
Ric is designing a new youth room. He wants to allow 9 square feet per person in the classroom area, and 15 square feet per person in the recreational area. If he wants room for 175 people in the classroom area and 75 people in the recreation area, how many square feet does the new classroom area need to be?

175 x 9 square feet = 1575 square feet

How many square feet does the new recreation area need to be?

75 x 15 square feet = 1125 square feet

How many square feet does the new youth room need to be?

1575 square feet + 1125 square feet = 2700 square feet

Ric has designed a classroom area with 2000 square feet to allow for growth. Is this space large enough to allow 9 square feet per person with 225 people in the room? NO

225 x 9 square feet = 2025 square feet

Teaching Tips, Cont.

➢ Emphasize that the answer will always be less than or equal to the smallest number in the given set.

➢ Ask the students why the answer must be less than or equal to the smallest number in the set. (Factors are numbers that multiply together to produce a new number. You can't multiply a natural number by another natural number and end up with a smaller number than one of your factors.)

➢ Complete the Classwork exercises. Have some students work the problems on the board for the class. All students should work the problems in their books.

Assignment

• Complete Lesson 16, Activities 2-5.

Lesson 17

Concepts
- Least common multiple
- Order of operations
- Prime factorization
- Greatest common factor
- Math in the real world

Learning Objectives
The student will be able to:
- Express the prime factorization of natural numbers using exponents
- Define *least common multiple*
- Identify the highest order primes from a set of 2 or 3 natural numbers
- Calculate the least common multiple of a set of 2 or 3 natural numbers

Materials Needed
- Student Book, Lesson 17

Teaching Tips
➤ Review prime factorization and exponents.

➤ Define *least common multiple* from the teaching box. Reinforce the difference between greatest common factor (which is always less than or equal to the smallest number in the set) and least common multiple (which is always greater than or equal to the largest number in the set).

➤ Hint: The *greatest* common factor can be *no greater than* the smallest given number, and the *least* common multiple must be *at least* as big as the biggest given number.

Least Common Multiple

The **least common multiple** of two or more numbers is the smallest number that is a multiple of all the given numbers.

To find the least common multiple, begin by finding the prime factorization of each number. For example, to find the least common multiple of 12 and 18, find the prime factorization of each number and express it using exponents.

$12 = 2 \times 2 \times 3 = 2^2 \times 3$

$18 = 2 \times 3 \times 3 = 2 \times 3^2$

Then, for each prime number, draw a box around the value with the largest exponent.

$12 = 2 \times 2 \times 3 = \boxed{2^2} \times 3$

$18 = 2 \times 3 \times 3 = 2 \times \boxed{3^2}$

Multiply the boxed factors to find the least common multiple.

$2^2 \times 3^2 = 4 \times 9 = 36$

The least common multiple of 12 and 18 is 36.

You can also list the factors of each number until you find a factor in common.

12: 12, 24, 36
18: 18, 36

① Classwork
Find the least common multiple of each set of numbers.

6 and 9
$6 = \boxed{2} \times 3$
$9 = 3 \times 3 = \boxed{3^2}$
LCM is $2 \times 3^2 = 2 \times 9 = 18$

9 and 12
$9 = 3 \times 3 = \boxed{3^2}$
$12 = 2 \times 2 \times 3 = \boxed{2^2} \times 3$
LCM is $2^2 \times 3^2 = 4 \times 9 = 36$

10, 15, and 20
$10 = 2 \times \boxed{5}$
$15 = \boxed{3} \times 5$
$20 = 2 \times 2 \times 5 = \boxed{2^2} \times 5$
LCM is $2^2 \times 3 \times 5 = 4 \times 3 \times 5 = 60$

Activities

② Find the least common multiple of each set of numbers.

3 and 5	4 and 6	8 and 12
$3 = 1 \times \boxed{3}$	$4 = 2 \times 2 = \boxed{2^2}$	$8 = 2 \times 2 \times 2 = \boxed{2^3}$
$5 = 1 \times \boxed{5}$	$6 = 2 \times \boxed{3}$	$12 = 2 \times 2 \times 3 = 2^2 \times \boxed{3}$
LCM: $3 \times 5 = 15$	LCM: $2^2 \times 3 = 4 \times 3 = 12$	LCM: $2^3 \times 3 = 8 \times 3 = 24$

9 and 15	12 and 15	12 and 16
$9 = 3 \times 3 = \boxed{3^2}$	$12 = 2 \times 2 \times 3 = \boxed{2^2} \times 3$	$12 = 2 \times 2 \times 3 = 2^2 \times \boxed{3}$
$15 = 3 \times \boxed{5}$	$15 = \boxed{3} \times \boxed{5}$	$16 = 2 \times 2 \times 2 \times 2 = \boxed{2^4}$
LCM: $3^2 \times 5 = 9 \times 5 = 45$	LCM: $2^2 \times 3 \times 5 = 60$	LCM: $3 \times 2^4 = 3 \times 16 = 48$

3, 4, and 5	6, 8, and 9	9, 12, and 15
$3 = 1 \times \boxed{3}$	$6 = 2 \times 3$	$9 = 3 \times 3 = \boxed{3^2}$
$4 = 2 \times 2 = \boxed{2^2}$	$8 = 2 \times 2 \times 2 = \boxed{2^3}$	$12 = 2 \times 2 \times 3 = \boxed{2^2} \times 3$
$5 = 1 \times \boxed{5}$	$9 = 3 \times 3 = \boxed{3^2}$	$15 = 3 \times \boxed{5}$
LCM: $2^2 \times 3 \times 5 = 60$	LCM: $2^3 \times 3^2 = 8 \times 9 = 72$	LCM: $2^2 \times 3^2 \times 5 = 180$

---

③ Simplify the following expressions, following the proper order of operations.

$\left(3(4+3)^0 + 4 - 1\right) \div 2 =$

$\left(3(7)^0 + 4 - 1\right) \div 2 = \left(3(1) + 4 - 1\right) \div 2 = (3 + 4 - 1) \div 2 = (7 - 1) \div 2 = 6 \div 2 = 3$

$\left(2 \times 3 \div (7 - 4)\right)^3 = \left(2 \times 3 \div 3\right)^3 = (6 \div 3)^3 = 2^3 = 8$

$\left(5^0 + 2^2 + 2^3(3^2 - 2 \times 4) - 3\right) \div 2 = \left(5^0 + 2^2 + 2^3(9 - 2 \times 4) - 3\right) \div 2 =$

$\left(5^0 + 2^2 + 2^3(9 - 8) - 3\right) \div 2 = \left(5^0 + 2^2 + 2^3(1) - 3\right) \div 2 = (1 + 4 + 8 - 3) \div 2 =$

$(5 + 8 - 3) \div 2 = (13 - 3) \div 2 = 10 \div 2 = 5$

$\left(3(6^2 - 5^2 - 3 \times 2) + 10 \div 2 + 3^0\right) \div 7^1 = \left(3(36 - 25 - 3 \times 2) + 10 \div 2 + 3^0\right) \div 7^1 =$

$\left(3(36 - 25 - 6) + 10 \div 2 + 3^0\right) \div 7^1 = \left(3(11 - 6) + 10 \div 2 + 3^0\right) \div 7^1 = \left(3(5) + 10 \div 2 + 3^0\right) \div 7^1 =$

$(15 + 10 \div 2 + 1) \div 7^1 = (15 + 5 + 1) \div 7 = (20 + 1) \div 7 = 21 \div 7 = 3$

④ Find the greatest common factor of each set of numbers.

9 and 12	12 and 15	18 and 24
9 = ③ × 3	12 = 2 × 2 × ③	18 = ② × ③ × 3
12 = 2 × 2 × ③	15 = ③ × 5	24 = ② × 2 × 2 × ③
GCF is 3	GCF is 3	GCF is 2 × 3 = 6
15 and 18	16 and 24	20 and 25
15 = ③ × 5	16 = ② × ② × ② × 2	20 = 2 × 2 × ⑤
18 = 2 × ③ × 3	24 = ② × ② × ② × 3	25 = ⑤ × 5
GCF is 3	GCF is 2 × 2 × 2 = 8	GCF is 5
9, 12, and 24	12, 15, and 21	16, 18, and 24
9 = ③ × 3	12 = 2 × 2 × ③	16 = ② × 2 × 2 × 2
12 = 2 × 2 × ③	15 = ③ × 5	18 = ② × 3 × 3
24 = 2 × 2 × 2 × ③	21 = ③ × 7	24 = ② × 2 × 2 × 3
GCF is 3	GCF is 3	GCF is 2

⑤ Solve. Remember to label your answers.

Ric is planning a family fun day at his church. In each race, he is allowing 10 minutes for the children's heats, 5 minutes for the adults' heats, and 2 minutes for instructions. What is the greatest number of races Ric can schedule between 3:00 and 5:00?   7 races
Total time available: 2 hours (120 minutes) Each race takes 10 min + 5 min + 2 min = 17 minutes. 120 ÷ 17 = 7 R1

If more adults signed up for the fun day races so that the adult' heats now required 10 minutes for each race, what is the greatest number of races Ric can schedule between 3:00 and 5:00?   5 races
Each race takes 10 min + 10 min + 2 min = 22 minutes. 120 ÷ 22 = 5 R10

Teaching Tips, Cont.

➢ Note: Circles have been used to mark the common factors for finding the greatest common factor, and squares have been used to mark the factors for the least common multiple. The visual of placing boxes around the exponential expressions and circles around individual prime numbers should help students remember what they are to do in each case. Your cupped palm (i.e. circle) is easily able to hold one thing at a time (individual prime numbers). A box is more practical for holding large or multiple items (exponential numbers). The individual *factors* (circled primes) are used to find the greatest common *factor*. The boxes with primes and *multiples* (exponents) are used to find the least common *multiple*.

➢ Complete the Classwork exercises. Have some students work the problems on the board for the class. All students should work the problems in their books.

Assignment
• Complete Lesson 17, Activities 2-5.

Lesson 18

Concepts

- Square roots
- Cube roots
- Root terminology
- Divisibility tests
- Prime/Composite numbers
- Greatest common factor
- Least common multiple

Learning Objectives

The student will be able to:

- Use proper terms relating to roots
- Calculate square roots and cube roots of numbers
- Identify perfect squares as factors of natural numbers
- Express exponential equations in radical form

Materials Needed

- Student Book, Lesson 18
- Worksheet 9

Teaching Tips

➤ Have students complete Worksheet 9 in class. This may be for added practice of earlier topics or graded as a quiz.

➤ Define terms relating to roots in the teaching box. Show students the relationship between the base, exponent, and answer in an exponential equation, and the radicand (or argument), index, and answer in a radical expression.

➤ Review square numbers. Have students list all perfect squares less than 150. (1, 4, 9, 16, 25, 36, 49, 64, 81, 100, 121, 144)

Square Roots

The opposite of raising a number to an exponent is taking the **root** of a number. The root is represented by the symbol $\sqrt{}$, called the **radical**. The number under the radical is called the **radicand** (or **argument**), and the number that indicates the root is called the **index** and corresponds to the exponent. For example, $2^3 = 8$. To express this as a root, write $\sqrt[3]{8} = 2$, where 8 is the radicand, 3 is the index, and 2 is the root. In this case, 3 is the cube root of 8.

To find the **square root** of a number, find a number that, when multiplied by itself, gives the radicand.

For example, $\sqrt{16} = \sqrt{4 \times 4} = 4$

For larger numbers, write the radicand as the product of perfect square factors and find the square roots.

$\sqrt{128} = \sqrt{8 \times 8 \times 2} = 8\sqrt{2}$

To add or subtract roots, the radicands and indexes must be equal. Add the numbers immediately to the left of the radical. If there is no number, treat it as a 1.

For example, $\sqrt{3} + \sqrt{3} = 2\sqrt{3}$ and $2\sqrt{5} + 4\sqrt{5} = 6\sqrt{5}$. If the radicands or indexes are not equal, the roots cannot be added or subtracted.

To multiply or divide roots with the same index, multiply or divide the radicands and write the answer under one radical. Multiply or divide the numbers outside the radical and write outside the radical in the answer. Simplify if necessary.

For example, $\sqrt{12} \times \sqrt{3} = \sqrt{12 \times 3} = \sqrt{36} = 6$

① Classwork

Rewrite the following expressions as roots.

$3^2 = 9 \qquad 3 = \sqrt{9}$

$4^3 = 64 \qquad 4 = \sqrt[3]{64}$

$2^4 = 16 \qquad 2 = \sqrt[4]{16}$

$5^2 = 25 \qquad 5 = \sqrt{25}$

$5^3 = 125 \qquad 5 = \sqrt[3]{125}$

Solve the following roots.

$\sqrt{16} = \sqrt{4 \times 4} = 4$

$\sqrt[3]{27} = \sqrt[3]{3 \times 3 \times 3} = 3$

$\sqrt{32} = \sqrt{2 \times 4 \times 4} = 4\sqrt{2}$

$\sqrt[3]{16} = \sqrt[3]{2 \times 2 \times 2 \times 2} = 2\sqrt[3]{2}$

$\sqrt{2} + \sqrt{2} = 2\sqrt{2}$

$\sqrt{5} + 2\sqrt{5} = 3\sqrt{5}$

$\sqrt[3]{10} + 5\sqrt[3]{10} = 6\sqrt[3]{10}$

$6\sqrt{7} - 4\sqrt{7} = 2\sqrt{7}$

$5\sqrt[3]{5} - 4\sqrt[3]{5} = \sqrt[3]{5}$

$\left(\sqrt{10}\right)\left(\sqrt{2}\right) =$
$\sqrt{10 \times 2} = \sqrt{20} = \sqrt{2 \times 2 \times 5} = 2\sqrt{5}$

$\left(3\sqrt{5}\right)\left(2\sqrt{2}\right) = (3 \times 2)\sqrt{5 \times 2} = 6\sqrt{10}$

$\sqrt{27} \div \sqrt{3} = \sqrt{27 \div 3} = \sqrt{9} = \sqrt{3 \times 3} = 3$

$10\sqrt[3]{16} \div 5\sqrt[3]{4} = (10 \div 5)\sqrt[3]{16 \div 4} = 2\sqrt[3]{4}$

$3 \div \sqrt{3} = \sqrt{3 \times 3} \div \sqrt{3} = \sqrt{9} \div 3 = \sqrt{3}$

Activities

② Rewrite the following expressions as roots.

$2^5 = 32 \qquad 2 = \sqrt[5]{32}$

$3^3 = 27 \qquad 3 = \sqrt[3]{27}$

$5^4 = 625 \qquad 5 = \sqrt[4]{625}$

$4^2 = 16 \qquad 4 = \sqrt{16}$

$7^2 = 49 \qquad 7 = \sqrt{49}$

$6^2 = 36 \qquad 6 = \sqrt{36}$

---

③ Solve the following roots.

$\sqrt{25} = \sqrt{5 \times 5} = 5$

$\sqrt{9} = \sqrt{3 \times 3} = 3$

$\sqrt{8} = \sqrt{2 \times 2 \times 2} = 2\sqrt{2}$

$\sqrt{12} = \sqrt{2 \times 2 \times 3} = 2\sqrt{3}$

$\sqrt[3]{27} = \sqrt[3]{3 \times 3 \times 3} = 3$

$\sqrt[3]{64} = \sqrt[3]{4 \times 4 \times 4} = 4$

$\sqrt{7} + 3\sqrt{7} = 4\sqrt{7}$

$8\sqrt[3]{11} - 5\sqrt[3]{11} = 3\sqrt[3]{11}$

$\left(\sqrt{6}\right)\left(\sqrt{3}\right) = \sqrt{18} = \sqrt{2 \times 3 \times 3} = 3\sqrt{2}$

$\left(\sqrt{2}\right)\left(3\sqrt{12}\right) =$
$3\sqrt{24} = 3\sqrt{2 \times 2 \times 6} = (3 \times 2)\sqrt{6} = 6\sqrt{6}$

$\sqrt{50} \div \sqrt{2} = \sqrt{50 \div 2} = \sqrt{25} = \sqrt{5 \times 5} = 5$

$4\sqrt{18} \div 2\sqrt{6} = (4 \div 2)\sqrt{18 \div 6} = 2\sqrt{3}$

$5 \div \sqrt{5} =$
$\sqrt{5 \times 5} \div \sqrt{5} = \sqrt{25} \div \sqrt{5} = \sqrt{25 \div 5} = \sqrt{5}$

④ Use the divisibility tests to identify each number as prime or composite.

163	Prime	173	Prime
165	Composite (3, 5)	175	Composite (5)
167	Prime	177	Composite (3)
171	Composite (3, 9)	179	Prime

⑤ Find the greatest common factor of each set of numbers.

12 and 18
$12 = ②\times 2 \times ③$
$18 = ②\times ③\times 3$
GCF: $2 \times 3 = 6$

18 and 28
$18 = ②\times 3 \times 3$
$28 = ②\times 2 \times 7$
CGF: 2

24 and 28
$24 = ②\times ②\times 2 \times 3$
$28 = ②\times ②\times 7$
GCF: $2 \times 2 = 4$

25 and 40
$25 = ⑤\times 5$
$40 = 2 \times 2 \times 2 \times ⑤$
GCF: 5

24 and 36
$24 = ②\times ②\times 2 \times ③$
$36 = ②\times ②\times ③\times 3$
GCF: $2 \times 2 \times 3 = 12$

28 and 42
$28 = ②\times 2 \times ⑦$
$42 = ②\times 3 \times ⑦$
GCF: $2 \times 7 = 14$

⑥ Find the least common multiple of each set of numbers.

3 and 4
$3 = 1 \times \boxed{3}$
$4 = 2 \times 2 = \boxed{2^2}$
LCM: $2^2 \times 3 = 4 \times 3 = 12$

4 and 7
$4 = 2 \times 2 = \boxed{2^2}$
$7 = 1 \times \boxed{7}$
LCM: $2^2 \times 7 = 4 \times 7 = 28$

8 and 10
$8 = 2 \times 2 \times 2 = \boxed{2^3}$
$10 = 2 \times \boxed{5}$
LCM: $2^3 \times 5 = 8 \times 5 = 40$

9 and 15
$9 = 3 \times 3 = \boxed{3^2}$
$15 = 3 \times \boxed{5}$
LCM: $3^2 \times 5 = 45$

12 and 16
$12 = 2 \times 2 \times 3 = 2^2 \times \boxed{3}$
$16 = 2 \times 2 \times 2 \times 2 = \boxed{2^4}$
LCM: $2^4 \times 3 = 16 \times 3 = 48$

14 and 24
$14 = 2 \times \boxed{7}$
$24 = 2 \times 2 \times 2 \times 3 = \boxed{2^3} \times \boxed{3}$
LCM:
$2^3 \times 3 \times 7 = 8 \times 3 \times 7 = 168$

Exponents, Divisibility Tests, GCF   Worksheet 9

① Simplify the expressions. You do not have to solve exponents greater than 3.

$7^0 = 1$
$16^1 = 16$
$5^2 \times 5^6 = 5^8$
$7^9 \div 7^7 = 7^2 = 49$
$(2 \times 3)^2 = 2^2 \times 3^2 = 4 \times 9 = 36$

$2^{-3} = \left(\dfrac{1}{2}\right)^3 = \dfrac{1^3}{2^3} = \dfrac{1}{8}$

$\left(\dfrac{1}{5}\right)^2 = \dfrac{1^2}{5^2} = \dfrac{1}{25}$

$\left(\dfrac{2}{3}\right)^{-2} = \left(\dfrac{3}{2}\right)^2 = \dfrac{3^2}{2^2} = \dfrac{9}{4}$

② Use the divisibility tests to determine which numbers are factors of the given numbers.

	2	3	4	5	6	9	10
471		x					
492	x	x	x		x		
459		x				x	
540	x	x	x	x	x	x	x
612	x	x	x		x	x	
606	x	x			x		
453		x					

③ Find the greatest common factor of each set of numbers.

9 and 15
$9 = ③ \times 3$
$15 = ③ \times 5$
GCF is 3

16 and 20
$16 = ② \times ② \times 2 \times 2$
$20 = ② \times ② \times 5$
GCF is $2 \times 2 = 4$

6, 9, and 15
$6 = 2 \times ③$
$9 = ③ \times 3$
$15 = ③ \times 5$
GCF is 3

Teaching Tips, Cont.

➢ Explain that it is not necessary to prime factor the radicand, but rather look for perfect squares that are factors.

➢ Have students express each of the following numbers as the product of a perfect square and another factor:
$12 = (4 \times 3)$, $18 = (9 \times 2)$, $20 = (4 \times 5)$, $24 = (4 \times 6)$.

➢ Show students that the process for finding any other root is the same as finding the square root, except the number of equal factors in the radicand must equal the number in the index. For example, the cube root of a number must have the same factor appearing three times in the radicand. The 4th root of a number must have the same factor appearing 4 times in the radicand. Encourage students to prime factor the radicand if they are having difficulty finding the root.

➢ Complete the Classwork exercises. Have some students work the problems on the board for the class. All students should work the problems in their books.

Assignment

• Complete Lesson 18, Activities 2-6.

Lesson 19

Concepts
- Writing expressions with one variable
- Signed numbers
- Least common multiple
- Roots
- Math in the real world

Learning Objectives
The student will be able to:
- Define *variable* and *constant*
- Translate words into mathematical expressions
- Use variables to represent unknown values
- Identify like terms in mathematical expressions
- Combine like terms

Materials Needed
- Student Book, Lesson 19
- 2 or more of each of the following items: pencils, pieces of paper, books
- Algebra tiles

Teaching Tips
➢ Define *variable* and *constant* in the teaching box. Explain that a variable simply represents an unknown amount – the amount they are looking for in a problem.

➢ Teach the rules for translating words into mathematical expressions. Point out that while this is not an exhaustive list, these are the most common words found in word problems.

Writing Expressions with One Variable

A **variable** is a letter used to represent an unknown numerical value. In algebra, x is the most common variable.

In an expression or equation, a letter appearing in more than one location always represents the same amount.

To write expressions with a variable, let x represent the unknown amount. Use the following rules to translate words into a numeric expression:
Addition: more than, total, sum, increased by, added to, together
Subtraction: less than, fewer than, difference, decreased by, reduced by
Multiplication: times, of, multiplied by, product, increased by a factor of
Division: per, a, ratio, quotient, percent, out of

When simplifying expressions, combine like terms. **Like terms** have identical variables with identical exponents or are constants. **Constants** (numbers with no variables) are all like terms and may be combined following the order of operations. Variables that are like terms may be combined following the order of operations.

① **Classwork**
Translate the following words into a mathematical expression.

5 more than a number $x + 5$

3 less than a number $x - 3$

A number increased by a factor of 4 $4x$

A number increased by 7 $x + 7$

6 decreased by a number $6 - x$

A number multiplied by 2 $2x$

Simplify by combining like terms.

$x + x = 2x$

$2 + 3 + x = 5 + x$ or $x + 5$

$2x + x + 4 + 1 = 3x + 5$ or $5 + 3x$

Activities
② Translate the following words into a mathematical expression.

The total of a number and 45 $x + 45$
9 fewer than a number $x - 9$
A number times 8 $8x$
The sum of 29 and a number $29 + x$
The quotient of a number and 9 $x \div 9$
7 less than a number $x - 7$
A number increased by a factor of 3 $3x$
43 more than a number $x + 43$
A number less than 83 $83 - x$
The product of 2 and a number $2x$
The ratio of a number to 10 $x \div 10$
A number increased by 23 $x + 23$

Using Algebra Tiles

When using algebra tiles, the red pieces always represent negative terms. All other colors represent positive terms. In this set, green pieces are constants, blue pieces are x-terms, and yellow pieces are x^2 terms. The colors and shapes will help the students identify like terms. A red piece may be combined with another color of the same size and shape. A red piece will always negate a corresponding green, blue, or yellow piece, and therefore remove both pieces. For example, if you have 5 green squares and 3 red squares, the three red squares cancel out 3 of the green squares, leaving 2 green squares. This is the representation of $5 - 3 = 2$.

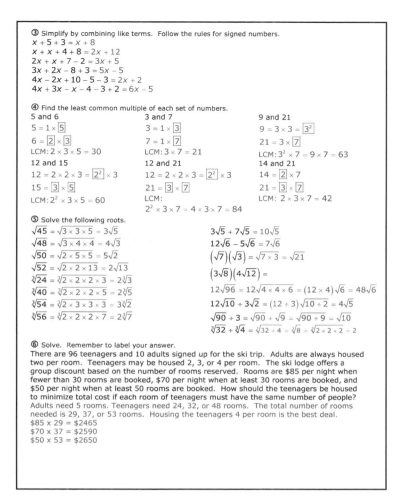

③ Simplify by combining like terms. Follow the rules for signed numbers.

$x + 5 + 3 = x + 8$
$x + x + 4 + 8 = 2x + 12$
$2x + x + 7 - 2 = 3x + 5$
$3x + 2x - 8 + 3 = 5x - 5$
$4x - 2x + 10 - 5 - 3 = 2x + 2$
$4x + 3x - x - 4 - 3 + 2 = 6x - 5$

④ Find the least common multiple of each set of numbers.

5 and 6
$5 = 1 \times \boxed{5}$
$6 = \boxed{2} \times \boxed{3}$
LCM: $2 \times 3 \times 5 = 30$

3 and 7
$3 = 1 \times \boxed{3}$
$7 = 1 \times \boxed{7}$
LCM: $3 \times 7 = 21$

9 and 21
$9 = 3 \times 3 = \boxed{3^2}$
$21 = 3 \times \boxed{7}$
LCM: $3^2 \times 7 = 9 \times 7 = 63$

12 and 15
$12 = 2 \times 2 \times 3 = \boxed{2^2} \times 3$
$15 = \boxed{3} \times \boxed{5}$
LCM: $2^2 \times 3 \times 5 = 60$

12 and 21
$12 = 2 \times 2 \times 3 = \boxed{2^2} \times 3$
$21 = \boxed{3} \times \boxed{7}$
LCM: $2^2 \times 3 \times 7 = 4 \times 3 \times 7 = 84$

14 and 21
$14 = \boxed{2} \times 7$
$21 = \boxed{3} \times \boxed{7}$
LCM: $2 \times 3 \times 7 = 42$

⑤ Solve the following roots.

$\sqrt{45} = \sqrt{3 \times 3 \times 5} = 3\sqrt{5}$
$\sqrt{48} = \sqrt{3 \times 4 \times 4} = 4\sqrt{3}$
$\sqrt{50} = \sqrt{2 \times 5 \times 5} = 5\sqrt{2}$
$\sqrt{52} = \sqrt{2 \times 2 \times 13} = 2\sqrt{13}$
$\sqrt[3]{24} = \sqrt[3]{2 \times 2 \times 2 \times 3} = 2\sqrt[3]{3}$
$\sqrt[3]{40} = \sqrt[3]{2 \times 2 \times 2 \times 5} = 2\sqrt[3]{5}$
$\sqrt[3]{54} = \sqrt[3]{2 \times 3 \times 3 \times 3} = 3\sqrt[3]{2}$
$\sqrt[3]{56} = \sqrt[3]{2 \times 2 \times 2 \times 7} = 2\sqrt[3]{7}$

$3\sqrt{5} + 7\sqrt{5} = 10\sqrt{5}$
$12\sqrt{6} - 5\sqrt{6} = 7\sqrt{6}$
$(\sqrt{7})(\sqrt{3}) = \sqrt{7 \times 3} = \sqrt{21}$
$(3\sqrt{8})(4\sqrt{12}) =$
$12\sqrt{96} = 12\sqrt{4 \times 4 \times 6} = (12 \times 4)\sqrt{6} = 48\sqrt{6}$
$12\sqrt{10} \div 3\sqrt{2} = (12 \div 3)\sqrt{10 \div 2} = 4\sqrt{5}$
$\sqrt{90} \div 3 = \sqrt{90} \div \sqrt{9} = \sqrt{90 \div 9} = \sqrt{10}$
$\sqrt[3]{32} \div \sqrt[3]{4} = \sqrt[3]{32 \div 4} = \sqrt[3]{8} = \sqrt[3]{2 \times 2 \times 2} = 2$

⑥ Solve. Remember to label your answer.

There are 96 teenagers and 10 adults signed up for the ski trip. Adults are always housed two per room. Teenagers may be housed 2, 3, or 4 per room. The ski lodge offers a group discount based on the number of rooms reserved. Rooms are $85 per night when fewer than 30 rooms are booked, $70 per night when at least 30 rooms are booked, and $50 per night when at least 50 rooms are booked. How should the teenagers be housed to minimize total cost if each room of teenagers must have the same number of people? Adults need 5 rooms. Teenagers need 24, 32, or 48 rooms. The total number of rooms needed is 29, 37, or 53 rooms. Housing the teenagers 4 per room is the best deal.

$85 \times 29 = \$2465$
$70 \times 37 = \$2590$
$50 \times 53 = \$2650$

2x + 3 is represented by

This visual makes is clear that the *x* terms cannot be combined with the constants.

2x – x + 3 – 2 is represented by

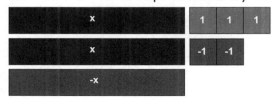

and simplifies to

or *x* + 1.

➢ Explain to students that any letter may be used as a variable. When solving word problems, they may want to use the letter that corresponds with the first letter of the unknown. Point out that *l* and *s* are not good variable choices since they tend to look like 1s and 5s.

➢ Teach students to identify and combine like terms. Show the students two pencils. (Make sure they are identical pencils, if possible.) Ask them if these two items are alike. (Yes.) Ask the students what one pencil plus one pencil equals. (Two pencils.) Now show the students a pencil and a book. Ask the students what one pencil plus one book equals. (One pencil plus one book – they cannot be combined because they are not alike.) Continue this process with the pencils, paper, and books until the students grasp the concept. Then illustrate the same concept using variables. Emphasize that the base and exponent must match to combine variables as like terms.

➢ Illustrate combining like terms using the algebra tiles. See the illustrations at the left. Encourage students to use their algebra tiles as necessary to check their work in the Classwork and Activities exercises for this lesson.

➢ Complete the Classwork exercises. Have some students work the problems on the board for the class. All students should work the problems in their books.

Assignment

- Complete Lesson 19, Activities 2-6.

Lesson 20

Concepts
- Equations with one variable
- Writing expressions
- Simplifying expressions
- Divisibility tests
- Prime/Composite numbers
- Greatest common factor
- Least common multiple
- Math in the real world

Learning Objectives
The student will be able to:
- Write equations with one variable
- Solve equations with one variable
- Combine like terms on opposite sides of the equal sign

Materials Needed
- Student Book, Lesson 20
- Worksheet 10
- Algebra tiles

Teaching Tips
➢ Review the rules for translating words into mathematical expressions.

➢ Review the rules for combining like terms.

➢ Teach the rules for placement of the equal sign in a mathematical expression from the teaching box.

➢ Show students the procedure for solving equations. Whatever is done to one side of the equal sign must also be done to the other side. Whatever is multiplied or divided by one term must be done to all terms on both sides of the equal sign. Order of operations must be followed, as well.

Horizons Pre-Algebra, Teacher's Guide

Equations with One Variable

To write equations with a variable, let x represent the unknown amount. Apply the rules for translating words into a numeric expression and separate the equal parts with an equal sign. Use the following rule to determine where to place the equal sign:
Equals: is , are, was, were, equals, yields, gives

To solve equations with one variable, combine the like terms, getting variables on one side of the equal sign and constants on the other side. When like terms appear on both sides of the equal sign, perform the same operation to both sides to maintain an equal equation. For example, to solve the equation $3x + 4 = 2x + 6$, begin by subtracting $2x$ from both sides to combine the like variable terms.
$3x + 4 = 2x + 6$
$3x + 4 - 2x = 2x + 6 - 2x$
$x + 4 = 6$
Then subtract 4 from both sides to combine the constant terms on the opposite side of the equal sign.
$x + 4 - 4 = 6 - 4$
$x = 2$
Check your answer by substituting the value of x into the original equation:
$3x + 4 = 2x + 6$
$3(2) + 4 = 2(2) + 6$
$6 + 4 = 4 + 6$
$10 = 10$

① **Classwork**
Translate the following words into a mathematical equation.

5 more than a number is 14.
$x + 5 = 14$
3 less than a number equals 5.
$x - 3 = 5$
A number increased by a factor of 4 yields 12.
$4x = 12$
A number increased by 7 gives 18.
$x - 7 = 18$
6 decreased by a number is 2.
$6 - x = 2$
A number multiplied by 2 equals 16.
$2x = 16$

Solve by combining like terms. Check your work by substituting into the original equation.

$x + x = 8 \Rightarrow 2x = 8 \Rightarrow x = 4$
Check: $4 + 4 = 8$

$2 + 3 + x = 9 \Rightarrow 5 + x = 9 \Rightarrow x = 4$
Check: $2 + 3 + 4 = 9$

$2x + x + 4 + 1 = 17$
$3x + 5 = 17 \Rightarrow 3x = 12 \Rightarrow x = 4$
Check: $2(4) + 4 + 4 + 1 = 17$
$\qquad 8 + 4 + 4 + 1 = 17$

Activities
② Translate the following words into a mathematical equation.
The total of a number and 45 is 56. $x + 45 = 56$
9 fewer than a number equals 5. $x - 9 = 5$
A number times 8 yields 32. $8x = 32$
The sum of 29 and a number is 47. $29 + x = 47$
The quotient of a number and 9 yields 6. $x \div 9 = 6$
7 less than a number is 18. $x - 7 = 18$
A number increased by a factor of 3 gives 21. $3x = 21$
43 more than a number is 77. $x + 43 = 77$
A number less than 83 equals 42. $83 - x = 42$

③ Solve by combining like terms. Follow the rules for signed numbers. Check your work.
$x + 5 + 3 = 13 \Rightarrow x + 8 = 13 \Rightarrow x = 5$
Check: $5 + 5 + 3 = 13$
$x + x + 4 + 8 = 26 \Rightarrow 2x + 12 = 26 \Rightarrow 2x = 14 \Rightarrow x = 7$
Check: $7 + 7 + 4 + 8 = 26$
$2x + x + 7 - 2 = 17 \Rightarrow 3x + 5 = 17 \Rightarrow 3x = 12 \Rightarrow x = 4$
Check: $2(4) + 4 + 7 - 2 = 17$
$\qquad 8 + 4 + 7 - 2 = 17$
$3x + 2x - 8 + 3 = 30 \Rightarrow 5x - 5 = 30 \Rightarrow 5x = 35 \Rightarrow x = 7$
Check: $3(7) + 2(7) - 8 + 3 = 30$
$\qquad 21 + 14 - 8 + 3 = 30$
$4x - 2x + 10 - 5 - 3 = 22 \Rightarrow 2x + 2 = 22 \Rightarrow 2x = 20 \Rightarrow x = 10$
Check: $4(10) - 2(10) + 10 - 5 - 3 = 22$
$\qquad 40 - 20 + 10 - 5 - 3 = 22$
$4x + 3x - x - 4 - 3 + 2 = 49 \Rightarrow 6x - 5 = 49 \Rightarrow 6x = 54 \Rightarrow x = 9$
Check: $4(9) + 3(9) - 9 - 4 - 3 + 2 = 49$
$\qquad 36 + 27 - 9 - 4 - 3 + 2 = 49$

④ Use the divisibility tests to identify each number as prime or composite.
181 Prime
183 Composite (3)
185 Composite (5)
189 Composite (3, 9)
191 Prime
193 Prime

⑤ Find the greatest common factor of each set of numbers.

18 and 26	24 and 36	32 and 48
$18 = ②\times 3 \times 3$	$24 = ②\times②\times 2 \times ③$	$32 = ②\times②\times②\times②\times 2$
$26 = ②\times 13$	$36 = ②\times②\times③\times 3$	$48 = ②\times②\times②\times②\times 3$
GCF: 2	GCF: $2 \times 2 \times 3 = 12$	GCF: $2 \times 2 \times 2 \times 2 = 2^4 = 16$

⑥ Find the least common multiple of each set of numbers.

6 and 15	8 and 12	10 and 15
$6 = \boxed{2} \times 3$	$8 = 2 \times 2 \times 2 = \boxed{2^3}$	$10 = \boxed{2} \times 5$
$15 = \boxed{3} \times \boxed{5}$	$12 = 2 \times 2 \times 3 = 2^2 \times \boxed{3}$	$15 = \boxed{3} \times \boxed{5}$
LCM: $2 \times 3 \times 5 = 30$	LCM: $2^3 \times 3 = 8 \times 3 = 24$	LCM: $2 \times 3 \times 5 = 30$

⑦ Set up an equation and solve. Remember to label your answers.
Each year, Ric designs a new t-shirt for the youth retreat. Company A charges $50 to make a custom design, $8 per shirt for the first 50 shirts, and $5 for each additional shirt. Ric is ordering 110 shirts for the youth retreat. If shipping costs $12, what is the total cost of the shirts from Company A? $762
Let x = the total cost of the shirts from Company A.
$x = \$50 + \$8(50) + \$5(110 - 50) + \$12$

$x = \$50 + \$400 + \$300 + \$12 = \$762$
Company B charges $7 per shirt, with no design fees and free shipping. Which company offers the better overall price for 110 shirts? $7(110) = $770. Company A is better.

① Find the greatest common factor of each set of numbers.

12 and 16
12 = ②×②×3
16 = ②×②×2×2
GCF is 2 × 2 = 4

16 and 18
16 = ②×2×2×2
18 = ②×3×3
GCF is 2

18 and 24
18 = ②×③×3
24 = ②×2×2×③
GCF is 2 × 3 = 6

15 and 24
15 = ③×5
24 = 2×2×2×③
CFG is 3

20 and 24
20 = ②×②×5
24 = ②×②×2×3
GCF is 2 × 2 = 4

12, 15, and 18
12 = 2 × 2 ×③
15 = ③×5
18 = 2 ×③×3
GCF is 3

② Find the least common multiple of each set of numbers.

4 and 6
4 = 2 × 2 = 2^2
6 = 2 × 3
LCM:
2^2 × 3 = 4 × 3 = 12

9 and 15
9 = 3 × 3 = 3^2
15 = 3 × 5
LCM:
3^2 × 5 = 9 × 5 = 45

12 and 16
12 = 2 × 2 × 3 = 2^2 × 3
16 = 2 × 2 × 2 × 2 = 2^4
LCM: 3 × 2^4 = 3 × 16 = 48

8 and 10
8 = 2 × 2 × 2 = 2^3
10 = 2 × 5
LCM:
2^3 × 5 = 8 × 5 = 40

12 and 15
12 = 2 × 2 × 3 = 2^2 × 3
15 = 3 × 5
LCM: 2^2 × 3 × 5 = 60

14 and 24
14 = 2 × 7
24 = 2 × 2 × 2 × 3 = 2^3 × 3
LCM:
2^3 × 3 × 7 = 8 × 3 × 7 = 168

③ Rewrite the following expressions as roots.

3^5 = 243   3 = $\sqrt[5]{243}$
9^2 = 81   9 = $\sqrt{81}$
4^3 = 64   4 = $\sqrt[3]{64}$

8^3 = 512   8 = $\sqrt[3]{512}$
10^4 = 10,000   10 = $\sqrt[4]{10,000}$
5^2 = 25   5 = $\sqrt{25}$

Solve $x + x = 8$ using algebra tiles.

Since each side has an even number of pieces of each color, divide by two by removing half of each color.

or $x = 4$

Solve $3x+4=x+6$ using algebra tiles.

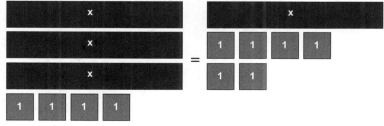

Each side has an x and 4 units in common. Remove these and you have

Remove half of each term, and $x = 1$.

Teaching Tips, Cont.

➤ Use algebra tiles to illustrate the process of solving single-variable equations. See the examples below. Encourage students to use their algebra tiles as necessary to check their work on the Classwork and Activities exercises for this lesson.

➤ Teach students how to check their work without using algebra tiles. Substitute the answer for x in the original problem and make sure it forms a true mathematical sentence. For example, in the problem $x + x = 8$, the student should get $x = 4$ for the answer. Substituting in the original problem gives $4 + 4 = 8$, which is a true statement. If the student said $x = 6$, substitution would show an incorrect answer: $6 + 6 \neq 8$.

➤ Complete the Classwork exercises. Have some students work the problems on the board for the class. All students should work the problems in their books.

Assignments
- Complete Lesson 20, Activities 2-7.
- Worksheet 10
- Study for test (Lessons 8-17)

Solve $x + 2 = -1$ using algebra tiles.

The two sides do not have matching pieces to remove. In this case, remove a green unit piece by *adding* a red unit piece to the opposite side.

$x = -3$

A positive on one side can always be removed by adding a corresponding negative to the opposite side.

Test 2

Testing Objectives

The student will:

- Identify 3-digit numbers as multiples of 2, 3, 4, 5, 6, 9, or 10
- Identify natural numbers as prime or composite
- Find the prime factorization of a given natural number
- Use exponents to express products
- Calculate the square of a natural number
- Apply the order of operations to mathematical expressions
- Calculate the greatest common factor of a set of natural numbers
- Calculate the least common multiple of a set of natural numbers

Materials Needed

- Test 2
- *It's College Test Prep Time!* from Student Book
- *A Math Minute with …* Billy G. from Student Book

Teaching Tips

➢ Administer Test 2, allowing the students 30-40 minutes to complete the test.

➢ When all students are finished taking the test, introduce the College Test Prep Time from the student book. This page may be completed in class or assigned as homework.

➢ Have students read the Math Minute interview for Lessons 21-30.

Test 2

① Use the divisibility tests to tell if 2, 3, 4, 5, 6, and 9 are factors of each number.   **19 points**

	90	91	92	93	94	95	96	115	116	117
2	X		X		X		X		X	
3	X			X			X			X
4			X				X		X	
5	X					X		X		
6	X						X			
9	X									X

② Identify each number as prime or composite.   **10 points**

2	Prime	11	Prime
3	Prime	13	Prime
4	Composite	15	Composite
5	Prime	19	Prime
7	Prime	21	Composite

③ Express the prime factorization of each number using exponents.   **9 points**

12
$12 = 2 \times 2 \times 3 = 2^2 \times 3$

16
$16 = 2 \times 2 \times 2 \times 2 = 2^4$

18
$18 = 2 \times 3 \times 3 = 2 \times 3^2$

20
$20 = 2 \times 2 \times 5 = 2^2 \times 5$

24
$24 = 2 \times 2 \times 2 \times 3 = 2^3 \times 3$

25
$25 = 5 \times 5 = 5^2$

28
$28 = 2 \times 2 \times 7 = 2^2 \times 7$

32
$32 = 2 \times 2 \times 2 \times 2 \times 2 = 2^5$

36
$36 = 2 \times 2 \times 3 \times 3 = 2^2 \times 3^2$

④ Find the square of each number.   **10 points**

2	$2^2 = 4$	9	$9^2 = 81$
3	$3^2 = 9$	10	$10^2 = 100$
5	$5^2 = 25$	11	$11^2 = 121$
6	$6^2 = 36$	12	$12^2 = 144$
8	$8^2 = 64$	13	$13^2 = 169$

Test 2

⑤ Solve, following the order of operations.   **10 points**

$5 + 3 \times 8 = 5 + 24 = 29$

$8 \div (2 + 6) + 1 = 8 \div 8 + 1 = 1 + 1 = 2$

$3 - (7 + 2) + 9 = 3 - 9 + 9 = -6 + 9 = 3$

$8^2 - 3^2 \times 4 = 64 - 9 \times 4 = 64 - 36 = 28$

$4 \times 3^2 - 6 \times 4 = 4 \times 9 - 6 \times 4 = 36 - 24 = 12$

$3^2 - 4^2 \div 8 - 7 = 9 - 16 \div 8 - 7 = 9 - 2 - 7 = 7 - 7 = 0$

$5^2 \times (4 - 6^2 \div 9) = 5^2 \times (4 - 36 \div 9) = 5^2 \times (4 - 4) = 25 \times 0 = 0$

$2 \times (3^2 + 1) - 5 \times 2 = 2 \times (9 + 1) - 5 \times 2 = 2 \times 10 - 5 \times 2 = 20 - 10 = 10$

$5 + (1 - 2^2) + 8 = 5 + (1 - 4) + 8 = 5 + (-3) + 8 = 5 - 3 + 8 = 2 + 8 = 10$

$2 \times 7 - (5 - 2 - 6) = 2 \times 7 - (3 - 6) = 2 \times 7 - (-3) = 2 \times 7 + 3 = 14 + 3 = 17$

⑥ Find the greatest common factor of each set of numbers.   **6 points**

12 and 15
$12 = 2 \times 2 \times ③$
$15 = ③ \times 5$
GCF: 3

16 and 24
$16 = ② \times ② \times ② \times 2$
$24 = ② \times ② \times ② \times 3$
GCF: $2 \times 2 \times 2 = 8$

9 and 12
$9 = ③ \times 3$
$12 = 2 \times 2 \times ③$
GCF: 3

20 and 32
$20 = ② \times ② \times 5$
$32 = ② \times ② \times 2 \times 2 \times 2$
GCF: $2 \times 2 = 4$

27 and 45
$27 = ③ \times ③ \times 3$
$45 = ③ \times ③ \times 5$
GCF: $3 \times 3 = 9$

28 and 42
$28 = ② \times 2 \times ⑦$
$42 = ② \times 3 \times ⑦$
GCF: $2 \times 7 = 14$

⑦ Find the least common multiple of each set of numbers.   **6 points**

6 and 9
$6 = \boxed{2} \times 3$
$9 = 3 \times 3 = \boxed{3^2}$
LCM: $2 \times 3^2 = 2 \times 9 = 18$

10 and 15
$10 = \boxed{2} \times 5$
$15 = \boxed{3} \times \boxed{5}$
LCM: $2 \times 3 \times 5 = 30$

12 and 18
$12 = 2 \times 2 \times 3 = \boxed{2^2} \times 3$
$18 = 2 \times 3 \times 3 = 2 \times \boxed{3^2}$
LCM: $2^2 \times 3^2 = 4 \times 9 = 36$

12 and 20
$12 = 2 \times 2 \times 3 = 2^2 \times \boxed{3}$
$20 = 2 \times 2 \times 5 = \boxed{2^2} \times \boxed{5}$
LCM: $2^2 \times 3 \times 5 = 60$

15 and 25
$15 = \boxed{3} \times 5$
$25 = 5 \times 5 = \boxed{5^2}$
LCM: $3 \times 5^2 = 3 \times 25 = 75$

16 and 24
$16 = 2 \times 2 \times 2 \times 2 = \boxed{2^4}$
$24 = 2 \times 2 \times 2 \times 3 = 2^3 \times \boxed{3}$
LCM: $2^4 \times 3 = 16 \times 3 = 48$

70 points total

It's College Test Prep Time!

1. Given $(4 + a)(5 - b) = 0$ and a is a natural number, what is the value of b?
   A. -5
   B. -4
   C. 0
   D. 4
   E. 5 A natural number is positive, making the first parentheses positive. The second parentheses MUST then equal zero.

2. Given $3(m + n) - 4 = 5$, what is the value of $m + n$?
   A. 2
   B. 3 $3(m + n) = 9$; $m + n = 9 \div 3 = 3$
   C. 6
   D. 9
   E. 27

3. If $9^6 \times 9^x = 9^{15}$, what is the value of x?
   A. 2.5
   B. 4.5
   C. 9 $9^{6+x} = 9^{15}$; $6 + x = 15$; $x = 9$
   D. 21
   E. 90

4. David made 42 sausage biscuits for the concession stand. He sold 36 of them at full price. Half of the remaining biscuits were sold at a discount before the rest were thrown away. How many sausage biscuits were thrown away?
   A. 3 $42 - 36 = 6$; $6 \div 2 = 3$
   B. 6
   C. 18
   D. 36
   E. 39

5. Let a represent any even integer and b represent any odd integer. Then, $7a + 4b$ MUST be:
   A. an even integer   Odd times even is always even. The sum of two evens is
   B. an odd integer   always even. Therefore this is always an even integer.
   C. a multiple of 7
   D. a multiple of 4
   E. an integer

A Math Minute with . . .

Billy G. – Volunteer Concessions

What do you do for volunteer work? I run the concession stand for a youth sports league.

Where do you volunteer? I serve as a volunteer at my church.

Did you attend college? If so, what was your major? I attended college where I majored in Accounting.

What parts of your job require the use of math? At the beginning of each season, I calculate the cost per item in order to set up the concession stand prices. I also must determine what to charge each team for their players' food for the games, so we break even. Before each game, I need to stock the concession stand. I determine how much money I need in order to do this. During the games, I use mental math to add up the total price of an individual's order and make the correct change for each purchase.

What is the biggest "problem" you have faced that required the use of math to solve? Because each player places an individual food order each week before the games, I don't know in advance what menu items will be ordered. I have to keep track of trends to estimate the amount of food to purchase prior to each game to ensure I have enough to fill the players' orders and still have enough to sell in the concession stand. Additionally, I do not want to have excess food at the end of the season.

Are there any other interesting math uses you have experienced? One interesting math problem I have done is to determine how many orders of fries I can fill from one bag of frozen fries. I also have to purchase cases of refrigerated biscuit dough to make donut holes. One pack of biscuits makes 160 donut holes, but the donut holes are packaged and sold in groups of 12. I also allow the coaches' families to charge their orders at the concession stand and pay the total at the end of the day. I need to write down the orders for each person in the family throughout the day. At the end, I find the sum to know what to charge each of the coaches.

Lesson 21

Concepts
- Solving word problems
- Math in the real world
- Absolute value
- Divisibility tests
- Prime and composite numbers
- Greatest common factor
- Roots

Learning Objectives
The student will be able to:
- Identify the unknown in a word problem
- Organize the information in a word problem in a mathematical expression
- Apply single-variable equations to real world scenarios

Materials Needed
- Student Book, Lesson 21

Teaching Tips
➢ Teach the steps for solving word problems using the acronym W.O.R.D.

➢ Remind students that any letter can be used for the variable, but *l* and *s* should be avoided. (See Lesson 19.)

➢ Read the following problem to the students, having them identify the extra information:
Last Saturday, Billy sold 37 energy drinks for $2 each, 112 cans of soda for $1 each, and 52 bottles of water for $1.50 each. How much money did the concession stand bring in on Saturday from the sales of energy drinks and soda? (The extra information is the water sales.)

Word Problems

Solving word problems is easy if you remember four steps that spell out **WORD**:

W: What are you asked to find? This is your unknown, represented by a variable.

O: Organize the information in the word problem by translating the words and phrases into a mathematical expression. Watch for extra information in the word problem that is not necessary for solving the problem. You will not necessarily use every number mentioned in the problem!

R: Rearrange the equation by isolating the variable on one side of the equal sign and combining like terms.

D: Does the answer make sense? If you start with 24 cookies in a jar and 4 people each eat 2 cookies for dessert, it does not make sense to say there are 32 cookies remaining in the jar!

① **Classwork**
Solve the word problem, using the four steps.

Last Saturday, Billy sold 37 energy drinks for $2 each and 112 cans of soda for $1 each. How much money did the concession stand bring in on Saturday from the sales of energy drinks and soda?
Let x=total sales of energy drinks and soda

$x = 37 \times \$2 + 112 \times \$1$

$x = \$74 + \$112$

$x = \$186$

Activities
② Solve the following word problems. Remember to label your answers.
At Billy's concession stand, soccer players may choose from a pouch of fruit punch, a bottle of sports drink, or a bottle of water for their beverage. Fruit punch costs 75 cents and water costs an additional 25 cents. If a sports drink costs twice as much as a bottle of water, how much does Billy charge for a sports drink? **$2**
Let x=charge for a sports drink
$x = 2(75¢ + 25¢)$ so $x = 2(100¢) = 200¢$ This is the number of cents, not dollars.
x=$2
Soccer players have the option of purchasing a full season meal plan from Billy's concession stand. The meal plan costs $10 for the eight-week season. Each game, players may choose a hot dog or hamburger along with their choice of fruit punch, water, or sports drink. If hot dogs cost $1 and hamburgers cost $2 and the drinks are priced according to the problem above, how much money will a player save if he orders a hamburger and sports drink each of the eight weeks? **$22**
Let x=total money saved for 8 weeks
$x = 8(\$2 + \$2) - \$10$ $x = 8(\$4) - \$10$ $x = \$32 - \$10 = \$22$
Billy lets the teenagers from the church youth group help in the concession stand. The profits are divided evenly among the teens who work. They purchase a case of 48 cans of soft drink from a warehouse club for $9. If they sell them for $1 per can, how much money would each of three teenagers earn from the sales of the soda? **$13**
Let x=amount of money each of three teenagers earns
$x = (\$48 - \$9) \div 3$ $x = (\$39) \div 3$ $x = \$13$

---

③ Solve, using the rules of absolute values.

$|-32| + |-17| = 32 + 17 = 49$ $-|42| - |-16| = -42 - 16 = -58$

$|-15| + |47| = 15 + 47 = 62$ $|18 + 26| + |27 - 5| = 44 + 22 = 66$

$|57| - |-33| = 57 - 33 = 24$ $-|53 - 24| + |14 - 21| = -29 + 7 = -22$

$-|14| + |-6| = -14 + 6 = -8$ $-|41 + 16| - |29 - 17| = -57 - 12 = -69$

④ Use the divisibility tests to identify each number as prime or composite.

195　Composite (3, 5)　　201　Composite (3)
197　Prime　　　　　　 205　Composite (5)
199　Prime　　　　　　 207　Composite (3, 9)

⑤ Find the greatest common factor of each set of numbers.

20 and 32
$20 = ②×②×5$
$32 = ②×②×2 × 2 × 2$
GCF: $2 × 2 = 4$

24 and 30
$24 = ②×2 × 2 ×③$
$30 = ②×③×5$
GCF: $2 × 3 = 6$

32 and 42
$32 = ②×2 × 2 × 2 × 2$
$42 = ②×3 × 7$
GCF: 2

15, 25, and 40
$15 = 3 × ⑤$
$25 = ⑤ × 5$
$40 = 2 × 2 × 2 × ⑤$
GCF: 5

16, 28, and 40
$16 = ②×②×2 × 2$
$28 = ②×②×7$
$40 = ②×②×2 × 5$
GCF: $2 × 2 = 4$

24, 32, and 36
$24 = ②×②×2 × 3$
$32 = ②×②×2 × 2 × 2$
$36 = ②×②×3 × 3$
GCF: $2 × 2 = 4$

⑥ Solve the following roots.

$\sqrt{27} = \sqrt{3 × 3 × 3} = 3\sqrt{3}$
$\sqrt{32} = \sqrt{2 × 4 × 4} = 4\sqrt{2}$
$\sqrt{40} = \sqrt{2 × 2 × 10} = 2\sqrt{10}$
$\sqrt{44} = \sqrt{2 × 2 × 11} = 2\sqrt{11}$
$\sqrt{45} = \sqrt{3 × 3 × 5} = 3\sqrt{5}$
$\sqrt{48} = \sqrt{3 × 4 × 4} = 4\sqrt{3}$
$\sqrt{50} = \sqrt{2 × 5 × 5} = 5\sqrt{2}$
$\sqrt{68} = \sqrt{2 × 2 × 17} = 2\sqrt{17}$

$\sqrt{75} = \sqrt{3 × 5 × 5} = 5\sqrt{3}$
$\sqrt[3]{32} = \sqrt[3]{2 × 2 × 4} = 2\sqrt[3]{4}$
$\sqrt[3]{40} = \sqrt[3]{2 × 2 × 2 × 5} = 2\sqrt[3]{5}$
$\sqrt[3]{54} = \sqrt[3]{2 × 3 × 3 × 3} = 3\sqrt[3]{2}$
$3\sqrt{11} + 6\sqrt{11} = (3 + 6)\sqrt{11} = 9\sqrt{11}$
$\sqrt{8} - \sqrt{2} = 2\sqrt{2} - \sqrt{2} = (2 - 1)\sqrt{2} = \sqrt{2}$
$\left(2\sqrt{6}\right)\left(5\sqrt{15}\right) = (2 × 5)\sqrt{6 × 15} = 10\sqrt{2 × 3 × 3 × 5}$
$= (10 × 3)\sqrt{2 × 5} = 30\sqrt{10}$

Teaching Tips, Cont.

➢ Review the procedure for solving equations with one variable. (See Lesson 20.)

➢ Review the order of operations (See Lesson 12), emphasizing that multiplication and division MUST be done before addition and subtraction.

➢ Complete the Classwork exercise. Have one student work the problem on the board for the class and explain the answer. All students should work the problem in their books.

Assignment

• Complete Lesson 21, Activities 2-6.

Lesson 22

Concepts
- Single-variable inequalities
- Absolute value
- Factors
- Roots
- Math puzzles
- Real world math

Learning Objectives
The student will be able to:
- Define *inequality*
- Use the symbols < and > to show relationships
- Apply mathematical concepts to solve inequalities

Materials Needed
- Student Book, Lesson 22
- Worksheet 11

Teaching Tips
➢ Have students complete Worksheet 11 in class. This may be for added practice of earlier topics, or graded as a quiz, if desired.

➢ Ask students what symbol is used to show that two amounts are equal. (=)

➢ Ask students how many players from each team are playing at any given time in a football game. (11) Have the students use a mathematical expression to show the relationship between the number of players on each team. (11 = 11) One team gets a penalty for having 12 players on the field. Is it fair for this team to be penalized? (Yes.) Why? (There are not an equal number of players on each team.)

Inequalities with One Variable

Inequalities show the relationship between two things that are not equal.
Use the > symbol to show that one object is greater than another. For example, 4 > 3.
Use the < symbol to show that one object is less than another.
For example, 3 < 4.

When working with inequalities in mathematical expressions, follow these rules:
- You may add or subtract the same amount from both sides of the inequality sign.
- You may multiply or divide both sides of the inequality sign by the same positive number.
- If you multiply or divide both sides of the inequality sign by a negative number, you must reverse the inequality sign.

For example, $-3x < 12$.
If we add $3x$ to each side and subtract 12 from each side, we get
$-3x + 3x < 12 + 3x$
$0 < 12 + 3x$
$-12 < 12 - 12 + 3x$
$-12 < 3x$

If we divide each side by 3, we know that $-4 < x$, which is the same as saying $x > -4$

Looking back at the original problem $-3x < 12$, if we divide both sides by -3 to isolate the variable and do not reverse the sign, we have $x < -4$. Choose any number that is less than -4, such as -5, and test in the original problem: $-3(-5) < 12$ and $15 < 12$. This is clearly not correct! Reverse the inequality sign to get $-4 < x$ or $x > -4$

① Classwork
Solve the inequalities.

$4x < 20$
$4x \div 4 < 20 \div 4$
$x < 5$

$-4x < 20$
$-4x \div 4 < 20 \div 4$
$-x < 5$
$x > -5$

$3x + 5 > 17$
$3x + 5 - 5 > 17 - 5$
$3x > 12$
$3x \div 3 > 12 \div 3$
$x > 4$

$4x - 2 < -x + 8$
$4x + x - 2 + 2 < -x + x + 8 + 2$
$5x < 10$
$x < 2$

$3x + 7 < 2x + 3$
$3x - 2x + 7 - 7 < 2x - 2x + 3 - 7$
$x < -4$

$6x + 13 > 5x - 16$
$6x - 5x + 13 - 13 > 5x - 5x - 16 - 13$
$x > -29$

Activities

② Solve the inequalities.

$3x < 9$
$3x \div 3 < 9 \div 3$
$x < 3$

$-3x < 9$
$-3x \div 3 < 9 \div 3$
$-x < 3$
$x > -3$

$5x + 8 > 13$
$5x + 8 - 8 > 13 - 8$
$5x > 5$
$5x \div 5 > 5 \div 5$
$x > 1$

$2x + 3 > x - 4$
$2x - x + 3 - 3 > x - x - 4 - 3$
$x > -7$

$3x - 5 < x + 11$
$3x - x - 5 + 5 < x - x + 11 + 5$
$2x < 16$
$2x \div 2 < 16 \div 2$
$x < 8$

$6x + 7 < 2x + 3$
$6x - 2x + 7 - 7 < 2x - 2x + 3 - 7$
$4x < -4$
$4x \div 4 < -4 \div 4$
$x < -1$

---

③ Solve, using the rules of absolute values.

$|-25| + |-14| = 25 + 14 = 39$

$-|34| - |-34| = -34 - 34 = -68$

$|-26| + |51| = 26 + 51 = 77$

$|23 + 21| + |19 - 22| = 44 + 3 = 47$

$|62| - |-43| = 62 - 43 = 19$

$-|27 - 33| + |16 - 15| = -6 + 1 = -5$

$-|26| + |-11| = -26 + 11 = -15$

$-|32 + 19| - |47 - 25| = -51 - 22 = -73$

④ Find all the natural number factors of each of the following numbers.

32	1, 2, 4, 8, 16, 32
33	1, 3, 11, 33
34	1, 2, 17, 34
35	1, 5, 7, 35

36	1, 2, 3, 4, 6, 9, 12, 18, 36
37	1, 37
38	1, 2, 19, 38
39	1, 3, 13, 39

⑤ Solve the following roots.

$\sqrt{54} = \sqrt{3 \times 3 \times 6} = 3\sqrt{6}$

$\sqrt{60} = \sqrt{2 \times 2 \times 15} = 2\sqrt{15}$

$\sqrt{64} = \sqrt{8 \times 8} = 8$

$\sqrt{72} = \sqrt{2 \times 6 \times 6} = 6\sqrt{2}$

$\sqrt{75} = \sqrt{3 \times 5 \times 5} = 5\sqrt{3}$

$\sqrt[3]{16} = \sqrt[3]{2 \times 2 \times 2 \times 2} = 2\sqrt[3]{2}$

$\sqrt[3]{24} = \sqrt[3]{2 \times 2 \times 2 \times 3} = 2\sqrt[3]{3}$

$\sqrt[3]{32} = \sqrt[3]{2 \times 2 \times 2 \times 4} = 2\sqrt[3]{4}$

⑥ Insert the values of 1^2, 2^2, 3^2, and 4^2 in the magic square to make the sum of each row, column, and diagonal equal. Each total equals 34.

16	5	9	4
3	10	6	15
2	11	7	14
13	8	12	1

⑦ Write an equation and solve. Remember to label your answer.
Biscuits are sold 36 per case, and sausage patties are sold 42 per case. Find the least common multiple. Then determine how many cases of each Billy should buy to ensure no extras when all biscuits are sold as sausage biscuits.

$36 = 2 \times 2 \times 3 \times 3 = \boxed{2^2} \times \boxed{3^2}$ $42 = 2 \times 3 \times \boxed{7}$ LCM: $2^2 \times 3^2 \times 7 = 252$

Let b = number of cases of biscuits
$36b = 252$
$36b \div 36 = 252 \div 36$
$b = 7$ cases of biscuits

Let p = number of cases of sausage patties
$42p = 252$
$42p \div 42 = 252 \div 42$
$p = 6$ cases of sausage patties

Radicals, Writing Mathematical Expressions Worksheet 11

① Rewrite the following expressions as roots.

$4^5 = 1024$ $4 = \sqrt[5]{1024}$ $13^2 = 169$ $13 = \sqrt{169}$

$8^2 = 64$ $8 = \sqrt{64}$ $3^4 = 81$ $3 = \sqrt[4]{81}$

$5^3 = 125$ $5 = \sqrt[3]{125}$ $11^2 = 121$ $11 = \sqrt{121}$

② Solve the following roots.

$\sqrt{16} = 4$

$\sqrt{36} = 6$

$\sqrt{12} = \sqrt{2 \times 2 \times 3} = 2\sqrt{3}$

$\sqrt{18} = \sqrt{3 \times 3 \times 2} = 3\sqrt{2}$

$\sqrt{32} = \sqrt{4 \times 4 \times 2} = 4\sqrt{2}$

$\sqrt{44} = \sqrt{2 \times 2 \times 11} = 2\sqrt{11}$

$\sqrt[3]{8} = 2$

$\sqrt[3]{27} = 3$

$\sqrt[3]{40} = \sqrt[3]{2 \times 2 \times 2 \times 5} = 2\sqrt[3]{5}$

$\sqrt[3]{54} = \sqrt[3]{3 \times 3 \times 3 \times 2} = 3\sqrt[3]{2}$

$\sqrt[3]{16} = \sqrt[3]{2 \times 2 \times 2 \times 2} = 2\sqrt[3]{2}$

$\sqrt[3]{64} = \sqrt[3]{4 \times 4 \times 4} = 4$

$6\sqrt{11} + 2\sqrt{11} =$
$(6 + 2)\sqrt{11} = 8\sqrt{11}$

$\sqrt{15} + 4\sqrt{15} = (1 + 4)\sqrt{15} = 5\sqrt{15}$

$16\sqrt{7} - 9\sqrt{7} = (16 - 9)\sqrt{7} = 7\sqrt{7}$

$(\sqrt{2})(\sqrt{5}) = \sqrt{2 \times 5} = \sqrt{10}$

$(2\sqrt{18})(3\sqrt{8}) =$
$(2 \times 3)(\sqrt{18} \times \sqrt{8}) = 6(3\sqrt{2} \times 2\sqrt{2}) =$
$6(3 \times 2)(\sqrt{4}) = 6 \times 6 \times 2 = 72$

$\sqrt[3]{40} \div \sqrt[3]{5} = \sqrt[3]{40 \div 5} = \sqrt[3]{8} = 2$

$15\sqrt{12} \div 3\sqrt{6} =$
$(15 \div 3)(\sqrt{12} \div \sqrt{6}) = 5\sqrt{2}$

$\sqrt{50} \div 5 = \sqrt{50} \div \sqrt{25} = \sqrt{2}$

③ Translate the following words into a mathematical expression.

The total of a number and 17	$x + 17$
6 fewer than a number	$x - 6$
A number times 9	$9x$
The sum of 35 and a number	$35 + x$
The quotient of a number and 8	$x \div 8$
13 less than a number	$x - 13$
A number increased by a factor of 4	$4x$
61 more than a number	$x + 61$
A number less than 72	$72 - x$
The product of 9 and a number	$9x$
The ratio of a number to 3	$x \div 3$
A number increased by 46	$x + 46$

Teaching Tips, Cont.

➢ Ask a student to write an expression showing that 11 is not equal to 12. (Most students will write $11 \neq 12$, although some may write $11 < 12$ or $12 > 11$.)

➢ Explain that a "not equal to" sign gives accurate information about the relationship between two values. However, inequalities give more specific information. They tell that two values are not equal, and they also tell which value is larger or smaller.

➢ If students are having trouble remembering which direction the inequality sign should point, have them picture it as an alligator mouth. Alligators would much rather eat a big meal than a small meal, so the mouth is open and facing the larger value.

➢ Complete the Classwork exercises. Have some students work the problems on the board for the class and explain their answers. All students should work the problems in their books.

Assignment
• Complete Lesson 22, Activities 2-7.

Lesson 23

Concepts
- Decimal system
- Addition of decimals
- Subtraction of decimals
- Multiples
- Least common multiple
- Single-variable equations
- Single-variable inequalities
- Real world math

Learning Objectives
The student will be able to:
- Explain the organization of the decimal system
- Read decimal place values correctly
- Add numbers with different place values after the decimal point
- Subtract numbers with more place values after the decimal point in the subtrahend than in the minuend

Materials Needed
- Student Book, Lesson 23
- Worksheet 12

Teaching Tips
➢ Review the terms *base* and *exponent*. (See Lesson 10.)

➢ Draw the place value chart on the board. (See the following page.) Explain that the decimal system is also called the base 10 system because every place value can be represented as an exponential number with 10 as the base.

➢ If you have more advanced students, you may wish to include the information about expressing numbers in other bases.

Decimal System

The **decimal system** is a base-10 system. This means that each place value is worth exactly 10 times the value of the place to its right.
For example, in the number 1, the digit 1 is worth 1. In the number 10, the digit 1 is worth $10 \times 1 = 10$. In the number 100, the digit 1 is worth $10 \times 10 = 100$, etc.

For values less than 1, the pattern continues, but a decimal point is placed after the digit in the ones, or units, place to signify which digits are in place values less than one.
For example, 0.1 is one-tenth, 0.01 is one-hundredth, 0.001 is one-thousandth, etc.

When adding or subtracting decimals, write the problem vertically, lining up the decimal points so that all digits of the same place value are aligned, and add or subtract as usual, placing the decimal point in its appropriate place in the answer. Write zeros in the spaces where necessary to give each term the same number of digits to the right of the decimal point.

① **Classwork**
Solve.

```
 112.53        67.44
  53.72        42.391
 +42.61       +77.1
 208.86       186.931


 251.038       47.990
 -17.469      -35.478
 233.569       12.512
```

Activities

② Solve.

```
  76.19      15.93      754.69     294.51     304.57
 +34.56     +46.72     +328.18    +347.83    +526.18
 110.75      62.65     1082.87     642.34     830.75


  46.71       9.478      97.48      52.493     781.46
 628.63      16.39      461.5        4.05       52.591
+293.458    +542.1     +391.468   +671.327   +329.5978
 968.798    567.968     950.448    727.87    1163.6488


  93.497     324.47     569.20     891.270    687.3200
 -61.372     -65.91     -74.32      -9.999    -29.5473
  32.125     258.56     494.88     881.271    657.7727
```

③ List 5 multiples of each number.
```
10   10, 20, 30, 40, 50
15   15, 30, 45, 60, 75
20   20, 40, 60, 80, 100
25   25, 50, 75, 100, 125
30   30, 60, 90, 120, 150
```

④ Find the least common multiple of each set of numbers.

5, 7, and 10

$5 = 1 \times \boxed{5}$
$7 = 1 \times \boxed{7}$
$10 = \boxed{2} \times 5$
LCM: $2 \times 5 \times 7 = 70$

6, 9, and 15

$6 = \boxed{2} \times 3$
$9 = 3 \times 3 = \boxed{3^2}$
$15 = 3 \times \boxed{5}$
LCM: $2 \times 3^2 \times 5 = 90$

12, 15, and 18

$12 = 2 \times 2 \times 3 = \boxed{2^2} \times 3$
$15 = 3 \times \boxed{5}$
$18 = 2 \times 3 \times 3 = 2 \times \boxed{3^2}$
LCM: $2^2 \times 3^2 \times 5 = 180$

⑤ Solve.

$x + 8 = 14$
$x + 8 - 8 = 14 - 8$
$x = 6$

$2x - 5 = 13$
$2x - 5 + 5 = 13 + 5$
$2x = 18$
$x = 9$

$4x + 3 = 2x + 7$
$4x - 2x + 3 - 3 = 2x - 2x + 7 - 3$
$2x = 4$
$x = 2$

$2(x - 3) = x + 8$
$2x - 6 = x + 8$
$2x - x - 6 + 6 = x - x + 8 + 6$
$x = 14$

$x + 12 \div 3 = 4x + 1$
$x + 4 = 4x + 1$
$x - 4x + 4 - 4 = 4x - 4x + 1 - 4$
$-3x = -3$
$x = 1$

$2(x - 4) = 3(x + 2)$
$2x - 8 = 3x + 6$
$2x - 3x - 8 + 8 = 3x - 3x + 6 + 8$
$-x = 14$
$x = -14$

$3x + 2 < x - 2$
$3x - x + 2 - 2 < x - x - 2 - 2$
$2x < -4$
$x < -2$

$4x - 3 > x + 6$
$4x - x - 3 + 3 > x - x + 6 + 3$
$3x > 9$
$x > 3$

$2(x + 1) < 3x + 5$
$2x + 2 < 3x + 5$
$2x - 3x + 2 < 3x - 3x + 5 - 2$
$-x < 3$
$x > -3$

⑥ Solve the real world math problem.

Concession Stand Menu

Fruit Punch – 75¢	Donut Holes – 12/$1	Chips – 50¢
Bottled Water – $1	Sausage Biscuit – $1	Candy Bars – 75¢
Soft Drink– $1.50	Hot Dog – $1	Bubble Gum – 5¢
Sports Drink Bottle – $2	Hamburger – $2	Hard Candy – 25¢

A family attending a basketball game ordered 2 hot dogs, a hamburger, one fruit punch, one soft drink, one bottle of water, one piece of hard candy, and 2 pieces of bubble gum from Billy's concession stand. If the family paid with a $10 bill, how much change should Billy give them?   Total ordered: $7.60 $10.00 - $7.60 = $2.40
$10.00 - [2($1) + $2 + $0.75 + $1.50 + $1 + $0.25 + 2($0.05)]

Addition and Subtraction of Decimals

① Add.

1454.18	7213.491	8353.5	2492.95
+8036.37	+3885.653	+7667.1	+4698.42
9490.55	11,099.144	16,020.6	7191.37

3426.8	680.96	65.345	248.88
+ 213.27	+4148.3	+3457.2	+ 2.4587
3640.07	4829.26	3522.545	251.3387

35.311	9492.69	31926.9	136.653
+1282.77	+65469.8	+ 84.7185	+ 37.5702
1318.081	74,962.49	32,011.6185	174.2232

② Subtract.

3357.679	9940.08	7897.4	8023.587
−1738.154	−2116.35	−6268.9	−6651.45
1619.525	7823.73	1628.5	1372.137

41940.267	81242.54	91661.7	7798.5
−22782.49	−74580.054	−36877.648	− 75.573
19,157.777	6662.486	54,784.052	7722.927

52085.2	507.669	452.478	7.02928
− 49.7823	− 30.4727	−251.9	−0.653841
52,035.4177	477.1963	200.578	6.375439

Hundreds	Tens	Ones	Decimal point	Tenths	Hundredths	Thousandths
10^2	10^1	10^0	.	10^{-1}	10^{-2}	10^{-3}
100	10	1	.	0.1	0.01	0.001
3	4	5	.	1	2	7

The number 345.127 can be represented using exponents by the expression $(3 \times 10^2) + (4 \times 10^1) +$
$(5 \times 10^0) + (1 \times 10^{-1}) + (2 \times 10^{-2}) +$
(7×10^{-3})

To represent a number in a different base, change the number in the base from 10 to whichever base you are looking for. The number twelve can be expressed in base 2 as $(1 \times 2^3) +$
$(1 \times 2^2) + (0 \times 2^0)$, or the number 110.

Teaching Tips, Cont.

➢ Write the following problem on the board in a horizontal direction:
1025 + 72 + 267 =
Ask a student to rewrite the problem vertically. The student should line up the digits in the ones column, as well as all place values to the left. Remind the students as necessary about the rules for writing problems vertically.

➢ Explain that lining those numbers up on the right works because all the place values are lined up. When working with decimals, line up the decimal points and all the place values will fall into the correct position. Point out the problems in the Classwork exercises as examples.

➢ Complete the Classwork exercises. Have some students work the problems on the board for the class and explain their answers. All students should work the problems in their books.

Assignments
- Complete Lesson 23, Activities 2-6.
- Worksheet 12 (Optional)

Lesson 24

Concepts
- Comparing decimals
- Rounding
- Adding decimals
- Factors
- Roots
- Single-variable equations
- Single-variable inequalities
- Math in the real world

Learning Objectives
The student will be able to:
- Compare decimals with equal place values using *greater than* and *less than*
- Compare decimals with different place values using *greater than* and *less than*
- Round numbers to place values to the right of the decimal point
- Write decimal problems vertically

Materials Needed
- Student Book, Lesson 24

Teaching Tips
- Write the following expression on the board: 134 _____ 431. Ask a student to fill in the blank with < or >. (<)

- Review less than and greater than as necessary. Remind students that they always compare the digits in the greatest place value. If the greatest place value is equal in both numbers, continue comparing place values one place at a time, moving to the right, until there is a digit that is different. The values of the digits in lower place values have no bearing on the comparison.

Comparing Decimals

Comparing decimals is the process of determining whether one decimal is greater than or less than another decimal. The easiest way to compare decimals is to begin working with the whole number portion of the decimal, or the portion to the left of the decimal point. If the whole number portions are not equal, then the decimal with the smaller whole number is the smaller decimal.	① Classwork
	Write < or > for each pair of decimals.
	134.297 __<__ 431.972
	29.542 __>__ 29.461
	32.16 __<__ 32.17
If the whole number portions are equal, compare the portion to the right of the decimal point, working from left to right. If the digits in the tenths place are different, the decimal with the smaller digit in the tenths place is the smaller decimal. If the digits in the tenths place are equal, move to the hundredths place and compare the digits. Continue in this manner until you do not have equal digits.	487.348 __<__ 487.4
	94.569 __<__ 94.579
	107.8134 __>__ 107.813

Activities

② Write < or > for each pair of decimals.

267.945 __<__ 762.549   318.725 __<__ 318.8

83.612 __>__ 83.154   77.462 __>__ 77.452

16.91 __>__ 16.89   900.002 __>__ 900.0005

③ Round each number to the nearest tenth.

| 14.62 | 14.6 | 615.99 | 616.0 |
| 123.943 | 123.9 | 4786.2534 | 4786.3 |

④ Round each number to the nearest hundredth.

| 6147.624 | 6147.62 | 15.994 | 15.99 |
| 284.349 | 284.35 | 593.998 | 594.00 |

⑤ Write the problem vertically and solve.

$115.46 + 846.62 =$ $672.6 + 43.79 =$ $672.85 + 49.148 + 5.7 =$

```
  115.46           672.6          672.85
 +846.62          +43.79           49.148
 ───────          ──────           +5.7
  962.08          716.39          ───────
                                  727.698
```

---

⑥ Find all the natural number factors.

41   1, 41
42   1, 2, 3, 6, 7, 14, 21, 42
43   1, 43
44   1, 2, 4, 11, 22, 44
45   1, 3, 5, 9, 15, 45

⑦ Solve the following roots.

$\sqrt{32} = \sqrt{2 \times 4 \times 4} = 4\sqrt{2}$

$\sqrt{32} + \sqrt{2} = 4\sqrt{2} + \sqrt{2} = (4+1)\sqrt{2} = 5\sqrt{2}$

$(\sqrt{32})(\sqrt{2}) = (4\sqrt{2})(\sqrt{2}) = 4\sqrt{2 \times 2} = 4(2) = 8$

$(\sqrt{32}) \div (\sqrt{2}) = \sqrt{32 \div 2} = \sqrt{16} = 4$

$\sqrt{2} + \sqrt{18} = \sqrt{2} + \sqrt{9 \times 2} = \sqrt{2} + 3\sqrt{2} = 4\sqrt{2}$

$(\sqrt{2})(\sqrt{18}) = \sqrt{2 \times 18} = \sqrt{36} = 6$

$(\sqrt{18}) \div (\sqrt{2}) = \sqrt{18 \div 2} = \sqrt{9} = 3$

$\sqrt[3]{7} + 4\sqrt[3]{7} = (1+4)\sqrt[3]{7} = 5\sqrt[3]{7}$

$(\sqrt[3]{56}) \div (\sqrt[3]{7}) = \sqrt[3]{56 \div 7} = \sqrt[3]{8} = 2$

$(3\sqrt[4]{5})(4\sqrt[4]{3}) = (3 \times 4)\sqrt[4]{5 \times 3} = 12\sqrt[4]{15}$

⑧ Solve.

$x + 13 = 27$
$x + 13 - 13 = 27 - 13$
$x = 14$

$3x - 7 = 14$
$3x - 7 + 7 = 14 + 7$
$3x = 21$
$x = 7$

$3x + 12 = 5x + 8$
$3x - 5x + 12 - 12 = 5x - 5x +$
$-2x = -4$
$x = 2$

$4(x - 1) = 3x + 7$
$4x - 4 = 3x + 7$
$4x - 3x - 4 + 4 = 3x - 3x +$
$x = 11$

$2x + 6 \div 3 = 5x + 8$
$2x + 2 = 5x + 8$
$2x - 5x + 2 - 2 = 5x - 5x +$
$-3x = 6$
$x = -2$

$2x - 7 = 3(x - 4)$
$2x - 7 = 3x - 12$
$2x - 3x - 7 + 7 = 3x - 3x - 12$
$-x = -5$
$x = 5$

$5x + 3 < 4x - 1$
$5x - 4x + 3 - 3 < 4x - 4x -$
$x < -4$

$6x - 5 > x + 5$
$6x - x - 5 + 5 > x - x + 5 +$
$5x > 10$
$x > 2$

$3(x - 2) < 4x - 7$
$3x - 6 < 4x - 7$
$3x - 4x - 6 + 6 < 4x - 4x - 7$
$-x < -1$
$x > 1$

⑨ Write an equation and solve.

At the local warehouse club where Billy buys supplies for the concession stand, a case of energy drinks costs twice as much as a case of water and a case of chips cost together. If a case of energy drinks costs $18 and a case of water costs $5, what is the cost of a case of chips?   **$4**

Let x = the cost of a case of chips.

$\$18 = 2(\$5 + x)$ $\$18 = \$10 + 2x$ $\$8 = 2x$ $\$4 = x$

Teaching Tips, Cont.

➢ Explain that the same rules apply when comparing numbers with decimals. Teach the rules for comparing decimals.

➢ Write the numbers 123 and 4786 on the board. Ask one student to round both number to the nearest 10 (120, 4790) and another student to round both numbers to the nearest 100 (100, 4800). Review the rules for rounding numbers as necessary. (See Lesson 2.) Point out that the same rules apply when working with decimals.

➢ Have students round the numbers in the first column of the Classwork exercises to the nearest tenth and hundredth as necessary to reinforce the rounding rules.
134.297: 134.3, 134.30
29.542: 29.5, 29.54
32.16: 32.2, 32.16
487.348: 487.3, 487.35
94.569: 94.6, 94.57
107.8134: 107.8, 107.81

➢ Complete the Classwork exercises. Have some students work the problems on the board for the class and explain their answers. All students should work the problems in their books.

Assignment

- Complete Lesson 24, Activities 2-9.

Lesson 25

Concepts
- Multiplying decimals
- Roots
- Single-variable equations
- Single-variable inequalities
- Math in the real world

Learning Objectives
The student will be able to:
- Multiply numbers with decimal points
- Correctly position the decimal point in the product

Materials Needed
- Student Book, Lesson 25
- Worksheet 13

Teaching Tips
➤ Have students complete Worksheet 13 in class. This may be for added practice of earlier topics, or graded as a quiz, if desired.

➤ Write the problem 762 × 124 on the board. Ask a student to solve the problem. (94,488)

➤ Insert a decimal point between the 2 and 4 in the second number so the problem now reads 762 × 12.4 and ask a student how that change would affect the answer. (9448.8)

➤ Teach the rules for multiplying decimals.

Multiplying Decimals

When multiplying decimals, treat the problem as a regular multiplication problem, ignoring the decimal point until the end. When you have the answer to the multiplication problem, count the total number of digits that come after the decimal point in the multiplicand and the multiplier. Count that number from the right of the answer and place the decimal point there. If the answer does not have enough digits, add zeros to the left side of the answer until you have enough digits to place the decimal point.

For example, .3 × .4 = .12 and .3 × .2 = .06

When multiplying vertically, work the problem as usual and add the decimal point at the end.

① Classwork
Multiply.

$0.2 \times 0.4 = 0.08$
$3 \times 0.5 = 1.5$
$1.1 \times 0.4 = 0.44$
$(1.1)^2 = 1.1 \times 1.1 = 1.21$

$$\begin{array}{r} 7.62 \\ \times 12.4 \\ \hline 3048 \\ 15240 \\ +76200 \\ \hline 94.488 \end{array}$$

Activities
② Multiply.

$0.3 \times 0.6 = 0.18$
$1.2 \times 0.6 = 0.72$
$4 \times 0.7 = 2.8$
$(0.8)^2 = 0.8 \times 0.8 = 0.64$

$1.1 \times 0.5 = 0.55$
$1.2 \times 1.1 = 1.32$
$0.8 \times 0.3 = 0.24$
$1.1 \times 0.9 = 0.99$

$$\begin{array}{r} 9.2 \\ \times 3.7 \\ \hline 644 \\ +2760 \\ \hline 34.04 \end{array} \quad \begin{array}{r} 5.6 \\ \times 0.33 \\ \hline 168 \\ +1680 \\ \hline 1.848 \end{array} \quad \begin{array}{r} 58.1 \\ \times 0.9 \\ \hline 52.29 \end{array} \quad \begin{array}{r} 8.24 \\ \times 3.7 \\ \hline 5768 \\ +24720 \\ \hline 30.488 \end{array} \quad \begin{array}{r} 0.743 \\ \times 0.91 \\ \hline 743 \\ +66870 \\ \hline .67613 \end{array}$$

$$\begin{array}{r} 61.8 \\ \times 45.7 \\ \hline 4326 \\ 30900 \\ +247200 \\ \hline 2824.26 \end{array} \quad \begin{array}{r} 1.26 \\ \times 32.4 \\ \hline 504 \\ 2520 \\ +37800 \\ \hline 40.824 \end{array} \quad \begin{array}{r} 9.14 \\ \times 2.63 \\ \hline 2742 \\ 54840 \\ +182800 \\ \hline 24.0382 \end{array} \quad \begin{array}{r} 5.23 \\ \times 0.758 \\ \hline 4184 \\ 26150 \\ +366100 \\ \hline 3.96434 \end{array} \quad \begin{array}{r} 0.354 \\ \times 0.925 \\ \hline 1770 \\ 7080 \\ +318600 \\ \hline .327450 \end{array}$$

③ Simplify the roots.

$\sqrt{48} = \sqrt{3 \times 4 \times 4} = 4\sqrt{3}$
$\sqrt{48} + \sqrt{3} = 4\sqrt{3} + \sqrt{3} = (4+1)\sqrt{3} = 5\sqrt{3}$
$(\sqrt{48})(\sqrt{3}) = (4\sqrt{3})(\sqrt{3}) = 4 \times 3 = 12$
$(\sqrt{48}) \div (\sqrt{3}) = \sqrt{48 \div 4} = \sqrt{16} = 4$
$\sqrt{3} + \sqrt{12} =$
$\sqrt{3} + \sqrt{2 \times 2 \times 3} = \sqrt{3} + 2\sqrt{3} = 3\sqrt{3}$

$(\sqrt{3})(\sqrt{12}) = (\sqrt{3})(2\sqrt{3}) = 3 \times 2 = 6$
$(\sqrt{12}) \div (\sqrt{3}) = \sqrt{12 \div 3} = \sqrt{4} = 2$
$\sqrt[3]{18} + 5\sqrt[3]{18} = (1+5)\sqrt[3]{18} = 6\sqrt[3]{18}$
$(\sqrt[3]{32}) \div (\sqrt[3]{4}) = \sqrt[3]{32 \div 4} = \sqrt[3]{8} = 2$
$(5\sqrt[4]{9})(3\sqrt[4]{9}) =$
$15\sqrt[4]{81} = 15\sqrt[4]{3 \times 3 \times 3 \times 3} = 15 \times 3 = 45$

④ Solve.

$3(2x-1) = 4x+5$	$3x - 12 \div 4 = 4x - 4$	$7x - 6 = 4(3x+1)$
$6x - 3 = 4x + 5$	$3x - 3 = 4x - 4$	$7x - 6 = 12x + 4$
$2x = 8$	$-x = -1$	$-5x = 10$
$x = 4$	$x = 1$	$x = -2$
$8x + 5 < 4x - 3$	$5x - 3 > 4x + 3$	$4(2x-3) < 6x - 8$
$4x < -8$	$x > 6$	$8x - 12 < 6x - 8$
$x < -2$		$2x < 4$
		$x < 2$

⑤ Write an equation and solve.
Billy buys a case of 36 biscuits for $5.76 and a case of 42 sausage patties for $9.24 to stock the concession stand for breakfast. If plain biscuits are sold for 50¢ and sausage biscuits for $1, how much money does the concession stand make on the sale of a plain biscuit? **$0.34**
Cost per biscuit: $5.76 ÷ 36 = $.16
Let x = profit from plain biscuit
x = $.50 - $.16 = $.34
How much money does the concession stand make on the sale of a sausage biscuit? **$0.62**
Cost per sausage patty: $9.24 ÷ 42 = $.22
Total cost per sausage biscuit: $.16 + $.22 = $.38
Let x = profit from sausage biscuit
x = $1.00 - $.38 = $.62
At the end of the breakfast serving time, the concession stand sells all remaining plain biscuits for 25¢ and the remaining sausage biscuits for 50¢. Is the concession stand still making money on the sale of the discounted biscuits? If so, how much does the concession stand make on the sale of a discounted plain biscuit? On the sale of a discounted sausage biscuit? **Yes, $0.09, Yes, $0.12**
Discounted plain biscuits: $.25 - $.16 = $.09
Discounted sausage biscuits: $.50 - $.38 = $.12

① Simplify by combining like terms.

$x + 6 + 2 = x + 8$

$x + 8 + 14 = x + 22$

$x + x + 9 + 2 = 2x + 11$

$x + x + 12 + 11 = 2x + 23$

$2x + x + 18 - 12 = 3x + 6$

$2x + 5x + 17 - 15 = 7x + 2$

$3x + 4x - 7 + 4 = 7x - 3$

$7x + 2x + 18 - 7 = 9x + 11$

$9x - 4x + 24 - 15 - 7 = 5x + 2$

$7x - 5x + 15 - 8 - 4 = 2x + 3$

$5x + 9x - 4x - 8 - 6 + 12 = 10x - 2$

$10x + 2x - 7x - 10 - 8 + 13 = 5x - 5$

② Solve by combining like terms.

$x + 12 = 23$

$x = 11$

$2x - 7 = 19$

$2x = 26; \; x = 13$

$x + 6 + 7 = 22$

$x + 13 = 22; \; x = 9$

$x + x + 3 + 11 = 30$

$2x + 14 = 30; \; 2x = 16; \; x = 8$

$2x + x + 9 - 5 = 22$

$3x + 4 = 22; \; 3x = 18; \; x = 6$

$3x + 2x - 18 + 13 = 35$

$5x - 5 = 35; \; 5x = 40; \; x = 8$

$4x - 2x + 15 - 10 - 6 = 19$

$2x - 1 = 19; \; 2x = 20; \; x = 10$

$4x + 3x - x - 8 - 6 + 4 = 32$

$6x - 10 = 32; \; 6x = 42; \; x = 7$

$5x + 6 = 4x + 11$

$x + 6 = 11; \; x = 5$

$x + 16 \div 4 = 4x + 1$

$x + 4 = 4x + 1; \; -3x + 4 = 1; \; -3x = -3; \; x = 1$

$3(x - 2) = 2x + 5$

$3x - 6 = 2x + 5; \; x - 6 = 5; \; x = 11$

$2(x - 3) = 3(x + 3)$

$2x - 6 = 3x + 9; \; -x - 6 = 9; \; -x = 15; \; x = -15$

Teaching Tips, Cont.

➢ Remind students that when multiplying decimals, there is no need to line up the decimal points as in addition and subtraction of decimals. Align all numbers on the right, and insert the decimal point in the appropriate place in the answer.

➢ Complete the Classwork exercises. Have some students work the problems on the board for the class. All students should work the problems in their books.

Assignment

• Complete Lesson 25, Activities 2-5.

Lesson 26

Concepts
- Dividing decimals
- Divisibility tests
- Prime/Composite numbers
- Single-variable equations
- Single-variable inequalities
- Multiplying decimals

Learning Objectives
The student will be able to:
- Divide two numbers containing decimal points
- Move the decimal point to the correct position in the dividend and divisor prior to dividing
- Correctly place the decimal point in the quotient

Materials Needed
- Student Book, Lesson 26

Teaching Tips
➢ Write the problem $216 \div 9$ on the board and ask a student to solve it. (24)

➢ Ask the students what would happen if a decimal point were added to make the problem $21.6 \div 9$. (2.4)

➢ Now change the problem to $216 \div 0.9$ and ask what effect that would have on the answer. (240)

➢ Teach the rules for dividing decimals.

Dividing Decimals

When dividing decimals, first look at the number of digits there are to the right of the decimal point in the divisor (the number you are dividing by). Move the decimal point in the divisor to the far right so you have a whole number. Move the decimal point in the dividend (the number you are dividing) to the right the same number of digits, adding zeros if necessary. For example, $2.5 \div 0.5$ becomes $25 \div 5$ and $25 \div 0.5$ becomes $250 \div 5$. Once you have eliminated the decimal point from the divisor, divide as usual. If there is a decimal point in the dividend, place the decimal point in the corresponding place in the quotient. For example:

$$1.2\overline{)1.44} \Rightarrow 12\overline{)14.4}$$

① Classwork
Divide.

$$.8\overline{)4.0} = 5$$

$$0.8\overline{).040} = .5$$

$$1.5\overline{)3.0} = 2$$

$$.015\overline{)3.00} = 20$$ remainder 30

Activities

② Divide.

$$0.2\overline{)1.0} = 5 \qquad 4\overline{)3.2} = .8 \qquad 5\overline{)2.5} = .5 \qquad 3\overline{)0.6} = .2$$

$$0.7\overline{)2.1} = 3 \qquad 0.5\overline{)2.5} = 5 \qquad 0.4\overline{)2.8} = 7 \qquad 0.9\overline{)2.7} = 3$$

$$1.8\overline{)23.4} = 13 \qquad 13\overline{)24.7} = 1.9 \qquad 0.9\overline{)13.5} = 15 \qquad 1.6\overline{)17.6} = 11$$

---

③ Use the divisibility tests to identify each number as prime or composite.

211   Prime
213   Composite (3)
215   Composite (5)
219   Composite (3)
223   Prime

④ Solve.

$4(x + 3) = 3x - 7$	$5x - 9 \div 3 = 3x + 1$	$8x - 5 = 3(2x + 3)$
$4x + 12 = 3x - 7$	$5x - 3 = 3x + 1$	$8x - 5 = 6x + 9$
$x = -19$	$2x = 4$	$2x = 14$
	$x = 2$	$x = 7$
$7x + 4 < 3x$	$4x + 3 < 3x - 3$	$3(x - 4) > 5x - 6$
$4x < -4$	$x < -6$	$3x - 12 > 5x - 6$
$x < -1$		$-2x > 6$
		$-x > 3$
		$x < -3$

⑤ Multiply.

45	73	26	41	69
×4.6	×8.5	×5.5	×2.2	×1.6
270	365	130	82	414
+1800	+5840	+1300	+820	+690
207.0	620.5	143.0	90.2	110.4

41.2	92.4	21.7	60.9	45.2
×5.3	×4.5	×6.8	×5.5	×3.7
1236	4620	1736	3045	3164
+20600	+36960	+13020	+30450	+13560
218.36	415.80	147.56	334.95	167.24

1.63	24.5	7.96	2.27	0.68
×0.71	×0.74	×8.2	×3.6	×0.85
163	980	1592	1362	340
+11410	+17150	+63680	+6810	+5440
1.1573	18.130	65.272	8.172	.5780

Teaching Tips, Cont.

➢ Remind students that the decimal point in the quotient will always line up with the decimal point in the dividend after the divisor has been converted to a whole number.

➢ Tell students that all division problems involving decimals should be written in long division format rather than horizontally to ensure correct placement of the decimal point in the answer.

➢ Complete the Classwork exercises. Have some students work the problems on the board for the class. All students should work the problems in their books.

Assignment

• Complete Lesson 26, Activities 2-5.

Lesson 27

Concepts
- Powers of 10
- Prime factorization
- Exponents
- Single-variable equations
- Multiplying decimals
- Dividing decimals
- Math in the real world

Learning Objectives
The student will be able to:
- Calculate the values of powers of 10 with positive exponents
- Calculate the values of powers of 10 with negative exponents
- Multiply powers of 10
- Divide powers of 10

Materials Needed
- Student Book, Lesson 27

Teaching Tips
➢ Review multiplying and dividing exponents with the same base. (See Lesson 14)

➢ Review the rules for zero exponents and negative exponents. (See Lesson 14)

➢ Write the first Powers of 10 chart from the teaching box on the board. Ask a student to identify the pattern formed as the value of the exponent increases.

➢ Teach the rules for Powers of 10 with positive exponents.

➢ Write the second Powers of 10 chart from the teaching box on the board. Ask a student to identify the pattern formed as the value of the exponent decreases.

Powers of 10

Powers of 10 are the exponential values when the base is equal to 10. Notice the pattern when the exponent increases in increments of 1:

$10^0 = 1$

$10^1 = 10$

$10^2 = 10 \times 10 = 100$

$10^3 = 10 \times 10 \times 10 = 1,000$

The answer always begins with the number 1. The number of zeros after the 1 is equal to the number in the exponent. In other words, move the decimal point to the right the number of places indicated in the exponent and fill in zeros in the blanks.

Notice the pattern when the exponent decreases in increments of 1:

$10^0 = 1$

$10^{-1} = \dfrac{1}{10} = 0.\underline{1}$

$10^{-2} = \dfrac{1}{10^2} = \dfrac{1}{100} = 0.\underline{01}$

$10^{-3} = \dfrac{1}{10^3} = \dfrac{1}{1000} = 0.\underline{001}$

The answer always ends with the number 1. The number of digits to the right of the decimal point is equal to the absolute value of the number in the exponent. In other words, for negative exponents, write the number 1 and move the decimal point to the left the number of places indicated in the exponent and fill in zeros in the blanks.

① **Classwork**
Solve.

$10^5 = 100,000$

$10^9 = 1,000,000,000$

$\left(10^2\right)\left(10^3\right) = 10^{2+3} = 10^5 = 100,000$

$\left(10^{10}\right) \div \left(10^7\right) = 10^{10-7} = 10^3 = 1,000$

$10^{-5} = 0.00001$

$10^{-9} = 0.000000001$

$\left(10^8\right)\left(10^{-6}\right) = 10^{8-6} = 10^2 = 100$

$\left(10^2\right) \div \left(10^{-1}\right) =$
$10^{2-(-1)} = 10^{2+1} = 10^3 = 1,000$

Activities
② Solve.

$10^4 = 10,000$

$10^7 = 10,000,000$

$\left(10^3\right)\left(10^6\right) =$
$10^{3+6} = 10^9 = 1,000,000,000$

$\left(10^{12}\right) \div \left(10^5\right) =$
$10^{12-5} = 10^7 = 10,000,000$

$10^{-6} = 0.000001$

$10^{-8} = 0.00000001$

$\left(10^7\right)\left(10^{-5}\right) = 10^{7-5} = 10^2 = 100$

$\left(10^4\right) \div \left(10^{-1}\right) =$
$10^{4-(-1)} = 10^{4+1} = 10^5 = 100,000$

---

③ Express the prime factorization using exponents where appropriate.

34	35	36
$34 = 2 \times 17$	$35 = 5 \times 7$	$36 = 2 \times 2 \times 3 \times 3$
		$36 = 2^2 \times 3^2$

④ Solve.

$5x - 1 = 2(x + 1)$
$5x - 1 = 2x + 2$
$3x = 3$
$x = 1$

$7x + 12 \div 4 = 4x + 3$
$7x + 3 = 4x + 3$
$3x = 0$
$x = 0$

$3x + 11 = x - 1$
$2x = -12$
$x = -6$

$2(2x + 1) = 3x$
$4x + 2 = 3x$
$x = -2$

$3x + 10 \div 2 = 2x - 4$
$3x + 5 = 2x - 4$
$x = -9$

$2x - 7 = 3(x + 2)$
$2x - 7 = 3x + 6$
$-x = 13$
$x = -13$

⑤ Multiply or divide as indicated.

```
  2.8        3.7         0.44       8.7        0.84
×0.9       ×1.6        ×4.8       ×0.55      ×0.31
 2.52        222         352        435          84
            +370       +1760      +4350       +2520
            5.92       2.112      4.785       .2604

      .9        1.4          15          9         170
1.7)1.53   1.9)2.66   0.15)2.25   0.12)1.08   0.13)22.10
            19           15                       13
            76           75          75           91
            76           75          75           91
```

⑥ Write an equation and solve.
If Billy purchases a case of sour candies for $7.68, what is the total cost, including 7% tax? (Multiply the price by 1.07 to find the final price including 7% sales tax.)   **$8.22**
(Round the answer to the nearest hundredth to get the nearest cent.)

```
  $7.68
 ×1.07
  5376
  0000
+76800
$8.2176
```

Teaching Tips, Cont.

➤ Teach the rules for Powers of 10 with negative exponents.

➤ Complete the Classwork exercises. Have some students work the problems on the board for the class. All students should work the problems in their books.

Assignment

• Complete Lesson 27, Activities 2-6.

Lesson 28

Concepts
- Multiplying by powers of 10
- Divisibility tests
- Prime/Composite numbers
- Order of operations
- Multiplying decimals
- Dividing decimals
- Math in the real world

Learning Objectives
The student will be able to:
- Multiply whole numbers by powers of 10
- Multiply decimals by powers of 10
- Solve powers of 10 problems as one-step problems

Materials Needed
- Student Book, Lesson 28
- Worksheet 14

Teaching Tips
➢ Have students complete Worksheet 14 in class. This may be for added practice of earlier topics, or graded as a quiz, if desired.

➢ Write the first chart from the teaching box on the board. Review the rules for working with Powers of 10 with zero and positive exponents. (See Lesson 27)

➢ Write the remaining charts from the teaching box on the board. Teach the rules for multiplying by powers of 10.

Multiplying by Powers of 10

Remember from Lesson 27:
$$10^0 = 1$$
$$10^1 = 10$$
$$10^2 = 10 \times 10 = 100$$
$$10^3 = 10 \times 10 \times 10 = 1,000$$

Now think of it this way:
$$1 \times 10^0 = 1 \times 1 = 1$$
$$1 \times 10^1 = 1 \times 10 = 10$$
$$1 \times 10^2 = 1 \times 10 \times 10 = 100$$
$$1 \times 10^3 = 1 \times 10 \times 10 \times 10 = 1,000$$

If you multiplied the powers of 10 by 5 instead of 1, then you would have this pattern:
$$5 \times 10^0 = 5 \times 1 = 5$$
$$5 \times 10^1 = 5 \times 10 = 50$$
$$5 \times 10^2 = 5 \times 10 \times 10 = 500$$
$$5 \times 10^3 = 5 \times 10 \times 10 \times 10 = 5,000$$

Now multiply the powers of 10 by a decimal and notice this pattern:
$$5.14 \times 10^0 = 5.14 \times 1 = 5.14$$
$$5.14 \times 10^1 = 5.14 \times 10 = 51.4$$
$$5.14 \times 10^2 = 5.14 \times 10 \times 10 = 514$$
$$5.14 \times 10^3 = 5.14 \times 10 \times 10 \times 10 = 5,140$$

The decimal point moves to the right the number of places indicated in the exponent.

① **Classwork**
Solve.

$$7 \times 10^0 = 7$$
$$2 \times 10^1 = 2 \times 10 = 20$$
$$9 \times 10^2 = 9 \times 100 = 900$$
$$8 \times 10^3 = 8 \times 1,000 = 8,000$$

$$3.27 \times 10^0 = 3.27$$
$$6.41 \times 10^1 = 6.41 \times 10 = 64.1$$
$$5.87 \times 10^2 = 5.87 \times 100 = 587$$
$$9.25 \times 10^3 = 9.25 \times 1,000 = 9,250$$

$$12.4 \times 10^0 = 12.4$$
$$69.5 \times 10^1 = 695$$
$$31.6 \times 10^2 = 3,160$$
$$74.2 \times 10^3 = 74,200$$

$$0.514 \times 10^0 = 0.514$$
$$0.873 \times 10^1 = 8.73$$
$$0.267 \times 10^2 = 26.7$$
$$0.951 \times 10^3 = 951$$

Activities
② Solve.

$$6 \times 10^0 = 6$$
$$0.4 \times 10^1 = 4$$
$$0.12 \times 10^2 = 12$$
$$7.85 \times 10^3 = 7,850$$

$$3.48 \times 10^0 = 3.48$$
$$0.683 \times 10^1 = 6.83$$
$$87.9 \times 10^2 = 8,790$$
$$0.056 \times 10^3 = 56$$

---

③ Use the divisibility tests to identify each number as prime or composite.

225	Composite (3, 5, 9)	231	Composite (3)
227	Prime	233	Prime
229	Prime	235	Composite (5)

④ Solve, following the proper order of operations.
$$8^2 \div (5+3) + 3 \times 1 = 64 \div 8 + 3 = 8 + 3 = 11$$
$$(3^2 - 8) - 9 = (9 - 8) - 9 = 1 - 9 = -8$$
$$7 - (7 - 3 + 4) = 7 - (4 + 4) = 7 - 8 = -1$$
$$(8^2 - 10) + 6 - 7 =$$
$$(64 - 10) + 6 - 7 = 54 + 6 - 7 = 60 - 7 = 53$$

$$(8 - 3^2) \times 9 = (8 - 9) \times 9 = (-1) \times 9 = -9$$
$$3^2 \times (9 - 3) \div 3 + 9 =$$
$$9 \times 6 \div 3 + 9 = 54 \div 3 + 9 = 18 + 9 = 27$$
$$9^2 - 8 \times 7 = 81 - 56 = 25$$
$$8^2 \div 4 - (6 + 3 + 2) =$$
$$64 \div 4 - (9 + 2) = 16 - 11 = 5$$

⑤ Multiply or divide as indicated.

2.1	5.3	6.41	4.38	0.754
×6.8	×0.35	×7.3	×0.47	×3.9
168	265	1923	3066	6786
+1260	+1590	+44870	+17520	+22620
14.28	1.855	46.793	2.0586	2.9406

.9	14	15	.9	170
1.7)1.53	1.9)26.6	0.15)2.25	0.12)0.108	0.13)22.10
	19	15		13
	76	75		91
	76	75		91

⑥ Write an equation and solve. Remember to label your answer.
Billy needs to purchase 2 cases of hot dogs at $11.28 each and 10 packages of hot dog buns at $1.98 each. What is the total cost for the hot dogs and buns? **$42.36**
Let x = total cost for hotdogs and buns
$$x = 2(\$11.28) + 10(\$1.98)$$
$$x = \$22.56 + \$19.80 = \$42.36$$

If there are 80 hot dogs in a case and 16 buns in a package, find the cost per hot dog in a bun, to the nearest cent. **$.26**
From the problem above, $42.36 will buy 160 hotdogs and 160 buns. Therefore, $42.36 ÷ 160 = 0.264, which rounds to $0.26

If Billy charges $1 for a hot dog in a bun, how much profit, to the nearest cent, does the concession stand earn on each hot dog sold? **$.74**
$1.00 − $.26 = $.74

---

① Solve the inequalities.

$4x < 20$
$x < 5$

$6x + 7 > 25$
$6x > 18$
$x > 3$

$5x - 3 < 2x + 9$
$3x - 3 < 9$
$3x < 12$
$x < 4$

$-4x < 20$
$-x < 5$
$x > -5$

$3x + 4 > x - 4$
$2x + 4 > -4$
$2x > -8$
$x > -4$

$6x + 7 < 8x + 5$
$-2x + 7 < 5$
$-2x < -2$
$-x < -1$
$x > 1$

② Solve.

```
  67.91        51.3        475.96       429.15       430.7
+43.65       +64.27       + 23.81      +743.3       + 26.81
------       ------       -------      -------      -------
111.56       115.57       499.77       1172.45      457.51
```

```
 39.749       243.74       695.2        189.72       768.2
-16.237      - 65.19      - 47.23      - 99.999     - 92.4537
-------      -------      -------      -------      --------
 23.512       178.55       647.97        89.721      675.7463
```

```
   9.2          6.5          85.1          8.42          .473
 ×  7         ×  .3        ×  .9         × 7.3         × .19
------       ------       ------        -----         -----
 64.4          1.95         76.59        2526          4257
                                        58940          4730
                                        ------         -----
                                        61.466        .08987
```

```
      4              .7               70               .5
.6)2.4          .4).28           .5)350            9)4.5
  24               28               35               45
  --               --               --               --
```

Teaching Tips, Cont.

➢ Once students understand the concept, show them that the problems can all be worked in one step as mental math simply by moving the decimal point.

➢ Complete the Classwork exercises. Have some students work the problems on the board for the class. All students should work the problems in their books.

Assignment

• Complete Lesson 28, Activities 2-6.

Lesson 29

Concepts
- Dividing by powers of 10
- Prime factorization
- Single-variable inequalities
- Multiplying decimals
- Dividing decimals

Learning Objectives
The student will be able to:
- Divide whole numbers by powers of 10
- Divide decimals by powers of 10
- Solve powers of 10 problems as one-step problems

Materials Needed
- Student Book, Lesson 29

Teaching Tips
➢ Write the first chart from the teaching box on the board. Review the rules for working with Powers of 10 with zero and positive exponents. (See Lesson 27)

➢ Review negative exponents. (See Lesson 14)

➢ Write the remaining charts from the teaching box on the board. Teach the rules for dividing by powers of 10.

➢ Once students understand the concept, show them that the problems can all be worked in one step as mental math simply by moving the decimal point.

➢ Review the mental math rules for powers of 10 using the summary chart at the right.

Dividing by Powers of 10

Remember from Lesson 27:

$$10^0 = 1$$

$$10^{-1} = \frac{1}{10} = 0.1$$

$$10^{-2} = \frac{1}{10^2} = \frac{1}{100} = 0.01$$

$$10^{-3} = \frac{1}{10^3} = \frac{1}{1000} = 0.001$$

Multiplying by a power of 10 with a negative exponent is the same as dividing by the power of 10 with the corresponding positive exponent.

$$5 \times 10^0 = 5 \times 1 = 5$$
$$5 \times 10^{-1} = 5 \div 10^1 = 5 \div 10 = 0.5$$
$$5 \times 10^{-2} = 5 \div 10^2 = 5 \div 100 = 0.05$$
$$5 \times 10^{-3} = 5 \div 10^3 = 5 \div 1,000 = 0.005$$

Now, divide a decimal by the powers of 10:
$$5.14 \div 10^0 = 5.14 \div 1 = 5.14$$
$$5.14 \div 10^1 = 5.14 \div 10 = 0.514$$
$$5.14 \div 10^2 = 5.14 \div 100 = 0.0514$$
$$5.14 \div 10^3 = 5.14 \div 1,000 = 0.00514$$

The decimal point moves to the left the number of places indicated in the exponent.

Note that if you are dividing by a power of 10 with a negative exponent, this is the same as multiplying by a power of 10 with a corresponding positive exponent.

① **Classwork**
Solve.

$$9 \times 10^0 = 9$$
$$3 \times 10^{-1} = 0.3$$
$$14 \times 10^{-2} = 0.14$$
$$22 \times 10^{-3} = 0.022$$

$$3.14 \div 10^0 = 3.14$$
$$9.26 \div 10^1 = 0.926$$
$$52.87 \div 10^2 = 0.5287$$
$$76.53 \div 10^3 = 0.07653$$

$$0.682 \div 10^0 = 0.682$$
$$0.54 \div 10^1 = 0.054$$
$$0.18 \div 10^2 = 0.0018$$
$$0.9 \div 10^3 = 0.0009$$

Activities
② Solve.

$7 \times 10^0 = 7$	$4.57 \div 10^0 = 4.57$	$0.385 \div 10^0 = 0.385$
$6 \times 10^{-1} = 0.6$	$2.95 \div 10^1 = 0.295$	$0.49 \div 10^1 = 0.049$
$25 \times 10^{-2} = 0.25$	$43.19 \div 10^2 = 0.4319$	$0.82 \div 10^2 = 0.0082$
$38 \times 10^{-3} = 0.038$	$86.27 \div 10^3 = 0.08627$	$0.1 \div 10^3 = 0.0001$

Powers of 10 Summary

Operation	Exponent	Decimal Direction
Multiply	Positive	Right
Multiply	Negative	Left
Divide	Positive	Left
Divide	Negative	Right

③ Express the prime factorization using exponents where appropriate.

38	39	40
$38 = 2 \times 19$	$39 = 3 \times 13$	$40 = 2 \times 2 \times 2 \times 5$
		$40 = 2^3 \times 5$

42	44	45
$42 = 2 \times 3 \times 7$	$44 = 2 \times 2 \times 11$	$45 = 3 \times 3 \times 5$
	$44 = 2^2 \times 11$	$45 = 3^2 \times 5$

④ Solve the inequalities.

$6x + 7 < 2x - 5$	$x - 10 < 4x + 5$	$3(2x - 1) > 5x + 11$
$4x < -12$	$-3x < 15$	$6x - 3 > 5x + 11$
$x < -3$	$-x < 5$	$x > 14$
	$x > -5$	

⑤ Multiply or divide as indicated.

```
 0.55      2.6        4.1        1.6        5.8
  ×6       ×6.5       ×2.7      ×0.69      ×0.75
 3.30      130        287        144        290
          +1560      +820       +960      +4060
          16.90      11.07      1.104      4.350

 0.46      0.41       0.67       0.73       0.58
×0.54      ×0.5       ×0.16      ×0.85      ×0.57
 184       .205       402        365        406
+2300                +670       +5840      +2900
.2484                .1072      .6205      .3306

       1.3        14        1.4         2          1.1
 1.8)2.34   0.1)1.4    0.9)1.26   1.5)30    0.16)0.176
    18          1          9                    16
    54          4         36                    16
    54          4         36                    16
```

➤ Explain that dividing by a power of 10 with a negative exponent is the same as multiplying by a power of 10 with a corresponding positive exponent. Also, dividing by a power of 10 with a positive exponent is the same as multiplying by a power of 10 with a corresponding negative exponent.

➤ Complete the Classwork exercises. Have some students work the problems on the board for the class. All students should work the problems in their books.

Assignment

• Complete Lesson 29, Activities 2-5.

Lesson 30

Concepts
- Metric system: Kilo-
- Like terms
- Order of operations
- Single-variable inequalities
- Powers of 10
- Dividing decimals

Learning Objectives
The student will be able to:
- Define *kilo-*
- Use proper abbreviations for metric units
- Convert kilo-units to base units
- Convert base units to kilo-units
- Apply powers of 10 to metric conversions

Materials Needed
- Student Book, Lesson 30
- Worksheet 15

Teaching Tips
- Review the rules for multiplying and dividing by powers of 10. (See Lessons 28-29)

- Explain that the metric system is a measurement system based on powers of 10. All conversions within the metric system will use multiplication and division of powers of 10.

- Teach the metric prefix *kilo-*. Make sure students correctly identify *kilo* as equal to one thousand.

- Ask the students how the number 1000 is represented as a power of 10. (10^3) Remind students that the three zeros after the one show that the exponent is 3.

Metric System: Kilo-

The metric prefix **kilo-** means *one thousand*. A kilogram is equal to 1000 grams. A kilometer is equal to 1,000 meters. The abbreviation for *kilo-* is *k*, and it is always followed by the abbreviation for the base units.
kilogram = kg; kilometer = km;
kiloliter = kL; kilowatt = kW

To determine the number of base units (grams, meters, liters, etc.) in a given number of kilos of that unit, multiply the number of kilos by 1,000.

For example, 4 kg = 4 x 1,000 = 4,000 grams
4.37 km = 4.37 x 1,000 = 4,370 meters
Note that this is the same as multiplying by 10^3.

To determine the number of kilos in a given number of base units (grams, meters, liters, etc.), divide the number of base units by 1000.

For example, 4000 grams = 4000 ÷ 1000 = 4 kg
4,370 meters = 4370 ÷ 1000 = 4.37 km
Note that this is the same as dividing by 10^3.

① Classwork
Multiply or divide as necessary to complete the metric conversions.

1 kg = ___1,000___ g

3 km = ___3,000___ m

4.2 kL = ___4,200___ L

6.17 kW = ___6,170___ W

2000 g = _____2_____ kg

5976 L = ___5.976___ kL

728 m = ___0.728___ km

Activities

② Multiply or divide the appropriate powers of 10 to complete the metric conversions.

7 kg = ___7,000___ g

0.9 km = ___900___ m

6.4 kL = ___6,400___ L

13.57 kW = ___13,570___ W

8000 g = ___8___ kg

7348 L = ___7.348___ kL

186 m = ___0.186___ km

39.5 W = ___0.0395___ kW

③ Simplify.

$x^3 + 8x^3 = 9x^3$

$8x^8 + 7x^8 = 15x^8$

$5x^3 + 9x^3 - 7x^3 =$
$14x^3 - 7x^3 = 7x^3$

$15x^7 - 13x^7 = 2x^7$

$4x^9 - x^9 = 3x^9$

$20x^{12} - 10x^{12} - 7x^{12} =$
$10x^{12} - 7x^{12} = 3x^{12}$

$(x^3)(x^2) = x^{2+3} = x^5$

$(x^5)(3x^5) = 3x^{5+5} = 3x^{10}$

$(7x^3)(2x^6) = 14x^{3+6} = 14x^9$

$(x^{15}) \div (x^5) = x^{15-5} = x^{10}$

$(3x^8) \div (x^5) = 3x^{8-5} = 3x^3$

$(18x^{13}) \div (3x^7) = 6x^{13-7} = 6x^6$

④ Solve, following the proper order of operations.

$6^2 \div (5-1) + 5 \times 2 = 36 \div 4 + 10 = 9 + 10 = 19$

$(5^2 - 7) \div 6 = (25 - 7) \div 6 = 18 \div 6 = 3$

$17 - (6 - 3 \times 5) = 17 - (6 - 15) = 17 - (-9) = 17 + 9 = 26$

$(7^2 - 13) - (6 - 7) = (49 - 13) - (-1) = 36 + 1 = 37$

$(5^2 - 3^2) \div 2^2 = (25 - 9) \div 4 = 16 \div 4 = 4$

$3^2 \times (8 - 5) \div 3 \times 2 = 9 \times 3 \div 3 \times 2 = 27 \div 3 \times 2 = 9 \times 2 = 18$

$7^2 - 6 \times 8 = 49 - 48 = 1$

$(11^2 + 4) \div (3 + 2)^2 = (121 + 4) \div 5^2 = 125 \div 25 = 5$

⑤ Solve the inequalities.

$11x + 16 < x - 4$	$15x - 4 > 9x + 2$	$7(3x - 4) < 11x - 8$
$10x < -20$	$6x > 6$	$21x - 28 < 11x - 8$
$x < -2$	$x > 1$	$10x < 20$
		$x < 2$

⑥ Solve.

$5.41 \times 10^0 = 5.41$

$89.13 \times 10^{-1} = 8.913$

$7.745 \times 10^{-2} = 0.07745$

$0.149 \times 10^{-3} = 0.000149$

$128 \times 10^0 = 128$

$354.48 \times 10^1 = 3,544.8$

$25.68 \div 10^2 = 0.2568$

$37.155 \div 10^3 = 0.037155$

$0.463 \div 10^0 = 0.463$

$0.95 \div 10^1 = 0.095$

$1.69 \div 10^2 = 0.0169$

$0.75 \div 10^3 = 0.00075$

⑦ Divide.

$$1.3\overline{)0.221} \quad \begin{array}{r} .17 \\ \hline \end{array}$$
13
91
91

$$0.12\overline{)10.80} \quad \begin{array}{r} 90 \\ \hline \end{array}$$
108

$$15\overline{)0.225} \quad \begin{array}{r} .015 \\ \hline \end{array}$$
15
75
75

$$1.9\overline{)26.6} \quad \begin{array}{r} 14 \\ \hline \end{array}$$
19
76
76

$$0.17\overline{)1.53} \quad \begin{array}{r} 9 \\ \hline \end{array}$$

$$0.19\overline{)209.00} \quad \begin{array}{r} 1100 \\ \hline \end{array}$$
19
19
19

$$12\overline{)2.04} \quad \begin{array}{r} .17 \\ \hline \end{array}$$
12
84
84

$$0.13\overline{)16.90} \quad \begin{array}{r} 130 \\ \hline \end{array}$$
13
39
39

$$1.7\overline{)2.72} \quad \begin{array}{r} 1.6 \\ \hline \end{array}$$
17
102
102

$$1.4\overline{)0.196} \quad \begin{array}{r} .14 \\ \hline \end{array}$$
14
56
56

① Solve.

$10^5 = 100,000$

$10^6 = 1,000,000$

$10^{-5} = .00001$

$10^{-7} = .0000001$

② Simplify.

$(10^4)(10^7) = 10^{4+7} = 10^{11}$

$(10^{14}) \div (10^8) = 10^{14-8} = 10^6$

$(10^8)(10^{-5}) = 10^{8-5} = 10^3$

$(10^3) \div (10^{-1}) = 10^{3-(-1)} = 10^{3+1} = 10^4$

③ Solve.

$9 \times 10^0 = 9 \times 1 = 9$

$.7 \times 10^1 = .7 \times 10 = 7$

$.35 \times 10^2 = .35 \times 100 = 35$

$8.14 \times 10^3 = 8.14 \times 1000 = 8140$

$4.83 \times 10^0 = 4.83 \times 1 = 4.83$

$.571 \times 10^1 = 0.571 \times 10 = 5.71$

$46.3 \times 10^2 = 46.3 \times 100 = 4630$

$.076 \times 10^3 = 0.076 \times 1000 = 76$

$19 \times 10^0 = 19 \times 1 = 19$

$13 \times 10^{-1} = 13 \times 0.1 = 1.3$

$27 \times 10^{-2} = 27 \times 0.01 = 0.27$

$39 \times 10^{-3} = 39 \times 0.001 = 0.039$

$3.28 \div 10^0 = 3.28 \div 1 = 3.28$

$7.48 \div 10^1 = 7.48 \div 10 = 0.748$

$26.91 \div 10^2 = 26.91 \div 100 = 0.2691$

$44.58 \div 10^3 = 44.58 \div 1000 = 0.04458$

$0.561 \div 10^0 = 0.561 \div 1 = 0.561$

$0.97 \div 10^1 = 0.97 \div 10 = 0.097$

$0.36 \div 10^2 = 0.36 \div 100 = 0.0036$

$0.4 \div 10^3 = 0.4 \div 1000 = 0.0004$

Memory Technique for Conversion Rules

Larger to smaller, multiply.
Larger – Have students hold their arms apart like they are carrying a large box.
Smaller – Have students bring their hands about shoulder width apart like they are carrying a small box.
Multiply – Have students move their arms in closer until they are crossed, forming a multiplication symbol.

Smaller to larger, divide.
Smaller – Have students hold their arms shoulder width apart like they are carrying a small box.
Larger – Have students move their arms farther apart like they are carrying a large box.
Divide – Have students extend their arms out straight from their shoulders, forming a horizontal division symbol. They may picture their arms as a fraction bar, or as the center line of ÷ with their head as the top dot.

Teaching Tips, Cont.

➢ Teach the conversion of kilo-units to base units. Ask the students what 1 kilometer is equal to. (1000 meters) Ask what 2 kilometers equal. (2000 meters) Ask the students how they found the number of meters in 2 kilometers. (Multiply by 1000)

➢ Teach the conversion of base units to kilo-units. Ask the students what 1000 meters is equal to. (1 kilometer) Ask what 2000 meters equal. (2 kilometers) Ask the students how they found the number of kilometers in 2000 meters. (Divide by 1000)

➢ Ask the students which is larger: a meter or a kilometer. (kilometer) Teach the rule for measurement conversions: Larger to smaller, multiply. Smaller to larger, divide. See the memory technique at the left.

➢ Teach capitalization rules for the metric system: All metric system abbreviations are written with lowercase letters EXCEPT those representing a unit named after a person. For example, watt is abbreviated W, and kilowatt is kW. The only exception is liter, which can have a capital or lowercase L. This book will always use a capital L so there is no confusion with the number 1.

➢ Complete the Classwork exercises. Have some students work the problems on the board for the class. All students should work the problems in their books.

Assignments
- Complete Lesson 30, Activities 2-7.
- Worksheet 15
- Study for test (Lessons 18-27)

Test 3

Testing Objectives
The student will:
- Simplify roots
- Translate words into mathematical expressions
- Solve single-variable equations
- Solve single-variable inequalities
- Add decimals
- Subtract decimals
- Multiply decimals
- Divide decimals
- Compare decimals
- Simplify powers of 10
- Apply math concepts to math in the real world

Materials Needed
- Test 3
- *It's College Test Prep Time!* from Student Book
- *A Math Minute with …* Diann J. from Student Book

Teaching Tips
➢ Administer Test 3, allowing the students 30-40 minutes to complete the test.

➢ When all students are finished taking the test, introduce the College Test Prep Time from the student book. This page may be completed in class or assigned as homework.

➢ Have students read the Math Minute interview for Lessons 31-40.

Horizons Pre-Algebra, Teacher's Guide   102

Test 3

① Simplify the roots.   **12 points**

$\sqrt{36} = 6$

$\sqrt{27} = \sqrt{3 \times 3 \times 3} = 3\sqrt{3}$

$\sqrt{18} = \sqrt{2 \times 3 \times 3} = 3\sqrt{2}$

$\sqrt[3]{8} = \sqrt[3]{2 \times 2 \times 2} = 2$

$\sqrt[3]{64} = \sqrt[3]{4 \times 4 \times 4} = 4$

$\sqrt{11} + 4\sqrt{11} = 5\sqrt{11}$

$6\sqrt[3]{5} - 2\sqrt[3]{5} = 4\sqrt[3]{5}$

$(\sqrt{8})(\sqrt{2}) = \sqrt{8 \times 2} = \sqrt{16} = 4$

$(\sqrt{3})(2\sqrt{15}) = 2\sqrt{3 \times 3 \times 5} = 2(3\sqrt{5}) = 6\sqrt{5}$

$\sqrt{48} \div \sqrt{3} = \sqrt{48 \div 3} = \sqrt{16} = 4$

$6\sqrt{24} \div 3\sqrt{8} = (6 \div 3)\sqrt{24 \div 8} = 2\sqrt{3}$

$7 \div \sqrt{7} = \sqrt{7 \times 7} \div \sqrt{7} = \sqrt{49} \div \sqrt{7} = \sqrt{7}$

② Translate the following words into a mathematical expression. Do not solve.   **10 points**

The product of 5 and a number $5x$

The ratio of a number to 8 $\dfrac{x}{8}$

A number increased by 31 $x + 31$

The total of a number and 28 is 61. $x + 28 = 61$

8 fewer than a number equals 3. $x - 8 = 3$

A number times 7 yields 42. $7x = 42$

The sum of 16 and a number is 29. $16 + x = 29$

6 less than a number is 19. $x - 6 = 19$

A number increased by a factor of 4 gives 32. $4x = 32$

51 more than a number is 88. $x + 51 = 88$

③ Solve.   **6 points**

$x + 6 + 5 = 18$
$x + 11 = 18$
$x = 7$

$x + 3x + 3 + 7 = 26$
$4x + 10 = 26$
$4x = 16$
$x = 4$

$2x + 3x + 6 - 1 = 20$
$5x + 5 = 20$
$5x = 15$
$x = 3$

$3x + x - 9 + 4 = 31$
$4x - 5 = 31$
$4x = 36$
$x = 9$

$5x - 2x + 11 - 4 - 1 = 24$
$3x + 6 = 24$
$3x = 18$
$x = 6$

$6x + 2x - x - 8 - 4 + 1 = 38$
$7x - 11 = 38$
$7x = 49$
$x = 7$

④ Solve the inequalities.   **6 points**

$4x < 12$
$x < 3$

$3x + 11 > 17$
$3x > 6$
$x > 2$

$3x - 8 < x + 14$
$2x < 22$
$x < 11$

$-5x < 15$
$-x < 3$
$x > -3$

$2x + 7 > x - 3$
$x > -10$

$7x + 9 < 3x + 1$
$4x < -8$
$x < -2$

Test 3

⑤ Solve.   **20 points**

19.67	39.51	694.57	519.4	457.09
+65.34	+27.64	+183.82	+73.38	+256.8
85.01	67.15	878.39	592.78	713.89

39.974	234.74	692.50	198.720	567.2300
−16.237	−56.19	−47.23	−9.999	−92.3745
23.737	178.55	645.27	188.721	474.8555

2.9	7.3	.33	7.8	.48
×.8	×6.1	×8.3	×.66	×.13
2.32	73	99	468	144
	+4380	+2640	+4680	+480
	44.53	2.739	5.148	.0624

$1.8)\overline{1.62}$ → .9, 162

$1.6)\overline{2.56}$ → 1.6, 16 96 96

$.14)\overline{1.96}$ → 14, 14 56 56

$.15)\overline{1.35}$ → 9, 135

$.16)\overline{20.80}$ → 130, 16 48 48

⑥ Write < or > for each pair of decimals.   **6 points**

314.954 __<__ 413.459   648.815 __<__ 648.9

92.763 __>__ 92.673   35.743 __<__ 35.753

21.89 __<__ 21.91   800.003 __>__ 800.0007

⑦ Solve.   **8 points**

$10^4 = 10,000$

$10^7 = 10,000,000$

$(10^3)(10^6) = 10^9 = 1,000,000,000$

$(10^{12}) \div (10^5) = 10^7 = 10,000,000$

$10^{-6} = 0.000001$

$10^{-8} = 0.00000001$

$(10^7)(10^{-5}) = 10^2 = 100$

$(10^4) \div (10^{-1}) = 10^5 = 100,000$

⑧ Write an equation and solve.   **2 points**
Four teenagers each worked 5 hours in Billy's concession stand on Saturday. If the concession stand made $115.80 profit, was there enough profit to pay each teenager $5 per hour toward youth activity fees? If so, how much extra was there? If not, how much money are they short?
Yes. There is $15.80 extra.
4 x 5 hours = 20 teenager-hours worked   20 x $5 = $100 pay.
$115.80 - $100 = $15.80 extra   **70 points total**

It's College Test Prep Time!

1. When 46,300 is written as 4.63×10^x, what is the value of x?
   A. -2
   B. 2
   C. 3
   D. <u>4</u>
   E. 5

2. At the beginning of the month, John had $57 and Levi had $62 in their youth group accounts. After working in Billy's concession stand for a month, John had $69 in his account. If Levi earned twice as much as John did during the month, how much money did Levi have in his account at the end of the month?
   A. $24
   B. $74
   C. $81
   D. <u>$86</u>
   E. $124

   John earned $62–$57 = $12. Levi earned twice as much, or $24. At the end of the month, Levi had $62+$24=$86

3. Find the value of x if $\left(\frac{1}{2}\right)^{x-5} = 1$.
   A. 0
   B. 3
   C. <u>5</u>
   D. 7
   E. 12

   $\left(\frac{1}{2}\right)^0 = 1$, therefore $x - 5 = 0$
   $x = 5$

4. If $x > 0$, which of the following are equivalent to $x^{\frac{5}{3}}$?
   I. $\sqrt[3]{x^5}$ $= \sqrt[3]{x \cdot x \cdot x \cdot x \cdot x} = x\sqrt[3]{x^2}$
   II. $\sqrt[5]{x^3}$
   III. $x\sqrt[3]{x^2}$

   A. None
   B. I only
   C. II only
   D. III only
   E. <u>I and III only</u>

A Math Minute with . . .

Diann J. – Seamstress, Cook

What is your hobby? I enjoy sewing alterations on clothing as well as volunteering as a cook for Wednesday night suppers at church.

Where do you do your volunteer work? I work both at home and at church.

Did you attend college? If so, what was your major? No.

What parts of your job require the use of math? With alterations, I need the right measurements to either increase or decrease garment sizes. For the suppers, I prepare the list of groceries and buy the necessary ingredients to cook the right amounts for the recipes.

What is the biggest "problem" you have faced that required the use of math to solve? I use math to carefully determine the right measurements on the garments. For Wednesday evening suppers, it is important I have the right quantities for the number of people to be fed.

Are there any other interesting math uses you have experienced? I find that knowing fractions is especially helpful in both sewing and baking.

Lesson 31

Concepts
- Metric system: Centi-
- Metric system: Milli-
- Metric system conversions
- Order of operations
- Greatest common factor
- Powers of 10
- Math in the real world

Learning Objectives
The student will be able to:
- Define *centi-*
- Define *milli-*
- Apply powers of 10 to convert values within the metric system

Materials Needed
- Student Book, Lesson 31

Teaching Tips
➢ Review the rules for multiplying and dividing by powers of 10. (See Lessons 28-29)

➢ Teach the metric prefixes *centi-* and *milli-*. Make sure students correctly identify *centi-* as equal to one hundred*th* and *milli-* as equal to one thousand*th*.

➢ Explain the additional information on the metric system in the right column. As students progress through their high school science courses, they will see metric units referred to as SI units. Emphasize that these are the same thing.

➢ Emphasize the capitalization rules for metric unit names and symbols.

Metric System: Centi- and Milli-

The metric prefix **centi-** (abbreviated c) means *one hundredth*, and the metric prefix **milli-** (abbreviated m) means one *thousandth*. One gram is equal to 100 <u>centi</u>grams or 1000 <u>milli</u>grams. 4 = 4
centigram = cg; millimeter = mm;

To determine the number of base units (grams, meters, liters, etc.) in a given number of centi-units, divide the number of centi-units by 100.

For example, 400 cg = 400 ÷ 100 = 4 grams
437 cm = 437 ÷ 100 = 4.37 meters
Note that this is the same as dividing by 10^2.

To determine the number of base units (grams, meters, liters, etc.) in a given number of milli-units, divide the number of milli-units by 1000.

4000 mg = 4000 ÷ 1000 = 4 grams
4370 mg = 4370 ÷ 1000 = 4.37 grams
Note that this is the same as dividing by 10^3.

Rule of thumb when converting measurements: When going from a larger unit to a smaller unit (such as from meters to millimeters), multiply. When going from a smaller unit to a larger unit (such as from millimeters to meters), divide.

① **Classwork**

1 g = _____100_____ cg

1 g = _____1000_____ mg

3 m = _____300_____ cm

4.2 L = _____420_____ cL

4.2 L = _____4200_____ mL

6.17 W = _____6,170_____ mW

2000 cg = _____20_____ g

2000 mg = _____2_____ g

5976 cL = _____59.76_____ L

728 cm = _____7.28_____ m

728 mm = _____0.728_____ m

Activities

② Multiply or divide the appropriate powers of 10 to complete the metric conversions.

7 g = _____700_____ cg   8000 cg = _____80_____ g

.9 m = _____900_____ mm   7348 mL = _____7.348_____ L

6.4 L = _____640_____ cL   186 cm = _____1.86_____ m

13.57 W = _____13,570_____ mW   39.5 mw = _____0.0395_____ W

③ Simplify.

$(4^2 + 5) \div (7 - 4) = (16 + 5) \div 3 = 21 \div 3 = 7$

$4 - (7 - 5^2) - (5 - 8) = 4 - (7 - 25) - (-3) = 4 - (-18) - (-3) = 4 + 18 + 3 = 22 + 3 = 25$

$(5^2 - (1^2 - 6^2)) \div (2 - 7) =$
$(25 - (1 - 36)) \div (-5) = (25 - (-35)) \div (-5) = (25 + 35) \div (-5) = 60 \div (-5) = -12$

$3^3 \times (9 - 3) \div (8 + 1) - 5 = 27 \times 6 \div 9 - 5 = 162 \div 9 - 5 = 18 - 5 = 13$

Additional Information on the Metric System

- The metric system is now referred to as the SI system, which stands for the *Système International d'Unités*, or the International System of Units.

- All units are spelled with all lowercase letters. The only exceptions are units that are the first word in a sentence, and Celsius, which is always capitalized.

- Prefix symbols representing values less than one million are written in lowercase. (m for milli- or one thousandth)

- Prefix symbol representing values of one million or more are capitalized. (M for mega- or one million)

④ Find the greatest common factor of each set of numbers.

18, 24, and 36	14, 35, and 42	20, 32, and 36
18 = ②×③×3	14 = 2 × ⑦	20 = ②×②×5
24 = ②×2 × 2 ×③	35 = 5 × ⑦	32 = ②×②×2 × 2 × 2
36 = ②×2 ×③×3	42 = 2 × 3 × ⑦	36 = ②×②×3 × 3
GCF: 2 × 3 = 6	GCF: 7	GCF: 2 × 2 = 4

⑤ Simplify.

$43.2 \times 10^0 = 43.2$ $0.063 \times 10^0 = 0.063$ $2.7 \div 10^0 = 2.7$

$0.871 \times 10^{-1} = 0.0871$ $27.96 \times 10^1 = 279.6$ $66.49 \div 10^1 = 6.649$

$6.492 \times 10^{-2} = 0.06492$ $3.18 \div 10^2 = 0.0318$ $31.45 \div 10^2 = 0.3145$

$0.5 \times 10^{-3} = 0.0005$ $549.618 \div 10^3 = 0.549618$ $0.088 \div 10^3 = 0.000088$

⑥ Solve the word problems. Remember to label your answers.

Recipe for Buttermilk Biscuits (Makes 4 dozen biscuits)	
8 cups flour	8 tablespoons butter
5 teaspoons baking powder	8 tablespoons shortening
1 teaspoon baking soda	4 cups buttermilk, chilled
1 tablespoon salt	

Diann is cooking for 192 people at church on Wednesday night. How much of each ingredient does Diann need to serve one biscuit to each person?
4 dozen = 4(12) = 48 biscuits per recipe. To cook for 192 people, Diann must prepare 192 ÷ 48 = 4 batches of biscuits. Multiply each ingredient amount in the recipe by 4.
Diann needs:
8×4=32 cups flour
5×4=20 teaspoons baking powder
1×4=4 teaspoons baking soda
1×4=4 teaspoons salt
8×4=32 tablespoons butter (Some students may recognize this as 1 pound of butter.)
8×4=32 tablespoons shortening
4×4=16 cups buttermilk, chilled

A 5-pound bag of flour contains about 20 cups of flour. How many 5-pound bags of flour must Diann purchase to ensure she has enough flour to bake biscuits for 192 people?
From the above problem, we know Diann needs 32 cups of flour. One 5-pound bag of flour contains about 20 cups, so Diann should purchase **2 bags** of flour.

Teaching Tips, Cont.

➤ Teach the conversion of base units to centi- and milli-units. Ask the students what 1 meter is equal to. (100 centimeters and 1000 millimeters) Ask what 2 meters equal. (200 centimeters or 2000 millimeters) Ask the students how they found the number of centimeters and millimeters in 2 meters. (Multiply by 100 for centimeters and 1000 for millimeters)

➤ Teach the conversion of centi-and milli-units to base units. Ask the students what 100 centimeters is equal to. (1 meter) Ask the students what 200 centimeters is equal to. (2 meters) Ask students what 1000 millimeters is equal to. (1 meter) Ask students what 2000 millimeters is equal to. (2 meters) Ask the students how they found the equivalent values. (Divide by 100 for centimeters and 1000 for millimeters)

➤ Review the memory technique for the conversion rules. (See Lesson 30)

➤ Complete the Classwork exercises. Have some students work the problems on the board for the class and explain their answers. All students should work the problems in their books.

Assignment
- Complete Lesson 31, Activities 2-6.

Lesson 32

Concepts
- Equivalent fraction
- Signed numbers
- Powers of 10
- Metric conversions
- Adding decimals
- Subtracting decimals

Learning Objectives
The student will be able to:
- Define *equivalent fractions*
- Calculate an equivalent fraction to a given fraction when given the new denominator

Materials Needed
- Student Book, Lesson 32
- 5 empty egg cartons (optional)
- Worksheet 16

Teaching Tips
➢ Have students complete Worksheet 16 in class. This may be for added practice of earlier topics, or graded as a quiz, if desired.

➢ Ask students how many quarters are in fifty cents. (2) Ask students how many quarters are in a dollar. (4) Have students express this as a fraction $\left(\frac{2}{4}\right)$.

➢ Repeat the above exercise with dimes, nickels, and pennies. (Dimes: 5,10, $\frac{5}{10}$; nickels:10, 20, $\frac{10}{20}$; pennies: 50,100, $\frac{50}{100}$)

➢ Show students that each of the above fractions represents $\frac{1}{2}$ of a dollar. Although the fractions appear to be different, they are all equal in value.

Equivalent Fractions

Equivalent fractions are fractions that have different numerators and denominators, but are equal in value.

For example, $\frac{1}{2}$ and $\frac{2}{4}$ are equivalent fractions because they both indicate equal amounts of something. When an object is divided into 2 equal parts and 1 part is chosen, that is the same amount as if the object were divided into 4 equal parts and 2 parts were chosen.

To find equivalent fractions, multiply both the numerator and denominator of one fraction by the same number to get the numerator and denominator of the equivalent fraction.

For example, given the fraction $\frac{2}{3}$, find an equivalent fraction by multiplying the 2 and 3 by the same number to get a new fraction:

$$\frac{2 \times 2}{3 \times 2} = \frac{4}{6}$$

① Classwork
Find the equivalent fractions.

$\frac{1}{2} = \frac{2}{4}$

$\frac{1}{3} = \frac{2}{6}$

$\frac{2}{3} = \frac{6}{9}$

$\frac{3}{5} = \frac{9}{15}$

Activities

② Solve the numerators to make equivalent fractions.

$\frac{1}{4} = \frac{2}{8}$	$\frac{5}{6} = \frac{10}{12}$	$\frac{3}{4} = \frac{9}{12}$
$\frac{2}{3} = \frac{4}{6}$	$\frac{1}{3} = \frac{4}{12}$	$\frac{1}{3} = \frac{2}{6}$
$\frac{1}{4} = \frac{2}{8}$	$\frac{3}{5} = \frac{9}{15}$	$\frac{1}{5} = \frac{4}{20}$
$\frac{3}{4} = \frac{6}{8}$	$\frac{3}{7} = \frac{9}{21}$	$\frac{1}{9} = \frac{2}{18}$
$\frac{2}{5} = \frac{4}{10}$	$\frac{5}{6} = \frac{15}{18}$	$\frac{4}{7} = \frac{12}{21}$
$\frac{1}{6} = \frac{2}{12}$	$\frac{6}{7} = \frac{12}{14}$	$\frac{5}{9} = \frac{15}{27}$

---

③ Solve, using the rules for signed numbers. Write the problem vertically, if necessary.

$(+34) + (+86) = 34 + 86 = 120$	$(+169) - (+498) = -(498 - 169) = -329$
$(+34) + (-86) = -(86 - 34) = -52$	$(+169) - (-498) = 169 + 498 = 667$
$(-34) + (+86) = 86 - 34 = 52$	$(-169) - (+498) = -(169 + 498) = -667$
$(-34) + (-86) = -(34 + 86) = -120$	$(-169) - (-498) = 498 - 169 = 329$

④ Multiply or divide by the appropriate powers of 10 to complete the metric conversions.

5 m = __5000__ mm	3000 cm = __30__ m
0.6 L = __600__ mL	4879 mL = __4.879__ L
8.1 g = __810__ cg	345 cW = __3.45__ W
26.49 W = __26,490__ mW	57.2 mg = __0.0572__ g

⑤ Write vertically and add or subtract as indicated.

14.39 + 5.267 =	275.96 + 43.8412 =	5.9 + 36.72 + 621.894 =
14.39 +5.267 19.657	275.96 +43.8412 319.8012	5.9 36.72 +621.894 664.514

755.759 + 65.5 + 9.99 =	7283.86 − 278.965 =	893.48 − 6.7853 =
755.759 65.5 +9.99 831.249	7283.860 − 278.965 7004.895	893.4800 − 6.7853 886.6947

7026.008 − 427.9005 =	9156.167 − 2648.1682 =	3185.276 − 999.9999 =
7026.0080 − 427.9005 6598.1075	9156.1670 −2648.1682 6507.9988	3185.2760 − 999.9999 2185.2761

Operations with Powers of Ten

Worksheet 16

① Solve.

$10^5 = 100{,}000$
$10^8 = 100{,}000{,}000$
$(10^2)(10^7) =$
$10^{2+7} = 10^9 = 1{,}000{,}000{,}000$
$(10^{15}) \div (10^9) =$
$10^{15-9} = 10^6 = 1{,}000{,}000$

$10^{-5} = 0.00001$
$10^{-2} = 0.01$
$(10^{10})(10^{-4}) = 10^{10-4} = 10^6 = 1{,}000{,}000$
$(10^5) \div (10^{-2}) =$
$10^{5-(-2)} = 10^{5+2} = 10^7 = 10{,}000{,}000$

② Multiply.

$12 \times 10^0 = 12$
$0.7 \times 10^1 = 7$
$0.63 \times 10^2 = 63$
$4.29 \times 10^3 = 4{,}290$
$54.29 \times 10^0 = 54.29$
$0.748 \times 10^1 = 7.48$
$8.19 \times 10^2 = 819$
$0.026 \times 10^3 = 26$

$0.15 \times 10^0 = 0.15$
$0.5796 \times 10^1 = 5.796$
$45.27 \times 10^2 = 4{,}527$
$0.072 \times 10^3 = 72$
$47.34 \times 10^0 = 47.34$
$0.982 \times 10^1 = 9.82$
$5.194 \times 10^2 = 519.4$
$0.008 \times 10^3 = 8$

③ Multiply or divide as indicated.

$16 \times 10^0 = 16$
$8 \times 10^{-1} = 0.8$
$4 \times 10^{-2} = 0.04$
$17 \times 10^{-3} = 0.017$
$8.34 \div 10^0 = 8.34$
$6.95 \div 10^1 = 0.695$
$5.49 \div 10^2 = 0.0549$
$47.13 \div 10^3 = 0.04713$

$6.4 \times 10^0 = 6.4$
$38 \times 10^{-1} = 3.8$
$67 \times 10^{-2} = 0.67$
$9.4 \times 10^{-3} = 0.0094$
$0.182 \div 10^0 = 0.182$
$0.493 \div 10^1 = 0.0493$
$0.047 \div 10^2 = 0.00047$
$0.7 \div 10^3 = 0.0007$

Cross Multiplication

To check for equivalent fractions, multiply the numerator of one fraction by the denominator of the other fraction. Repeat this process with the second denominator and numerator. If the two products are equal, the fractions are equivalent.

$$\frac{2}{4} = \frac{5}{10}$$

$2 \times 10 = 20$

$4 \times 5 = 20$

Because both products are equal, the fractions are equivalent.

Teaching Tips, Cont.

➢ Teach equivalent fractions from the teaching box.

➢ For students who are having difficulty "seeing" equivalent fractions, you may wish to use empty egg cartons cut into sections. See egg carton illustration below.

➢ Show students how to use cross multiplication to check their work on equivalent fractions. Note: Cross multiplication is not presented in the student text. This is an additional concept you may incorporate as you see fit.

➢ Complete the Classwork exercises. Have some students work the problems on the board for the class and explain their answers. If you have taught cross multiplication, have the students include this step in their explanations. All students should work the problems in their books.

Assignment

• Complete Lesson 32, Activities 2-5.

Egg Carton Illustration

Divide 5 egg cartons (12 sections each) as follows:

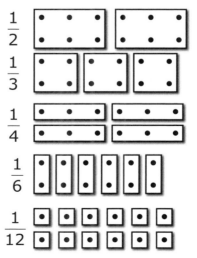

Horizons Pre-Algebra, Teacher's Guide

Lesson 33

Concepts
- Fraction-decimal equivalents
- Absolute value
- Divisibility tests
- Prime/Composite numbers
- Multiplying by powers of 10
- Dividing by powers of 10
- Real world math

Learning Objectives
The student will be able to:
- Use division to convert a fraction to a decimal
- Write a decimal as a fraction
- Reduce fractions to simplest form
- Memorize common fraction-decimal equivalents

Materials Needed
- Student Book, Lesson 33
- Fraction-decimal flashcards
- Worksheet 17

Teaching Tips
➤ Ask students how many quarters are in a dollar. (4) Ask students what fraction of a dollar is one quarter. $\left(\frac{1}{4}\right)$ Ask students what the value of a quarter is. ($0.25) Repeat this procedure with 2 quarters ($\frac{1}{2}$, $0.50), and 3 quarters ($\frac{3}{4}$, $0.75).

➤ Show students the relationship between the fraction and decimal representations in the above examples.

➤ Introduce the fraction-decimal equivalents in the student book. Students should memorize these values. They are not expected to memorize fractions that are not on this list.

Fraction-Decimal Conversion

To convert a fraction to a decimal, divide the numerator by the denominator.

$\frac{1}{2} = 1 \div 2 = 0.5$

If a fraction results in a repeating decimal, put a bar above the digit or digits that repeat to indicate a repeating decimal. For example,

$\frac{1}{3} = 0.\overline{3}$, read, "zero point three repeating."

To convert a decimal to a fraction, write the numeric portion on the right side of the decimal point as the numerator, and the place value of the digit on the right as the denominator.

$0.3 = \frac{3}{10}$

Reduce the resulting fraction, if possible.

$0.5 = \frac{5}{10} = \frac{5 \div 5}{10 \div 5} = \frac{1}{2}$

① **Classwork**

Convert each fraction to a decimal.

$\frac{1}{4} = 0.25$ $\frac{3}{8} = 0.375$

$\frac{2}{5} = 0.4$ $\frac{2}{3} = 0.\overline{6}$

Convert each decimal to a fraction.

$0.7 = \frac{7}{10}$ $0.4 = \frac{2}{5}$

$0.2 = \frac{1}{5}$ $0.8\overline{3} = \frac{5}{6}$

Memorize these fraction-decimal equivalents.

$\frac{1}{2} = 0.5$ $\frac{1}{5} = 0.2$ $\frac{5}{6} = 0.8\overline{3}$ $\frac{1}{10} = 0.1$

$\frac{1}{3} = 0.\overline{3}$ $\frac{2}{5} = 0.4$ $\frac{1}{8} = 0.125$ $\frac{3}{10} = 0.3$

$\frac{2}{3} = 0.\overline{6}$ $\frac{3}{5} = 0.6$ $\frac{3}{8} = 0.375$ $\frac{7}{10} = 0.7$

$\frac{1}{4} = 0.25$ $\frac{4}{5} = 0.8$ $\frac{5}{8} = 0.625$ $\frac{9}{10} = 0.9$

$\frac{3}{4} = 0.75$ $\frac{1}{6} = 0.1\overline{6}$ $\frac{7}{8} = 0.875$

Activities

② Write the following fractions as decimals.

$\frac{1}{2} = 0.5$ $\frac{1}{5} = 0.2$ $\frac{2}{3} = 0.\overline{6}$ $\frac{3}{5} = 0.6$ $\frac{5}{8} = 0.625$

$\frac{1}{3} = 0.\overline{3}$ $\frac{1}{6} = 0.1\overline{6}$ $\frac{2}{5} = 0.4$ $\frac{3}{8} = 0.375$ $\frac{7}{8} = 0.875$

$\frac{1}{4} = 0.25$ $\frac{1}{8} = 0.125$ $\frac{3}{4} = 0.75$ $\frac{5}{6} = 0.8\overline{3}$

③ Write the following decimals as fractions.

$0.5 = \frac{1}{2}$ $0.1\overline{6} = \frac{1}{6}$ $0.75 = \frac{3}{4}$ $0.625 = \frac{5}{8}$

$0.\overline{3} = \frac{1}{3}$ $0.125 = \frac{1}{8}$ $0.6 = \frac{3}{5}$ $0.875 = \frac{7}{8}$

$0.25 = \frac{1}{4}$ $0.\overline{6} = \frac{2}{3}$ $0.375 = \frac{3}{8}$ $0.7 = \frac{7}{10}$

$0.2 = \frac{1}{5}$ $0.4 = \frac{2}{5}$ $0.8\overline{3} = \frac{5}{6}$ $0.9 = \frac{9}{10}$

④ Solve the absolute values.

$|-25| + |-61| = 25 + 61 = 86$ $-|58| - |-46| = -58 - 46 = -104$

$|-34| + |58| = 34 + 58 = 92$ $|33 + 45| + |18 - 7| = 78 + 11 = 89$

$|93| - |-65| = 93 - 65 = 28$ $-|74 - 46| + |26 - 33| = -28 + 7 = -21$

$-|26| + |-9| = -26 + 9 = -17$ $-|54 + 21| - |44 - 32| = -75 - 12 = -87$

⑤ Use the divisibility tests to identify each number as prime or composite.

237	Composite (3)	243	Composite (3, 9)
239	Prime	245	Composite (5)
241	Prime	249	Composite (3)

⑥ Simplify.

$2.48 \times 10^0 = 2.48$ $0.075 \times 10^0 = 0.075$ $5.7 \div 10^0 = 5.7$

$17.95 \times 10^{-1} = 1.795$ $19.48 \times 10^1 = 194.8$ $88.29 \div 10^1 = 8.829$

$0.1983 \times 10^{-2} = 0.001983$ $7.31 \div 10^2 = 0.0731$ $43.57 \div 10^2 = 0.4357$

$2.6 \times 10^{-3} = 0.0026$ $938.174 \div 10^3 = 0.938174$ $0.062 \div 10^3 = 0.000062$

⑦ Solve.

The bottle of vanilla Diann uses in her baking contains 0.473 liters. If her cookie recipe calls for 1 teaspoon of vanilla (1 teaspoon = 5 milliliters), how many batches of cookies can Diann make with one bottle of vanilla?   **94 batches**

0.473 liters = 473 milliliters

$473 \div 5 = 94.6$ Diann can make 94 batches of cookies with one bottle of vanilla.

After making as many batches as possible, how many milliliters of vanilla will Diann have left?   **3 milliliters** $5 \times 94 = 470$ Diann will have 3 milliliters left.

① Convert the fractions to decimals.

$\frac{3}{20} = 3 \div 20 = 0.15$ $\frac{5}{16} = 5 \div 16 = 0.3125$

$\frac{7}{50} = 7 \div 50 = 0.14$ $\frac{7}{9} = 7 \div 9 = 0.\overline{7}$

$\frac{9}{25} = 9 \div 25 = 0.36$ $\frac{13}{20} = 13 \div 20 = 0.65$

$\frac{4}{15} = 4 \div 15 = 0.2\overline{6}$ $\frac{37}{50} = 37 \div 50 = 0.74$

$\frac{1}{9} = 1 \div 9 = 0.\overline{1}$ $\frac{11}{30} = 11 \div 30 = 0.3\overline{6}$

$\frac{9}{40} = 9 \div 40 = 0.225$ $\frac{19}{40} = 19 \div 40 = 0.475$

② Convert the decimals to fractions. Reduce all fractions to lowest terms.

$0.18 = \frac{18}{100} = \frac{9}{50}$ $0.018 = \frac{18}{1000} = \frac{9}{500}$

$0.36 = \frac{36}{100} = \frac{9}{25}$ $0.036 = \frac{36}{1000} = \frac{9}{250}$

$0.49 = \frac{49}{100}$ $0.049 = \frac{49}{1000}$

$0.66 = \frac{66}{100} = \frac{33}{50}$ $0.066 = \frac{66}{1000} = \frac{33}{500}$

$0.24 = \frac{24}{100} = \frac{6}{25}$ $0.024 = \frac{24}{1000} = \frac{3}{125}$

$0.55 = \frac{55}{100} = \frac{11}{20}$ $0.055 = \frac{55}{1000} = \frac{11}{200}$

Teaching Tips, Cont.

➢ Drill the fraction-decimal equivalents using flash cards. Students should say the value on the front of the card, followed by "equals" and the equivalent value on the back of the card. If time allows, drill all values fraction-to-decimal as well as decimal-to-fraction.

➢ Teach the procedure for converting fractions to decimals by division.

➢ Teach the procedure for converting decimals to fractions. Emphasize the importance of reducing all fractions to simplest form.

➢ Complete the Classwork exercises. Have some students work the problems on the board for the class and explain their answers. All students should work the problems in their books.

➢ Worksheet 17 is strongly encouraged for this lesson. It contains fraction-decimal conversions that are not on the memorized list and must be converted mathematically.

Assignments
- Complete Lesson 33, Activities 2-7.
- Worksheet 17

Lesson 34

Concepts
- Adding fractions
- Greatest common factor
- Metric system conversion
- Multiplying by powers of 10
- Dividing by powers of 10
- Least common multiple
- Absolute value
- Math in the real world

Learning Objectives
The student will be able to:
- Add fractions with a common denominator
- Calculate the lowest common denominator of two fractions
- Add fractions with different denominators
- Reduce fractions to simplest form

Materials Needed
- Student Book, Lesson 34
- Fraction-decimal flashcards

Teaching Tips
➢ Drill the fraction-decimal equivalents using flashcards. Follow the same procedure from Lesson 33.

➢ Write the following problem on the board: $2x + 3x =$
Ask the students if the problem can be simplified. (Yes. $5x$)

➢ Write the following problem on the board: $2x + 3y =$
Ask the students if the problem can be simplified. (No.) Why not? (The terms are not alike.)

Adding Fractions

When adding fractions, follow these steps:
1. Make sure the fractions have the same denominator. If the denominators are not equal, find the lowest common multiple (also called the **lowest common denominator**) and rewrite each fraction as an equivalent fraction having the lowest common denominator.
2. Add the numerators of the new fractions. Write this number as the numerator of the answer.
3. The lowest common denominator is the denominator of the answer. DO NOT add the denominators!
4. Check the answer to see if it can be reduced. Divide the numerator and the denominator of the answer by their greatest common factor.

$$\frac{1}{2} + \frac{1}{3} = ? \quad \text{The LCD is 6. Therefore,}$$

$$\frac{1 \times 3}{2 \times 3} + \frac{1 \times 2}{3 \times 2} = \frac{3}{6} + \frac{2}{6} = \frac{3+2}{6} = \frac{5}{6}$$

① **Classwork**
Add. Reduce.

$$\frac{1}{5} + \frac{3}{5} = \frac{1+3}{5} = \frac{4}{5}$$

$$\frac{1}{8} + \frac{3}{8} = \frac{1+3}{8} = \frac{4}{8} = \frac{4 \div 4}{8 \div 4} = \frac{1}{2}$$

$$\frac{1}{3} + \frac{1}{6} = \frac{1 \times 2}{3 \times 2} + \frac{1}{6} = \frac{2}{6} + \frac{1}{6} = \frac{2+1}{6} = \frac{3 \div 3}{6 \div 3} = \frac{1}{2}$$

$$\frac{2}{3} + \frac{1}{4} = \frac{2 \times 4}{3 \times 4} + \frac{1 \times 3}{4 \times 3} = \frac{8}{12} + \frac{3}{12} = \frac{8+3}{12} = \frac{11}{12}$$

$$\frac{3}{10} + \frac{1}{2} = \frac{3}{10} + \frac{1 \times 5}{2 \times 5} = \frac{3}{10} + \frac{5}{10} = \frac{8 \div 2}{10 \div 2} = \frac{4}{5}$$

$$\frac{2}{3} + \frac{3}{10} = \frac{2 \times 10}{3 \times 10} + \frac{3 \times 3}{10 \times 3} = \frac{20}{30} + \frac{9}{30} = \frac{29}{30}$$

Activities
② Add the following fractions. Reduce.

$$\frac{1}{3} + \frac{1}{3} = \frac{1+1}{3} = \frac{2}{3}$$

$$\frac{1}{5} + \frac{2}{5} = \frac{1+2}{5} = \frac{3}{5}$$

$$\frac{4}{7} + \frac{2}{7} = \frac{4+2}{7} = \frac{6}{7}$$

$$\frac{1}{6} + \frac{1}{6} = \frac{1+1}{6} = \frac{2}{6} = \frac{2 \div 2}{6 \div 2} = \frac{1}{3}$$

$$\frac{3}{10} + \frac{1}{10} = \frac{3+1}{10} = \frac{4}{10} = \frac{4 \div 2}{10 \div 2} = \frac{2}{5}$$

$$\frac{1}{2} + \frac{1}{4} = \frac{1 \times 2}{2 \times 2} + \frac{1}{4} = \frac{2}{4} + \frac{1}{4} = \frac{3}{4}$$

$$\frac{2}{3} + \frac{1}{6} = \frac{2 \times 2}{3 \times 2} + \frac{1}{6} = \frac{4}{6} + \frac{1}{6} = \frac{5}{6}$$

$$\frac{1}{2} + \frac{1}{10} = \frac{1 \times 5}{2 \times 5} + \frac{1}{10} = \frac{5}{10} + \frac{1}{10} = \frac{5+1}{10} = \frac{6 \div 2}{10} = \frac{3}{5}$$

$$\frac{1}{3} + \frac{1}{5} = \frac{1 \times 5}{3 \times 5} + \frac{1 \times 3}{5 \times 3} = \frac{5}{15} + \frac{3}{15} = \frac{5+3}{15} = \frac{8}{15}$$

$$\frac{4}{5} + \frac{1}{10} = \frac{4 \times 2}{5 \times 2} + \frac{1}{10} = \frac{8}{10} + \frac{1}{10} = \frac{8+1}{10} = \frac{9}{10}$$

$$\frac{3}{4} + \frac{1}{6} = \frac{3 \times 3}{4 \times 3} + \frac{1 \times 2}{6 \times 2} = \frac{9}{12} + \frac{2}{12} = \frac{9+2}{12} = \frac{11}{12}$$

$$\frac{3}{10} + \frac{3}{5} = \frac{3}{10} + \frac{3 \times 2}{5 \times 2} = \frac{3}{10} + \frac{6}{10} = \frac{3+6}{10} = \frac{9}{10}$$

Horizons Pre-Algebra, Teacher's Guide   110

③ Find the greatest common factor of each set of numbers.

12, 15, and 18	9, 12, and 24	10, 18, and 30
$12 = 2 \times 2 \times ③$	$9 = ③ \times 3$	$10 = ② \times 5$
$15 = ③ \times 5$	$12 = 2 \times 2 \times ③$	$18 = ② \times 3 \times 3$
$18 = 2 \times ③ \times 3$	$24 = 2 \times 2 \times 2 \times ③$	$30 = ② \times 3 \times 5$
GCF is 3	GCF is 3	GCF is 2

④ Multiply or divide by powers of 10 to convert the metric measurements.

13 g = ____1300____ cg   4000 cg = ____40_____ g

0.6 m = _____600___ mm   1576 mL = ____1.576__ L

5.9 L = ___590____ cL   352 cm = ___3.52___ m

49.74 W = ___49,740__ mW   26.8 mW = ___0.0268___ W

⑤ Find the least common multiple of each set of numbers.

3, 4, and 5	6, 8, and 9	9, 12, and 15
$3 = 1 \times \boxed{3}$	$6 = 2 \times 3$	$9 = 3 \times 3 = \boxed{3^2}$
$4 = 2 \times 2 = \boxed{2^2}$	$8 = 2 \times 2 \times 2 = \boxed{2^3}$	$12 = 2 \times 2 \times 3 = \boxed{2^2} \times 3$
$5 = 1 \times \boxed{5}$	$9 = 3 \times 3 = \boxed{3^2}$	$15 = 3 \times \boxed{5}$
LCM: $2^2 \times 3 \times 5 = 60$	LCM: $2^3 \times 3^2 = 8 \times 9 = 72$	LCM: $2^2 \times 3^2 \times 5 = 180$

⑥ Simplify the absolute values.

$|85| - |-29| = 85 - 29 = 56$ $|21 + 35| + |42 - 9| = 56 + 33 = 89$

$-|38| + |-17| = -38 + 17 = -21$ $-|71 - 38| + |36 - 19| = -33 + 17 = -16$

$-|77| - |-55| = -77 - 55 = -132$ $-|97 + 22| - |61 - 23| = -119 - 38 = -157$

⑦ Solve.
Diann is baking a recipe that calls for ½ cup of butter for one part of the recipe, and ¼ cup of butter for another part of the recipe. How much butter does Diann need to make the entire recipe?

$\dfrac{1}{2} + \dfrac{1}{4} = \dfrac{1 \times 2}{2 \times 2} + \dfrac{1}{4} = \dfrac{2}{4} + \dfrac{1}{4} = \dfrac{2+1}{4} = \dfrac{3}{4}$ cups of butter.

If ¼ cup of butter is equal to 4 tablespoons of butter, how many tablespoons of butter does Diann need to make the recipe?
3×4 tablespoons = 12 tablespoons

Teaching Tips, Cont.

➢ Explain that adding fractions follows a similar rule. The denominators must be alike before fractions can be added. Just like the coefficients are added and the variable stays the same in the example above, the numerators are added and the denominators stay the same when adding fractions.

➢ Teach the procedure for adding fractions from the teaching box.

➢ Review least common multiple as necessary. (See Lesson 17)

➢ Remind students to reduce all fractions in their answers to simplest form.

➢ Complete the Classwork exercises. Have some students work the problems on the board for the class and explain their answers. All students should work the problems in their books.

Assignment
- Complete Lesson 34, Activities 2-7.

Lesson 35

Concepts
- Subtracting fractions
- Divisibility tests
- Prime/composite numbers
- Roots
- Fraction-decimal equivalents
- Math in the real world

Learning Objectives
The student will be able to:
- Subtract fractions with a common denominator
- Calculate the lowest common denominator of two fractions
- Subtract fractions with different denominators
- Reduce fractions to simplest form

Materials Needed
- Student Book, Lesson 35
- Worksheet 18
- Fraction-decimal flashcards

Teaching Tips
➢ Have students complete Worksheet 18 in class. This may be for added practice of earlier topics, or graded as a quiz, if desired.

➢ Drill the fraction-decimal equivalents using flashcards. Follow the same procedure from Lesson 33.

➢ Review adding fractions. (See Lesson 34)

➢ Explain that the same rules apply to subtracting fractions.

Subtracting Fractions

When subtracting fractions, follow these steps:
1. Make sure the fractions have the same denominator. If the denominators are not equal, find the lowest common multiple (also called the **lowest common denominator**) and rewrite each fraction as an equivalent fraction having the lowest common denominator.
2. Subtract the numerators of the new fractions. Write this number as the numerator of the answer.
3. The lowest common denominator is the denominator of the answer. DO NOT subtract the denominators!
4. Check the answer to see if it can be reduced. Divide the numerator and the denominator of the answer by their greatest common factor.

$\frac{1}{2} - \frac{1}{3} = ?$ The LCD is 6. Therefore,

$\frac{1 \times 3}{2 \times 3} - \frac{1 \times 2}{3 \times 2} = \frac{3}{6} - \frac{2}{6} = \frac{3-2}{6} = \frac{1}{6}$

① Classwork
Subtract.

$\frac{3}{5} - \frac{1}{5} = \frac{3-1}{5} = \frac{2}{5}$

$\frac{3}{8} - \frac{1}{8} = \frac{3-1}{8} = \frac{2}{8} = \frac{2 \div 2}{8 \div 2} = \frac{1}{4}$

$\frac{1}{3} - \frac{1}{6} = \frac{1 \times 2}{3 \times 2} - \frac{1}{6} = \frac{2}{6} - \frac{1}{6} = \frac{2-1}{6} = \frac{1}{6}$

$\frac{2}{3} - \frac{1}{4} = \frac{2 \times 4}{3 \times 4} - \frac{1 \times 3}{4 \times 3} = \frac{8}{12} - \frac{3}{12} = \frac{8-3}{12} = \frac{5}{12}$

$\frac{1}{2} - \frac{3}{10} = \frac{1 \times 5}{2 \times 5} - \frac{3}{10} = \frac{5}{10} - \frac{3}{10} = \frac{5-3}{10} = \frac{2}{10} = \frac{2 \div 2}{10 \div 2} = \frac{1}{5}$

$\frac{2}{3} - \frac{3}{10} = \frac{2 \times 10}{3 \times 10} - \frac{3 \times 3}{10 \times 3} = \frac{20}{30} - \frac{9}{30} = \frac{20-9}{30} = \frac{11}{30}$

Activities
② Subtract the following fractions.

$\frac{2}{3} - \frac{1}{3} = \frac{2-1}{3} = \frac{1}{3}$

$\frac{4}{5} - \frac{2}{5} = \frac{4-2}{5} = \frac{2}{5}$

$\frac{6}{7} - \frac{4}{7} = \frac{6-4}{7} = \frac{2}{7}$

$\frac{5}{6} - \frac{1}{6} = \frac{5-1}{6} = \frac{4}{6} = \frac{4 \div 2}{6 \div 2} = \frac{2}{3}$

$\frac{3}{10} - \frac{1}{10} = \frac{3-1}{10} = \frac{2}{10} = \frac{2 \div 2}{10 \div 2} = \frac{1}{5}$

$\frac{1}{2} - \frac{1}{4} = \frac{1 \times 2}{2 \times 2} - \frac{1}{4} = \frac{2}{4} - \frac{1}{4} = \frac{2-1}{4} = \frac{1}{4}$

$\frac{2}{3} - \frac{1}{6} = \frac{2 \times 2}{3 \times 2} - \frac{1}{6} = \frac{4}{6} - \frac{1}{6} = \frac{4-1}{6} = \frac{3}{6} = \frac{3 \div 3}{6 \div 3} = \frac{1}{2}$

$\frac{1}{2} - \frac{1}{10} = \frac{1 \times 5}{2 \times 5} - \frac{1}{10} = \frac{5}{10} - \frac{1}{10} = \frac{5-1}{10} = \frac{4}{10} = \frac{4 \div 2}{10 \div 2} = \frac{2}{5}$

$\frac{1}{3} - \frac{1}{5} = \frac{1 \times 5}{3 \times 5} - \frac{1 \times 3}{5 \times 3} = \frac{5}{15} - \frac{3}{15} = \frac{5-3}{15} = \frac{2}{15}$

$\frac{4}{5} - \frac{1}{10} = \frac{4 \times 2}{5 \times 2} - \frac{1}{10} = \frac{8}{10} - \frac{1}{10} = \frac{8-1}{10} = \frac{7}{10}$

$\frac{3}{4} - \frac{1}{6} = \frac{3 \times 3}{4 \times 3} - \frac{1 \times 2}{6 \times 2} = \frac{9}{12} - \frac{2}{12} = \frac{9-2}{12} = \frac{7}{12}$

$\frac{3}{5} - \frac{3}{10} = \frac{3 \times 2}{5 \times 2} - \frac{3}{10} = \frac{6}{10} - \frac{3}{10} = \frac{6-3}{10} = \frac{3}{10}$

③ Use the divisibility tests to identify each number as prime or composite.

251	Prime	261	Composite (3, 9)
255	Composite (3, 5)	263	Prime
257	Prime	265	Composite (5)

④ Simplify the roots.

$\sqrt{63} = \sqrt{9 \times 7} = 3\sqrt{7}$

$\sqrt{63} + \sqrt{7} = 3\sqrt{7} + \sqrt{7} = 4\sqrt{7}$

$\left(\sqrt{63}\right)\left(\sqrt{7}\right) = \left(3\sqrt{7}\right)\left(\sqrt{7}\right) = 3(7) = 21$

$\left(\sqrt{63}\right) \div \left(\sqrt{7}\right) = 3\sqrt{7} \div \sqrt{7} = 3$

$\sqrt{2} + \sqrt{72} = \sqrt{2} + \sqrt{36 \times 2} = \sqrt{2} + 6\sqrt{2} = 7\sqrt{2}$

$\left(\sqrt{2}\right)\left(\sqrt{72}\right) = \left(\sqrt{2}\right)\left(6\sqrt{2}\right) = 2(6) = 12$

$\left(\sqrt{72}\right) \div \left(\sqrt{2}\right) = 6\sqrt{2} \div \sqrt{2} = 6$

$\sqrt[3]{40} + 4\sqrt[3]{5} = \sqrt[3]{8 \times 5} + 4\sqrt[3]{5} = 2\sqrt[3]{5} + 4\sqrt[3]{5} = 6\sqrt[3]{5}$

$\left(\sqrt[3]{40}\right) \div \left(\sqrt[3]{5}\right) = 2\sqrt[3]{5} \div \sqrt[3]{5} = 2$

$\left(3\sqrt[3]{4}\right)\left(4\sqrt[3]{4}\right) =$
$\left(3\sqrt[3]{2 \times 2}\right)\left(4\sqrt[3]{2 \times 2}\right) = (3)(4)\left(\sqrt[3]{2 \times 2 \times 2}\right) = (3)(4)(2) = 24$

⑤ Complete the chart to show proper fraction-decimal equivalents.

Fraction	Decimal		Fraction	Decimal
$\frac{1}{4}$	0.25		$\frac{2}{3}$	$0.\overline{6}$
$\frac{3}{5}$	0.6		$\frac{3}{4}$	0.75
$\frac{5}{6}$	$0.8\overline{3}$		$\frac{1}{6}$	$0.1\overline{6}$
$\frac{7}{8}$	0.875		$\frac{5}{8}$	0.625
$\frac{9}{10}$	0.9		$\frac{7}{10}$	0.7

⑥ Solve.
Diann bought a remnant of fabric that is 0.875 yards long. She is sewing an apron that takes ⅔ of a yard. How much fabric will Diann have left over after she sews the apron? (Express your answer as a fraction.)

$0.875 = \frac{7}{8}$

$\frac{7}{8} - \frac{2}{3} = \frac{7 \times 3}{8 \times 3} - \frac{2 \times 8}{3 \times 8} = \frac{21}{24} - \frac{16}{24} = \frac{5}{24}$

Diann uses fabric scraps to make quilt squares. If she needs ⅕ of a yard to make quilt squares, will she have enough left over from the apron to make any quilt squares? **Yes.**
Find the least common denominator and make equivalent fractions to compare.

$\frac{1}{5} = \frac{1 \times 24}{5 \times 24} = \frac{24}{120}$ $\frac{5}{24} = \frac{5 \times 5}{24 \times 5} = \frac{25}{120}$

Metric Conversions

① Multiply or divide the appropriate powers of 10 to complete the metric conversions.

54 kg = ___54,000__ g

0.13 km = ___130___ m

5.8 kL = ___5,800___ L

32.49 kW = ___32,490__ W

17,000 g = ____17____ kg

4971 L = ___4.971___ kL

394 m = ___0.394___ km

45.7 W = ___0.0457___ kW

2 kg = ___2,000___ g

0.5 km = ___500_____ m

0.8 kL = ___800___ L

72.18 kW = ___72,180__ W

6481 g = ____6.481_ kg

9157 L = ___9.157___ kL

329 m = ___0.329___ km

17.4 W = ___0.0174___ kW

0.8 kg = ___800___ g

0.17 km = ___170_____ m

13.8 kL = ___13,800___ L

62.4 kW = ___62,400__ W

9080 g = _____9.08___ kg

716.8 L = ___0.7168__ kL

319 m = ___0.319___ km

43 g = __4300_____ cg

0.87 m = ____870___ mm

3.7 L = ____370___ cL

54.91 W = ___54,910__ mW

3000 cg = ____30_____ g

1943 mL = ___1.943__ L

325 cm = _____3.25__ m

39.5 mW = ___0.0395_ W

10 g = ____1000____ cg

0.4 m = ____400___ mm

1.2 L = ____120___ cL

2.49 W = ___2490___ mW

5614 cg = ___56.14__ g

914 mL = ___0.914__ L

83 cm = ____0.83__ m

95.43 mW = __0.09543_ W

1 g = ____100___ cg

1 m = ____1000__ mm

6.7 L = ____670___ cL

1.817 W = __1817___ mW

43 cg = ___0.43___ g

90,483 mL = __90.483__ L

5 cm = ___0.05___ m

Teaching Tips, Cont.

➢ Teach the procedure for subtracting fractions from the teaching box. Review least common multiple as necessary. (See Lesson 17)

➢ Complete the Classwork exercises. Have some students work the problems on the board for the class. All students should work the problems in their books.

Assignment

• Complete Lesson 35, Activities 2-6

Lesson 36

Concepts
- Multiplying fractions
- Fraction-decimal equivalents
- Multiplying by powers of 10
- Dividing by powers of 10
- Metric system conversion
- Math in the real world

Learning Objectives
The student will be able to:
- Multiply two fractions
- Multiply a whole number by a fraction
- Simplify fractions before multiplying

Materials Needed
- Student Book, Lesson 36
- Fraction-decimal flashcards

Teaching Tips
➤ Drill the fraction-decimal equivalents using flashcards. Follow the same procedure from Lesson 33. These will appear on a quiz in Lesson 38.

➤ Review the rules of adding and subtracting fractions:
- The denominators must be equal
- Add or subtract the numerators and keep the same denominator

➤ Write the following problem on the board: $4(x+2) =$

Ask students to simplify and all on a student to explain the answer. $(4x + 8)$

➤ Point out that both the variable and the constant were multiplied by the value outside the parentheses.

Multiplying Fractions

When multiplying fractions, follow these steps:
1. Multiply the numerators to get the numerator of the answer.
2. Multiply the denominators to get the denominator of the answer.
3. Reduce the fraction in the answer by dividing both the numerator and the denominator by the greatest common factor.

Note: You may find it easier to multiply if you reduce the individual fractions before multiplying. You will still need to check the answer to see if it needs to be reduced.

$\frac{2}{3} \times \frac{3}{4} = ?$ Neither fraction can be reduced, so

$\frac{2 \times 3}{3 \times 4} = \frac{6}{12}$ The greatest common factor is 6.

$\frac{6 \div 6}{12 \div 6} = \frac{1}{2}$

When multiplying a whole number by a fraction, multiply the whole number by the numerator to get the new numerator, and keep the denominator the same. This is because a whole number has a denominator of 1, which will not change the value of the fraction denominator when multiplied.

$3\left(\frac{1}{4}\right) = \left(\frac{3}{1}\right)\left(\frac{1}{4}\right) = \frac{3}{4}$ or $3\left(\frac{1}{4}\right) = \frac{3 \times 1}{4} = \frac{3}{4}$

① **Classwork**

Multiply.

$\frac{1}{3} \times \frac{1}{6} = \frac{1 \times 1}{3 \times 6} = \frac{1}{18}$

$\frac{3}{5} \times \frac{5}{8} = \frac{3 \times 5}{5 \times 8} = \frac{15}{40} = \frac{15 \div 5}{40 \div 5} = \frac{3}{8}$

$\frac{3}{8} \times \frac{4}{5} = \frac{3 \times 4}{8 \times 5} = \frac{12}{40} = \frac{12 \div 4}{40 \div 4} = \frac{3}{10}$

$\frac{2}{3} \times \frac{1}{4} = \frac{2 \times 1}{3 \times 4} = \frac{2}{12} = \frac{2 \div 2}{12 \div 2} = \frac{1}{6}$

$\frac{1}{2} \times \frac{4}{5} = \frac{1 \times \overset{2}{\cancel{4}}}{\underset{1}{\cancel{2}} \times 5} = \frac{2}{5}$

$\frac{2}{3} \times \frac{3}{10} = \frac{\overset{1}{\cancel{2}} \times \overset{1}{\cancel{3}}}{\underset{1}{\cancel{3}} \times \underset{5}{\cancel{10}}} = \frac{1}{5}$

$5 \times \frac{2}{5} = \frac{\overset{1}{\cancel{5}} \times 2}{\underset{1}{\cancel{5}}} = 2$

$3 \times \frac{5}{8} = \frac{3 \times 5}{8} = \frac{15}{8}$

Activities

② Multiply the following fractions.

$\frac{2}{3} \times \frac{1}{3} = \frac{2 \times 1}{3 \times 3} = \frac{2}{9}$

$\frac{4}{5} \times \frac{1}{8} = \frac{4 \times 1}{5 \times 8} = \frac{4}{40} = \frac{4 \div 4}{40 \div 4} = \frac{1}{10}$

$\frac{6}{7} \times \frac{2}{3} = \frac{\overset{2}{\cancel{6}} \times 2}{7 \times \underset{1}{\cancel{3}}} = \frac{2 \times 2}{7 \times 1} = \frac{4}{7}$

$\frac{5}{6} \times \frac{1}{2} = \frac{5 \times 1}{6 \times 2} = \frac{5}{12}$

$\frac{7}{8} \times \frac{1}{10} = \frac{7 \times 1}{8 \times 10} = \frac{7}{80}$

$\frac{1}{2} \times \frac{2}{5} = \frac{1 \times \overset{1}{\cancel{2}}}{\underset{1}{\cancel{2}} \times 5} = \frac{1}{5}$

$4 \times \frac{1}{6} = \frac{\overset{2}{\cancel{4}} \times 1}{\underset{3}{\cancel{6}}} = \frac{2}{3}$

$5 \times \frac{1}{6} = \frac{5 \times 1}{6} = \frac{5}{6}$

③ Complete the chart to show proper fraction-decimal equivalents.

Fraction	Decimal		Fraction	Decimal
$\frac{2}{3}$	$0.\overline{6}$		$\frac{1}{4}$	0.25
$\frac{3}{4}$	0.75		$\frac{3}{5}$	0.6
$\frac{1}{6}$	$0.1\overline{6}$		$\frac{5}{6}$	$0.8\overline{3}$
$\frac{5}{8}$	0.625		$\frac{7}{8}$	0.875
$\frac{7}{10}$	0.7		$\frac{9}{10}$	0.9

④ Multiply or divide by powers of 10 to convert the metric measurements.

24.8 g = _____2480_____ cg   9000 cg = _____90_____ g

0.7 L = _____700_____ mL   8267 mm = _____8.267___ m

21.4 m = _____2140___ cm   519 cL = ____5.19___ L

76.48 W = _____76,480___ mW   521.49 mW = ___0.52149___ W

⑤ Write an equation and solve.
Diann's cake recipe calls for 2 eggs, $\frac{1}{4}$ cup of oil, and $\frac{1}{3}$ cup of water. If each egg is equal to $\frac{1}{4}$ cup, what is the total volume of the eggs, oil, and water?

$$2\left(\frac{1}{4}\right) + \frac{1}{4} + \frac{1}{3} = \frac{2}{4} + \frac{1}{4} + \frac{1}{3} = \frac{3}{4} + \frac{1}{3} = \frac{3 \times 3}{4 \times 3} + \frac{1 \times 4}{3 \times 4} = \frac{9}{12} + \frac{4}{12} = \frac{13}{12} \text{ cups}$$

Students may write the answer as $1\frac{1}{12}$ cups.

Diann is making a triple batch of the cake recipe for her church. Will a 4-cup mixing bowl be large enough to mix the liquid ingredients?   **Yes.**

$$3\left(\frac{13}{12}\right) = \frac{\overset{1}{\cancel{3}} \times 13}{\underset{4}{\cancel{12}}} = \frac{13}{4} \text{ cups.}$$

A 4-cup mixing bowl will hold $4\left(\frac{4}{4}\right) = \frac{16}{4}$ cups.

Teaching Tips, Cont.

➢ Explain that unlike addition and subtraction, where the denominators must be equal, multiplication works with any numerator and any denominator. Just like multiplication with algebra, there is no need for like terms.

➢ Demonstrate the procedure for multiplying fractions using the problem in the teaching box. Show the students how to cancel terms prior to multiplying as follows:

$$\frac{\overset{1}{\cancel{2}}}{\underset{1}{\cancel{3}}} \times \frac{\overset{1}{\cancel{3}}}{\underset{2}{\cancel{4}}} = \frac{1 \times 1}{1 \times 2} = \frac{1}{2}$$

➢ Complete the Classwork exercises. Have some students work the problems on the board for the class. All students should work the problems in their books.

Assignment

- Complete Lesson 36, Activities 2-5.

Lesson 37

Concepts
- Dividing fractions
- Roots
- Divisibility tests
- Factors
- Multiplying by powers of 10
- Dividing by powers of 10
- Metric system conversion
- Math in the real world

Learning Objectives
The student will be able to:
- Divide two fractions
- Reduce fractions after inverting the divisor
- Define *reciprocal*

Materials Needed
- Student Book, Lesson 37
- Fraction-decimal flashcards

Teaching Tips
➢ Drill the fraction-decimal equivalents using flashcards. Follow the same procedure from Lesson 33. These will appear on a quiz in Lesson 38.

➢ Review the procedure for multiplying fractions. (See Lesson 36)

➢ Write 12 ÷ 3 = x on the board. Explain that this problem is really asking, "What times 3 equals 12?" Ask students how to express "What times 3 equals 12?" algebraically. (3x = 12)

➢ Show students that dividing both sides by 3 is the same as multiplying by $\frac{1}{3}$.

$$\frac{1}{3}(3x) = 12\left(\frac{1}{3}\right)$$
$$x = 4$$

Dividing Fractions

When dividing fractions, follow these steps:
1. Take the **reciprocal** of the divisor (the second fraction). This means you must invert the second fraction so the numerator is now the denominator and the denominator is now the numerator.
2. Multiply the first fraction by the reciprocal of the second fraction.
3. Reduce the fraction in the answer by dividing both the numerator and the denominator by the greatest common factor.

Note: You may find it easier if you reduce the individual fractions before multiplying. You will still need to check the answer to see if it needs to be reduced.

$\frac{1}{6} \div \frac{1}{2} = ?$ Neither fraction can be reduced, so take the reciprocal of the second fraction and multiply: $\frac{1}{6} \times \frac{2}{1} = \frac{1 \times 2}{6 \times 1} = \frac{2}{6}$

The greatest common factor is 2.

$\frac{2 \div 2}{6 \div 2} = \frac{1}{3}$

① Classwork
Divide. Leave answers as improper fractions.

$\frac{1}{3} \div \frac{1}{6} = \frac{1}{\cancel{3}_1} \times \frac{\cancel{6}^2}{1} = \frac{2}{1} = 2$

$\frac{3}{5} \div \frac{1}{3} = \frac{3}{5} \times \frac{3}{1} = \frac{3 \times 3}{5 \times 1} = \frac{9}{5}$

$\frac{3}{8} \div \frac{1}{4} = \frac{3}{\cancel{8}_2} \times \frac{\cancel{4}^1}{1} = \frac{3}{2}$

$\frac{2}{3} \div \frac{1}{4} = \frac{2}{3} \times \frac{4}{1} = \frac{2 \times 4}{3 \times 1} = \frac{8}{3}$

$\frac{1}{2} \div \frac{4}{5} = \frac{1}{2} \times \frac{5}{4} = \frac{1 \times 5}{2 \times 4} = \frac{5}{8}$

$\frac{2}{3} \div \frac{4}{5} = \frac{2}{3} \times \frac{5}{\cancel{4}_2} = \frac{1 \times 5}{3 \times 2} = \frac{5}{6}$

$\frac{3}{5} \div \frac{2}{5} = \frac{3}{\cancel{5}_1} \times \frac{\cancel{5}^1}{2} = \frac{3}{2}$

Activities
② Divide the following fractions. Leave answers as improper fractions.

$\frac{2}{3} \div \frac{1}{3} = \frac{2}{\cancel{3}_1} \times \frac{\cancel{3}^1}{1} = \frac{2}{1} = 2$

$\frac{4}{5} \div \frac{1}{5} = \frac{4}{\cancel{5}_1} \times \frac{\cancel{5}^1}{1} = \frac{4}{1} = 4$

$\frac{6}{7} \div \frac{2}{3} = \frac{\cancel{6}^3}{7} \times \frac{3}{\cancel{2}_1} = \frac{3 \times 3}{7 \times 1} = \frac{9}{7}$

$\frac{5}{6} \div \frac{5}{2} = \frac{5}{\cancel{6}_3} \times \frac{\cancel{2}^1}{5} = \frac{5}{3}$

$\frac{5}{8} \div \frac{1}{10} = \frac{5}{\cancel{8}_4} \times \frac{\cancel{10}^5}{1} = \frac{5 \times 5}{4 \times 1} = \frac{25}{4}$

$\frac{1}{2} \div \frac{2}{5} = \frac{1}{2} \times \frac{5}{2} = \frac{1 \times 5}{2 \times 2} = \frac{5}{4}$

$\frac{4}{5} \div \frac{1}{6} = \frac{4}{5} \times \frac{6}{1} = \frac{4 \times 6}{5 \times 1} = \frac{24}{5}$

$\frac{5}{6} \div \frac{1}{6} = \frac{5}{\cancel{6}_1} \times \frac{\cancel{6}^1}{1} = \frac{5}{1} = 5$

$\frac{5}{6} \div \frac{1}{3} = \frac{5}{\cancel{6}_2} \times \frac{\cancel{3}^1}{1} = \frac{5}{2}$

$\frac{7}{8} \div \frac{1}{10} = \frac{7}{\cancel{8}_4} \times \frac{\cancel{10}^5}{1} = \frac{7 \times 5}{4 \times 1} = \frac{35}{4}$

$\frac{1}{10} \div \frac{2}{5} = \frac{1}{\cancel{10}_2} \times \frac{\cancel{5}^1}{2} = \frac{1 \times 1}{2 \times 2} = \frac{1}{4}$

$\frac{1}{2} \div \frac{3}{10} = \frac{1}{\cancel{2}_1} \times \frac{\cancel{10}^5}{3} = \frac{5}{3}$

---

③ Simplify the following roots.

$\sqrt{75} = \sqrt{5 \times 5 \times 3} = 5\sqrt{3}$

$\sqrt{75} + \sqrt{3} =$

$5\sqrt{3} + \sqrt{3} = (5+1)\sqrt{3} = 6\sqrt{3}$

$(\sqrt{75})(\sqrt{3}) = 5\sqrt{3}(\sqrt{3}) = 5(3) = 15$

$(\sqrt{75}) \div (\sqrt{3}) = 5\sqrt{3} \div \sqrt{3} = 5$

$\sqrt{11} + \sqrt{99} =$

$\sqrt{11} + \sqrt{3 \times 3 \times 11} = \sqrt{11} + 3\sqrt{11} = 4\sqrt{11}$

$(\sqrt{11})(\sqrt{99}) = \sqrt{11}(3\sqrt{11}) = 11(3) = 33$

$(\sqrt{99}) \div (\sqrt{11}) = 3\sqrt{11} \div \sqrt{11} = 3$

$\sqrt[3]{54} + 7\sqrt[3]{2} =$

$\sqrt[3]{3 \times 3 \times 3 \times 2} + 7\sqrt[3]{2} = 3\sqrt[3]{2} + 7\sqrt[3]{2} =$

$(3+7)\sqrt[3]{2} = 10\sqrt[3]{2}$

$(\sqrt[3]{54}) \div (\sqrt[3]{2}) = 3\sqrt[3]{2} \div \sqrt[3]{2} = 3$

$(2\sqrt[4]{25})(5\sqrt[4]{25}) =$

$(2\sqrt[4]{5 \times 5})(5\sqrt[4]{5 \times 5}) = (2 \times 5)(\sqrt[4]{5 \times 5 \times 5 \times 5}) =$

$10(5) = 50$

④ Use the divisibility tests to identify factors of each number.

251   Prime
255   Composite (3, 5)
257   Prime

261   Composite (3, 9)
263   Prime
265   Composite (5)

⑤ Multiply or divide by the proper powers of 10 to convert the metric conversions.

32 m = ___32,000__ mm

1.7 L = ___1700___ mL

28.4 g = ___2840___ cg

163.59 W = _163,590_ mW

2196 cm = __21.96___ m

681 mL = ___0.681___ L

65 cW = ___0.65_____ W

496.4 mg = ___0.4964__ g

⑥ Solve.
Diann has purchased a remnant of fabric that is ¾ of a yard in length. She cuts the fabric into strips that are ¹⁄₁₂ of a yard wide. How many strips of fabric can Diann cut from the remnant of fabric?

$\dfrac{3}{4} \div \dfrac{1}{12} = \dfrac{3}{\cancel{4}_1} \times \dfrac{\cancel{12}^3}{1} = \dfrac{9}{1} = 9$ strips of fabric.

Teaching Tips, Cont.

➢ Teach the definition of reciprocal.

➢ Teach the procedure for dividing fractions from the teaching box. Relate this to the algebra problem you have already worked out.

➢ Complete the Classwork exercises. Have some students work the problems on the board for the class. All students should work the problems in their books.

Assignment

• Complete Lesson 37, Activities 2-6.

Lesson 38

Concepts
- Improper fractions
- Single-variable equations
- Divisibility tests
- Multiples
- Math in the real world

Learning Objectives
The student will be able to:
- Define *improper fraction*
- Add improper fractions
- Subtract improper fractions
- Multiply improper fractions
- Divide improper fractions

Materials Needed
- Student Book, Lesson 38
- Worksheet 19

Teaching Tips
➤ Have students complete Worksheet 19 in class. This is intended as a quiz over the memorized fraction-decimal equivalents.

➤ Draw the first circle diagram from the teaching box on the board. Ask students to express the shaded area as a fraction. $\left(\frac{3}{4}\right)$

➤ Draw the second circle diagram from the teaching box on the board. Ask students to express the shaded area as a fraction. $\left(\frac{4}{4}\right)$

Improper Fractions

An **improper fraction** is a fraction whose numerator is greater than its denominator.

An improper fraction always has a value greater than 1, so any improper fraction is always greater than any proper fraction.

$\frac{3}{4}$ is less than 1.

$\frac{4}{4}$ is exactly 1.

$\frac{5}{4}$ is greater than 1.

Improper fractions can be added, subtracted, multiplied, and divided following the same rules that apply to regular fractions.

① Classwork
Add, subtract, multiply, or divide as indicated. Leave answers as improper fractions.

$\frac{4}{3}+\frac{7}{6}=\frac{4\times2}{3\times2}+\frac{7}{6}=\frac{8}{6}+\frac{7}{6}=\frac{15}{6}=\frac{15\div3}{6\div3}=\frac{5}{2}$

$\frac{5}{3}-\frac{5}{6}=\frac{5\times2}{3\times2}-\frac{5}{6}=\frac{10}{6}-\frac{5}{6}=\frac{5}{6}$

$\frac{11}{8}\times\frac{4}{3}=\frac{11}{2\,\cancel{8}}\times\frac{\cancel{4}^{1}}{3}=\frac{11}{2}\times\frac{1}{3}=\frac{11\times1}{2\times3}=\frac{11}{6}$

$\frac{8}{3}\div\frac{12}{5}=\frac{\cancel{8}^{2}}{3}\times\frac{5}{\cancel{12}_{3}}=\frac{2}{3}\times\frac{5}{3}=\frac{2\times5}{3\times3}=\frac{10}{9}$

Activities
② Add, subtract, multiply, or divide as indicated. Leave answers as improper fractions.

$\frac{4}{3}+\frac{7}{5}=\frac{4\times5}{3\times5}+\frac{7\times3}{5\times3}=\frac{20}{15}+\frac{21}{15}=\frac{41}{15}$

$\frac{6}{5}+\frac{13}{10}=\frac{6\times2}{5\times2}+\frac{13}{10}=\frac{12}{10}+\frac{13}{10}=\frac{25\div5}{10\div5}=\frac{5}{2}$

$\frac{7}{4}+\frac{5}{6}=\frac{7\times3}{4\times3}+\frac{5\times2}{6\times2}=\frac{21}{12}+\frac{10}{12}=\frac{31}{12}$

$\frac{11}{10}+\frac{9}{5}=\frac{11}{10}+\frac{9\times2}{5\times2}=\frac{11}{10}+\frac{18}{10}=\frac{29}{10}$

$\frac{7}{3}-\frac{7}{5}=\frac{7\times5}{3\times5}-\frac{7\times3}{5\times3}=\frac{35}{15}-\frac{21}{15}=\frac{35-21}{15}=\frac{14}{15}$

$\frac{9}{5}-\frac{11}{10}=\frac{9\times2}{5\times2}-\frac{11}{10}=\frac{18}{10}-\frac{11}{10}=\frac{18-11}{10}=\frac{7}{10}$

$\frac{11}{4}-\frac{13}{6}=\frac{11\times3}{4\times3}-\frac{13\times2}{6\times2}=\frac{33}{12}-\frac{26}{12}=\frac{33-26}{12}=\frac{7}{12}$

$\frac{7}{5}-\frac{11}{10}=\frac{7\times2}{5\times2}-\frac{11}{10}=\frac{14}{10}-\frac{11}{10}=\frac{3}{10}$

$\frac{10}{7}\times\frac{7}{3}=\frac{10}{1\,\cancel{7}}\times\frac{\cancel{7}^{1}}{3}=\frac{10}{3}$

$\frac{7}{6}\times\frac{3}{2}=\frac{7}{2\,\cancel{6}}\times\frac{\cancel{3}^{1}}{2}=\frac{7}{2}\times\frac{1}{2}=\frac{7\times1}{2\times2}=\frac{7}{4}$

$\frac{15}{8}\times\frac{11}{10}=\frac{\cancel{15}^{3}}{8}\times\frac{11}{\cancel{10}_{2}}=\frac{3}{8}\times\frac{11}{2}=\frac{3\times11}{8\times2}=\frac{33}{16}$

$\frac{5}{2}\times\frac{7}{5}=\frac{\cancel{5}^{1}}{2}\times\frac{7}{\cancel{5}_{1}}=\frac{7}{2}$

$\frac{11}{6}\div\frac{7}{6}=\frac{11}{1\,\cancel{6}}\times\frac{\cancel{6}^{1}}{7}=\frac{11}{7}$

$\frac{13}{6}\div\frac{5}{3}=\frac{13}{2\,\cancel{6}}\times\frac{\cancel{3}^{1}}{5}=\frac{13\times1}{2\times5}=\frac{13}{10}$

$\frac{9}{8}\div\frac{13}{10}=\frac{9}{4\,\cancel{8}}\times\frac{\cancel{10}^{5}}{13}=\frac{9\times5}{4\times13}=\frac{45}{52}$

$\frac{13}{10}\div\frac{6}{5}=\frac{13}{2\,\cancel{10}}\times\frac{\cancel{5}^{1}}{6}=\frac{13\times1}{2\times6}=\frac{13}{12}$

---

③ Solve.

$3x+28=46$
$\quad 3x=46-28$
$\quad 3x=18$
$\quad x=6$

$5x-11=24-2x$
$\quad 5x+2x=24+11$
$\quad 7x=35$
$\quad x=5$

$14x+1=6x+17$
$\quad 14x-6x=17-1$
$\quad 8x=16$
$\quad x=2$

$3(x-5)=2x+18$
$\quad 3x-15=2x+18$
$\quad 3x-2x=18+15$
$\quad x=33$

$3x+18\div2=x+3$
$\quad 3x+9=x+3$
$\quad 3x-x=3-9$
$\quad 2x=-6$
$\quad x=-3$

$3(x-1)=5(x+3)$
$\quad 3x-3=5x+15$
$\quad 3x-5x=15+3$
$\quad -2x=18$
$\quad x=-9$

④ Use the divisibility tests to identify multiples of each number.

	2	3	4	5	6	9
268	x		x			
270	x	x		x	x	x
272	x		x			
273		x				
274	x					
275				x		

⑤ Solve.
Diann is baking cookies for a church social. If one batch of cookies takes ¾ of a cup of sugar, how many batches of cookies can Diann make from a 4-pound bag of sugar if one 4-pound bag of sugar contains 9 cups of sugar?

$9\div\frac{3}{4}=\frac{9}{1}\div\frac{3}{4}=\frac{\cancel{9}^{3}}{1}\times\frac{4}{\cancel{3}_{1}}=\frac{3\times4}{1}=12$ batches of cookies.

Before Diann made the cookies, she baked 6 pans of brownies that each took ⅔ of a cup of sugar. How much sugar did she use to make 6 pans of brownies?

$6\times\frac{2}{3}=\frac{\cancel{6}^{2}}{1}\times\frac{2}{\cancel{3}_{1}}=\frac{2\times2}{1\times1}=4$ cups of sugar.

How much sugar was left in the 4-pound bag after making 6 pans of brownies?

9 cups – 4 cups = 5 cups

Does Diann have enough sugar left to make 7 batches of cookies?   **No.**

$7\times\frac{3}{4}=\frac{7}{1}\times\frac{3}{4}=\frac{7\times3}{1\times4}=\frac{21}{4}$ cups of sugar in 7 batches.

$5\times\frac{4}{4}=\frac{5}{1}\times\frac{4}{4}=\frac{20}{4}$ cups of sugar left after making the brownies.

① Complete the fraction-decimal equivalents.

$\frac{1}{2} = 0.5$　　　　　　　　$0.1 = \frac{1}{10}$

$\frac{1}{3} = 0.\bar{3}$　　　　　　　　$0.125 = \frac{1}{8}$

$\frac{1}{4} = 0.25$　　　　　　　　$0.1\bar{6} = \frac{1}{6}$

$\frac{1}{5} = 0.2$　　　　　　　　$0.2 = \frac{1}{5}$

$\frac{1}{6} = 0.1\bar{6}$　　　　　　　$0.25 = \frac{1}{4}$

$\frac{1}{8} = 0.125$　　　　　　　$0.3 = \frac{3}{10}$

$\frac{1}{10} = 0.1$　　　　　　　$0.\bar{3} = \frac{1}{3}$

$\frac{2}{3} = 0.\bar{6}$　　　　　　　$0.375 = \frac{3}{8}$

$\frac{2}{5} = 0.4$　　　　　　　　$0.4 = \frac{2}{5}$

$\frac{3}{4} = 0.75$　　　　　　　$0.5 = \frac{1}{2}$

$\frac{3}{5} = 0.6$　　　　　　　　$0.6 = \frac{3}{5}$

$\frac{3}{8} = 0.375$　　　　　　　$0.625 = \frac{5}{8}$

$\frac{3}{10} = 0.3$　　　　　　　$0.\bar{6} = \frac{2}{3}$

$\frac{4}{5} = 0.8$　　　　　　　　$0.7 = \frac{7}{10}$

$\frac{5}{6} = 0.8\bar{3}$　　　　　　　$0.75 = \frac{3}{4}$

$\frac{5}{8} = 0.625$　　　　　　　$0.8 = \frac{4}{5}$

$\frac{7}{8} = 0.875$　　　　　　　$0.8\bar{3} = \frac{5}{6}$

$\frac{7}{10} = 0.7$　　　　　　　$0.875 = \frac{7}{8}$

$\frac{9}{10} = 0.9$　　　　　　　$0.9 = \frac{9}{10}$

Teaching Tips, Cont.

➢ Draw the last set of circles on the board. Ask students to express the total shaded area as a single fraction. $\left(\frac{5}{4}\right)$ Students may express the area as a mixed number, but point out that it is not a single fraction, but rather a whole number and a fraction.

➢ Define *improper fraction* from the teaching box. Explain that proper fractions always have a numerator that is less than the denominator. Improper fractions also include fractions whose numerator is equal to the denominator. Therefore, the fraction expressed in the second example would be considered an improper fraction.

➢ Tell the students that improper fractions are added, subtracted, multiplied, and divided just like proper fractions. Because mixed numbers are not introduced until Lesson 39, students are expected to leave answers as improper fractions in this lesson.

➢ Complete the Classwork exercises. Have some students work the problems on the board for the class. All students should work the problems in their books.

Assignment
• Complete Lesson 38, Activities 2-5.

Lesson 39

Concepts
- Mixed numbers
- Adding mixed numbers
- Subtracting mixed numbers
- Single-variable equations
- Math in the real world

Learning Objectives
The student will be able to:
- Define *mixed number*
- Convert improper fractions to mixed numbers
- Convert mixed numbers to improper fractions
- Add mixed numbers
- Subtract mixed numbers

Materials Needed
- Student Book, Lesson 39

Teaching Tips
➢ Review improper fractions. (See Lesson 38)

➢ Review the proper procedure for adding and subtracting fractions. Remind students that they must have equal denominators.

➢ Introduce mixed numbers from the teaching box.

➢ Review the circle diagrams from Lesson 38. Ask students how the third set of circles could be expressed without using an improper fraction. $\left(1\frac{1}{4}\right)$

➢ Teach the addition of mixed numbers from the teaching box.

Mixed Numbers

A **mixed number** is the result of adding a whole number and a fraction. A mixed number can be written as an improper fraction by following these steps:
1. Multiply the whole number by the denominator. Add this to the numerator to get the new numerator.
2. Keep the denominator for the improper fraction the same as it is in the mixed number.

Why does this work? See what happens when we convert $2\frac{1}{4}$ to a mixed number:

Think: $2 = 1 + 1$. Therefore,

$$2\frac{1}{4} = 1 + 1 + \frac{1}{4}$$

Rewriting 1 as a fraction with a common denominator, we get

$$\frac{4}{4} + \frac{4}{4} + \frac{1}{4} = 2\left(\frac{4}{4}\right) + \frac{1}{4} = \frac{8}{4} + \frac{1}{4} = \frac{9}{4}$$

Following the steps above, we see that

$$2\frac{1}{4} = \frac{2(4)+1}{4} = \frac{8+1}{4} = \frac{9}{4}$$

To add mixed numbers, add the whole numbers to get the new whole number, and add the fractions to get the new fraction. Simplify if necessary.

$$1\frac{3}{4} + 2\frac{3}{4} = 3\frac{6}{4} = 3 + 1\frac{2}{4} = 4\frac{1}{2}$$

To subtract mixed numbers, convert to improper fractions and subtract. Convert the answer to a mixed number.

$$5\frac{3}{4} - 2\frac{1}{2} = \frac{23}{4} - \frac{5}{2} = \frac{23}{4} - \frac{10}{4} = \frac{13}{4} = 3\frac{1}{4}$$

Alternately,

$$5\frac{3}{4} - 2\frac{1}{2} = (5-2) + \left(\frac{3}{4} - \frac{1}{2}\right) = 3 + \left(\frac{3}{4} - \frac{2}{4}\right) = 3\frac{1}{4}$$

---

① Classwork

Convert to an improper fraction.

$$1\frac{1}{2} = \frac{1 \times 2 + 1}{2} = \frac{2+1}{2} = \frac{3}{2}$$

$$2\frac{2}{5} = \frac{2 \times 5 + 2}{5} = \frac{10+2}{5} = \frac{12}{5}$$

$$4\frac{3}{8} = \frac{4 \times 8 + 3}{8} = \frac{32+3}{8} = \frac{35}{8}$$

Convert to a mixed number.

$$\frac{5}{2} = 5 \div 2 = 2R1 = 2\frac{1}{2}$$

$$\frac{4}{3} = 4 \div 3 = 1R1 = 1\frac{1}{3}$$

$$\frac{9}{5} = 9 \div 5 = 1R4 = 1\frac{4}{5}$$

Add or subtract as indicated.

$$2\frac{1}{5} + 3\frac{2}{5} = (2+3) + \frac{1+2}{5} = 5\frac{3}{5}$$

$$1\frac{1}{5} + 4\frac{2}{5} = (1+4) + \frac{1+2}{5} = 5\frac{3}{5}$$

$$6\frac{7}{8} - 2\frac{3}{8} =$$

$$\frac{6 \times 8 + 7}{8} - \frac{2 \times 8 + 3}{8} = \frac{55-19}{8} = \frac{36}{8} = \frac{9}{2} = 4\frac{1}{2}$$

$$7\frac{3}{8} - 3\frac{1}{2} =$$

$$\frac{7 \times 8 + 3}{8} - \frac{3 \times 2 + 1}{2} = \frac{59}{8} - \frac{7}{2} = \frac{59}{8} - \frac{28}{8} = \frac{31}{8} = 3\frac{7}{8}$$

Activities

② Complete the chart to convert between improper fractions and mixed numbers.

Improper Fraction	Mixed Number	Improper Fraction	Mixed Number
$\frac{5}{2}$	$2\frac{1}{2}$	$\frac{19}{5}$	$3\frac{4}{5}$
$\frac{5}{3}$	$1\frac{2}{3}$	$\frac{17}{8}$	$2\frac{1}{8}$
$\frac{9}{4}$	$2\frac{1}{4}$	$\frac{22}{5}$	$4\frac{2}{5}$
$\frac{17}{5}$	$3\frac{2}{5}$	$\frac{9}{7}$	$1\frac{2}{7}$

③ Add or subtract as indicated.

$1\frac{3}{5} + 2\frac{1}{5} = (1+2) + \frac{3+1}{5} = 3\frac{4}{5}$

$3\frac{1}{3} + 2\frac{1}{3} = (3+2) + \frac{1+1}{3} = 5\frac{2}{3}$

$2\frac{2}{7} + 5\frac{4}{7} = (2+5) + \frac{2}{7} + \frac{4}{7} = 7 + \frac{2+4}{7} = 7\frac{6}{7}$

$2\frac{3}{8} + 3\frac{1}{4} =$

$(2+3) + \frac{3}{8} + \frac{1}{4} = 5 + \frac{3}{8} + \frac{2}{8} = 5 + \frac{3+2}{8} = 5\frac{5}{8}$

$1\frac{3}{5} + 6\frac{3}{10} =$

$(1+6) + \frac{3}{5} + \frac{3}{10} = 7 + \frac{6}{10} + \frac{3}{10} = 7 + \frac{6+3}{10} = 7\frac{9}{10}$

$7\frac{5}{8} - 4\frac{1}{8} =$

$\frac{7 \times 8 + 5}{8} - \frac{4 \times 8 + 1}{8} = \frac{61 - 33}{8} = \frac{28}{8} = \frac{7}{2} = 3\frac{1}{2}$

$4\frac{3}{4} - 2\frac{1}{2} =$

$\frac{4 \times 4 + 3}{4} - \frac{2 \times 2 + 1}{2} = \frac{19}{4} - \frac{5}{2} = \frac{19}{4} - \frac{10}{4} = \frac{9}{4} = 2\frac{1}{4}$

$3\frac{2}{3} - 1\frac{1}{6} = \frac{3 \times 3 + 2}{3} - \frac{1 \times 6 + 1}{6} = \frac{11}{3} - \frac{7}{6}$

$\frac{22}{6} - \frac{7}{6} = \frac{22 - 7}{6} = \frac{15}{6} = \frac{5}{2} = 2\frac{1}{2}$

$8\frac{3}{10} - 5\frac{1}{5} =$

$\frac{8 \times 10 + 3}{10} - \frac{5 \times 5 + 1}{5} = \frac{83}{10} - \frac{26}{5} = \frac{83}{10} - \frac{52}{10} = \frac{31}{10} = 3\frac{1}{10}$

$4\frac{1}{4} - 2\frac{7}{8} =$

$\frac{4 \times 4 + 1}{4} - \frac{2 \times 8 + 7}{8} = \frac{17}{4} - \frac{23}{8} = \frac{34}{8} - \frac{23}{8} = \frac{34 - 23}{8} = \frac{11}{8} = 1\frac{3}{8}$

④ Solve.

$5x + 17 = x - 19$
$5x - x = -19 - 17$
$4x = -36$
$x = -9$

$7x - 16 = 44 - 3x$
$7x + 3x = 44 + 16$
$10x = 60$
$x = 6$

$11x - 7 = 6x + 23$
$11x - 6x = 23 + 7$
$5x = 30$
$x = 6$

$4(2x - 1) = 5x + 14$
$8x - 4 = 5x + 14$
$8x - 5x = 14 + 4$
$3x = 18$
$x = 6$

$7x + 27 \div 3 = 8x + 13$
$7x + 9 = 8x + 13$
$7x - 8x = 13 - 9$
$-x = 4$
$x = -4$

$2(3x - 1) = 5(2x + 2)$
$6x - 2 = 10x + 10$
$6x - 10x = 10 + 2$
$-4x = 12$
$x = -3$

⑤ Write an equation and solve.
Diann is purchasing fabric to sew a dress. The pattern calls for $2\frac{3}{4}$ yards of fabric in the main color, and $1\frac{7}{8}$ yards of fabric in a contrasting color. How many total yards of fabric does Diann need to purchase to sew the dress?

$2\frac{3}{4} + 1\frac{7}{8} = (2+1) + \left(\frac{3}{4} + \frac{7}{8}\right) = 3 + \frac{3 \times 2}{4 \times 2} + \frac{7}{8} = 3 + \frac{6}{8} + \frac{7}{8} = 3 + \frac{13}{8} = 3 + 1\frac{5}{8} = 4\frac{5}{8}$

yards of fabric
If the fabric costs $4 per yard, how much will the fabric cost? (Convert the fraction to a decimal.)

$\frac{5}{8} = 0.625$

$\$4 \times 4.625 = \$18.50$

Teaching Tips, Cont.

➤ Teach the subtraction of mixed numbers from the teaching box.

➤ Subtraction of mixed numbers is possible without rewriting as an improper fraction, but it often involves regrouping, which can lead to errors. (See the example below.)

➤ Complete the Classwork exercises. Have some students work the problems on the board for the class. All students should work the problems in their books.

Assignment

• Complete Lesson 39, Activities 2-5.

Subtraction of Mixed Numbers with Regrouping

$3\frac{1}{4} - 1\frac{1}{2} =$

$3\frac{1}{4} - 1\frac{2}{4} =$

$2\frac{5}{4} - 1\frac{2}{4} =$

$(2 - 1) + \left(\frac{5}{4} - \frac{2}{4}\right) =$

$1 + \frac{5 - 2}{4} =$

$1\frac{3}{4}$

This method tends to be more tedious and prone to errors.

Lesson 40

Concepts
- English and metric lengths
- English length equivalents
- English-metric length equivalents
- Metric-English length equivalents
- Prime factorization
- Dividing decimals
- Adding mixed numbers
- Subtracting mixed numbers

Learning Objectives
The student will be able to:
- Explain the difference between English and metric units
- Convert lengths among miles, yards, feet, and inches
- Convert English lengths to metric units
- Convert metric lengths to English units

Materials Needed
- Student Book, Lesson 40
- Worksheet 20

Teaching Tips
➢ Review the metric prefixes *kilo-*, *centi-*, and *milli-* from Lessons 30-31.

➢ Review the information on the SI system from Lesson 31.

➢ Write the following problem on the board:

$$\frac{2}{3} \times \frac{9}{16} =$$

Ask students how to simplify this problem before multiplying. (Cancel terms) They should get

$$\frac{\overset{1}{\cancel{2}}}{\underset{1}{\cancel{3}}} \times \frac{\overset{3}{\cancel{9}}}{\underset{8}{\cancel{16}}} = \frac{1 \times 3}{1 \times 8} = \frac{3}{8}$$

English and Metric Lengths

English length equivalents:
1 mile = 5280 feet = 1760 yards
1 yard = 3 feet = 36 inches

English-Metric length equivalents:
1 inch = 2.54 cm = 25.4 mm
1 yard = 0.91 meter
1 mile = 1.61 km

Metric-English length equivalents:
1 cm = 0.39 inch
1 meter = 1.09 yards
1 km = 0.62 mile

To convert from one measurement to another, multiply the given number of units by the conversion factor of the units you are looking for.

For example, convert 2 miles to feet:
2(5280 feet) = 10,560 feet

Set up an equation including the units to ensure accuracy. Think of 5280 feet as "5280 feet per mile," or 5280 feet/mile.

$$2 \text{ miles} \left(\frac{5280 \text{ feet}}{1 \text{ mile}} \right) = 10,560 \text{ feet}$$

① **Classwork**
Convert the English lengths.
2 miles = __3520__ yards
$$2 \text{ miles} \left(\frac{1760 \text{ yards}}{1 \text{ mile}} \right) = 3520 \text{ yards}$$
3 miles = __15,840__ feet
$$3 \text{ miles} \left(\frac{5280 \text{ feet}}{1 \text{ mile}} \right) = 15,840 \text{ feet}$$
3 yards = __108__ inches
$$3 \text{ yards} \left(\frac{36 \text{ inches}}{1 \text{ yard}} \right) = 108 \text{ inches}$$
12 feet = __4__ yards
$$12 \text{ feet} \left(\frac{1 \text{ yard}}{3 \text{ feet}} \right) = 4 \text{ yards}$$
3.5 yards = __10.5__ feet
$$3.5 \text{ yards} \left(\frac{3 \text{ feet}}{1 \text{ yard}} \right) = 10.5 \text{ feet}$$

Convert the lengths from English to metric.
5 inches = __12.7__ cm $5 \text{ inches} \left(\frac{2.54 \text{ cm}}{1 \text{ inch}} \right) = 12.7 \text{ cm}$
3 inches = __76.2__ mm
$$3 \text{ inches} \left(\frac{25.4 \text{ mm}}{1 \text{ inch}} \right) = 76.2 \text{ mm}$$
4 yards = __3.64__ meters
$$4 \text{ yards} \left(\frac{0.91 \text{ meter}}{1 \text{ yard}} \right) = 3.64 \text{ meters}$$
3 miles = __4.83__ km $3 \text{ miles} \left(\frac{1.61 \text{ km}}{1 \text{ mile}} \right) = 4.83 \text{ km}$

Convert the lengths from metric to English.
10 cm = __3.9__ inches
$$10 \text{ cm} \left(\frac{0.39 \text{ in.}}{1 \text{ cm}} \right) = 3.9 \text{ inches}$$
3 meters = __3.27__ yards
$$3 \text{ meters} \left(\frac{1.09 \text{ yd.}}{1 \text{ meter}} \right) = 3.27 \text{ yards}$$
4 km = __2.48__ miles $4 \text{ km} \left(\frac{0.62 \text{ mi.}}{1 \text{ km}} \right) = 2.48 \text{ miles}$

Activities
② Complete the chart to show correct English-Metric conversions.

16 inches	$16 \text{ inches} \left(\frac{2.54 \text{ cm}}{1 \text{ inch}} \right) = 40.64$	cm
11 inches	$11 \text{ inches} \left(\frac{25.4 \text{ mm}}{1 \text{ inch}} \right) = 279.4$	mm
9 yards	$9 \text{ yards} \left(\frac{0.91 \text{ meter}}{1 \text{ yard}} \right) = 8.19$	meters
14 miles	$14 \text{ miles} \left(\frac{1.61 \text{ km}}{1 \text{ mile}} \right) = 22.54$	km
25 cm	$25 \text{ cm} \left(\frac{0.39 \text{ in.}}{1 \text{ cm}} \right) = 9.75$	inches
7 meters	$7 \text{ meters} \left(\frac{1.09 \text{ yd.}}{1 \text{ meter}} \right) = 7.63$	yards
12 km	$12 \text{ km} \left(\frac{0.62 \text{ mi.}}{1 \text{ km}} \right) = 7.44$	miles

③ Complete the chart to show correct English length equivalents.

9 miles	$9 \text{ miles} \left(\frac{1760 \text{ yards}}{1 \text{ mile}} \right) = 15,840$	yards
7 miles	$7 \text{ miles} \left(\frac{5280 \text{ feet}}{1 \text{ mile}} \right) = 36,960$	feet
10 yards	$10 \text{ yards} \left(\frac{36 \text{ inches}}{1 \text{ yard}} \right) = 360$	inches
69 feet	$_{23}\cancel{69} \text{ feet} \left(\frac{1 \text{ yard}}{\cancel{3} \text{ feet}} \right) = 23$	yards
11 yards	$11 \text{ yards} \left(\frac{3 \text{ feet}}{1 \text{ yard}} \right) = 33$	feet
21,120 feet	$_4\cancel{21,120} \text{ feet} \left(\frac{1 \text{ mile}}{\cancel{5280} \text{ feet}} \right) = 4$	miles
15,840 yards	$_9\cancel{15,840} \text{ yards} \left(\frac{1 \text{ mile}}{\cancel{1760} \text{ yards}} \right) = 9$	miles
13 feet	$13 \text{ feet} \left(\frac{12 \text{ inches}}{1 \text{ foot}} \right) = 156$	inches
108 inches	$108 \text{ inches} \left(\frac{1 \text{ foot}}{12 \text{ inches}} \right) = 9$	feet
396 inches	$396 \text{ inches} \left(\frac{1 \text{ yard}}{36 \text{ inches}} \right) = 11$	yards

④ Give the prime factorization of each number. Use exponents where appropriate.

72	84	96
$72 = 2 \times 2 \times 2 \times 3 \times 3$	$84 = 2 \times 2 \times 3 \times 7$	$96 = 2 \times 2 \times 2 \times 2 \times 2 \times 3$
$72 = 2^3 \times 3^2$	$84 = 2^2 \times 3 \times 7$	$96 = 2^5 \times 3$

⑤ Divide.

$$1.7\overline{)5.44} \rightarrow 3.2$$
$$\begin{array}{r} 3.2 \\ 1.7\overline{)5.44} \\ \underline{5\,1} \\ 34 \\ \underline{34} \end{array} \quad \begin{array}{r} 42 \\ 2.7\overline{)113.4} \\ \underline{108} \\ 54 \\ \underline{54} \end{array} \quad \begin{array}{r} 110 \\ .57\overline{)62.70} \\ \underline{57} \\ 57 \\ \underline{57} \end{array} \quad \begin{array}{r} 12 \\ .605\overline{)7.260} \\ \underline{605} \\ 1210 \\ \underline{1210} \end{array}$$

⑥ Add or subtract as indicated. Express your answer as a mixed number.

$$3\frac{3}{5} + 2\frac{1}{8} = (3+2) + \frac{3 \times 8}{5 \times 8} + \frac{1 \times 5}{8 \times 5} = 5 + \frac{24}{40} + \frac{5}{40} = 5 + \frac{24+5}{40} = 5\frac{29}{40}$$

$$5\frac{2}{3} + 11\frac{4}{5} = (5+11) + \frac{2 \times 5}{3 \times 5} + \frac{4 \times 3}{5 \times 3} = 16 + \frac{10}{15} + \frac{12}{15} = 16 + \frac{10+12}{15} = 16 + \frac{22}{15} = 16 + 1 + \frac{7}{15} = 17\frac{7}{15}$$

$$14\frac{7}{8} - 9\frac{1}{4} = \frac{14 \times 8 + 7}{8} - \frac{9 \times 4 + 1}{4} = \frac{119}{8} - \frac{37}{4} = \frac{119}{8} - \frac{37 \times 2}{4 \times 2} = \frac{119}{8} - \frac{74}{8} = \frac{119-74}{8} = \frac{45}{8} = 5\frac{5}{8}$$

$$8\frac{1}{7} - 5\frac{1}{3} = \frac{8 \times 7 + 1}{7} - \frac{5 \times 3 + 1}{3} = \frac{57}{7} - \frac{16}{3} = \frac{57 \times 3}{7 \times 3} - \frac{16 \times 7}{3 \times 7} = \frac{171}{21} - \frac{112}{21} = \frac{171-112}{21} = \frac{59}{21} = 2\frac{17}{21}$$

English to Metric Conversions

① Complete the chart to show correct English length equivalents.

12 miles	$12 \text{ miles}\left(\frac{1760 \text{ yards}}{1 \text{ mile}}\right) = 21{,}120$ yards
12 miles	$12 \text{ miles}\left(\frac{5280 \text{ feet}}{1 \text{ mile}}\right) = 63{,}360$ feet
6 yards	$6 \text{ yards}\left(\frac{36 \text{ inches}}{1 \text{ yards}}\right) = 216$ inches
132 feet	$_{44}132 \text{ feet}\left(\frac{1 \text{ yard}}{3 \text{ feet}}\right) = 44$ yards
15 yards	$15 \text{ yards}\left(\frac{3 \text{ feet}}{1 \text{ yards}}\right) = 45$ feet
36,960 feet	$_{7}36{,}960 \text{ feet}\left(\frac{1 \text{ mile}}{5280 \text{ feet}}\right) = 7$ miles
19,360 yards	$_{11}19{,}360 \text{ yards}\left(\frac{1 \text{ mile}}{1760 \text{ yards}}\right) = 11$ miles
14 feet	$14 \text{ feet}\left(\frac{12 \text{ inches}}{1 \text{ feet}}\right) = 168$ inches
192 inches	$_{16}192 \text{ inches}\left(\frac{1 \text{ foot}}{12 \text{ inches}}\right) = 16$ feet
504 inches	$_{14}504 \text{ inches}\left(\frac{1 \text{ yard}}{36 \text{ inches}}\right) = 14$ yards
8 miles	$8 \text{ miles}\left(\frac{5280 \text{ feet}}{1 \text{ mile}}\right) = 42{,}240$ feet
9 yards	$9 \text{ yards}\left(\frac{36 \text{ inches}}{1 \text{ yards}}\right) = 324$ inches
96 feet	$_{32}96 \text{ feet}\left(\frac{1 \text{ yard}}{3 \text{ feet}}\right) = 32$ yards

② Complete the chart to show correct English-Metric conversions.

19 inches	$19 \text{ inches}\left(\frac{2.54 \text{ cm}}{1 \text{ inch}}\right) = 48.26$ cm
14 inches	$14 \text{ inches}\left(\frac{25.4 \text{ mm}}{1 \text{ inch}}\right) = 355.6$ mm
11 yards	$11 \text{ yards}\left(\frac{0.91 \text{ meter}}{1 \text{ yard}}\right) = 10.01$ meters
9 miles	$9 \text{ miles}\left(\frac{1.61 \text{ km}}{1 \text{ mile}}\right) = 14.49$ km
32 cm	$32 \text{ cm}\left(\frac{0.39 \text{ in.}}{1 \text{ cm}}\right) = 12.48$ inches
8 meters	$8 \text{ meters}\left(\frac{1.09 \text{ yd.}}{1 \text{ meter}}\right) = 8.72$ yards
13 km	$13 \text{ km}\left(\frac{0.62 \text{ mi.}}{1 \text{ km}}\right) = 8.06$ miles
20 inches	$20 \text{ inches}\left(\frac{2.54 \text{ cm}}{1 \text{ inch}}\right) = 50.8$ cm
8 inches	$8 \text{ inches}\left(\frac{25.4 \text{ mm}}{1 \text{ inch}}\right) = 203.2$ mm
15 yards	$15 \text{ yards}\left(\frac{0.91 \text{ meter}}{1 \text{ yard}}\right) = 13.65$ meters
18 miles	$18 \text{ miles}\left(\frac{1.61 \text{ km}}{1 \text{ mile}}\right) = 28.98$ km
17 cm	$17 \text{ cm}\left(\frac{0.39 \text{ in.}}{1 \text{ cm}}\right) = 6.63$ inches
11 meters	$11 \text{ meters}\left(\frac{1.09 \text{ yd.}}{1 \text{ meter}}\right) = 11.99$ yards
10 km	$10 \text{ km}\left(\frac{0.62 \text{ mi.}}{1 \text{ km}}\right) = 6.2$ miles

Note concerning memorization of conversion factors and standardized tests: The only conversion factors students are expected to have memorized for standardized tests are those relating to time. This includes seconds, minutes, hours, days, weeks, months, and years. All other conversion factors that appear in test questions will either be provided as part of the question or will appear on a formula and conversion sheet provided as part of the test.

Teaching Tips, Cont.

➢ Now rewrite the problem using words.

$$\text{miles}\left(\frac{\text{yards}}{\text{miles}}\right) =$$

Show student that units can cancel just like numbers:

$$\cancel{\text{miles}}\left(\frac{\text{yards}}{\cancel{\text{miles}}}\right) = \text{yards}$$

➢ Teach the conversion of English and metric length equivalents. Students are NOT expected to memorize the conversion equivalents in the teaching box. All standardized tests provide the conversion factors as part of the question. The questions simply test whether or not the student can apply the information to calculate the proper conversion.

➢ Emphasize the importance of including the units in the conversion equation. This will eliminate much of the risk of error in the conversion. Also, if students are used to this method of conversion, they will have an easier transition to the mathematics required in chemistry and physics.

➢ Complete the Classwork exercises. Have some students work the problems on the board for the class. All students should work the problems in their books.

Assignments
- Complete Lesson 40, Activities 2-6.
- Worksheet 20
- Study for Test 4. (Lessons 28-37)
- Study for Exam 1. (Lessons 1-37)

Test 4

Testing Objectives
The student will:
- Multiply by powers of 10
- Divide by powers of 10
- Apply powers of 10 to metric conversions
- Form equivalent fractions
- Convert fractions to decimals
- Convert decimals to fractions
- Add fractions
- Subtract fractions
- Multiply fractions
- Divide fractions

Materials Needed
- Test 4
- *It's College Test Prep Time!* from Student Book
- *A Math Minute with…* Steve G. from Student Book

Teaching Tips
➢ Administer Test 4, allowing the students 30-40 minutes to complete the test.

➢ When all students are finished taking the test, introduce the College Test Prep Time from the student book. This page may be completed in class or assigned as homework.

➢ Have students read the Math Minute interview for Lessons 41-50.

Test 4

① Solve. **24 points**

$5 \times 10^0 = 5$ $5.19 \div 10^0 = 5.19$

$0.7 \times 10^1 = 7$ $18.38 \div 10^1 = 1.838$

$0.36 \times 10^2 = 36$ $6.21 \div 10^2 = 0.0621$

$9.42 \times 10^3 = 9420$ $99.26 \div 10^3 = 0.09926$

$9.54 \times 10^0 = 9.54$ $13.92 \div 10^0 = 13.92$

$0.816 \times 10^1 = 8.16$ $5.63 \div 10^1 = 0.563$

$94.5 \times 10^2 = 9450$ $3.91 \div 10^2 = 0.0391$

$0.071 \times 10^3 = 71$ $2.61 \div 10^3 = 0.00261$

$8.17 \times 10^0 = 8.17$ $0.048 \div 10^0 = 0.048$

$0.352 \times 10^{-1} = 0.0352$ $0.61 \div 10^{-1} = 6.1$

$46.87 \times 10^{-2} = 0.4687$ $0.09 \div 10^{-2} = 9$

$0.0079 \times 10^{-3} = 0.0000079$ $1.3 \div 10^{-3} = 1300$

② Multiply or divide the appropriate powers of 10 to complete the metric conversions. **8 points**

10 kg = __10,000__ g   9000 g = __9__ kg

0.4 km = __400__ m   8163 L = __8.163__ kL

3.2 kL = __3200__ L   266 m = __0.266__ km

62.46 kW = __62,460__ W   54.1 W = __0.0541__ kW

③ Multiply or divide the appropriate powers of 10 to complete the metric conversions. **8 points**

13 g = __1300__ cg   2000 cg = __20__ g

0.6 m = __600__ mm   8168 mL = __8.168__ L

1.4 L = __140__ cL   357 cm = __3.57__ m

54.19 W = __54,190__ mW   8.19 mW = __0.00819__ W

④ Solve the numerators to make equivalent fractions. **6 points**

$\dfrac{1 \times 3}{4 \times 3} = \dfrac{3}{12}$ $\dfrac{3 \times 4}{4 \times 4} = \dfrac{12}{16}$

$\dfrac{2 \times 4}{3 \times 4} = \dfrac{8}{12}$ $\dfrac{2 \times 5}{5 \times 5} = \dfrac{10}{25}$

$\dfrac{1 \times 5}{4 \times 5} = \dfrac{5}{20}$ $\dfrac{1 \times 4}{6 \times 4} = \dfrac{4}{24}$

Test 4

⑤ Write the following fractions as decimals. **8 points**

$\dfrac{1}{2} = 0.5$ $\dfrac{3}{4} = 0.75$ $\dfrac{5}{6} = 0.8\overline{3}$ $\dfrac{1}{3} = 0.\overline{3}$

$\dfrac{1}{6} = 0.1\overline{6}$ $\dfrac{2}{5} = 0.4$ $\dfrac{3}{8} = 0.375$ $\dfrac{4}{5} = 0.8$

⑥ Write the following decimals as fractions. **8 points**

$0.25 = \dfrac{1}{4}$ $0.625 = \dfrac{5}{8}$ $0.7 = \dfrac{7}{10}$ $0.6 = \dfrac{3}{5}$

$0.\overline{6} = \dfrac{2}{3}$ $0.4 = \dfrac{2}{5}$ $0.2 = \dfrac{1}{5}$ $0.3 = \dfrac{3}{10}$

⑦ Add, subtract, multiply, or divide as indicated. **20 points**

$\dfrac{1}{5} + \dfrac{3}{5} = \dfrac{1+3}{5} = \dfrac{4}{5}$ $\dfrac{2}{5} \times \dfrac{1}{5} = \dfrac{2 \times 1}{5 \times 5} = \dfrac{2}{25}$

$\dfrac{1}{7} + \dfrac{4}{7} = \dfrac{1+4}{7} = \dfrac{5}{7}$ $\dfrac{\overset{1}{\cancel{4}}}{5} \times \dfrac{3}{\cancel{8}_2} = \dfrac{1 \times 3}{5 \times 2} = \dfrac{3}{10}$

$\dfrac{1}{3} + \dfrac{1}{6} = \dfrac{1 \times 2}{3 \times 2} + \dfrac{1}{6} = \dfrac{2}{6} + \dfrac{1}{6} = \dfrac{3}{6} = \dfrac{1}{2}$ $\dfrac{\overset{1}{\cancel{5}}}{\cancel{7}_{17}} \times \dfrac{\cancel{7}^1}{\cancel{10}_2} = \dfrac{1}{2}$

$\dfrac{1}{4} + \dfrac{3}{8} = \dfrac{1 \times 2}{4 \times 2} + \dfrac{3}{8} = \dfrac{2}{8} + \dfrac{3}{8} = \dfrac{5}{8}$ $\dfrac{5}{8} \times \dfrac{1}{2} = \dfrac{5 \times 1}{8 \times 2} = \dfrac{5}{16}$

$\dfrac{5}{8} + \dfrac{1}{12} = \dfrac{5 \times 3}{8 \times 3} + \dfrac{1 \times 2}{12 \times 2} = \dfrac{15}{24} + \dfrac{2}{24} = \dfrac{17}{24}$ $\dfrac{\overset{1}{\cancel{5}}}{\cancel{2}_2} \times \dfrac{\cancel{4}^1}{\cancel{5}_1} = \dfrac{1}{2}$

$\dfrac{4}{5} - \dfrac{3}{5} = \dfrac{4-3}{5} = \dfrac{1}{5}$ $\dfrac{2}{5} \div \dfrac{1}{2} = \dfrac{2}{\cancel{5}_1} \times \dfrac{\cancel{5}^1}{1} = \dfrac{2}{1} = 2$

$\dfrac{2}{3} - \dfrac{1}{6} = \dfrac{2 \times 2}{3 \times 2} - \dfrac{1}{6} = \dfrac{4}{6} - \dfrac{1}{6} = \dfrac{3}{6} = \dfrac{1}{2}$ $\dfrac{3}{8} \div \dfrac{1}{8} = \dfrac{3}{\cancel{8}_1} \times \dfrac{\cancel{8}^1}{1} = \dfrac{3}{1} = 3$

$\dfrac{9}{10} - \dfrac{3}{4} = \dfrac{9 \times 2}{10 \times 2} - \dfrac{3 \times 5}{4 \times 5} = \dfrac{18}{20} - \dfrac{15}{20} = \dfrac{3}{20}$ $\dfrac{4}{7} \div \dfrac{2}{3} = \dfrac{\overset{2}{\cancel{4}}}{7} \times \dfrac{3}{\cancel{2}_1} = \dfrac{2 \times 3}{7 \times 1} = \dfrac{6}{7}$

$\dfrac{7}{9} - \dfrac{2}{3} = \dfrac{7}{9} - \dfrac{2 \times 3}{3 \times 3} = \dfrac{7}{9} - \dfrac{6}{9} = \dfrac{1}{9}$ $\dfrac{5}{8} \div \dfrac{3}{4} = \dfrac{5}{\cancel{8}_2} \times \dfrac{\cancel{4}^1}{3} = \dfrac{5 \times 1}{2 \times 3} = \dfrac{5}{6}$

$\dfrac{5}{8} - \dfrac{1}{4} = \dfrac{5}{8} - \dfrac{1 \times 2}{4 \times 2} = \dfrac{5}{8} - \dfrac{2}{8} = \dfrac{3}{8}$ $\dfrac{3}{8} \div \dfrac{9}{10} = \dfrac{\overset{1}{\cancel{3}}}{\cancel{8}_4} \times \dfrac{\cancel{10}^5}{\cancel{9}_3} = \dfrac{1 \times 5}{4 \times 3} = \dfrac{5}{12}$

82 points total

It's College Test Prep Time!

1. The aerial bucket ride at an amusement park allows a maximum of 8 park guests to exit or board at each stop. The chart below shows how many guests boarded and exited the bucket ride in each of the first 5 stops. If there were 38 guests on the ride at the start, how many were on the ride after the 5th stop?

Stop	A	B	C	D	E
Boarded	6	4	7	8	8
Exited	2	8	5	4	3

   A. 10 $6 + 4 + 7 + 8 + 8 = 33$ guests boarded.
   B. 16 $2 + 8 + 5 + 4 + 3 = 22$ guests exited.
   C. 34 $33 - 22 = 11$ additional guests were on the ride.
   D. 38 $38 + 11 = 49$
   E. 49

2. Given $x + 3 = 7$ and $y + 12 = 20$, what is the value of $x + y$?
   A. 4 $x = 7 - 3$ $x = 4$
   B. 8 $y = 20 - 12$ $y = 8$
   C. 12 $x + y = 4 + 8 = 12$
   D. 32
   E. 42

3. In a football game, a touchdown with an extra point is worth a total of 7 points. A field goal is worth 3 points. If a team has 23 points, how many field goals have they scored? (Assume all extra points were made and no safeties or 2-point conversions were scored.)
   A. 1
   B. 2   Use trial and error to solve.
   C. 3   3 touchdowns = 21 points. Only 2 points remain.
   D. 4   2 touchdowns = 14 points, leaving 9 points.
   E. 5 $9 \div 3 = 3$ field goals.

4. Given x is the square of an integer and a multiple of 9 and 18, find the value of x.
   A. 3   Since 18 is a multiple of 9, look for multiples of 18
   B. 6   that are perfect squares. 18, 36, 54, . . .
   C. 9   You should recognize 36 as a perfect square. This
   D. 18   is the value of x. Notice that x is the square, not
   E. 36   the integer.

A Math Minute with . . .

Steve G. – Race Car Driver

What is your hobby? Auto Racing

Where do you do this? I race on $\frac{3}{8}$- to $\frac{1}{2}$-mile asphalt tracks around the state of Georgia.

Did you attend college? If so, what was your major? I studied Automotive Management and Service at Western Michigan University.

What parts of your hobby require the use of math? Before each race I use math to set up the race car suspension, weight balance, and tire dimensions.

What is the biggest "problem" you have faced that required the use of math to solve? A race car has four footprints, or tire prints. Each tire must carry a certain percentage of the total vehicle weight in order to handle well. I place the car on electronic scales to determine front to rear and side to side bias, or balance. Those numbers help me to determine the cross weight, which is the right front tire and left rear tire, as a percentage of the total weight, or *wedge*.

In addition to calculating weight percentages, the angles on the suspension parts are critical in keeping the tires as flat as possible on the track when cornering. These angles help determine the center of gravity, roll centers, and moment of inertia.

The circumference of the tires, measured around the center, is critical to the car's handling. This is called *tire stagger*.

Mathematical formulas help calculate all these different car measurements. I use a race car computer program to set up the calculations to make the car race faster.

Are there any other interesting math uses you have experienced? The biggest challenge in preparing to race is to set up the car so the front and rear suspensions are balanced. This ensures they work together instead of against each other. While this takes a great deal of measuring and calculating, it hopefully pays off during the race. Sometimes determining what will help a car's performance is simply trial and error.

Assignments
- Complete *It's College Test Prep Time!*
- Read *A Math Minute with …* Steve G. – Race Car Driver

Exam 1

Testing Objectives

The student will:

- Apply the divisibility tests to find factors of numbers
- Estimate sums and products
- Round numbers to the nearest ten and thousand
- Apply rules of signed numbers
- Apply rules of absolute value
- Add whole numbers
- Subtract whole numbers
- Multiply whole numbers
- Divide whole numbers
- Find the prime factorization of composite numbers
- Use exponents correctly
- Follow the order of operations
- Find the greatest common factor
- Find the least common multiple
- Simplify roots
- Solve single-variable equations
- Solve single-variable inequalities
- Add decimals
- Subtract decimals
- Multiply decimals
- Divide decimals
- Multiply by powers of 10
- Divide by powers of 10
- Apply principles of math to real world scenarios
- Convert measurements in the metric system
- Form equivalent fractions
- State fraction-decimal equivalents
- Add fractions
- Subtract fractions
- Multiply fractions
- Divide fractions

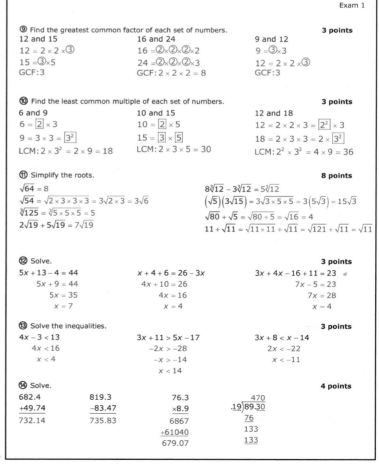

① Use the divisibility tests to tell if 2, 3, 4, 5, 6, and 9 are factors of each number. **24 points**

	114	115	116	117	118	120	123	124	126	135
2	x		x		x	x		x	x	
3	x			x		x	x		x	x
4			x			x		x		
5		x				x				x
6	x					x			x	
9				x					x	x

② Estimate the sum by rounding to the nearest thousand. **3 points**

$$2809 \approx 3000$$
$$+1207 \approx +1000$$
$$4,000$$

$$4118 \approx 4000$$
$$+8978 \approx +9000$$
$$13,000$$

$$3987 \approx 4000$$
$$+4016 \approx +4000$$
$$8,000$$

③ Estimate each product by rounding to the nearest ten. **2 points**

$19 \times 132 \approx 20 \times 130 = 2,600$ $72 \times 28 \approx 70 \times 30 = 2,100$

④ Solve, using the rules for signed numbers. **4 points**

$(+52) + (+23) = 52 + 23 = 75$ $(-11)(5)(-2) = (-55)(-2) = 110$
$(-11) + (+37) = 37 - 11 = 26$ $(-6)(-9)(-1) = (54)(-1) = -54$

⑤ Solve, using the rules of absolute values. **4 points**

$|-8| + |-49| = 8 + 49 = 57$ $|84| - |-16| = 84 - 16 = 68$
$|-13| + |92| = 13 + 92 = 105$ $-|24| + |-6| = (-24) + (+6) = -(24 - 6) = -18$

⑥ Solve. **4 points**

$$82194$$
$$+12917$$
$$95,111$$

$$61,591$$
$$-31,467$$
$$30,124$$

$$248$$
$$\times 76$$
$$1488$$
$$+17360$$
$$18,848$$

$$53\overline{)1272}$$
$$\frac{24}{}$$
$$106$$
$$212$$
$$212$$
$$000$$

⑦ Express the prime factorization of each number using exponents. **3 points**

$\quad\quad 81 \quad\quad\quad\quad\quad 84 \quad\quad\quad\quad\quad 100$
$81 = 3 \times 3 \times 3 \times 3 = 3^4 \quad 84 = 2 \times 2 \times 3 \times 7 = 2^2 \times 3 \times 7 \quad 100 = 2 \times 2 \times 5 \times 5 = 2^2 \times 5^2$

⑧ Solve, following the order of operations. **2 points**

$3 \times (2^3 + 1) - 5 \times 3 = 3 \times (8 + 1) - 5 \times 3 = 3 \times 9 - 5 \times 3 = 27 - 15 = 12$
$3 \times 8 - (3^2 - 2^2 - 7) = 3 \times 8 - (9 - 4 - 7) = 3 \times 8 - (5 - 7) = 3 \times 8 - (-2) = 24 + 2 = 26$

⑨ Find the greatest common factor of each set of numbers. **3 points**

12 and 15
$12 = 2 \times 2 \times ③$
$15 = ③ \times 5$
GCF: 3

16 and 24
$16 = ② \times ② \times ② \times 2$
$24 = ② \times ② \times ② \times 3$
GCF: $2 \times 2 \times 2 = 8$

9 and 12
$9 = ③ \times 3$
$12 = 2 \times 2 \times ③$
GCF: 3

⑩ Find the least common multiple of each set of numbers. **3 points**

6 and 9
$6 = \boxed{2} \times 3$
$9 = 3 \times 3 = \boxed{3^2}$
LCM: $2 \times 3^2 = 2 \times 9 = 18$

10 and 15
$10 = \boxed{2} \times 5$
$15 = \boxed{3} \times \boxed{5}$
LCM: $2 \times 3 \times 5 = 30$

12 and 18
$12 = 2 \times 2 \times 3 = \boxed{2^2} \times 3$
$18 = 2 \times 3 \times 3 = 2 \times \boxed{3^2}$
LCM: $2^2 \times 3^2 = 4 \times 9 = 36$

⑪ Simplify the roots. **8 points**

$\sqrt{64} = 8$
$\sqrt{54} = \sqrt{2 \times 3 \times 3 \times 3} = 3\sqrt{2 \times 3} = 3\sqrt{6}$
$\sqrt[3]{125} = \sqrt[3]{5 \times 5 \times 5} = 5$
$2\sqrt{19} + 5\sqrt{19} = 7\sqrt{19}$

$8\sqrt[3]{12} - 3\sqrt[3]{12} = 5\sqrt[3]{12}$
$(\sqrt{5})(3\sqrt{15}) = 3\sqrt{3 \times 5 \times 5} = 3(5\sqrt{3}) = 15\sqrt{3}$
$\sqrt{80} \div \sqrt{5} = \sqrt{80 \div 5} = \sqrt{16} = 4$
$11 \div \sqrt{11} = \sqrt{11 \times 11} \div \sqrt{11} = \sqrt{121} \div \sqrt{11} = \sqrt{11}$

⑫ Solve. **3 points**

$5x + 13 - 4 = 44$
$5x + 9 = 44$
$5x = 35$
$x = 7$

$x + 4 + 6 = 26 - 3x$
$4x + 10 = 26$
$4x = 16$
$x = 4$

$3x + 4x - 16 + 11 = 23$
$7x - 5 = 23$
$7x = 28$
$x = 4$

⑬ Solve the inequalities. **3 points**

$4x - 3 < 13$
$4x < 16$
$x < 4$

$3x + 11 > 5x - 17$
$-2x > -28$
$-x > -14$
$x < 14$

$3x + 8 < x - 14$
$2x < -22$
$x < -11$

⑭ Solve. **4 points**

$$682.4$$
$$+49.74$$
$$732.14$$

$$819.3$$
$$-83.47$$
$$735.83$$

$$76.3$$
$$\times 8.9$$
$$6867$$
$$+61040$$
$$679.07$$

$$.19\overline{)89.30}$$
$$\frac{470}{}$$
$$\frac{76}{}$$
$$133$$
$$\underline{133}$$

⑮ Solve. **12 points**

$10^5 = 100,000$

$(10^2)(10^7) = 10^9 = 1,000,000,000$

$(10^{18}) \div (10^{11}) = 10^7 = 10,000,000$

$10^{-3} = 0.001$

$67.1 \times 10^2 = 6710$

$0.038 \times 10^3 = 38$

$0.483 \times 10^{-1} = 0.0483$

$69.15 \times 10^{-2} = 0.6915$

$54.19 \div 10^0 = 54.19$

$3.45 \div 10^3 = 0.00345$

$0.32 \div 10^{-1} = 3.2$

$0.04 \div 10^{-2} = 4$

⑯ Write an equation and solve. **2 points**

At Billy's concession stand, a cheeseburger with potato chips costs 4 times as much as a candy-filled sucker and 2 pieces of bubble gum. If a candy-filled sucker costs 25 cents and bubble gum costs 5 cents each, how much does Billy charge for a cheeseburger with potato chips?

Let x = the cost of a cheeseburger with potato chips.

$x = 4(\$0.25 + 2(\$0.05))$

$x = 4(\$0.25 + \$0.10) \qquad x = 4(\$0.35) \qquad x = \$1.40$

⑰ Multiply or divide the appropriate powers of 10 to complete the metric conversions. **8 points**

0.3 km = _____300_____ m

6.7 kL = _____6700__ L

1794 L = _____1.794_ kL

32.8 W = ___0.0328__ kW

0.25 m = _____250___ mm

6.5 L = _____650____ cL

6791 mL = ___6.791__ L

826 cm = _____8.26__ m

⑱ Solve the numerators to make equivalent fractions. **4 points**

$\dfrac{3 \times 3}{8 \times 3} = \dfrac{9}{24}$

$\dfrac{2 \times 4}{5 \times 4} = \dfrac{8}{20}$

$\dfrac{9 \times 9}{10 \times 9} = \dfrac{81}{90}$

$\dfrac{5 \times 4}{6 \times 4} = \dfrac{20}{24}$

⑲ Complete the fraction-decimal equivalents. **8 points**

$\dfrac{1}{2} = 0.5$

$\dfrac{1}{6} = 0.1\overline{6}$

$\dfrac{3}{4} = 0.75$

$\dfrac{2}{5} = 0.4$

$0.25 = \dfrac{1}{4}$

$0.\overline{6} = \dfrac{2}{3}$

$0.625 = \dfrac{5}{8}$

$0.4 = \dfrac{2}{5}$

⑳ Add, subtract, multiply, or divide as indicated. **4 points**

$\dfrac{2}{3} + \dfrac{1}{4} = \dfrac{2 \times 4}{3 \times 4} + \dfrac{1 \times 3}{4 \times 3} = \dfrac{8}{12} + \dfrac{3}{12} = \dfrac{11}{12}$

$\dfrac{7}{10} - \dfrac{2}{3} = \dfrac{7 \times 3}{10 \times 3} - \dfrac{2 \times 10}{3 \times 10} = \dfrac{21}{30} - \dfrac{20}{30} = \dfrac{1}{30}$

$\dfrac{\overset{1}{\cancel{4}}}{\underset{1}{\cancel{5}}} \times \dfrac{\overset{3}{\cancel{15}}}{\underset{4}{\cancel{16}}} = \dfrac{1 \times 3}{1 \times 4} = \dfrac{3}{4}$

$\dfrac{3}{5} \div \dfrac{7}{10} = \dfrac{3}{\underset{1}{\cancel{5}}} \times \dfrac{\overset{2}{\cancel{10}}}{7} = \dfrac{3 \times 2}{1 \times 7} = \dfrac{6}{7}$

108 points total

Materials Needed
- Exam 1

Teaching Tips
➢ Administer Exam 1, allowing the students 45-50 minutes to complete the test.

Assignment
- There is no assignment for this lesson.

Lesson 41

Concepts

- Multiplying mixed numbers
- Divisibility tests
- Prime/composite numbers
- Multiplying decimals
- Dividing fractions
- Improper fraction-mixed number conversions
- Math in the real world

Learning Objectives

The student will be able to:

- Convert mixed numbers to improper fractions
- Multiply mixed numbers
- Convert improper fractions to mixed numbers

Materials Needed

- Student Book, Lesson 41
- Formula strip, Lesson 41

Teaching Tips

- Review the rules for multiplying fractions. (See Lesson 36)

- Review the rules for converting between mixed numbers and improper fractions. (See Lesson 39)

- Explain that multiplying mixed numbers follows the same rules as multiplying fractions.

- Teach multiplying mixed numbers from the lesson box.

Multiplying Mixed Numbers

To multiply mixed numbers, follow these steps:
- Convert each mixed number to an improper fraction.
- Multiply the improper fractions.
- Reduce, if possible.
- Convert the answer to a mixed number.

$$3\frac{1}{5} \times 5\frac{1}{2} = \frac{16}{5} \times \frac{11}{4} =$$

$$\frac{16}{5} \times \frac{11}{4} = \frac{4 \times 11}{5 \times 1} =$$

$$\frac{44}{5} = 8\frac{4}{5}$$

① Classwork

Multiply.

$$2\frac{1}{2} \times 3\frac{1}{3} = \frac{5}{2} \times \frac{10}{3} = \frac{5 \times 5}{1 \times 3} = \frac{25}{3} = 8\frac{1}{3}$$

$$4\frac{2}{5} \times 3\frac{3}{4} = \frac{22}{5} \times \frac{15}{4} = \frac{11 \times 3}{1 \times 2} = \frac{33}{2} = 16\frac{1}{2}$$

$$1\frac{3}{7} \times 2\frac{5}{8} = \frac{10}{7} \times \frac{21}{8} = \frac{5 \times 3}{1 \times 4} = \frac{15}{4} = 3\frac{3}{4}$$

$$5\frac{1}{7} \times 2\frac{1}{4} = \frac{36}{7} \times \frac{9}{4} = \frac{9 \times 9}{7 \times 1} = \frac{81}{7} = 11\frac{4}{7}$$

Activities

② Multiply.

$$2\frac{1}{4} \times 3\frac{2}{3} = \frac{9}{4} \times \frac{11}{3} = \frac{3 \times 11}{4 \times 1} = \frac{33}{4} = 8\frac{1}{4}$$

$$3\frac{4}{7} \times 4\frac{1}{5} = \frac{25}{7} \times \frac{21}{5} = \frac{5 \times 3}{1 \times 1} = \frac{15}{1} = 15$$

$$7\frac{1}{7} \times 2\frac{1}{10} = \frac{50}{7} \times \frac{21}{10} = \frac{5 \times 3}{1 \times 1} = \frac{15}{1} = 15$$

$$5\frac{4}{7} \times 2\frac{2}{13} = \frac{39}{7} \times \frac{28}{13} = \frac{3 \times 4}{1 \times 1} = \frac{12}{1} = 12$$

$$3\frac{1}{2} \times 4\frac{2}{3} = \frac{7}{2} \times \frac{14}{3} = \frac{7 \times 7}{1 \times 3} = \frac{49}{3} = 16\frac{1}{3}$$

$$4\frac{2}{9} \times 3\frac{3}{4} = \frac{38}{9} \times \frac{15}{4} = \frac{19 \times 5}{3 \times 2} = \frac{95}{6} = 15\frac{5}{6}$$

$$7\frac{3}{4} \times 4\frac{1}{2} = \frac{31}{4} \times \frac{9}{2} = \frac{31 \times 9}{4 \times 2} = \frac{279}{8} = 34\frac{7}{8}$$

$$5\frac{1}{3} \times 2\frac{1}{8} = \frac{16}{3} \times \frac{17}{8} = \frac{2 \times 17}{3 \times 1} = \frac{34}{3} = 11\frac{1}{3}$$

$$2\frac{5}{8} \times 3\frac{2}{3} = \frac{21}{8} \times \frac{11}{3} = \frac{7 \times 11}{8 \times 1} = \frac{77}{8} = 9\frac{5}{8}$$

$$2\frac{2}{5} \times 3\frac{3}{4} = \frac{12}{5} \times \frac{15}{4} = \frac{3 \times 3}{1 \times 1} = \frac{9}{1} = 9$$

$$1\frac{3}{11} \times 3\frac{1}{7} = \frac{14}{11} \times \frac{22}{7} = \frac{2 \times 2}{1 \times 1} = \frac{4}{1} = 4$$

$$2\frac{9}{13} \times 2\frac{1}{5} = \frac{35}{13} \times \frac{11}{5} = \frac{7 \times 11}{13 \times 1} = \frac{77}{13} = 5\frac{12}{13}$$

$$2\frac{1}{6} \times 3\frac{3}{5} = \frac{13}{6} \times \frac{18}{5} = \frac{13 \times 3}{1 \times 5} = \frac{39}{5} = 7\frac{4}{5}$$

$$1\frac{2}{9} \times 6\frac{3}{4} = \frac{11}{9} \times \frac{27}{4} = \frac{11 \times 3}{1 \times 4} = \frac{33}{4} = 8\frac{1}{4}$$

$$1\frac{5}{7} \times 2\frac{5}{8} = \frac{12}{7} \times \frac{21}{8} = \frac{3 \times 3}{1 \times 2} = \frac{9}{2} = 4\frac{1}{2}$$

$$3\frac{4}{7} \times 1\frac{1}{5} = \frac{25}{7} \times \frac{6}{5} = \frac{5 \times 6}{7 \times 1} = \frac{30}{7} = 4\frac{2}{7}$$

③ Use the divisibility tests to identify each number as prime or composite.

267	Composite (3)	273	Composite (3)
269	Prime	275	Composite (5)
271	Prime	277	Prime

④ Multiply.

```
  12.49          374.6           8.72           61.08
×   3.4        ×0.064         ×0.591         ×  2.07
  4996          14984            872           42756
+37470        +224760          78480           00000
 42.466        23.9744       +436000        +1221600
                               5.15352       126.4356
```

⑤ Divide. Convert improper fractions to mixed numbers.

$$\frac{3}{4} \div \frac{7}{10} = \frac{3}{\cancel{4}_2} \times \frac{\cancel{10}^5}{7} = \frac{3 \times 5}{2 \times 7} = \frac{15}{14} = 1\frac{1}{14}$$

$$\frac{5}{9} \div \frac{1}{6} = \frac{5}{\cancel{9}_3} \times \frac{\cancel{6}^2}{1} = \frac{5 \times 2}{3 \times 1} = \frac{10}{3} = 3\frac{1}{3}$$

$$\frac{4}{7} \div \frac{8}{9} = \frac{\cancel{4}^1}{7} \times \frac{9}{\cancel{8}_2} = \frac{1 \times 9}{7 \times 2} = \frac{9}{14}$$

$$\frac{5}{8} \div \frac{7}{10} = \frac{5}{\cancel{8}_4} \times \frac{\cancel{10}^5}{7} = \frac{5 \times 5}{4 \times 7} = \frac{25}{28}$$

$$\frac{6}{11} \div \frac{2}{7} = \frac{\cancel{6}^3}{11} \times \frac{7}{\cancel{2}_1} = \frac{3 \times 7}{11 \times 1} = \frac{21}{11} = 1\frac{10}{11}$$

$$\frac{1}{6} \div \frac{5}{12} = \frac{1}{\cancel{6}_1} \times \frac{\cancel{12}^2}{5} = \frac{1 \times 2}{1 \times 5} = \frac{2}{5}$$

⑥ Solve.

Steve raced 75 laps on a $\frac{1}{2}$-mile track and 100 laps on a $\frac{3}{8}$-mile track. How many miles did Steve race on each track?

$$75\left(\frac{1}{2}\right) = \frac{75}{1}\left(\frac{1}{2}\right) = \frac{75}{2} = 37\frac{1}{2} \text{ miles on the } \frac{1}{2} \text{ mile track}$$

$$100\left(\frac{3}{8}\right) = \frac{\cancel{100}^{25}}{1}\left(\frac{3}{\cancel{8}_2}\right) = \frac{25 \times 3}{1 \times 2} = \frac{75}{2} = 37\frac{1}{2} \text{ miles on the } \frac{3}{8} \text{ mile track}$$

How many yards did Steve race on each track?

$$37\frac{1}{2} \text{ miles} \left(\frac{1760 \text{ yards}}{1 \text{ mile}}\right) = 37.5(1760 \text{ yards}) = 66,000 \text{ yards}$$

How many feet did Steve race on each track?

$$66,000 \text{ yards} \left(\frac{3 \text{ feet}}{1 \text{ yard}}\right) = 66,000(3) = 198,000 \text{ feet}$$

Teaching Tips, Cont.

➢ Explain to students that they cannot multiply the whole numbers to get the new whole number and multiply the fractions to get the new fraction.

➢ Use the example in the lesson box to show students that multiplying mixed numbers is the same as multiplying two sums:

$$3\frac{1}{5} \times 5\frac{1}{2} = \left(3 + \frac{1}{5}\right)\left(5 + \frac{1}{2}\right)$$

➢ Ask students what the order of operations requires them to do first. (Solve inside the parentheses.) Explain that this means they need to simplify each set of parentheses to a single term, if possible. In other words, convert to an improper fraction.

➢ Complete the Classwork exercises. Have some students work the problems on the board for the class and explain their answers. All students should work the problems in their books.

➢ Give students the strip labeled "For use in Lesson 41" from the formula strip page.

Assignments

- Complete Lesson 41, Activities 2-6.
- If possible, bring instructions for building or construction sets to be used in Lesson 45.

Horizons Pre-Algebra, Teacher's Guide

Lesson 42

Concepts
- Dividing mixed numbers
- Prime factorization
- Exponents
- Order of operations
- Distributive property
- Single-variable equations
- Single-variable inequalities
- Dividing decimals
- Adding mixed numbers

Learning Objectives
The student will be able to:
- Divide mixed numbers
- Convert between mixed numbers and improper fractions
- Add mixed numbers without converting to improper fractions

Materials Needed
- Student Book, Lesson 42
- Worksheet 21

Teaching Tips
➢ Have students complete Worksheet 21, Activity 1 in class. This may be for added practice of earlier topics, or graded as a quiz, if desired.

➢ Review the procedure for dividing fractions. (See Lesson 37)

➢ Review the rules for multiplying mixed numbers. (See Lesson 41)

➢ Explain that dividing mixed numbers also requires the conversion to improper fractions. Teach dividing mixed numbers from the lesson box.

Dividing Mixed Numbers

To divide mixed numbers, follow these steps:
- Convert each mixed number to an improper fraction.
- Find the reciprocal of the second improper fraction and multiply.
- Reduce, if possible.
- Convert the answer to a mixed number, if necessary.

$$5\frac{1}{5} \div 3\frac{1}{4} = \frac{26}{5} \div \frac{13}{4} = \frac{26}{5} \times \frac{4}{13} =$$

$$\frac{\overset{2}{26}}{5} \times \frac{4}{\underset{1}{13}} = \frac{2 \times 4}{5 \times 1} = \frac{8}{5} = 1\frac{3}{5}$$

① Classwork
Divide.

$$2\frac{1}{3} \div 5\frac{7}{9} = \frac{7}{3} \div \frac{52}{9} = \frac{7}{\underset{1}{3}} \times \frac{\overset{3}{9}}{52} = \frac{21}{52}$$

$$6\frac{3}{8} \div 2\frac{3}{7} = \frac{51}{8} \div \frac{17}{7} = \frac{\overset{3}{51}}{8} \times \frac{7}{\underset{1}{17}} = \frac{21}{8} = 2\frac{5}{8}$$

$$5\frac{1}{4} \div 2\frac{1}{3} = \frac{21}{4} \div \frac{7}{3} = \frac{\overset{3}{21}}{4} \times \frac{3}{\underset{1}{7}} = \frac{9}{4} = 2\frac{1}{4}$$

Activities

② Divide.

$$2\frac{3}{4} \div 7\frac{1}{3} = \frac{11}{4} \div \frac{22}{3} = \frac{\overset{1}{11}}{4} \times \frac{3}{\underset{2}{22}} = \frac{3}{8}$$

$$4\frac{1}{5} \div 4\frac{2}{3} = \frac{21}{5} \div \frac{14}{3} = \frac{\overset{3}{21}}{5} \times \frac{3}{\underset{2}{14}} = \frac{9}{10}$$

$$5\frac{1}{2} \div 4\frac{2}{5} = \frac{11}{2} \div \frac{22}{5} = \frac{\overset{1}{11}}{2} \times \frac{5}{\underset{2}{22}} = \frac{5}{4} = 1\frac{1}{4}$$

$$5\frac{1}{3} \div 6\frac{2}{5} = \frac{16}{3} \div \frac{32}{5} = \frac{\overset{1}{16}}{3} \times \frac{5}{\underset{2}{32}} = \frac{5}{6}$$

$$3\frac{1}{2} \div 1\frac{1}{4} = \frac{7}{2} \div \frac{5}{4} = \frac{7}{\underset{1}{2}} \times \frac{\overset{2}{4}}{5} = \frac{14}{5} = 2\frac{4}{5}$$

$$1\frac{3}{12} \div 2\frac{1}{7} = \frac{15}{12} \div \frac{15}{7} = \frac{\overset{1}{15}}{12} \times \frac{7}{\underset{1}{15}} = \frac{7}{12}$$

$$1\frac{3}{8} \div 3\frac{1}{7} = \frac{11}{8} \div \frac{22}{7} = \frac{\overset{1}{11}}{8} \times \frac{7}{\underset{2}{22}} = \frac{7}{16}$$

$$3\frac{3}{4} \div 1\frac{2}{3} = \frac{15}{4} \div \frac{5}{3} = \frac{\overset{3}{15}}{4} \times \frac{3}{\underset{1}{5}} = \frac{9}{4} = 2\frac{1}{4}$$

$$4\frac{1}{4} \div 3\frac{1}{3} = \frac{17}{4} \div \frac{10}{3} = \frac{17}{4} \times \frac{3}{10} = \frac{51}{40} = 1\frac{11}{40}$$

$$5\frac{1}{3} \div 4\frac{4}{5} = \frac{16}{3} \div \frac{24}{5} = \frac{\overset{2}{16}}{3} \times \frac{5}{\underset{3}{24}} = \frac{10}{9} = 1\frac{1}{9}$$

$$4\frac{2}{3} \div 3\frac{4}{9} = \frac{14}{3} \div \frac{31}{9} = \frac{14}{3} \times \frac{\overset{3}{9}}{31} = \frac{42}{31} = 1\frac{11}{31}$$

$$2\frac{5}{8} \div 1\frac{3}{4} = \frac{21}{8} \div \frac{7}{4} = \frac{\overset{3}{21}}{8} \times \frac{\overset{1}{4}}{\underset{2}{7}} = \frac{3}{2} = 1\frac{1}{2}$$

$$4\frac{2}{3} \div 7\frac{7}{8} = \frac{14}{3} \div \frac{63}{8} = \frac{\overset{2}{14}}{3} \times \frac{8}{\underset{9}{63}} = \frac{16}{27}$$

$$6\frac{1}{4} \div 3\frac{1}{3} = \frac{25}{4} \div \frac{10}{3} = \frac{\overset{5}{25}}{4} \times \frac{3}{\underset{2}{10}} = \frac{15}{8} = 1\frac{7}{8}$$

$$1\frac{7}{8} \div 3\frac{4}{7} = \frac{15}{8} \div \frac{25}{7} = \frac{\overset{3}{15}}{8} \times \frac{7}{\underset{5}{25}} = \frac{21}{40}$$

$$5\frac{1}{3} \div 3\frac{5}{9} = \frac{16}{3} \div \frac{32}{9} = \frac{\overset{1}{16}}{3} \times \frac{\overset{3}{9}}{\underset{2}{32}} = \frac{3}{2} = 1\frac{1}{2}$$

$$2\frac{1}{3} \div 3\frac{3}{4} = \frac{7}{3} \div \frac{15}{4} = \frac{7}{3} \times \frac{4}{15} = \frac{28}{45}$$

$$8\frac{3}{4} \div 2\frac{4}{5} = \frac{35}{4} \div \frac{14}{5} = \frac{\overset{5}{35}}{4} \times \frac{5}{\underset{2}{14}} = \frac{25}{8} = 3\frac{1}{8}$$

$$2\frac{5}{6} \div 6\frac{4}{5} = \frac{17}{6} \div \frac{34}{5} = \frac{\overset{1}{17}}{6} \times \frac{5}{\underset{2}{34}} = \frac{5}{12}$$

$$2\frac{1}{4} \div 2\frac{7}{8} = \frac{9}{4} \div \frac{15}{8} = \frac{\overset{3}{9}}{4} \times \frac{7}{\underset{5}{15}} = \frac{21}{20} = 1\frac{1}{20}$$

$$3\frac{3}{8} \div 1\frac{2}{7} = \frac{27}{8} \div \frac{9}{7} = \frac{\overset{3}{27}}{8} \times \frac{7}{\underset{1}{9}} = \frac{21}{8} = 2\frac{5}{8}$$

$$2\frac{1}{4} \div 5\frac{5}{8} = \frac{9}{4} \div \frac{45}{8} = \frac{\overset{1}{9}}{\underset{1}{4}} \times \frac{\overset{2}{8}}{\underset{5}{45}} = \frac{2}{5}$$

---

③ Find the prime factorization of each number. Use exponents where appropriate.

105	120	124
$105 = 3 \times 5 \times 7$	$120 = 2 \times 2 \times 2 \times 3 \times 5$	$124 = 2 \times 2 \times 31$
	$120 = 2^3 \times 3 \times 5$	$124 = 2^2 \times 31$

④ Solve. Follow proper order of operations, and use the distributive property when necessary.
Hint: Multiply each term by the denominator to eliminate fractions.

$$5(x+3) - 4 = 6 + 9 \div 3 + 3x$$
$$5x + 15 - 4 = 6 + 3 + 3x$$
$$5x + 11 = 9 + 3x$$
$$2x = -2$$
$$x = -1$$

$$6x + 12 \div 4 - 1 = 2(x-1) - 6 + 2x$$
$$6x + 3 - 1 = 2x - 2 - 6 + 2x$$
$$6x + 2 = 4x - 8$$
$$2x = -10$$
$$x = -5$$

$$4(x+1) - 3(x+2) = 5$$
$$4x + 4 - 3x - 6 = 5$$
$$x - 2 = 5$$
$$x = 7$$

$$\frac{x}{2} + 2 = -1$$
$$\frac{x}{2} = -3$$
$$\cancel{2}\left(\frac{x}{\cancel{2}}\right) = 2(-3)$$
$$x = -6$$

$$\frac{x}{3} + 5 = x + 1$$
$$\frac{x}{3} = x - 4$$
$$\cancel{3}\left(\frac{x}{\cancel{3}}\right) = 3(x-4)$$
$$x = 3x - 12$$
$$-2x = -12$$
$$x = 6$$

$$\frac{x-1}{2} - 3 = 2x + 1$$
$$\frac{x-1}{2} = 2x + 4$$
$$\cancel{2}\left(\frac{x-1}{\cancel{2}}\right) = 2(2x+4)$$
$$x - 1 = 4x + 8$$
$$-3x = 9$$
$$x = -3$$

$$3(2x+1) < 5x + 12 \div 4$$
$$6x + 3 < 5x + 3$$
$$x < 0$$

$$5(x-2) - (2-5) > (18 \div 2 - 3) \div 2$$
$$5x - 10 - (-3) > (9-3) \div 2$$
$$5x - 10 + 3 > 6 \div 2$$
$$5x - 7 > 3$$
$$5x > 10$$
$$x > 2$$

$$\frac{x+2}{3} < 2x - 1$$
$$\cancel{3}\left(\frac{x+2}{\cancel{3}}\right) < 3(2x-1)$$
$$x + 2 < 6x - 3$$
$$-5x < -5$$
$$x > 1$$

⑤ Divide.

$$1.5)\overline{43.35} \quad \frac{28.9}{}$$
$$\frac{30}{133}$$
$$\frac{120}{135}$$
$$\frac{135}{0}$$

$$.23)\overline{4.14} \quad \frac{18}{}$$
$$\frac{23}{184}$$
$$\frac{184}{0}$$

$$1.2)\overline{54} \quad \frac{45}{}$$
$$\frac{48}{60}$$
$$\frac{60}{0}$$

$$.38)\overline{9.5} \quad \frac{25}{}$$
$$\frac{76}{190}$$
$$\frac{190}{0}$$

① Add.

$$2\frac{3}{7} + 3\frac{1}{7} = \left(\frac{17}{7} + \frac{22}{7}\right) = \frac{39}{7} = 5\frac{4}{7}$$

$$3\frac{1}{3} + 2\frac{1}{3} = \left(\frac{10}{3} + \frac{7}{3}\right) = \frac{17}{3} = 5\frac{2}{3}$$

$$2\frac{2}{7} + 5\frac{4}{7} = \left(\frac{16}{7} + \frac{39}{7}\right) = \frac{55}{7} = 7\frac{6}{7}$$

$$2\frac{3}{8} + 3\frac{1}{4} = \left(\frac{19}{8} + \frac{13}{4}\right) = \left(\frac{19}{8} + \frac{26}{8}\right) = \frac{45}{8} = 5\frac{5}{8}$$

$$1\frac{3}{5} + 6\frac{3}{10} = \left(\frac{8}{5} + \frac{63}{10}\right) = \left(\frac{16}{10} + \frac{63}{10}\right) = \frac{79}{10} = 7\frac{9}{10}$$

$$2\frac{2}{3} + 5\frac{3}{4} = \left(\frac{8}{3} + \frac{23}{4}\right) = \left(\frac{32}{12} + \frac{69}{12}\right) = \frac{101}{12} = 8\frac{5}{12}$$

② Add, using the alternate method.

$$2\frac{3}{7} + 3\frac{1}{7} = (2+3) + \left(\frac{3}{7} + \frac{1}{7}\right) = 5 + \frac{4}{7} = 5\frac{4}{7}$$

$$3\frac{1}{3} + 2\frac{1}{3} = (3+2) + \left(\frac{1}{3} + \frac{1}{3}\right) = 5 + \frac{2}{3} = 5\frac{2}{3}$$

$$2\frac{2}{7} + 5\frac{4}{7} = (2+5) + \left(\frac{2}{7} + \frac{4}{7}\right) = 7 + \frac{6}{7} = 7\frac{6}{7}$$

$$2\frac{3}{8} + 3\frac{1}{4} = (2+3) + \left(\frac{3}{8} + \frac{1}{4}\right) = 5 + \left(\frac{3}{8} + \frac{2}{8}\right) = 5 + \frac{5}{8} = 5\frac{5}{8}$$

$$1\frac{3}{5} + 6\frac{3}{10} = (1+6) + \left(\frac{3}{5} + \frac{3}{10}\right) = 7 + \left(\frac{6}{10} + \frac{3}{10}\right) = 7 + \frac{9}{10} = 7\frac{9}{10}$$

$$2\frac{2}{3} + 5\frac{3}{4} = (2+5) + \left(\frac{2}{3} + \frac{3}{4}\right) = 7 + \left(\frac{8}{12} + \frac{9}{12}\right) = 7 + \frac{17}{12} = 7 + 1\frac{5}{12} = 8\frac{5}{12}$$

Alternate Method for Adding Mixed Numbers

Once students are comfortable adding mixed numbers that have been converted to improper fractions, you may wish to teach an alternate method.

- Add the whole number portions.
- Rewrite all fractions as equivalent fractions having a common denominator and add.
- If the sum of the fractions is an improper fraction, convert to a mixed number.
- Add the sum of the fractions to the sum of the whole numbers to get the answer.

Example:

$$2\frac{3}{4} + 1\frac{1}{2} = (2+1) + \left(\frac{3}{4} + \frac{1}{2}\right) =$$

$$3 + \left(\frac{3}{4} + \frac{2}{4}\right) = 3 + \frac{5}{4} = 3 + 1\frac{1}{4} + 4\frac{1}{4}$$

Teaching Tips, Cont.

➢ If students still do not understand why they must convert to improper fractions, use this example.

$$3\frac{3}{4} \div 1\frac{1}{4} =$$

What happens if you just divide?

$$3 \div 1 = 3$$

$$\frac{3}{4} \div \frac{1}{4} = 3$$

Adding the answer from the whole number portion to the answer from the fraction portion gives 3 + 3 = 6. This does not even make sense! The correct answer is 3.

$$3\frac{3}{4} \div 1\frac{1}{4} = \frac{15}{4} \div \frac{5}{4} =$$

$$\frac{\overset{3}{\cancel{15}}}{\underset{1}{\cancel{4}}} \times \frac{\overset{1}{\cancel{4}}}{\underset{1}{\cancel{5}}} = 3$$

➢ Teach the alternate method for adding mixed numbers. Worksheet 21 section 2 provides practice in the new method using the same problems as section 1.

➢ Complete the Classwork exercises. Have some students work the problems on the board for the class and explain their answers. All students should work the problems in their books.

Assignments
- Complete Lesson 42, Activities 2-5.
- Worksheet 21, Activity 2
- If possible, bring instructions for building or construction sets to be used in Lesson 45.

Lesson 43

Concepts
- Ratios
- Single-variable inequalities
- Multiplying fractions
- Dividing fractions
- Multiplying mixed numbers
- Dividing mixed numbers
- Subtracting mixed numbers

Learning Objectives
The student will be able to:
- Define *ratio*
- Write a ratio in three different formats
- Reduce ratios to simplest form
- Calculate ratios from given sets of data
- Subtract mixed numbers without converting to improper fractions

Materials Needed
- Student Book, Lesson 43
- Worksheet 22

Teaching Tips
➤ Teach ratios from the teaching box.

➤ Show students the three ways to write a ratio. Explain that all three ways are correct and equivalent.

➤ Emphasize that ratios forming improper fractions *must* be left as improper fractions. A mixed number is *not* an acceptable way of writing a ratio because it does not show a comparison between two distinct values.

Ratios

A ratio is an expression that compares two quantities. For example, if a class has 9 girls and 12 boys, the ratio of girls to boys would be 9 to 12.

Ratios can be written in one of three formats. The ratio in the above example can be written in any of the following ways:
9 to 12
9:12
$\frac{9}{12}$

Just as in fractions, ratios should be written in lowest terms. In the above example, both 9 and 12 are divisible by 3, so the proper way to express the ratio is 3 to 4, 3:4, or $\frac{3}{4}$.

To express the ratio of boys to girls, switch the terms. The ratios would then be written 4 to 3, 4:3, or $\frac{4}{3}$.

When working with ratios, always leave improper fractions as improper fractions. Never convert a ratio to a mixed number. Ratios that can reduce to a whole number are written as an improper fraction with 1 as the denominator or with 1 as the second term.

Any of the three methods for writing ratios is acceptable, but you will find that expressing ratios as fractions will make working with them easier later on.

① Classwork
Write ratios in simplest form.

The following car numbers finished in the top 10 of a recent race: 12, 1, 2, 8, 73, 5, 9, 13, 58, 24

What is the ratio of odd numbers to even numbers?
Odd: 1, 73, 5, 9, 13
Even: 12, 2, 8, 58, 24
Ratio: $\frac{5}{5} = \frac{1}{1}$ or 1:1 or 1 to 1

What is the ratio of prime numbers to composite numbers?
·Prime: 2, 73, 5, 13
Composite: 12, 8, 9, 58, 24
Ratio: $\frac{4}{5}$ or 4:5 or 4 to 5

What is the ratio of multiples of 2 to multiples of 3?
Multiples of 2: 12, 2, 8, 58, 24
Multiples of 3: 12, 9, 24
Ratio: $\frac{5}{3}$ or 5:3 or 5 to 3

Activities
② Write ratios in simplest form.

The numbers and colors of the top ten finishing cars of a recent race are as follows: 12: red, 1: blue, 2: white, 8: black, 73: green, 5: grey, 9: grey, 13: green, 58: yellow, and 24: red.

What is the ratio of primary colors (red, blue, yellow) to secondary colors (purple, green, orange)?
$\frac{4}{2} = \frac{2}{1}$ or 2:1 or 2 to 1

What is the ratio of cars that are black, grey, and white to cars that are colored?
$\frac{4}{6} = \frac{2}{3}$ or 2:3 or 2 to 3

---

③ Solve.

$-5(-2+4x) < 2(-6x-7)$
$10-20x < -12x-14$
$-8x < -24$
$-x < -3$
$x > 3$

$-5(2x+6) > 2^2(-5-2x)+3x$
$-10x-30 > 4(-5-2x)+3x$
$-10x-30 > -20-8x+3x$
$-10x-30 > -20-5x$
$-5x > 10$
$-x > 2$
$x < -2$

$-11-5x > (3^2-3)(5x+4)$
$-11-5x > (9-3)(5x+4)$
$-11-5x > 6(5x+4)$
$-11-5x > 30x+24$
$-35x > 35$
$-x > 1$
$x < -1$

④ Multiply or divide as indicated.

$\frac{2}{3} \times \frac{2}{9} = \frac{2 \times 2}{3 \times 9} = \frac{4}{27}$

$\frac{1}{4} \times \frac{4}{5} = \frac{1}{{}_1\cancel{4}} \times \frac{\cancel{4}^1}{5} = \frac{1}{5}$

$\frac{3}{8} \times \frac{4}{9} = \frac{{}^1\cancel{3}}{{}_2\cancel{8}} \times \frac{\cancel{4}^1}{\cancel{9}_3} = \frac{1}{6}$

$\frac{8}{9} \times \frac{1}{4} = \frac{{}^2\cancel{8}}{9} \times \frac{1}{\cancel{4}_1} = \frac{2}{9}$

$2\frac{1}{6} \times \frac{2}{5} = \frac{13}{{}_3\cancel{6}} \times \frac{\cancel{2}^1}{5} = \frac{13}{15}$

$2\frac{1}{4} \times \frac{8}{9} = \frac{{}^1\cancel{9}}{{}_1\cancel{4}} \times \frac{\cancel{8}^2}{\cancel{9}_1} = \frac{2}{1} = 2$

$4\frac{5}{7} \times \frac{2}{3} = \frac{{}^{11}\cancel{33}}{7} \times \frac{2}{\cancel{3}_1} = \frac{22}{7} = 3\frac{1}{7}$

$4\frac{1}{2} \times \frac{1}{6} = \frac{{}^3\cancel{9}}{2} \times \frac{1}{\cancel{6}_2} = \frac{3}{4}$

$1\frac{1}{2} \times 3\frac{1}{6} = \frac{{}^1\cancel{3}}{2} \times \frac{19}{\cancel{6}_2} = \frac{19}{4} = 4\frac{3}{4}$

$4\frac{1}{8} \times 4\frac{2}{3} = \frac{{}^{11}\cancel{33}}{{}_4\cancel{8}} \times \frac{\cancel{14}^7}{\cancel{3}_1} = \frac{77}{4} = 19\frac{1}{4}$

$1\frac{3}{4} \times 4\frac{4}{9} = \frac{7}{{}_1\cancel{4}} \times \frac{\cancel{40}^{10}}{9} = \frac{70}{9} = 7\frac{7}{9}$

$4\frac{2}{3} \times 5\frac{1}{2} = \frac{{}^7\cancel{14}}{3} \times \frac{11}{\cancel{2}_1} = \frac{77}{3} = 25\frac{2}{3}$

$\frac{2}{9} \div \frac{1}{3} = \frac{2}{{}_3\cancel{9}} \times \frac{\cancel{3}^1}{1} = \frac{2}{3}$

$\frac{3}{4} \div \frac{5}{8} = \frac{3}{{}_1\cancel{4}} \times \frac{\cancel{8}^2}{5} = \frac{6}{5} = 1\frac{1}{5}$

$\frac{1}{6} \div \frac{3}{4} = \frac{1}{{}_3\cancel{6}} \times \frac{\cancel{4}^2}{3} = \frac{2}{9}$

$\frac{2}{3} \div \frac{2}{7} = \frac{2}{3} \times \frac{7}{\cancel{2}_1} = \frac{7}{3} = 2\frac{1}{3}$

$1\frac{5}{7} \div \frac{1}{6} = \frac{12}{7} \div \frac{1}{6} = \frac{12}{7} \times \frac{6}{1} = \frac{72}{7} = 10\frac{2}{7}$

$2\frac{8}{9} \div \frac{2}{3} = \frac{26}{9} \div \frac{2}{3} = \frac{{}^{13}\cancel{26}}{{}_3\cancel{9}} \times \frac{\cancel{3}^1}{\cancel{2}_1} = \frac{13}{3} = 4\frac{1}{3}$

$4\frac{2}{3} \div \frac{4}{7} = \frac{14}{3} \div \frac{4}{7} = \frac{{}^7\cancel{14}}{3} \times \frac{7}{\cancel{4}_2} = \frac{49}{6} = 8\frac{1}{6}$

$4\frac{2}{7} \div \frac{3}{4} = \frac{30}{7} \div \frac{3}{4} = \frac{{}^{10}\cancel{30}}{7} \times \frac{4}{\cancel{3}_1} = \frac{40}{7} = 5\frac{5}{7}$

$2\frac{1}{4} \div 2\frac{1}{3} = \frac{9}{4} \div \frac{7}{3} = \frac{9}{4} \times \frac{3}{7} = \frac{27}{28}$

$3\frac{3}{7} \div 4\frac{1}{2} = \frac{24}{7} \div \frac{9}{2} = \frac{{}^8\cancel{24}}{7} \times \frac{2}{\cancel{9}_3} = \frac{16}{21}$

$1\frac{6}{7} \div 2\frac{8}{9} = \frac{13}{7} \div \frac{26}{9} = \frac{{}^1\cancel{13}}{7} \times \frac{9}{\cancel{26}_2} = \frac{9}{14}$

$1\frac{1}{2} \div 3\frac{3}{5} = \frac{3}{2} \div \frac{18}{5} = \frac{{}^1\cancel{3}}{2} \times \frac{5}{\cancel{18}_6} = \frac{5}{12}$

① Subtract.

$$8\frac{5}{8} - 5\frac{1}{8} = \frac{69}{8} - \frac{41}{8} = \frac{28}{8} = 3\frac{4}{8} = 3\frac{1}{2}$$

$$5\frac{3}{4} - 1\frac{1}{2} = \frac{23}{4} - \frac{3}{2} = \frac{23}{4} - \frac{6}{4} = \frac{17}{4} = 4\frac{1}{4}$$

$$7\frac{2}{3} - 3\frac{1}{6} = \frac{23}{3} - \frac{19}{6} = \frac{46}{6} - \frac{19}{6} = \frac{27}{6} = 4\frac{3}{6} = 4\frac{1}{2}$$

$$5\frac{3}{10} - 2\frac{1}{5} = \frac{53}{10} - \frac{11}{5} = \frac{53}{10} - \frac{22}{10} = \frac{31}{10} = 3\frac{1}{10}$$

$$3\frac{1}{4} - 1\frac{7}{8} = \frac{13}{4} - \frac{15}{8} = \frac{26}{8} - \frac{15}{8} = \frac{11}{8} = 1\frac{3}{8}$$

$$8\frac{1}{4} - 5\frac{2}{3} = \frac{33}{4} - \frac{17}{3} = \frac{99}{12} - \frac{68}{12} = \frac{31}{12} = 2\frac{7}{12}$$

② Subtract, using the alternate method.

$$8\frac{5}{8} - 5\frac{1}{8} = (8-5) + \left(\frac{5}{8} - \frac{1}{8}\right) = 3 + \frac{4}{8} = 3\frac{4}{8} = 3\frac{1}{2}$$

$$5\frac{3}{4} - 1\frac{1}{2} = (5-1) + \left(\frac{3}{4} - \frac{1}{2}\right) = 4 + \left(\frac{3}{4} - \frac{2}{4}\right) = 4 + \frac{1}{4} = 4\frac{1}{4}$$

$$7\frac{2}{3} - 3\frac{1}{6} = (7-3) + \left(\frac{2}{3} - \frac{1}{6}\right) = 4 + \left(\frac{4}{6} - \frac{1}{6}\right) = 4 + \frac{3}{6} = 4\frac{3}{6} = 4\frac{1}{2}$$

$$5\frac{3}{10} - 2\frac{1}{5} = (5-2) + \left(\frac{3}{10} - \frac{1}{5}\right) = 3 + \left(\frac{3}{10} - \frac{2}{10}\right) = 3 + \frac{1}{10} = 3\frac{1}{10}$$

$$3\frac{1}{4} - 1\frac{7}{8} = (3-1) + \left(\frac{1}{4} - \frac{7}{8}\right) = 2 + \left(\frac{2}{8} - \frac{7}{8}\right) = 1 + \left(\frac{8+2}{8} - \frac{7}{8}\right) = 1 + \frac{3}{8} = 1\frac{3}{8}$$

$$8\frac{1}{4} - 5\frac{2}{3} = (8-5) + \left(\frac{1}{4} - \frac{2}{3}\right) = 3 + \left(\frac{3}{12} - \frac{8}{12}\right) = 2 + \left(\frac{12+3}{12} - \frac{8}{12}\right) = 2 + \frac{7}{12} = 2\frac{7}{12}$$

Alternate Method for Subtracting Mixed Numbers

Once students are comfortable subtracting mixed numbers that have been converted to improper fractions, you may wish to teach an alternate method.

- Rewrite all fractions as equivalent fractions having a common denominator and subtract. If necessary, regroup to form an improper fraction.
- Subtract the whole numbers.
- Subtract the fractions.
- Add the difference of the whole numbers to the difference of the fractions to get the answer.

Example:

$$3\frac{1}{2} - 1\frac{3}{4} = (3-1) + \left(\frac{1}{2} - \frac{3}{4}\right) =$$

$$2 + \left(\frac{2}{4} - \frac{3}{4}\right) = 1 + \left(\frac{6}{4} - \frac{3}{4}\right) = 1 + \frac{3}{4} = 1\frac{3}{4}$$

Teaching Tips, Cont.

➢ Review multiplication and division of fractions and mixed numbers as necessary. (See Lessons 36-37, and 41-42)

➢ Teach the alternate method for subtracting mixed numbers. Worksheet 22 provides practice in the new method. Each problem is given twice. Students should solve the top half by forming improper fractions and the bottom half using the new method. They should then compare their answers in the two sections to check their work.

➢ Complete the Classwork exercises. Have some students work the problems on the board for the class and explain their answers. All students should work the problems in their books.

Assignments

- Complete Lesson 43, Activities 2-4.
- Worksheet 22
- If possible, bring instructions for building or construction sets to be used in Lesson 45.

Lesson 44

Concepts

- Identifying proportions
- Solving proportions
- Metric system conversion
- Multiplying by powers of 10
- Dividing by powers of 10
- Order of operations
- Single-variable equations
- Math in the real world

Learning Objectives

The student will be able to:

- Define *proportions*
- Use cross multiplication to solve proportions
- Identify if pairs of ratios form a proportion

Materials Needed

- Student Book, Lesson 44

Teaching Tips

➢ Review ratios. (See Lesson 43)

➢ Review equivalent fractions. (See Lesson 32)

➢ Teach proportions. Point out that equivalent fractions form a proportion. Emphasize that when working with proportions, the terms are called *ratios*, not *fractions*.

Proportions

A **proportion** is a mathematical sentence showing two ratios are equal. For example, $\frac{1}{2} = \frac{2}{4}$ is a proportion. Notice that a proportion looks the same as two equivalent fractions.

The easiest method to solve a proportion is to **cross multiply**. Multiply the numerator of the first ratio by the denominator of the second ratio. Multiply the denominator of the first ratio by the numerator of the second ratio. In a true proportion, these values will always be equal.

For example, $\frac{6}{9} = \frac{4}{6}$ is a proportion because $6 \times 6 = 9 \times 4$.

When the ratios are not written as fractions, the product of the outer terms will equal the product of the inner terms. For example, 6:9 = 4:6 because $6 \times 6 = 9 \times 4$ and 6 to 9 = 4 to 6 because $6 \times 6 = 9 \times 4$.

To solve for an unknown in a proportion, let a variable represent the unknown term. Cross multiply and solve for the variable.

$$\frac{3}{5} = \frac{6}{x}$$
$$3x = 5(6)$$
$$3x = 30$$
$$x = 10$$

① Classwork

Write = or ≠ to indicate if each pair of ratios forms a proportion.

$\frac{6}{20} \neq \frac{12}{26}$ $6 \times 26 = 156;\ 20 \times 12 = 240$

$\frac{5}{3} = \frac{15}{9}$ $5 \times 9 = 45;\ 3 \times 15 = 45$

$\frac{5}{8} \neq \frac{18}{32}$ $5 \times 32 = 160;\ 8 \times 18 = 144$

$\frac{4}{9} = \frac{20}{36}$ $4 \times 36 = 144;\ 9 \times 20 = 180$

Solve the proportions. Leave answers as improper fractions where appropriate.

$\frac{4}{8} = \frac{x}{10}$ $4(10) = 8x \Rightarrow 40 = 8x \Rightarrow 5 = x$

$\frac{x}{6} = \frac{8}{3}$ $3x = 6(8) \Rightarrow 3x = 48 \Rightarrow x = 16$

$\frac{11}{22} = \frac{x}{9}$ $11(9) = 22x \Rightarrow 99 = 22x \Rightarrow \frac{9}{2} = x$

$\frac{3}{7} = \frac{5}{x}$ $3x = 7(5) \Rightarrow 3x = 35 \Rightarrow x = \frac{35}{3}$

Activities

② Write = or ≠ to indicate if each pair of ratios forms a proportion.

$\frac{12}{60} = \frac{5}{25}$ $12 \times 25 = 300;\ 60 \times 5 = 300$

$\frac{4}{34} \neq \frac{17}{8}$ $4 \times 8 = 32;\ 34 \times 17 = 578$

$\frac{11}{15} \neq \frac{5}{7}$ $11 \times 7 = 77;\ 5 \times 15 = 75$

$\frac{15}{27} = \frac{10}{18}$ $15 \times 18 = 270;\ 27 \times 10 = 270$

$\frac{33}{100} \neq \frac{1}{3}$ $33 \times 3 = 99;\ 100 \times 1 = 100$

$\frac{14}{26} = \frac{21}{39}$ $14 \times 39 = 546;\ 26 \times 21 = 546$

$\frac{18}{24} \neq \frac{24}{36}$ $18 \times 36 = 648;\ 24 \times 24 = 576$

$\frac{36}{10} = \frac{54}{15}$ $36 \times 15 = 540;\ 54 \times 10 = 540$

---

③ Solve the proportions. Leave answers as improper fractions where appropriate.

$\dfrac{x}{6} = \dfrac{26}{4}$

$4x = 6(26)$

$4x = 156$

$x = 39$

$\dfrac{6}{39} = \dfrac{x}{156}$

$6(156) = 39x$

$936 = 39x$

$24 = x$

$\dfrac{12}{x} = \dfrac{8}{12}$

$12(12) = 8x$

$144 = 8x$

$18 = x$

$\dfrac{4}{7} = \dfrac{28}{x}$

$4x = 7(28)$

$4x = 196$

$x = 49$

$\dfrac{x}{2} = \dfrac{9}{7}$

$7x = 2(9)$

$7x = 18$

$x = \dfrac{18}{7}$

$\dfrac{4}{34} = \dfrac{x}{8}$

$4(8) = 34x$

$32 = 34x$

$\dfrac{32}{34} = x$

$x = \dfrac{16}{17}$

$\dfrac{21}{x} = \dfrac{14}{9}$

$21(9) = 14x$

$189 = 14x$

$\dfrac{189}{14} = x$

$x = \dfrac{27}{2}$

$\dfrac{5}{6} = \dfrac{2}{x}$

$5x = 6(2)$

$5x = 12$

$x = \dfrac{12}{5}$

④ Multiply or divide by the correct powers of 10 to convert the metric measurements.

7 m = __7000__ mm

0.42 L = __420__ mL

6.7 g = __670__ cg

31.48 W = __31,480__ mW

25,000 cm = __250__ m

8365 mL = __8.365__ L

129 cW = __1.29__ W

6.13 mg = __0.00613__ g

⑤ Solve, following the proper order of operations.

$4(x+1) - 5 = 3 + 8 \div 4 + 2x$

$4x + 4 - 5 = 3 + 2 + 2x$

$4x - 1 = 5 + 2x$

$2x = 6$

$x = 3$

$7x + 15 \div 3 - 2 = 3(x-2) + 7 + 2x$

$7x + 5 - 2 = 3x - 6 + 7 + 2x$

$7x + 3 = 5x + 1$

$2x = -2$

$x = -1$

$2(3x+1) - (x+3) = 14$

$6x + 2 - x - 3 = 14$

$5x - 1 = 14$

$5x = 15$

$x = 3$

⑥ Solve. Write your answer as a mixed number.
Steve has completed 72 of the 100 laps in a race on a $\frac{3}{8}$-mile track. How many miles must he still drive to finish the race?
Steve must complete 100 − 72 = 28 laps.

$\overset{7}{\cancel{28}}\left(\dfrac{3}{\underset{2}{\cancel{8}}}\right) = \dfrac{21}{2} = 10\dfrac{1}{2}$ miles

Teaching Tips, Cont.

➢ Explain that the ratios may be written in any of the three ways to form a proportion, but that writing ratios in fraction form will be the easiest to work with.

➢ Show students how to cross multiply to solve proportions. (See Lesson 32)

➢ Remind students that ratios are left as improper fractions rather than mixed numbers. Explain that the same rule applies when working with proportions since a proportion is two equivalent ratios.

➢ Complete the Classwork exercises. Have some students work the problems on the board for the class and explain their answers. All students should work the problems in their books.

Assignments

- Complete Lesson 44, Activities 2-6.
- If possible, bring instructions for building or construction sets to be used in Lesson 45.

Horizons Pre-Algebra, Teacher's Guide

Lesson 45

Concepts
- Scale drawings
- Ratios
- Solving proportions
- Math in the real world
- Greatest common factor
- Multiplying mixed numbers
- Dividing mixed numbers
- Absolute value

Learning Objectives
The student will be able to:
- Define *scale drawing*
- Set up a proportion for a scale drawing
- Calculate the measurements for a scale drawing based on actual measurements and a given ratio.

Materials Needed
- Student Book, Lesson 45
- Worksheet 23
- Formula strip, Lesson 45
- Examples of scale drawings

Teaching Tips
➢ Have students complete Worksheet 23 in class. This may be for added practice of earlier topics, or graded as a quiz, if desired. Give students the strip labeled "For use in Lesson 45" from the formula strip page.

➢ Review cross multiplication and solving proportions. (See Lessons 32 and 44)

➢ Teach scale drawings. Ask students when having a scale drawing would be important. (Examples: blueprint for construction; assembly instructions; schematics and wiring diagrams; floor plans)

Scale Drawings

A **scale drawing** is a proportionally accurate representation of a real thing. A scale drawing may be larger or smaller than the actual object. All measurements on the scale drawing must be the same ratio as the corresponding measurements on the actual object. The ratio on a scale drawing is usually expressed using a colon or the word *to*.

For example, if 1 inch on a scale drawing represents 12 inches on the real object, the ratio is expressed as 1:12 or 1 to 12. Make sure the same measurements are used for both parts of the ratio and make the necessary conversions. For example, if 1 inch on a scale drawing represents 2 feet on the real object, the ratio is 1:24, not 1:2, because there are 24 inches in 2 feet.

To find missing lengths on a scale drawing, set up a proportion. If the ratio is known, use that as one of the fractions in the proportion. Otherwise, use known corresponding lengths to find the ratio.

Example:
If a 6-inch line is used to represent a 3-foot length, how long should a line be to represent a 4-foot length?

First, set up a proportion, letting a variable represent the unknown length. Make sure you are consistent in your placement of the terms in the ratios. If the measurement from the original is in the denominator on one ratio, it must be in the denominator of the other ratio. ALWAYS include the units, if given, on all known measurements. The units will cancel, letting you know the proper units for the answer.

$$\frac{6 \text{ inches}}{3 \text{ feet}} = \frac{x}{4 \text{ feet}}$$

Cross multiply and cancel identical units. Solve for the unknown variable.

$6 \text{ inches}(4 \text{ feet}) = 3 \text{ feet}(x)$

$24 \text{ inches} = 3x$

$8 \text{ inches} = x$

The line should be 8 inches long.

① **Classwork**
Label the scale drawing if the ratio of the scale drawing to the actual measurements is 1:6.

Actual measurements

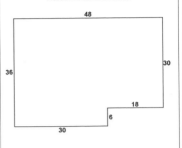

Scale drawing measurements

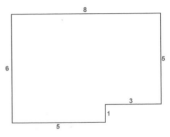

Set up proportions so each of the following ratios are equal to $\frac{1}{6}$:

$$\frac{x}{48}, \frac{x}{30}, \frac{x}{18}, \frac{x}{6}, \frac{x}{36}$$

Solve for x in each proportion to find the length of the sides in the scale drawing.

Activities

② Solve.
Steve is building a pine car replica of his race car using a ratio of 1:35. The pine car he builds is $5\frac{1}{2}$ inches long, $2\frac{1}{4}$ inches wide and $1\frac{1}{10}$ inches high. What are the length, width, and height of Steve's race car? Express answers as mixed numbers where necessary.

Length:
$$\frac{1}{35} = \frac{5\frac{1}{2}}{x}$$
$x = 35\left(\frac{11}{2}\right)$
$x = \frac{385}{2}$
$x = 192\frac{1}{2}$ inches

Width:
$$\frac{1}{35} = \frac{2\frac{1}{4}}{x}$$
$x = 35\left(\frac{9}{4}\right)$
$x = \frac{315}{4}$
$x = 78\frac{3}{4}$ inches

Height:
$$\frac{1}{35} = \frac{1\frac{1}{10}}{x}$$
$x = \overset{7}{35}\left(\frac{11}{10_2}\right)$
$x = \frac{77}{2}$
$x = 38\frac{1}{2}$ inches

③ Find the greatest common factor of each set of numbers.

48 and 72
$48 = ②×②×②×2×③$
$72 = ②×②×②×③×3$
GCF: $2^3 × 3 = 8 × 3 = 24$

42 and 63
$42 = 2×③×⑦$
$63 = ③×3×⑦$
GCF: $3 × 7 = 21$

36 and 42
$36 = ②×2×③×3$
$42 = ②×③×7$
GCF: $2 × 3 = 6$

④ Multiply or divide as indicated.

$6\frac{3}{7} × 3\frac{1}{9} = \frac{\overset{5}{\cancel{45}}}{\cancel{7}_1} × \frac{\overset{4}{\cancel{28}}}{\cancel{9}_1} = \frac{20}{1} = 20$

$2\frac{7}{12} ÷ 5\frac{5}{6} = \frac{31}{12} ÷ \frac{35}{6} = \frac{31}{_2\cancel{12}} × \frac{\cancel{6}^1}{35} = \frac{31}{70}$

$6\frac{3}{5} × 1\frac{7}{11} = \frac{\overset{3}{\cancel{33}}}{5} × \frac{18}{\cancel{11}_1} = \frac{54}{5} = 10\frac{4}{5}$

$1\frac{5}{8} ÷ 2\frac{8}{9} = \frac{13}{8} ÷ \frac{26}{9} = \frac{\overset{1}{\cancel{13}}}{8} × \frac{9}{\cancel{26}_2} = \frac{9}{16}$

$4\frac{3}{8} × 5\frac{1}{3} = \frac{35}{\cancel{8}_1} × \frac{\cancel{16}^2}{3} = \frac{70}{3} = 23\frac{1}{3}$

$4\frac{1}{2} ÷ 5\frac{2}{5} = \frac{9}{2} ÷ \frac{27}{5} = \frac{\overset{1}{\cancel{9}}}{2} × \frac{5}{\cancel{27}_3} = \frac{5}{6}$

⑤ Solve the proportions. Leave answers as improper fractions where appropriate.

$\frac{x}{7} = \frac{48}{42}$
$42x = 7(48)$
$42x = 336$
$x = 8$

$\frac{9}{17} = \frac{x}{153}$
$9(153) = 17x$
$1377 = 17x$
$81 = x$

$\frac{11}{x} = \frac{8}{11}$
$11(11) = 8x$
$121 = 8x$
$\frac{121}{8} = x$

$\frac{4}{7} = \frac{1}{x}$
$4x = 7(1)$
$4x = 7$
$x = \frac{7}{4}$

⑥ Solve the absolute values.

$|27 + 19| + |43 - 61| = 46 + 18 = 64$

$-|27 + 19| + |43 - 61| = -46 + 18 = -28$

$-|43 - 61| + |19 - 27| = -18 + 8 = -10$

$|62 - 43| - |43 - 87| = 19 - 44 = -25$

$-|62 - 43| - |43 - 87| = -19 - 44 = -63$

$-|87 - 43| - |43 - 62| = -44 - 19 = -63$

English to Metric Length Conversion

Worksheet 23

① Complete the chart to show correct English length equivalents.

7 miles	7 miles $\left(\frac{1760 \text{ yards}}{1 \text{ mile}}\right) = 12{,}320$ yards
4 yards	4 yards $\left(\frac{36 \text{ inches}}{1 \text{ yard}}\right) = 144$ inches
102 feet	102 feet $\left(\frac{1 \text{ yard}}{3 \text{ feet}}\right) = 34$ yards
31,680 feet	31,680 feet $\left(\frac{1 \text{ mile}}{5280 \text{ feet}}\right) = 6$ miles
15,840 yards	15,840 yards $\left(\frac{1 \text{ mile}}{1760 \text{ yards}}\right) = 9$ miles
360 inches	360 inches $\left(\frac{1 \text{ yard}}{36 \text{ inches}}\right) = 10$ yards
4 miles	4 miles $\left(\frac{5280 \text{ feet}}{1 \text{ mile}}\right) = 21{,}120$ feet

② Complete the chart to show correct English-Metric conversions.

11 inches	11 inches $\left(\frac{2.54 \text{ cm}}{1 \text{ inch}}\right) = 27.94$ cm
13 inches	13 inches $\left(\frac{25.4 \text{ mm}}{1 \text{ inch}}\right) = 330.2$ mm
12 yards	12 yards $\left(\frac{0.91 \text{ meter}}{1 \text{ yard}}\right) = 10.92$ meters
6 miles	6 miles $\left(\frac{1.61 \text{ km}}{1 \text{ mile}}\right) = 9.66$ km
20 cm	20 cm $\left(\frac{0.39 \text{ in.}}{1 \text{ cm}}\right) = 7.8$ inches
7 meters	7 meters $\left(\frac{1.09 \text{ yd.}}{1 \text{ meter}}\right) = 7.63$ yards
5 km	5 km $\left(\frac{0.62 \text{ mi.}}{1 \text{ km}}\right) = 3.1$ miles

Sources for Scale Drawings

Many apartment and builder websites have scale drawings of their floor plans posted on the internet. Note that these are not always posted in high enough resolution for printing. Another option is to stop by the model home in a new construction area and pick up several floor plans.

Several days in advance, you may ask students to bring the instructions for toys or games to class for this lesson. Especially appropriate are instructions for building and construction sets, such as blocks, bricks, logs, electronic components, etc.

You may also want to bring in a toy race car or model train. These are often built to scale from an actual item and have the ratio listed on the product packaging.

Teaching Tips, Cont.

➤ Show students the examples of scale drawings you brought. Ask what would happen if all of the drawings were done actual size. (They would be too big to be readable and usable, in most cases.)

➤ Ask students who brought instructions for building or construction sets to look for scale drawings and share their findings with the class.

➤ Explain that the measurements in a scale drawing can be calculated using proportions. The same ratio must be used for every measurement on the same scale drawing.

➤ Complete the Classwork exercises. Have some students work the problems on the board for the class. All students should work the problems in their books.

Assignment
Complete Lesson 45, Activities 2-6.

Horizons Pre-Algebra, Teacher's Guide

Lesson 46

Concepts
- Scientific notation
- Multiplying mixed numbers
- Dividing mixed numbers
- Divisibility tests
- Prime/composite numbers
- Math in the real world

Learning Objectives
The student will be able to:
- Define *scientific notation*
- Define *mantissa*
- Write numbers in scientific notation
- Convert numbers from scientific notation to standard form

Materials Needed
- Student Book, Lesson 46

Teaching Tips
➤ Review multiplying and dividing by powers of 10. (See Lessons 28-29)

➤ Write the numbers in the first paragraph of the teaching box on the board. Ask students if they can read them. (59 ten-quadrillionths and 467 trillion)

➤ Explain that scientists have devised a method of writing very small and very large numbers to make them much easier to read and work with.

➤ Teach scientific notation, showing that every notation includes multiplying by a power of 10.

Scientific Notation

Do you find it difficult to read the number 0.0000000000000059 without losing track of the number of zeros? It is also difficult to work with large numbers like 467,000,000,000,000 since most calculators will not accommodate that number of characters.

Scientists and mathematicians have developed a way to make working with these kinds of numbers easier. **Scientific notation** is a method of writing very large and very small numbers. Using this notation, numbers are written in the format $m \times 10^p$. M is the **mantissa** (also called the **significand**) and p is the exponent, or power of 10. The mantissa, or significand, is ALWAYS a number greater than or equal to 1 and less than 10. In other words, $1 \leq m < 10$.

The mantissa begins with the first non-zero digit of the standard notation number, and ends with the last non-zero digit. In the first example above, the mantissa is 5.9 because 5 is the first non-zero digit. A decimal point is always placed after the first non-zero digit so the mantissa will be less than 10.

In the second example, the mantissa is 4.67 because 4 is the first non-zero digit.

To find the value of p, count the number of places the decimal point must move from its place in the mantissa to its place in the standard form number. In the first example, the decimal point in 5.9 must move 15 places to the left. This makes p equal to -15 and the scientific notation is 5.9×10^{-15}.

In the second example, the decimal point in 4.67 moves 14 places to the right. This makes p equal to 14 and the scientific notation is 4.67×10^{14}.

① **Classwork**
Write each number in scientific notation.

652,000 6.52×10^5

37,000 3.7×10^4

7,500,000 7.5×10^6

92,300,000 9.23×10^7

0.00056 5.6×10^{-4}

0.00000049 4.9×10^{-7}

0.00000716 7.16×10^{-6}

0.000000008 8×10^{-9}

Write each number in standard form.

2.7×10^5 270,000

3.54×10^7 35,400,000

8.216×10^6 8,216,000

9×10^8 900,000,000

6.4×10^{-6} 0.0000064

3.98×10^{-7} 0.000000398

1.487×10^{-9} 0.000000001487

3×10^{-5} 0.00003

Activities
② Write each number in scientific notation.

170,000,000 1.7×10^8 0.000000814 8.14×10^{-7}

32,000,000 3.2×10^7 0.00037 3.7×10^{-4}

6,190,000,000 6.19×10^9 0.0000005674 5.674×10^{-7}

9,000,000 9×10^6 0.000000002 2×10^{-9}

---

③ Write each number in standard form.

3.8×10^6 3,800,000

7.481×10^9 7,481,000,000

9.26×10^7 92,600,000

6×10^5 600,000

5.8×10^{-7} 0.00000058

9.12×10^{-6} 0.00000912

3.875×10^{-8} 0.00000003875

7×10^{-5} 0.00007

④ Multiply or divide as indicated. Write answers as mixed numbers where necessary.

$$4\frac{1}{6} \times 3\frac{3}{5} = \frac{\overset{5}{\cancel{25}}}{\underset{1}{\cancel{6}}} \times \frac{\overset{3}{\cancel{18}}}{\underset{1}{\cancel{5}}} = \frac{15}{1} = 15$$

$$6\frac{3}{4} \times 1\frac{5}{9} = \frac{\overset{3}{\cancel{27}}}{\underset{2}{\cancel{4}}} \times \frac{\overset{7}{\cancel{14}}}{\underset{1}{\cancel{9}}} = \frac{21}{2} = 10\frac{1}{2}$$

$$3\frac{3}{10} \times 4\frac{1}{6} = \frac{\overset{11}{\cancel{33}}}{\underset{2}{\cancel{10}}} \times \frac{\overset{5}{\cancel{25}}}{\underset{2}{\cancel{6}}} = \frac{55}{4} = 13\frac{3}{4}$$

$$5\frac{3}{5} \div 3\frac{1}{9} = \frac{28}{5} \div \frac{28}{9} = \frac{\cancel{28}}{5} \times \frac{9}{\cancel{28}} = \frac{9}{5} = 1\frac{4}{5}$$

$$2\frac{5}{8} \div 1\frac{5}{9} = \frac{21}{8} \div \frac{14}{9} = \frac{\overset{3}{\cancel{21}}}{8} \times \frac{9}{\underset{2}{\cancel{14}}} = \frac{27}{16} = 1\frac{11}{16}$$

$$6\frac{2}{3} \div 3\frac{3}{4} = \frac{20}{3} \div \frac{15}{4} = \frac{\overset{4}{\cancel{20}}}{3} \times \frac{4}{\underset{3}{\cancel{15}}} = \frac{16}{9} = 1\frac{7}{9}$$

⑤ Use the divisibility tests to identify each number as prime or composite.

279   Composite (3, 9)

281   Prime

283   Prime

285   Composite (3, 5)

291   Composite (3)

293   Prime

⑥ Solve.

The tires on a race car are not all the same size. Tire stagger refers to the difference in sizes of the tires. The outside tires have about a 2-inch larger circumference (distance around the tire) than the inside tires. This allows for better handling on the turns of a circular or oval race track, since the outer tires must cover a greater distance. The tire stagger on Steve's car is given by the ratio 58:59. If the inside tire has a diameter of 29 inches, what is the diameter of the outside tire? (Express your answer as a mixed number.)

Do not make the mistake of adding 2 inches to the diameter. The *circumference* is 2 inches larger, not the diameter.

Set up a proportion using the tire stagger ratio and the diameter of the inside (smaller) tire:

$$\frac{58}{59} = \frac{29}{x}$$

Cross multiply and solve for x:

$$58x = 59(29)$$

$$58x = 1711$$

$$x = \frac{1711}{58}$$

$$x = 29\frac{29}{58}$$

$$x = 29\frac{1}{2} \text{ inches}$$

Teaching Tips, Cont.

➢ Tell students to pay careful attention to the exponent. Remind them that positive exponents will make the number larger and move the decimal point to the right. Negative exponents will make the number smaller and move the decimal point to the left.

➢ Complete the Classwork exercises. Have some students work the problems on the board for the class. All students should work the problems in their books.

Assignment

• Complete Lesson 46, Activities 2-6.

Lesson 47

Concepts
- Percent
- Percent-decimal conversion
- Least common multiple
- Fraction-decimal equivalents
- Solving proportions
- Scale drawings

Learning Objectives
The student will be able to:
- Define *percent*
- Express a percent as a decimal
- Express a decimal as a percent

Materials Needed
- Student Book, Lesson 47

Teaching Tips
➤ Review multiplying and dividing by powers of 10, focusing on 10^2 and 10^{-2}. (See Lessons 28-29)

➤ Teach the meaning of *percent*. Emphasize the *per hundred* portion of the definition. Make sure students understand that a percent of something does not require there to be exactly 100 to begin with, but the percent indicates an equivalent fraction with 100 as the denominator.

➤ Remind students that the word *per* in a problem indicates division, so in the case of percents, the equivalent fraction has a denominator of 100.

➤ Teach the conversion of percents to decimals. Write "90%" on the board. Ask a student to read it using the definition of percent rather than the word *percent*. (90 per hundred)

Percent

Percent means *hundredth* or *per hundred*. It is used to show how one quantity compares in size to another quantity. For example, if you receive a 90% on your test, you have correctly answered the equivalent of 90 out of 100 questions. It does not mean there were 100 questions on the test, but that the ratio of questions you answered correctly was equivalent to $\frac{90}{100}$.

To express a percent as a decimal, divide by 100. If you have 100% of something, you have 1 whole of that thing. If you have 200% of something, you have 2 of that thing. If you have 50% of something, you have the equivalent of 0.50, or half of that thing.

Conversely, to express a decimal as a percent, multiply by 100. If you have 1 whole, you have 100%. If you have 2 of something, you have 200%. If you have half, or 0.50 of something, you have 50%.

① Classwork
Convert each percent to a decimal.

8%	0.08
25%	0.25
33%	0.33
80%	0.8
150%	1.5
275%	2.75

Convert each decimal to a percent.

0.1	10%
0.67	67%
0.99	99%
1.4	140%
2.66	266%
3	300%

Activities

② Convert each percent to a decimal.

14%	0.14	92.7%	0.927
30%	0.3	2.8%	0.028
45%	0.45	133%	1.33
70%	0.7	498.1%	4.981
125%	1.25	5.7%	0.057
180%	1.8	0.67%	0.0067
3%	0.03	1%	0.01
10%	0.1	0.7%	0.007
85%	0.85	99.9%	0.999

③ Convert each decimal to a percent.

0.49	49%	0.583	58.3%
0.97	97%	0.019	1.9%
0.26	26%	4	400%
3.4	340%	7.523	752.3%
6.71	671%	0.09	9%
8	800%	0.005	0.5%
0.2	20%	0.00036	0.036%
0.07	7%	8.19	819%
1.01	101%	4.08	408%

④ Find the least common multiple of each set of numbers.

6, 10, and 12
$6 = 2 \times \boxed{3}$
$10 = 2 \times \boxed{5}$
$12 = 2 \times 2 \times 3 = \boxed{2^2} \times 3$
LCM: $2^2 \times 3 \times 5 = 60$

10, 15, and 20
$10 = 2 \times \boxed{5}$
$15 = \boxed{3} \times 5 =$
$20 = 2 \times 2 \times 5 = \boxed{2^2} \times 5$
LCM: $2^2 \times 3 \times 5 = 60$

9, 12, and 15
$9 = 3 \times 3 = \boxed{3^2}$
$12 = 2 \times 2 \times 3 = \boxed{2^2} \times 3$
$15 = 3 \times \boxed{5}$
LCM: $2^2 \times 3^2 \times 5 = 180$

⑤ Complete the chart to show proper fraction-decimal equivalents.

Fraction	Decimal	Fraction	Decimal
$\frac{3}{4}$	0.75	$\frac{1}{3}$	$0.\overline{3}$
$\frac{2}{5}$	0.4	$\frac{1}{4}$	0.25
$\frac{1}{6}$	$0.1\overline{6}$	$\frac{5}{6}$	$0.8\overline{3}$
$\frac{5}{8}$	0.625	$\frac{1}{8}$	0.125
$\frac{3}{10}$	0.3	$\frac{9}{10}$	0.9

⑥ Solve the proportions. Leave answers as improper fractions where appropriate.

$\frac{x}{12} = \frac{15}{40}$
$40x = 12(15)$
$40x = 180$
$x = \frac{\overset{9}{\cancel{180}}}{\underset{2}{\cancel{40}}}$
$x = \frac{9}{2}$

$\frac{12}{25} = \frac{x}{175}$
$12(175) = 25x$
$2100 = 25x$
$84 = x$

$\frac{7}{x} = \frac{11}{7}$
$7(7) = 11x$
$49 = 11x$
$\frac{49}{11} = x$

$\frac{8}{17} = \frac{1}{x}$
$8x = 17(1)$
$8x = 17$
$x = \frac{17}{8}$

⑦ Label the scale drawing using the ratio 1:12 if the original dimensions are length: 204 inches, width: 84 inches, and height: 42 inches. Write your answer as a mixed number where appropriate.

length:
$\frac{1}{12} = \frac{x}{204}$
$12x = 204$
$x = 17$ inches

width:
$\frac{1}{12} = \frac{x}{84}$
$12x = 84$
$x = 7$ inches

height:
$\frac{1}{12} = \frac{x}{42}$
$12x = 42$
$x = \frac{\overset{7}{\cancel{42}}}{\underset{2}{\cancel{12}}}$
$x = \frac{7}{2} = 3\frac{1}{2}$ inches

Teaching Tips, Cont.

➢ Demonstrate that 90% can be correctly written $\frac{90}{100}$. Ask a student to convert the fraction to a decimal. (0.9 or 0.90)

➢ Show students that converting a decimal to a percent is really dividing the number portion by 100 or dividing by 10^2. Point out that this is the same as multiplying by 10^{-2}.

➢ Teach the conversion of decimals to percents. Write "0.9" on the board. Ask the students how they could get the decimal back to a percent. (Multiplying by 10^2 or dividing by 10^{-2}) Point out that this is the opposite of going from a percent to a decimal.

➢ Complete the Classwork exercises. Have some students work the problems on the board for the class. All students should work the problems in their books.

Assignment

- Complete Lesson 47, Activities 2-7.

Lesson 48

Concepts
- Finding the percent of a number
- Prime factorization
- Roots
- Scientific notation
- Math in the real world

Learning Objectives
The student will be able to:
- Find the percent of a number
- Solve for a number when a percent of that number is given
- Calculate the percent when two numbers are given

Materials Needed
- Student Book, Lesson 48
- Worksheet 24

Teaching Tips
➢ Have students complete Worksheet 24 in class. This may be for added practice of earlier topics, or graded as a quiz, if desired.

➢ Review terminology for writing equations with one variable. (See Lessons 19-20)

➢ Explain that percent problems follow the same rules. A variable should be substituted for the word *what*, and an equal sign should be substituted for the word *is*.

➢ Write the following problem on the board: 25 is what percent of 50? Show students that the question can be written as a mathematical equation:
$25 = x\%(50)$ or $25 = 50x$

Finding the Percent of a Number

To solve percent problems, follow these steps:
- Change the percent to a decimal, if one is given.
- Set up an equation, using a variable to represent the unknown.
- Solve for the variable.
- Change the decimal to a percent if you are asked to find a percent.

For example, what is 25% of 50?
First, change 25% to a decimal: 25% = 0.25
Then, set up an equation: $x = 0.25(50)$
Now, solve for x.
$x = 0.25 \times 50$
$x = 12.5$

① Classwork
Solve.
What is 15% of 60?
$x = 0.15(60)$
$x = 9$

30 is 40% of what number?
$30 = 0.40x$
$30 \div 0.40 = x$
$75 = x$

40 is what percent of 125?
$40 = 125x$
$40 \div 125 = x$
$0.32 = x$
$32\% = x$

Activities

② Solve.

What is 30% of 90?	What is 25% of 92?	What is 18% of 40?
$x = 0.3(90)$	$x = 0.25(92)$	$x = 0.18(40)$
$x = 27$	$x = 23$	$x = 7.2$

What is 7% of 50?	What is 1.5% of 60?	What is 220% of 80?
$x = 0.07(50)$	$x = 0.015(60)$	$x = 2.2(80)$
$x = 3.5$	$x = 0.9$	$x = 176$

25 is 40% of what number?	66 is 55% of what number?	30 is 120% of what number?
$25 = 0.4x$	$66 = 0.55x$	$30 = 1.2x$
$25 \div 0.4 = x$	$66 \div 0.55 = x$	$30 \div 1.2 = x$
$x = 62.5$	$x = 120$	$x = 25$

30 is what percent of 150?	75 is what percent of 30?	9 is what percent of 180?
$30 = 150x$	$75 = 30x$	$9 = 180x$
$30 \div 150 = x$	$75 \div 30 = x$	$9 \div 180 = x$
$0.2 = x$	$2.5 = x$	$0.05 = x$
$x = 20\%$	$x = 250\%$	$x = 5\%$

③ Find the prime factorization of each argument and simplify the roots.

$\sqrt{96} = \sqrt{2 \times 2 \times 2 \times 2 \times 2 \times 3} = (2 \times 2)\sqrt{2 \times 3} = 4\sqrt{6}$

$\sqrt{72} = \sqrt{2 \times 2 \times 2 \times 3 \times 3} = (2 \times 3)\sqrt{2} = 6\sqrt{2}$

$3\sqrt{75} = 3\sqrt{3 \times 5 \times 5} = (3 \times 5)\sqrt{3} = 15\sqrt{3}$

$\sqrt{216} = \sqrt{2 \times 2 \times 2 \times 3 \times 3 \times 3} = (2 \times 3)\sqrt{2 \times 3} = 6\sqrt{6}$

$5\sqrt{300} = 5\sqrt{2 \times 2 \times 3 \times 5 \times 5} = (5 \times 2 \times 5)\sqrt{3} = 50\sqrt{3}$

④ Complete the chart to show proper conversion between scientific notation and standard form.

Scientific notation	Standard form	Standard form	Scientific notation
6.519×10^8	651,900,000	4,850,000,000	4.85×10^9
3.47×10^9	3,470,000,000	27,600,000,000	2.76×10^{10}
8.4×10^{-6}	0.0000084	0.0000000007	7×10^{-10}
3×10^{-7}	0.0000003	0.000000000812	8.12×10^{-10}

⑤ Solve.
The cross weight of a race car is calculated by finding the sum of the weight on the right front and left rear tires. For a race car to handle properly, the cross weight should be between 52% and 58% of the car's total weight. If the total weight of Steve's car is 3400 pounds, what is the minimum cross weight Steve should have on his car? What is the maximum cross weight Steve should have on his car?

Minimum cross weight: $0.52 \times 3400 = 1768$ pounds
Maximum cross weight: $0.58 \times 3400 = 1972$ pounds

The weight on each of the four tires of Steve's car is as follows: Right front – 925 pounds; Left front – 825 pounds; Right rear – 775 pounds; Left rear – 875 pounds. Does his car's cross weight fall within the acceptable range? What percent of the total weight is the cross weight of Steve's car? (Round to the nearest tenth of a percent.)
Right front + left rear = 925 pounds + 875 pounds = 1800 pounds
This is within the range of 1768 to 1972 pounds.
$1800 \div 3400 =$

```
       .5294
17)9.0000          0.5294 = 52.94% rounds to 52.9%
    85
    50
    34
    160
    153
      70
      68
```

① Write = or ≠ to indicate if each pair of ratios forms a proportion.

$\dfrac{12}{75} = \dfrac{16}{100}$ $12 \times 100 = 1200;\ 75 \times 16 = 1200$ $\dfrac{15}{25} \neq \dfrac{25}{35}$ $15 \times 35 = 525;\ 25 \times 25 = 625$

$\dfrac{4}{5} \neq \dfrac{16}{25}$ $4 \times 25 = 100;\ 5 \times 16 = 80$ $\dfrac{64}{24} = \dfrac{24}{9}$ $64 \times 9 = 576;\ 24 \times 24 = 576$

$\dfrac{10}{15} \neq \dfrac{25}{30}$ $10 \times 30 = 300;\ 15 \times 25 = 375$ $\dfrac{16}{100} \neq \dfrac{32}{50}$ $16 \times 50 = 800;\ 100 \times 32 = 3200$

$\dfrac{28}{30} = \dfrac{14}{15}$ $28 \times 15 = 420;\ 30 \times 14 = 420$ $\dfrac{16}{28} = \dfrac{48}{84}$ $16 \times 84 = 1344;\ 28 \times 48 = 1344$

$\dfrac{66}{100} \neq \dfrac{2}{3}$ $66 \times 3 = 198;\ 100 \times 2 = 200$ $\dfrac{4}{16} \neq \dfrac{5}{25}$ $4 \times 25 = 100;\ 16 \times 5 = 80$

$\dfrac{9}{12} = \dfrac{27}{36}$ $9 \times 36 = 324;\ 12 \times 27 = 324$ $\dfrac{36}{20} = \dfrac{54}{30}$ $36 \times 30 = 1080;\ 20 \times 54 = 1080$

② Solve the proportions. Leave answers as improper fractions where appropriate.

$\dfrac{x}{60} = \dfrac{1}{5}$	$\dfrac{2}{17} = \dfrac{x}{8}$	$\dfrac{11}{x} = \dfrac{5}{7}$	$\dfrac{5}{9} = \dfrac{10}{x}$
$5x = 60(1)$	$2(8) = 17x$	$11(7) = 5x$	$5x = 9(10)$
$5x = 60$	$16 = 17x$	$77 = 5x$	$5x = 90$
$x = 12$	$x = \dfrac{16}{17}$	$x = \dfrac{77}{5}$	$x = 18$
$\dfrac{x}{100} = \dfrac{1}{3}$	$\dfrac{7}{13} = \dfrac{x}{39}$	$\dfrac{18}{x} = \dfrac{2}{3}$	$\dfrac{18}{5} = \dfrac{54}{x}$
$3x = 1(100)$	$7(39) = 13x$	$18(3) = 2x$	$18x = 5(54)$
$3x = 100$	$273 = 13x$	$54 = 2x$	$18x = 270$
$x = \dfrac{100}{3}$	$\dfrac{273}{13} = x$	$x = 27$	$x = \dfrac{270}{18}$
	$x = 21$		$x = 15$

Teaching Tips, Cont.

➢ Ask a student to solve the equation 25 = 50x. ($x = \frac{1}{2}$)

➢ Show students that while this is a correct value of x, it does not answer the question. 25 is not $\frac{1}{2}$% of 50. The fraction must be changed to a percent.

➢ Review fraction-decimal equivalents, if needed.

➢ Review decimal-percent conversions. (See Lesson 47)

➢ Ask a student to convert $\frac{1}{2}$ to a decimal and then to a percent. ($\frac{1}{2} = 0.5 = 50\%$)

➢ Complete the Classwork exercises. Have some students work the problems on the board for the class. All students should work the problems in their books.

Assignment

• Complete Lesson 48, Activities 2-5.

Lesson 49

Concepts

- Fraction-percent conversion
- Least common multiple
- Prime factorization
- Roots
- Finding percents
- Scientific notation

Learning Objectives

The student will be able to:

- Convert fractions to percents
- Convert percents to fractions
- Convert repeating decimals to percents

Materials Needed

- Student Book, Lesson 49
- Fraction-decimal flashcards

Teaching Tips

➢ Review fraction-decimal equivalents using the flashcards.

➢ Review decimal-percent conversions. (See Lesson 47)

➢ Teach fraction-percent conversion. Explain that converting from a fraction to a percent is simple when fraction-decimal equivalents are used.

➢ Emphasize the importance of memorizing the fraction-decimal equivalents. (See Lesson 33)

➢ Show students how to work with repeating decimals. See the example in the column to the right.

Fraction-Percent Conversion

To change a fraction to a percent, first change the fraction to a decimal. Then change the decimal to a percent by multiplying by 100 and placing a percent symbol (%) after the number.

Express $\frac{1}{8}$ as a percent.

Change $\frac{1}{8}$ to a decimal: $\frac{1}{8} = 0.125$

Multiply 0.125 by 100: $0.125 \times 100 = 12.5\%$

To change a percent to a fraction, reverse the process. First, remove the percent symbol and divide by 100. Then convert the resulting decimal to a fraction.

Express 75% as a fraction.
Remove the percent symbol and divide by 100: $75 \div 100 = 0.75$
Convert 0.75 to a fraction: $\frac{3}{4}$

① Classwork

Complete the fraction-percent conversions.

Fraction	Percent
$\frac{1}{2}$	50%
$\frac{1}{6}$	$16.\overline{6}\%$
$\frac{3}{8}$	37.5%
$\frac{1}{3}$	$33.\overline{3}\%$
$\frac{3}{5}$	60%
$\frac{1}{4}$	25%

Activities

② Complete the fraction-percent conversions.

Fraction	Percent
$\frac{1}{4}$	25%
$\frac{1}{3}$	$33.\overline{3}\%$
$\frac{1}{5}$	20%
$\frac{1}{10}$	10%
$\frac{3}{5}$	60%
$\frac{5}{6}$	$83.\overline{3}\%$
$\frac{5}{8}$	62.5%
$\frac{9}{10}$	90%
$\frac{7}{8}$	87.5%

Percent	Fraction
$66.\overline{6}\%$	$\frac{2}{3}$
40%	$\frac{2}{5}$
$16.\overline{6}\%$	$\frac{1}{6}$
12.5%	$\frac{1}{8}$
75%	$\frac{3}{4}$
30%	$\frac{3}{10}$
80%	$\frac{4}{5}$
70%	$\frac{7}{10}$
37.5%	$\frac{3}{8}$

Converting Repeating Decimals to Percents

$$\frac{1}{3} = 0.\overline{3}$$

This means that there are an infinite number of 3s following the decimal.

To convert the decimal to a percent, write two additional 3s after the decimal point and multiply by 100.

$$0.\overline{3} = 0.33\overline{3} = 33.\overline{3}\%$$

③ Find the least common multiple of each set of numbers.

9 and 12

$9 = 3 \times 3 = \boxed{3^2}$
$12 = 2 \times 2 \times 3 = \boxed{2^2} \times 3$
LCM: $2^2 \times 3^2 = 36$

12 and 15

$12 = 2 \times 2 \times 3 = \boxed{2^2} \times 3$
$15 = 3 \times \boxed{5}$
LCM: $2^2 \times 3 \times 5 = 60$

24 and 30

$24 = 2 \times 2 \times 2 \times 3 = \boxed{2^3} \times \boxed{3}$
$30 = 2 \times 3 \times \boxed{5}$
LCM: $2^3 \times 3 \times 5 = 120$

④ Find the prime factorization of each argument and simplify the roots.

$\sqrt{240} = \sqrt{2 \times 2 \times 2 \times 2 \times 3 \times 5} = (2 \times 2)\sqrt{3 \times 5} = 4\sqrt{15}$

$\sqrt{108} = \sqrt{2 \times 2 \times 3 \times 3 \times 3} = (2 \times 3)\sqrt{3} = 6\sqrt{3}$

$3\sqrt{45} = 3\sqrt{3 \times 3 \times 5} = (3 \times 3)\sqrt{5} = 9\sqrt{5}$

$\sqrt{432} = \sqrt{2 \times 2 \times 2 \times 2 \times 3 \times 3 \times 3} = (2 \times 2 \times 3)\sqrt{3} = 12\sqrt{3}$

$2\sqrt{700} = 2\sqrt{2 \times 2 \times 5 \times 5 \times 7} = (2 \times 2 \times 5)\sqrt{7} = 20\sqrt{7}$

⑤ Solve.

What is 27% of 150?
$x = 0.27(150)$
$x = 40.5$

What is 3.6% of 80?
$x = 0.036(80)$
$x = 2.88$

What is 238% of 75?
$x = 2.38(75)$
$x = 178.5$

18 is 60% of what number?
$18 = 0.6x$
$18 \div 0.6 = x$
$x = 30$

52 is 1.3% of what number?
$52 = 0.013x$
$52 \div 0.013 = x$
$x = 4000$

351 is 117% of what number?
$351 = 1.17x$
$351 \div 1.17 = x$
$x = 300$

41 is what percent of 205?
$41 = 205x$
$41 \div 205 = x$
$0.2 = x$
$x = 20\%$

81 is what percent of 27?
$81 = 27x$
$81 \div 27 = x$
$3 = x$
$x = 300\%$

3 is what percent of 1000?
$3 = 1000x$
$3 \div 1000 = x$
$0.003 = x$
$x = 0.3\%$

⑥ Complete the chart to show proper conversion between scientific notation and standard form.

Scientific notation	Standard form
5.71×10^7	57,100,000
4.892×10^8	489,200,000
7.4×10^{-7}	0.00000074
6×10^{-8}	0.00000006

Standard form	Scientific notation
9,723,000,000	9.723×10^9
251,600,000,000	2.516×10^{11}
0.00000000102	1.02×10^{-9}
0.00000000054	5.4×10^{-10}

Teaching Tips, Cont.

➢ Tell students that some problems may be easier to solve if they convert the percent to a fraction before solving for the variable. This is especially true when the percent involves repeating decimals.

➢ Complete the Classwork exercises. Have some students work the problems on the board for the class. All students should work the problems in their books.

Assignment

• Complete Lesson 49, Activities 2-6.

Lesson 50

Concepts
- Percent decrease
- Math in the real world
- Greatest common factor
- Fraction-decimal-percent equivalents
- English-metric conversions
- English length equivalents

Learning Objectives
The student will be able to:
- Calculate the percent decrease when given two numbers
- Apply the concepts of percent to real world math

Materials Needed
- Student Book, Lesson 50
- Formula strip, Lesson 50
- Worksheet 25

Teaching Tips
➢ Review fraction-percent conversions from Lesson 49.

➢ Teach percent decrease. Emphasize that when there is a decrease, the new amount will be smaller than the original amount.

➢ Work through the sample problem with the students. Point out that 75 laps is the original number of laps to race, and 60 laps is the new number of laps to race. Some students may be tempted to calculate that Steve has raced 15 laps and use this as the new amount, but this is incorrect.

Lesson 50

Percent Decrease

To find the percent decrease, start by finding the difference between the original amount and the new amount. Then divide the difference by the original amount.

$$\% \text{ decrease} = \frac{\text{original} - \text{new}}{\text{original}}$$

Steve has 60 of the 75 laps remaining in the race. What percent of the laps has Steve completed?
Original amount: 75 laps
New amount: 60 laps

$$\% \text{ decrease} = \frac{75 - 60}{75} = \frac{15}{75} = \frac{1}{5}$$

Change the fraction to a percent:

$$\frac{1}{5} = 0.20 = 20\%$$

① Classwork
Find the percent decrease.

Original amount: 50
New amount: 35
Percent decrease: 30%

$$\frac{50 - 35}{50} = \frac{\overset{3}{\cancel{15}}}{\cancel{50}_{10}} = \frac{3}{10} = 0.3 = 30\%$$

Original amount: 144
New amount: 96
Percent decrease: 33.$\overline{3}$%

$$\frac{144 - 96}{144} = \frac{\overset{1}{\cancel{48}}}{\cancel{144}_3} = \frac{1}{3} = 0.\overline{3} = 33.\overline{3}\%$$

Activities

② Solve.

New tires have an average tread depth of $\frac{11}{32}$ of an inch. Most states have laws allowing cars to legally run with tires having at least $\frac{1}{16}$ of an inch of tread. What percent decrease in tread depth is the maximum allowed by most state laws?

$$\frac{\frac{11}{32} - \frac{1}{16}}{\frac{11}{32}} = \frac{\frac{11}{32} - \frac{2}{32}}{\frac{11}{32}} = \frac{\frac{9}{32}}{\frac{11}{32}} = \frac{9}{32} \div \frac{11}{32} = \frac{9}{\cancel{32}} \times \frac{\cancel{32}}{11} = \frac{9}{11} = 9 \div 11 = 0.\overline{81} = 81.\overline{81}\%$$

Tires are considered safe to use in rainy conditions if they have at least $\frac{1}{8}$ of an inch of tread. What is the maximum percent decrease in tread depth that is still safe for rainy conditions?

$$\frac{\frac{11}{32} - \frac{1}{8}}{\frac{11}{32}} = \frac{\frac{11}{32} - \frac{4}{32}}{\frac{11}{32}} = \frac{\frac{7}{32}}{\frac{11}{32}} = \frac{7}{32} \div \frac{11}{32} = \frac{7}{\cancel{32}} \times \frac{\cancel{32}}{11} = \frac{7}{11} = 7 \div 11 = 0.\overline{63} = 63.\overline{63}\%$$

Tires are considered safe to use in snowy conditions if they have at least $\frac{3}{16}$ of an inch of tread. What is the maximum percent decrease in tread depth that is still safe for snowy conditions?

$$\frac{\frac{11}{32} - \frac{3}{16}}{\frac{11}{32}} = \frac{\frac{11}{32} - \frac{6}{32}}{\frac{11}{32}} = \frac{\frac{5}{32}}{\frac{11}{32}} = \frac{5}{32} \div \frac{11}{32} = \frac{5}{\cancel{32}} \times \frac{\cancel{32}}{11} = \frac{5}{11} = 5 \div 11 = 0.\overline{45} = 45.\overline{45}\%$$

---

③ Find the greatest common factor of each set of numbers.

36 and 54	42 and 70	48 and 92
$36 = ② \times 2 \times ③ \times ③$	$42 = ② \times 3 \times ⑦$	$48 = ② \times ② \times 2 \times 2 \times 3$
$54 = ② \times ③ \times ③ \times 3$	$70 = ② \times ③ \times 5 \times ⑦$	$92 = ② \times ② \times 23$
GCF: $2 \times 3 \times 3 = 18$	GCF: $2 \times 7 = 14$	GCF: $2 \times 2 = 4$

④ Complete the chart to show proper fraction-decimal-percent equivalents.

Fraction	Decimal	Percent	Fraction	Decimal	Percent
$\frac{1}{3}$	$0.\overline{3}$	33.$\overline{3}$%	$\frac{3}{4}$	0.75	75%
$\frac{1}{8}$	0.125	12.5%	$\frac{2}{3}$	$0.\overline{6}$	66.$\overline{6}$%
$\frac{2}{5}$	0.4	40%	$\frac{7}{8}$	0.875	87.5%
$\frac{1}{2}$	0.5	50%	$\frac{3}{5}$	0.6	60%

⑤ Complete the chart to show correct English-Metric conversions. (See Lesson 40.)

7 inches	7 inches $\left(\frac{2.54 \text{ cm}}{1 \text{ inch}}\right) = 17.78$	cm
21 inches	21 inches $\left(\frac{25.4 \text{ mm}}{1 \text{ inch}}\right) = 533.4$	mm
12 yards	12 yards $\left(\frac{0.91 \text{ meter}}{1 \text{ yard}}\right) = 10.92$	meters
8 miles	8 miles $\left(\frac{1.61 \text{ km}}{1 \text{ mile}}\right) = 12.88$	km
30 cm	30 cm $\left(\frac{0.39 \text{ in.}}{1 \text{ cm}}\right) = 11.7$	inches
4 meters	4 meters $\left(\frac{1.09 \text{ yd.}}{1 \text{ meter}}\right) = 4.36$	yards
14 km	14 km $\left(\frac{0.62 \text{ mi.}}{1 \text{ km}}\right) = 8.68$	miles

⑥ Complete the chart to show correct English length equivalents. (See Lesson 40.)

11 miles	11 miles $\left(\frac{1760 \text{ yards}}{1 \text{ mile}}\right) = 19,360$	yards
4 miles	4 miles $\left(\frac{5280 \text{ feet}}{1 \text{ mile}}\right) = 21,120$	feet
15 yards	15 yards $\left(\frac{36 \text{ inches}}{1 \text{ yard}}\right) = 540$	inches
72 feet	$_{24}\cancel{72}$ feet $\left(\frac{1 \text{ yard}}{\cancel{3} \text{ feet}}\right) = 24$	yards
7 yards	7 yards $\left(\frac{3 \text{ feet}}{1 \text{ yard}}\right) = 21$	feet
36,960 feet	$_7\cancel{36,960}$ feet $\left(\frac{1 \text{ mile}}{\cancel{5280} \text{ feet}}\right) = 7$	miles
22,880 yards	$_{13}\cancel{22,880}$ yards $\left(\frac{1 \text{ mile}}{\cancel{1760} \text{ yards}}\right) = 13$	miles
8 feet	8 feet $\left(\frac{12 \text{ inches}}{1 \text{ feet}}\right) = 96$	inches
132 inches	$_{11}\cancel{132}$ inches $\left(\frac{1 \text{ foot}}{\cancel{12} \text{ inches}}\right) = 11$	feet
468 inches	$_{13}\cancel{468}$ inches $\left(\frac{1 \text{ yard}}{\cancel{36} \text{ inches}}\right) = 13$	yards

① Solve.

What is 40% of 90? $x = 0.4(90)$ $x = 36$	What is 35% of 92? $x = 0.35(92)$ $x = 32.2$	What is 36% of 40? $x = 0.36(40)$ $x = 14.4$
What is 8% of 50? $x = 0.08(50)$ $x = 4$	What is 1.8% of 60? $x = 0.018(60)$ $x = 1.08$	What is 210% of 80? $x = 2.1(80)$ $x = 168$
25 is 20% of what number? $25 = 0.2x$ $25 \div 0.2 = x$ $x = 125$	66 is 40% of what number? $66 = 0.4x$ $66 \div 0.4 = x$ $x = 165$	30 is 150% of what number? $30 = 1.5x$ $30 \div 1.5 = x$ $x = 20$
30 is what percent of 120? $30 = 120x$ $30 \div 120 = x$ $0.25 = x$ $x = 25\%$	75 is what percent of 60? $75 = 60x$ $75 \div 60 = x$ $1.25 = x$ $x = 125\%$	9 is what percent of 72? $9 = 72x$ $9 \div 72 = x$ $0.125 = x$ $x = 12.5\%$
What is $33.\overline{3}\%$ of 66? $x = 0.\overline{3}(66)$ $x = \frac{1}{3}(66)$ $x = 22$	What is $66.\overline{6}\%$ of 96? $x = 0.\overline{6}(96)$ $x = \frac{2}{3}(96)$ $x = 64$	What is $16.\overline{6}\%$ of 42? $x = 0.1\overline{6}(42)$ $x = \frac{1}{6}(42)$ $x = 7$
What is $83.\overline{3}\%$ of 54? $x = 0.8\overline{3}(54)$ $x = \frac{5}{6}(54)$ $x = 45$	What is 1.5% of 40? $x = 0.015(40)$ $x = 0.6$	What is 240% of 120? $x = 2.4(120)$ $x = 288$
36 is 75% of what number? $36 = 0.75x$ $36 \div 0.75 = x$ $x = 48$	62 is 50% of what number? $62 = 0.5x$ $62 \div 0.5 = x$ $x = 124$	75 is 120% of what number? $75 = 1.2x$ $75 \div 1.2 = x$ $x = 62.5$

Teaching Tips, Cont.

➤ Ask students for examples of when calculating percent decrease would be helpful. Examples include determining what percent discount a sale price is, tracking attendance or sales trends, stock market accounts, etc.

➤ Complete the Classwork exercises. Have some students work the problems on the board for the class. All students should work the problems in their books.

➤ Give students the strip labeled "For use in Lesson 50" from the formula strip page to be used in completing the assignment.

Assignments

- Complete Lesson 50, Activities 2-6.
- Worksheet 25
- Study for Test 5 (Lessons 38-47)

Test 5

Testing Objectives
The student will:
- Add, subtract, multiply, and divide improper fractions
- Add, subtract, multiply, and divide mixed numbers
- Convert length measurements in the English system
- Convert length measurements between the English and metric systems
- Form ratios from a given set of data
- Determine if a pair of ratios is a proportion
- Solve proportions
- Calculate measurements on a scale drawing from a given ratio
- Write numbers in scientific notation
- Convert percents to decimals
- Convert decimals to percents

Materials Needed
- Test 5
- Formula strip, Test 5
- *It's College Test Prep Time!* from Student Book
- *A Math Minute with…* Denny S. from Student Book

Teaching Tips
➢ Administer Test 5, allowing the students 30-40 minutes to complete the test. Give students the strip labeled "For use on Test 5" from the formula strip page.

➢ When all students are finished taking the test, introduce *It's College Test Prep Time* from the student book. This page may be completed in class or assigned as homework.

Test 5

① Add, subtract, multiply, or divide as indicated. Convert answers with improper fractions to mixed numbers if the problem has mixed numbers. **8 points**

$$\frac{5}{2} + \frac{9}{5} = \frac{5 \times 5}{2 \times 5} + \frac{9 \times 2}{5 \times 2} = \frac{25}{10} + \frac{18}{10} = \frac{43}{10}$$

$$\frac{8}{5} \times \frac{9}{4} = \frac{^2 8}{5} \times \frac{9}{4_1} = \frac{2}{5} \times \frac{9}{1} = \frac{2 \times 9}{5 \times 1} = \frac{18}{5}$$

$$3\frac{1}{8} + 2\frac{3}{5} = (3+2) + \left(\frac{1}{8} + \frac{3}{5}\right) = 5 + \frac{5}{40} + \frac{24}{40} = 5\frac{29}{40}$$

$$2\frac{1}{3} \times 3\frac{4}{7} = \frac{7}{3} \times \frac{25}{7} = \frac{25}{3} = 8\frac{1}{3}$$

$$\frac{7}{4} - \frac{8}{5} = \frac{7 \times 5}{4 \times 5} - \frac{8 \times 4}{5 \times 4} = \frac{35}{20} - \frac{32}{20} = \frac{35 - 32}{20} = \frac{3}{20}$$

$$\frac{13}{4} \div \frac{5}{2} = \frac{13}{4} \times \frac{2^1}{5} = \frac{13 \times 1}{2 \times 5} = \frac{13}{10}$$

$$5\frac{3}{5} - 3\frac{1}{3} =$$

$$4\frac{1}{3} \div 3\frac{1}{4} = \frac{13}{3} \div \frac{13}{4} = \frac{13}{3} \times \frac{4}{13} = \frac{4}{3} = 1\frac{1}{3}$$

$$\frac{5 \times 5 + 3}{5} - \frac{3 \times 3 + 1}{3} = \frac{28}{5} - \frac{10}{3} = \frac{84}{15} - \frac{50}{15} = \frac{34}{15} = 2\frac{4}{15}$$

② Set up a proper conversion formula and calculate the equivalent length for each given length. **16 points**

3 miles	$3 \text{ miles} \left(\frac{1760 \text{ yards}}{1 \text{ mile}}\right) = 5280$	yards
4 miles	$4 \text{ miles} \left(\frac{5280 \text{ feet}}{1 \text{ mile}}\right) = 21,120$	feet
5 yards	$5 \text{ yards} \left(\frac{36 \text{ inches}}{1 \text{ yard}}\right) = 180$	inches
39 feet	$_{13}39 \text{ feet} \left(\frac{1 \text{ yard}}{3 \text{ feet}}\right) = 13$	yards
10 inches	$10 \text{ inches} \left(\frac{2.54 \text{ cm}}{1 \text{ inch}}\right) = 25.4$	cm
12 inches	$12 \text{ inches} \left(\frac{25.4 \text{ mm}}{1 \text{ inch}}\right) = 304.8$	mm
11 yards	$11 \text{ yards} \left(\frac{0.91 \text{ meter}}{1 \text{ yard}}\right) = 10.01$	meters
6 miles	$6 \text{ miles} \left(\frac{1.61 \text{ km}}{1 \text{ mile}}\right) = 9.66$	km

③ Write ratios in simplest form. **6 points**
A band has 25 clarinets, 20 flutes, 15 saxophones, 10 oboes, and 5 bassoons in the woodwind section.

What is the ratio of flutes to oboes?
$\frac{20}{10} = \frac{2}{1}$ or 2:1 or 2 to 1

What is the ratio of oboes to saxophones?
$\frac{10}{15} = \frac{2}{3}$ or 2:3 or 2 to 3

What is the ratio of bassoons to flutes?
$\frac{5}{20} = \frac{1}{4}$ or 1:4 or 1 to 4

What is the ratio of clarinets to oboes?
$\frac{25}{10} = \frac{5}{2}$ or 5:2 or 5 to 2

What is the ratio of oboes and bassoons to clarinets and flutes?
$\frac{10+5}{25+20} = \frac{15}{45} = \frac{1}{3}$ or 1:3 or 1 to 3

What is the ratio of clarinets to all woodwinds?
$\frac{25}{75} = \frac{2}{3}$ or 2:3 or 2 to 3

④ Write = or ≠ to indicate if each pair of ratios forms a proportion. **4 points**

$\frac{39}{51} = \frac{13}{17}$ $\quad 39 \times 17 = 663; \ 51 \times 13 = 663$

$\frac{11}{15} \neq \frac{7}{11}$ $\quad 11 \times 11 = 121; \ 15 \times 7 = 105$

$\frac{4}{24} = \frac{6}{36}$ $\quad 4 \times 36 = 144; \ 6 \times 24 = 144$

$\frac{15}{35} = \frac{3}{7}$ $\quad 15 \times 7 = 105; \ 35 \times 3 = 105$

Test 5

⑤ Solve the proportions. **4 points**

$$\frac{x}{8} = \frac{24}{6}$$
$6x = 8(24)$
$6x = 192$
$x = 32$

$$\frac{9}{21} = \frac{x}{112}$$
$9(112) = 21x$
$1008 = 21x$
$48 = x$

$$\frac{15}{x} = \frac{25}{15}$$
$15(15) = 25x$
$225 = 25x$
$9 = x$

$$\frac{4}{9} = \frac{36}{x}$$
$4x = 9(36)$
$4x = 324$
$x = 81$

⑥ Label the scale drawing if the ratio of the scale drawing to the actual measurements is 1:3. **6 points**

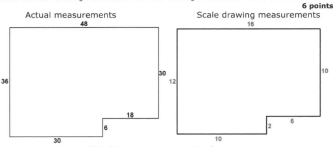

Actual measurements

Scale drawing measurements

Set up proportions so each of the following ratios are equal to $\frac{1}{3}$:

$$\frac{x}{48}, \frac{x}{30}, \frac{x}{18}, \frac{x}{6}, \frac{x}{36}$$

Solve for x in each proportion to find the length of the sides in the scale drawing.

⑦ Write each number in scientific notation. **8 points**

320,000,000	3.2×10^8
97,000,000	9.7×10^7
4,180,000,000	4.18×10^9
6,000,000	6×10^6

0.000000375	3.75×10^{-7}
0.00089	8.9×10^{-4}
0.0000007612	7.612×10^{-7}
0.000000001	1×10^{-9}

⑧ Convert each percent to a decimal. **6 points**

17%	0.17	32%	0.32
80%	0.8	314%	3.14
66%	0.66	200%	2 or 2.00

⑨ Convert each decimal to a percent. **6 points**

0.88	88%	7.6	760%
0.07	7%	9.15	915%
0.31	31%	6	600%

64 points total

It's College Test Prep Time!

1. Which of the following expressions represents 8% of x?
   A. $800x$
   B. $80x$
   C. $8x$
   D. $0.8x$
   E. <u>$0.08x$</u>   8% = 0.08 Therefore, 8% of x is $0.08x$

2. There are 250 7th and 8th graders in a club. 60% of the club members are boys, and 54% of the boys in the club are in 7th grade. How many 7th grade boys are in the club?
   A. <u>81</u>   60% of 250 = 150 boys. 54% of 150 = 81 7th graders.
   B. 100
   C. 115
   D. 135
   E. 150

3. Denny has 20 packages of red pens and 20 packages of blue pens in his store. How many packages of red pens must he sell without selling any blue pens to make the ratio of red pens to blue pens equal to 4:5?
   A. 2   Let x = the number of packages of red pens sold.
   B. <u>4</u>   Set up a proportion. $\dfrac{20-x}{20} = \dfrac{4}{5}$
   C. 5   Cross multiply and solve for x: $5(20-x) = 80$
   D. 8 $100 - 5x = 80$
   E. 10 $20 = 5x;\ x = 4$

4. Given x is a non-zero digit in the number $0.00x$, which of the following expressions is equivalent to $\dfrac{5}{0.00x}$?
   A. $\dfrac{5}{x}$
   B. $\dfrac{200}{x}$
   C. $\dfrac{5000}{x}$ $0.00x = \dfrac{x}{1000}$
   D. $\dfrac{x}{200}$ Therefore, $\dfrac{5}{0.00x} = 5 \div \dfrac{x}{1000} = \dfrac{5}{1} \times \dfrac{1000}{x} = \dfrac{5000}{x}$
   E. $\dfrac{x}{5000}$

Denny S. – Store Owner/Operator

What is your occupation? I am a store owner and operator.

Where do you work? I work at my store.

Did you attend college? If so, what was your major? No, I did not attend college.

What parts of your job require the use of math? Just about everything I do involves math. For example, purchasing, invoicing, sales, profit and loss, profit margins, tax, and payroll all involve math. I also make deliveries for my local customers. I need to figure in delivery expenses, calculate the estimated time for each delivery, the best order for delivering the items, and the best route to each destination.

What is the biggest "problem" you have faced that required the use of math to solve? My biggest challenge is inventory control. I need to know what items sell well at different times during the year. I need to order my inventory in time to have enough of each item in stock when it is most needed. Also, I do not want to order too much of an item and have extras left in storage.

Are there any other interesting math uses you have experienced? It is impossible to run a business without a good basic math background. Math is an exact science. It will always tell you if you are right or wrong in your business decisions.

Teaching Tips, Cont.
➢ Have students read the Math Minute interview for Lessons 51-60.

Assignments
- Complete *It's College Test Prep Time!*
- Read *A Math Minute with…* Denny S. – Store Owner/ Operator

Lesson 51

Concepts
- Discounts
- Sale prices
- One-variable equations
- Multiplying fractions
- Multiplying mixed numbers
- Scale drawings
- Math in the real world

Learning Objectives
The student will be able to:
- Calculate the sale price when the percent discount is given
- Calculate the percent discount when the sale price is given
- Apply percent decrease to discounts and sale prices

Materials Needed
- Student Book, Lesson 51
- Variety of store ads showing sale prices (Save for Lesson 52.)

Teaching Tips
➢ Review percent decrease. (See Lesson 50)

➢ Show students the ads, pointing out the sale prices. Ask the students how they could find the percent discount the store is giving on an item, assuming they know both the regular price and the sale price.

➢ Teach finding the percent discount from the teaching box. Explain that this is an application of percent decrease. Use an item from one of the ads to do a sample problem with the students.

Discounts and Sale Prices

Discounts and **sale prices** are calculated as a percent decrease from the original price. Remember the formula for percent decrease:

$$\% \text{ decrease} = \frac{\text{original price - new price}}{\text{original price}}$$

Solving for the new price, we get this formula:
new price = original price − (original price)(% decrease)

We can rewrite this formula to simplify it.
new price = original price(1 − % decrease)

To find the discounted price or sale price, change the percent discount to a decimal and subtract from 1. Multiply this number by the original price to get the discounted price. When working with money problems, round all answers to the nearest cent (hundredth).

Denny has marked all clearance items 75% off. If the original price is $9.95, what is the discounted price?
Let x = the discounted price
$x = \$9.95(1 - 0.75)$
$x = \$9.95(0.25)$
$x = \$2.4875$
Rounded to the nearest cent: $x = \$2.49$

① Classwork
Solve.

If the original price of an item was $5.99, find the sale price for the following discounts:

10%
Let x = the sale price
$x = \$5.99(1 - 0.10)$
$x = \$5.99(0.90)$
$x = \$5.39$

25%
Let x = the sale price
$x = \$5.99(1 - 0.25)$
$x = \$5.99(0.75)$
$x = \$4.49$

60%
Let x = the sale price
$x = \$5.99(1 - 0.60)$
$x = \$5.99(0.40)$
$x = \$2.40$

Activities
② Solve.
Denny sells five different staplers with prices of $7.29, $8.79, $10.29, $12.99, and $14.99. Denny gives all teachers and homeschoolers a 10% discount. What is the discounted price of each stapler for teachers and homeschoolers? Let x = the sale price

$x = \$7.29(1 - 0.10)$	$x = \$8.79(1 - 0.10)$	$x = \$10.29(1 - 0.10)$	$x = \$12.99(1 - 0.10)$	$x = \$14.99(1 - 0.10)$
$x = \$7.29(0.90)$	$x = \$8.79(0.90)$	$x = \$10.29(0.90)$	$x = \$12.99(0.90)$	$x = \$14.99(0.90)$
$x = \$6.56$	$x = \$7.91$	$x = \$9.26$	$x = \$11.69$	$x = \$13.49$

If Denny has a special sale and offers all staplers for $7 each, what is the percent discount for each stapler? (Round answers to the nearest tenth of a percent.) Let x = % discount

$x = \dfrac{\$7.29 - \$7}{\$7.29}$	$x = \dfrac{\$8.79 - \$7}{\$8.79}$	$x = \dfrac{\$10.29 - \$7}{\$10.29}$	$x = \dfrac{\$12.99 - \$7}{\$12.99}$	$x = \dfrac{\$14.99 - \$7}{\$14.99}$
$x = \dfrac{\$0.29}{\$7.29}$	$x = \dfrac{\$1.79}{\$8.79}$	$x = \dfrac{\$3.29}{\$10.29}$	$x = \dfrac{\$5.99}{\$12.99}$	$x = \dfrac{\$7.99}{\$14.99}$
$x = 0.0397$	$x = 0.2036$	$x = 0.3197$	$x = 0.4611$	$x = 0.5330$
$x = 4.0\%$	$x = 20.4\%$	$x = 32.0\%$	$x = 46.1\%$	$x = 53.3\%$

---

③ Solve. Remember to multiply each term by the denominator to eliminate fractions.

$$3(x-2)+7 = 5+12 \div 3 - x$$
$$3x - 6 + 7 = 5 + 4 - x$$
$$3x + 1 = 9 - x$$
$$4x = 8$$
$$x = 2$$

$$5x + 14 \div 7 + 4 = 3(x-1) - x$$
$$5x + 2 + 4 = 3x - 3 - x$$
$$5x + 6 = 2x - 3$$
$$3x = -9$$
$$x = -3$$

$$4(2-x) - 3(1-x) = x - 3$$
$$8 - 4x - 3 + 3x = x - 3$$
$$-x + 5 = x - 3$$
$$-2x = -8$$
$$x = 4$$

$$\frac{2x}{3} + 1 = -5$$
$$\frac{2x}{3} = -6$$
$$3\left(\frac{2x}{3}\right) = 3(-6)$$
$$2x = -18$$
$$x = -9$$

$$\frac{3x}{2} + 3 = 2x + 1$$
$$\frac{3x}{2} = 2x - 2$$
$$2\left(\frac{3x}{2}\right) = 2(2x - 2)$$
$$3x = 4x - 4$$
$$-x = -4$$
$$x = 4$$

$$\frac{x+1}{2} - 5 = 2x - 3$$
$$\frac{x+1}{2} = 2x + 2$$
$$2\left(\frac{x+1}{2}\right) = 2(2x + 2)$$
$$x + 1 = 4x + 4$$
$$-3x = 3$$
$$x = -1$$

④ Multiply.

$$\frac{7}{10} \times \frac{4}{11} = \frac{7}{5\,\cancel{10}} \times \frac{\cancel{4}^2}{11} = \frac{7 \times 2}{5 \times 11} = \frac{14}{55}$$

$$\frac{5}{12} \times \frac{18}{25} = \frac{\cancel{5}^1}{2\,\cancel{12}} \times \frac{\cancel{18}^3}{\cancel{25}_5} = \frac{1 \times 3}{2 \times 5} = \frac{3}{10}$$

$$\frac{13}{21} \times \frac{14}{19} = \frac{13}{3\,\cancel{21}} \times \frac{\cancel{14}^2}{19} = \frac{13 \times 2}{3 \times 19} = \frac{26}{57}$$

$$\frac{3}{25} \times \frac{5}{18} = \frac{\cancel{3}^1}{5\,\cancel{25}} \times \frac{\cancel{5}^1}{\cancel{18}_6} = \frac{1 \times 1}{5 \times 6} = \frac{1}{30}$$

$$3\frac{4}{7} \times \frac{3}{5} = \frac{\cancel{25}^5}{7} \times \frac{3}{\cancel{5}_1} = \frac{5 \times 3}{7 \times 1} = \frac{15}{7} = 2\frac{1}{7}$$

$$3\frac{3}{8} \times \frac{4}{9} = \frac{\cancel{27}^3}{2\,\cancel{8}} \times \frac{\cancel{4}^1}{\cancel{9}_1} = \frac{3 \times 1}{2 \times 1} = \frac{3}{2} = 1\frac{1}{2}$$

$$5\frac{4}{7} \times 2\frac{1}{3} = \frac{\cancel{39}^{13}}{\cancel{7}_1} \times \frac{\cancel{7}^1}{\cancel{3}_1} = \frac{13 \times 1}{1 \times 1} = \frac{13}{1} = 13$$

$$4\frac{3}{8} \times 3\frac{3}{7} = \frac{\cancel{35}^5}{\cancel{8}_1} \times \frac{\cancel{24}^3}{\cancel{7}_1} = \frac{5 \times 3}{1 \times 1} = \frac{15}{1} = 15$$

⑤ Label the scale drawing using the ratio 1:10.
The small bed is $5\frac{2}{5}$ inches wide, $7\frac{1}{2}$ inches long, and 3 inches tall.

$$\text{wide}: \frac{5\frac{2}{5}}{x} = \frac{1}{10}$$

$$\text{long}: \frac{7\frac{1}{2}}{x} = \frac{1}{10}$$

$$\text{high}: \frac{3}{x} = \frac{1}{10}$$

54 inches wide
75 inches long
30 inches high

Teaching Tips, Cont.

➢ Ask the students how they would be able to determine the price of an item on a clearance rack if the sign said to take an extra 20% off the lowest marked price. (Students will most likely say to find 20% of the marked price and subtract that amount from the marked price.)

➢ Explain that there is a more direct way of finding the discounted price. Teach finding the discounted price from the teaching box.

➢ Complete the Classwork exercises. Have some students work the problems on the board for the class and explain their answers. All students should work the problems in their books.

Assignment

• Complete Lesson 51, Activities 2-5.

Lesson 52

Concepts

- Percent increase
- Scientific notation
- One-variable equations
- Multiplying decimals
- Adding mixed numbers
- Subtracting mixed numbers
- Math in the real world

Learning Objectives

The student will be able to:

- Calculate percent increase
- Apply percent increase to real world scenarios

Materials Needed

- Student Book, Lesson 52
- Worksheet 26
- Store ads from Lesson 51

Teaching Tips

➤ Have students complete Worksheet 26 in class. This may be for added practice of earlier topics, or graded as a quiz, if desired.

➤ Review discounts and sale prices. (See Lesson 51)

➤ Show students the store ads from Lesson 51. Ask the students how they could calculate the percent the price will go up after the sale ends.

➤ Teach percent increase from the teaching box. Use an item from one of the ads to do a sample problem with the students.

Percent Increase

To find the percent increase, start by finding the difference between the original amount and the new amount. Divide the difference by the original amount.

$$\% \text{ increase} = \frac{\text{new amount - original amount}}{\text{original amount}}$$

One of Denny's suppliers is raising the suggested retail prices of their products at the beginning of next year. The suggested retail price is $9.95 this year and will be raised to $10.45 next year. What is the percent increase? (Round to the nearest tenth.)

Let x = % increase

$$x = \frac{\$10.45 - \$9.95}{\$9.95}$$

$$x = \frac{\$0.50}{\$9.95}$$

$$x = 5.0\%$$

① **Classwork**
Solve.

A church had 70 children enrolled in its Bible club at the beginning of the year. At the end of the year, there were 84 children enrolled. What was the percent increase in enrollment during the year?

Let x = % increase

$$x = \frac{84 - 70}{70}$$

$$x = \frac{14}{70}$$

$$x = 0.2$$

$$x = 20\%$$

Activities

② Solve. Round answers to the nearest tenth when necessary.
In preparation for the upcoming school year, Denny ordered 50 each of grade books and lesson plan books. If he had 6 grade books and 8 lesson plan books before he placed his order, what is the percent increase Denny will have in his inventory of grade books and lesson plan books when his order arrives? (Assume no other grade books or lesson plan books were sold.)

Let x = % increase of grade books

$$x = \frac{56 - 6}{6}$$

$$x = \frac{50}{6}$$

$$x = 8.3$$

$$x = 833.\overline{3}\% \text{ or } 833\frac{1}{3}\%$$

Let x = % increase of lesson plan books

$$x = \frac{58 - 8}{8}$$

$$x = \frac{50}{8}$$

$$x = 6.25$$

$$x = 625\%$$

Denny usually averages 150 customers per day in his store. On a special customer appreciation day, there were 250 customers. What was the percent increase in customers for the special appreciation day?

Let x = % increase

$$x = \frac{250 - 150}{150}$$

$$x = \frac{100}{150}$$

$$x = .\overline{6}$$

$$x = 66.\overline{6}\% \text{ or } 66\frac{2}{3}\%$$

---

③ Complete the chart to show the conversion between scientific notation and standard form.

Scientific notation	Standard form	Standard form	Scientific notation
3.14×10^9	3,140,000,000	125,400,000,000	1.254×10^{11}
2.007×10^8	200,700,000	21,030,000,000	2.103×10^{10}
9.247×10^{-7}	0.0000009247	0.0000000307	3.07×10^{-8}
6.0201×10^{-6}	0.0000060201	0.0000000099037	9.99037×10^{-9}

④ Solve.

$$\frac{2x+1}{3} - 2 = -7$$
$$\frac{2x+1}{3} = -5$$
$$3\left(\frac{2x+1}{3}\right) = 3(-5)$$
$$2x+1 = -15$$
$$2x = -16$$
$$x = -8$$

$$\frac{3x+5}{2} + 1 = 5x + 3$$
$$\frac{3x+5}{2} = 5x + 2$$
$$2\left(\frac{3x+5}{2}\right) = 2(5x+2)$$
$$3x+5 = 10x + 4$$
$$-7x = -1$$
$$x = \frac{1}{7}$$

$$\frac{2x-1}{3} - 1 = 3(x-2)$$
$$\frac{2x-1}{3} - 1 = 3x - 6$$
$$\frac{2x-1}{3} = 3x - 5$$
$$3\left(\frac{2x-1}{3}\right) = 3(3x-5)$$
$$2x - 1 = 9x - 15$$
$$-7x = -14$$
$$x = 2$$

⑤ Multiply.

43.68	3.89	432.59	0.061
× 8.1	×0.07	× 6.07	×0.321
4368	0.2723	302813	61
+349440		+25955400	1220
353.808		2625.8213	+18300
			0.019581

⑥ Add or subtract as indicated.

$$6\frac{5}{9} + 5\frac{7}{12} = (6+5) + \left(\frac{5}{9} + \frac{7}{12}\right) = 11 + \frac{20}{36} + \frac{21}{36} = 11 + \frac{41}{36} = 11 + 1 + \frac{5}{36} = 12\frac{5}{36}$$

$$3\frac{4}{7} + 4\frac{2}{3} = (3+4) + \left(\frac{4}{7} + \frac{2}{3}\right) = 7 + \frac{12}{21} + \frac{14}{21} = 7 + \frac{26}{21} = 7 + 1 + \frac{5}{21} = 8\frac{5}{21}$$

$$8\frac{3}{4} - 3\frac{7}{12} = (8-3) + \left(\frac{3}{4} - \frac{7}{12}\right) = 5 + \left(\frac{9}{12} - \frac{7}{12}\right) = 5 + \frac{2}{12} = 5\frac{1}{6}$$

$$9\frac{1}{3} - 5\frac{4}{5} = (9-5) + \left(\frac{1}{3} - \frac{4}{5}\right) = 4 + \left(\frac{5}{15} - \frac{12}{15}\right) = 3 + \frac{15}{15} + \frac{5}{15} - \frac{12}{15} = 3\frac{8}{15}$$

Fraction to Percent Conversions, Percent Decrease

① Complete the fraction-percent conversions.

Fraction	Percent
$\frac{1}{4}$	25%
$\frac{1}{3}$	33.$\overline{3}$%
$\frac{1}{5}$	20%
$\frac{1}{10}$	10%
$\frac{3}{5}$	60%
$\frac{5}{6}$	83.$\overline{3}$%
$\frac{5}{8}$	62.5%
$\frac{9}{10}$	90%
$\frac{7}{8}$	87.5%

Percent	Fraction
66.$\overline{6}$%	$\frac{2}{3}$
40%	$\frac{2}{5}$
16.$\overline{6}$%	$\frac{1}{6}$
12.5%	$\frac{1}{8}$
75%	$\frac{3}{4}$
30%	$\frac{3}{10}$
80%	$\frac{4}{5}$
70%	$\frac{7}{10}$
37.5%	$\frac{3}{8}$

② Find the percent decrease.

Original amount: 50
New amount: 30
Percent decrease: 40%

$$\frac{50-30}{50} = \frac{\overset{2}{\cancel{20}}}{\underset{5}{\cancel{50}}} = \frac{2}{5} = 0.4 = 40\%$$

Original amount: 75
New amount: 50
Percent decrease: 33.$\overline{3}$%

$$\frac{75-50}{75} = \frac{\overset{1}{\cancel{25}}}{\underset{3}{\cancel{75}}} = \frac{1}{3} = 0.\overline{3} = 33.\overline{3}\%$$

Original amount: 64
New amount: 40
Percent decrease: 37.5%

$$\frac{64-40}{64} = \frac{\overset{3}{\cancel{24}}}{\underset{8}{\cancel{64}}} = \frac{3}{8} = 0.375 = 37.5\%$$

Original amount: 80
New amount: 70
Percent decrease: 12.5%

$$\frac{80-70}{80} = \frac{\overset{1}{\cancel{10}}}{\underset{8}{\cancel{80}}} = \frac{1}{8} = 0.125 = 12.5\%$$

Original amount: 30
New amount: 25
Percent decrease: 16.$\overline{6}$%

$$\frac{30-25}{30} = \frac{\overset{1}{\cancel{5}}}{\underset{6}{\cancel{30}}} = \frac{1}{6} = 0.1\overline{6} = 16.\overline{6}\%$$

Original amount: 42
New amount: 7
Percent decrease: 83.$\overline{3}$%

$$\frac{42-7}{42} = \frac{\overset{5}{\cancel{35}}}{\underset{6}{\cancel{42}}} = \frac{5}{6} = 0.8\overline{3} = 83.\overline{3}\%$$

Teaching Tips, Cont.

> Complete the Classwork exercises. Have some students work the problems on the board for the class and explain their answers. If you have taught cross multiplication, have the students include this step in their explanations. All students should work the problems in their books.

Assignment

- Complete Lesson 52, Activities 2-6.

Lesson 53

Concepts
- Calculating mark-up
- Prime factorization
- Exponents
- Dividing decimals
- Multiplying fractions
- Multiplying mixed numbers
- Roots
- Math in the real world

Learning Objectives
The student will be able to:
- Define *mark-up*
- Calculate the percent mark-up
- Calculate the new price, given the percent mark-up

Materials Needed
- Student Book, Lesson 53
- Worksheet 27

Teaching Tips
➢ Review percent increase. (See Lesson 52.)

➢ Ask students when finding the percent increase would be important. Some examples would include purchasing and reselling, sales tax, warehouse club memberships, etc.)

➢ Teach the definition of mark-up and give some examples, such as those above.

➢ Ask students how they would know what the new price will be after a 10% mark-up. (Students will most likely say to find 10% of the price and add it to the original price.)

Calculating Mark-Up

Mark-up is the amount the price of an item is increased. To calculate mark-up, use a variation of the percent increase formula.

To find the new amount when the percent increase is given, use the formula
new price = original price$(1 + \%$ increase$)$

Denny currently sells a product for $11.95. After a 5% price increase next year, what will the new price be?

Let x = the new price
$x = \$11.95(1 + 0.05)$
$x = \$11.95(1.05)$
$x = \$12.55$

To find the amount of mark-up, use a variation of the formula.
mark-up = original price$(\%$ increase$)$

Denny currently sells a product for $11.95. After a 5% price increase next year, how much more will his customers be charged for the same item?

Let x = the amount of mark-up
$x = \$11.95(0.05)$
$x = \$0.60$

① **Classwork**
Solve.

A warehouse club allows non-members to shop, but charges them a 10% mark-up on all items purchased. If a computer costs $549.99 for members, what is the non-member price?

Let x = the new price
$x = \$549.99(1 + .10)$
$x = \$549.99(1.10)$
$x = \$604.99$

If the warehouse club charges $40 for a membership, should the customer join the club prior to purchasing the computer?

Yes.
The mark-up for non-members would cost the customer $604.99 - $549.99 = $55.00

Activities

② Solve. Round answers to the nearest cent.

To cover his expenses, Denny marks the price of each item 30% more than his purchase price. What does Denny charge for items that cost him $1.04, $7.23, $9.99, and $42.77?
Let x = the new price

$x = \$1.04(1+.30)$	$x = \$7.23(1+.30)$	$x = \$9.99(1+.30)$	$x = \$42.77(1+.30)$
$x = \$1.04(1.30)$	$x = \$7.23(1.30)$	$x = \$9.99(1.30)$	$x = \$42.77(1.30)$
$x = \$1.35$	$x = \$9.40$	$x = \$12.99$	$x = \$55.60$

When Denny has a sale, he marks the price 15% more than his purchase price. What is the sale price of each of the above items?
Let x = the new price

$x = \$1.04(1+.15)$	$x = \$7.23(1+.15)$	$x = \$9.99(1+.15)$	$x = \$42.77(1+.15)$
$x = \$1.04(1.15)$	$x = \$7.23(1.15)$	$x = \$9.99(1.15)$	$x = \$42.77(1.15)$
$x = \$1.20$	$x = \$8.31$	$x = \$11.49$	$x = \$49.19$

---

③ Express the prime factorization of each number using exponents.

64	72	81	100
$64 = 2 \times 2 \times 2 \times 2 \times 2 \times 2$	$72 = 2 \times 2 \times 2 \times 3 \times 3$	$81 = 3 \times 3 \times 3 \times 3$	$100 = 2 \times 2 \times 5 \times 5$
$64 = 2^6$	$72 = 2^3 \times 3^2$	$81 = 3^4$	$100 = 2^2 \times 5^2$

④ Divide.

$$0.13\overline{)0.08957} \quad \begin{array}{r} 0.689 \\ \hline \end{array}$$
78
115
104
117
117

$$2.3\overline{)148.81} \quad \begin{array}{r} 64.7 \\ \hline \end{array}$$
138
108
92
161
161

$$0.95\overline{)30.4} \quad \begin{array}{r} 32 \\ \hline \end{array}$$
285
190
190

$$0.092\overline{)2.668} \quad \begin{array}{r} 29 \\ \hline \end{array}$$
184
828
828

⑤ Multiply. Express answers as mixed numbers where appropriate.

$\dfrac{7}{12} \times \dfrac{18}{21} = \dfrac{^1 7}{_2 12} \times \dfrac{18^3}{21_3} = \dfrac{1}{2}$

$\dfrac{8}{15} \times \dfrac{9}{20} = \dfrac{^2 8}{_5 15} \times \dfrac{9^3}{20_5} = \dfrac{6}{25}$

$\dfrac{20}{27} \times \dfrac{18}{25} = \dfrac{^4 20}{_3 27} \times \dfrac{18^2}{25_5} = \dfrac{8}{15}$

$\dfrac{16}{35} \times \dfrac{25}{28} = \dfrac{^4 16}{_7 35} \times \dfrac{25^5}{28_7} = \dfrac{20}{49}$

$\dfrac{24}{35} \times \dfrac{49}{56} = \dfrac{^3 24}{_5 35} \times \dfrac{49^7}{56_7} = \dfrac{3}{5}$

$\dfrac{\sqrt{2}}{5} \times \dfrac{\sqrt{8}}{4} = \dfrac{\sqrt{2} \times \sqrt{8}}{5 \times 4} = \dfrac{\sqrt{16}}{20} = \dfrac{4^1}{20_5} = \dfrac{1}{5}$

$\dfrac{\sqrt{12}}{3} \times \dfrac{\sqrt{3}}{2} = \dfrac{\sqrt{12} \times \sqrt{3}}{3 \times 2} = \dfrac{\sqrt{36}}{6} = \dfrac{6}{6} = 1$

$\dfrac{2\sqrt{6}}{15} \times \dfrac{3\sqrt{2}}{12} =$
$\dfrac{^1 2\sqrt{6}}{_5 15} \times \dfrac{^1 3\sqrt{2}}{12_6} = \dfrac{\sqrt{6 \times 2}}{5 \times 6} = \dfrac{\sqrt{12}}{30} = \dfrac{2\sqrt{3}}{30} = \dfrac{\sqrt{3}}{15}$

$\dfrac{12}{25} \times 4\dfrac{3}{8} = \dfrac{^3 12}{_5 25} \times \dfrac{35^7}{8_2} = \dfrac{21}{10} = 2\dfrac{1}{10}$

$\dfrac{16}{21} \times 3\dfrac{3}{4} = \dfrac{^4 16}{_7 21} \times \dfrac{15^5}{4_1} = \dfrac{20}{7} = 2\dfrac{6}{7}$

$6\dfrac{1}{8} \times 5\dfrac{1}{7} = \dfrac{^7 49}{_2 8} \times \dfrac{36^9}{7_1} = \dfrac{63}{2} = 31\dfrac{1}{2}$

$7\dfrac{1}{9} \times 5\dfrac{5}{8} = \dfrac{^8 64}{_1 9} \times \dfrac{45^5}{8_1} = \dfrac{40}{1} = 40$

$4\dfrac{4}{9} \times 7\dfrac{1}{5} = \dfrac{^8 40}{_1 9} \times \dfrac{36^4}{5_1} = \dfrac{32}{1} = 32$

$\dfrac{\sqrt{8}}{3} \times \dfrac{3\sqrt{2}}{4} = \dfrac{3\sqrt{16}}{3 \times 4} = \dfrac{4}{4} = 1$

$2\dfrac{2}{3} \times \dfrac{3\sqrt{6}}{2} = \dfrac{^4 8}{_1 3} \times \dfrac{3\sqrt{6}}{2_1} = 4\sqrt{6}$

$\dfrac{4\sqrt{3}}{5} \times \dfrac{5\sqrt{15}}{3} = \dfrac{4 \times 5\sqrt{3 \times 15}}{5 \times 3} =$
$\dfrac{4\sqrt{45}}{3} = \dfrac{4\sqrt{3 \times 3 \times 5}}{3} = \dfrac{4 \times 3\sqrt{5}}{3} = 4\sqrt{5}$

① Calculate the sale price, given the percent discount.

Original Price	Percent Discount	Sale Price
$15	20%	$15(1 - 0.2) = $15(0.8) = $12
$20	15%	$20(1 - 0.15) = $20(0.85) = $17
$25	30%	$25(1 - 0.3) = $25(0.7) = $17.50
$30	33.$\overline{3}$%	$30(1 - 0.\overline{3}) = $30(1 - \frac{1}{3}) =$ $30(\frac{2}{3}) = $20
$40	40%	$40(1 - 0.4) = $40(0.6) = $24
$50	25%	$50(1 - 0.25) = $50(0.75) = $37.50

② Calculate the new price, given the percent mark-up.

Original Price	Percent Mark-up	New Price
$15	20%	$15(1 + 0.2) = $15(1.2) = $18
$20	15%	$20(1 + 0.15) = $20(1.15) = $23
$25	30%	$25(1 + 0.3) = $25(1.3) = $32.50
$30	33.$\overline{3}$%	$30(1 + 0.\overline{3}) = $30(1 + \frac{1}{3}) =$ $30(\frac{4}{3}) = $40
$40	40%	$40(1 + 0.4) = $40(1.4) = $56
$50	25%	$50(1 + 0.25) = $50(1.25) = $62.50

Teaching Tips, Cont.

➤ Explain that there is a more direct way of finding the price after the mark-up. Teach how to calculate mark-up from the teaching box. Explain that this is an application of percent increase.

➤ Show students that the total cost of an item including sales tax is really a percent mark-up on the item equivalent to the percentage of the sales tax.

➤ Remind students that sometimes working with percents is easier if they first convert to a fraction. This is especially true when working with repeating decimals.

➤ Complete the Classwork exercises. Have some students work the problems on the board for the class and explain their answers. All students should work the problems in their books.

Assignments
- Complete Lesson 53, Activities 2-5.
- Worksheet 27
- Bring a scientific calculator beginning in Lesson 58.

Lesson 54

Concepts
- Simple interest
- One-variable inequalities
- Divisibility tests
- Prime/composite numbers
- Multiplying decimals
- Math in the real world

Learning Objectives
The student will be able to:
- Define *interest*
- Define *principal*
- Define *simple interest*
- Give the formula for simple interest
- Calculate the amount of simple interest on a loan or investment
- Calculate the total amount due on a loan with simple interest
- Calculate the amount due per month on a loan with simple interest

Materials Needed
- Student Book, Lesson 54

Teaching Tips
- When going over the assignment from Lesson 53, point out to the students that the dollar amount a price is discounted to get a sale price is equal to the dollar amount the price is raised for the same percent mark-up.

- Review the applications of percent that have been taught so far: Discounts and sale prices (See Lesson 51), and mark-up (See Lesson 53).

- Introduce another application of percent: interest.

Simple Interest

Interest is the fee paid for the use of money. Whenever you get a loan, you will be charged interest. You will also earn interest on money you invest. Interest rates are always stated as a percent of the amount borrowed or invested.

The **principal** is the amount of money borrowed or invested. The **interest rate** is the percent of the principal that is paid each term.

Simple interest is interest charged on the original amount of the principal.

To calculate the amount of simple interest, use the formula $i = Prt$, where i is the amount of interest, P is the original amount of principal, r is the interest rate (given as a percent), and t is the time of the loan or investment in years.

How much simple interest will be charged on a $25,000 loan with a 6% interest rate that is paid back in 5 years?

i = the amount of interest
P = \$25,000
r = 6% = 0.06
t = 5
Use the formula $i = Prt$.
i = (\$25,000)(0.06)(5)
i = \$7500

What will be the total amount paid on the $25,000 loan?

$25,000 + \$7500 = \$32,500

① Classwork
Solve.

Denny allows businesses a 30-day grace period to pay for purchases with no interest. After 30 days, he charges them 18% simple interest per year on the unpaid balance. If a business purchases $9500 worth of supplies from Denny and pays $2500 in the first 30 days, what will be the total cost of the supplies if they take a year to pay the remaining balance?

Unpaid balance = \$9500 - \$2500 = \$7000
$I = Prt$
P = \$7000
r = 0.18
t = 1

I = (\$7000)(0.18)(1)
I = \$1260

This is the amount of interest – not the total cost.

Total cost = \$9500 + \$1260 = \$10,760

Activities
② Solve.
How much simple interest will be charged on a $40,000 loan with a 7% interest rate that is paid back in 4 years?
$I = Prt$
P = \$40,000 r = 0.07 t = 4
I = (\$40,000)(0.07)(4) = \$11,200
What will be the total amount paid on the $40,000 loan?
\$40,000 + \$11,200 = \$51,200
How much is paid each month to pay off the loan in 4 years? (Round to the nearest cent.)
4 years = 4 × 12 = 48 months
\$51,200 ÷ 48 months = \$1066.67 per month

---

③ Complete the chart. Round the monthly payment to the nearest cent.

Amount of loan	Interest rate	Number of years	Amount of interest paid	Total amount paid	Amount paid per month
$5,000	21%	2	($5000)(0.21)(2) = $2100	$5000 + $2100 = $7100	$7100 / 24 = $295.83
$11,000	18%	7	($11,000)(0.18)(7) = $13,860	$11,000 + $13,860 = $24,860	$24,860 / 84 = $295.95
$20,000	8.125%	15	($20,000)(0.08125)(15) = $24,375	$20,000 + $24,375 = $44,375	$44,375 / 180 = $246.53
$97,000	7%	20	($97,000)(0.07)(20) = $135,800	$97,000 + $135,800 = $232,800	$232,800 / 240 = $970.00
$175,000	5.5%	30	($175,000)(0.055)(30) = $288,750	$175,000 + $288,750 = $463,750	$463,750 / 360 = $1288.19

④ Solve.

$5(x-1)+4 < 1+20 \div 4 - 2x$

$5x - 5 + 4 < 1 + 5 - 2x$

$5x - 1 < 6 - 2x$

$7x < 7$

$x < 1$

$3x + 2 \times 3 - 1 > 4(x+2) - 3x$

$3x + 6 - 1 > 4x + 8 - 3x$

$3x + 5 > x + 8$

$2x > 3$

$x > \dfrac{3}{2}$

$6(1-2x) - 2(1-3x) < 5x - 7$

$6 - 12x - 2 + 6x < 5x - 7$

$-6x + 4 < 5x - 7$

$-11x < -11$

$x > 1$

⑤ Use the divisibility tests to identify each number as prime or composite.

295 Composite (5)
297 Composite (3, 9)
303 Composite (3)

305 Composite (5)
307 Prime
309 Composite (3)

⑥ Multiply.

```
   510.6
 × 3.14
  20424
  51060
+1531800
1603.284
```

```
  12.96
 ×1.08
 10368
+129600
13.9968
```

```
    2.0607
  ×0.3098
   164856
  1854630
+61821000
0.63840486
```

```
   0.061
 ×0.321
     61
   1220
 +18300
0.019581
```

Additional information for teaching interest:

You may wish to look up the current interest rates being paid by banks for checking, savings, CDs, etc. This will give the students a better idea of what interest rates are, and will show them the difference in rates depending on the type of investment. You may also wish to tell what credit card interest rates are. Many students may be shocked to see the difference in interest rates between what the consumer is charged versus what the consumer is paid. If you wish, you may work sample problems based on these numbers.

Teaching Tips, Cont.

➢ Explain that interest can be good or bad for the consumer. If the consumer is earning interest on an investment, then it is good. If the consumer is paying interest on a loan, it is bad for the consumer. Emphasize that the person using the money is responsible for paying the interest. When you put money in the bank, the bank is using your money, so they pay you the interest.

➢ Teach the definitions of *interest*, *principal*, and *simple interest* from the teaching box.

➢ Introduce the formula for calculating simple interest and teach how to do the calculations. Students should memorize this formula.

➢ Complete the Classwork exercises. Have some students work the problems on the board for the class and explain their answers. All students should work the problems in their books.

Assignments

• Complete Lesson 54, Activities 2-6.
• Bring a scientific calculator beginning in Lesson 58.

Lesson 55

Concepts
- Commission
- Prime factorization
- Exponents
- One-variable equations
- Dividing fractions
- Dividing mixed numbers
- Simple interest
- Math in the real world

Learning Objectives
The student will be able to:
- Define *commission*
- Calculate commission
- Apply principles of commission to real life scenarios

Materials Needed
- Student Book, Lesson 55
- Worksheet 28

Teaching Tips
- ➤ Have students complete Worksheet 28 in class. This may be for added practice of earlier topics, or graded as a quiz, if desired.

- ➤ Review finding the percent of a number. (See Lesson 48.)

- ➤ Have students give examples of applications of percents that they have learned so far. (Discounts, sale prices, mark-up, and interest have been taught; sales tax and cross weight have been mentioned)

- ➤ Introduce commission as another application of percent.

Lesson 55

Commission

Commission is the amount a sales person earns based on a percent of the price of the item sold. To calculate commission, convert the percent to a decimal and multiply by the price of the item sold.

If a real estate agent earns 4% commission on the sale of a house, how much does the agent earn after the sale of house for $179,500?

$179,500(0.04) = $7180

① Classwork

A real estate listing agent has agreed to split the commission equally with whomever finds a buyer for a piece of property. If the property sells for $248,250 and the commission rate is 6%, how much commission does the listing agent earn?
Half of 6% is 3%. The listing agent will earn ($248,250)(0.03) = $7447.50

Activities

② Solve.

A real estate agent offers to sell a house for a set fee of $7500 or 6% of the selling price of the house, whichever the seller chooses. If the house sells for $127,400, which option should the seller choose? How much will the seller save over the other option?
(127,400)(0.06) = $7644
The seller should choose the set fee of $7500.
The savings would be $7644 - $7500 = $144

At what selling price would the 6% commission equal $7500?
Let x = the selling price
$7500 = 0.06x$
$7500 \div 0.06 = x$
$125,000 = x$

An appliance salesman gets paid $300 per week plus 10% commission on the selling price of any appliances he sells. If the salesman sold a refrigerator for $890, a washer and dryer for $1175, and an oven for $325, how much commission did the salesman earn during the week?
Total sales = $890 + $1175 + $325 = $2390
Commission = $2390(0.10) = $239

What did the salesman get paid for the week?
Earnings = $300 + $239 = $539

---

③ Find the prime factorization of each number. Use exponents where appropriate.

124	126	132
$124 = 2 \times 2 \times 31$	$126 = 2 \times 3 \times 3 \times 7$	$132 = 2 \times 2 \times 3 \times 11$
$124 = 2^2 \times 31$	$126 = 2 \times 3^2 \times 7$	$132 = 2^2 \times 3 \times 11$

④ Solve.

$3x + (6-4)^2 = 2(x-1)$
$3x + 2^2 = 2x - 2$
$3x + 4 = 2x - 2$
$x = -6$

$7x + 2(3-x) = x - (3^2 - 2^3)$
$7x + 6 - 2x = x - (9-8)$
$5x + 6 = x - 1$
$4x = -7$
$x = -\dfrac{7}{4}$

$3(3x-4) + \sqrt{2^2 \times 6 + 1} = 5x + 1$
$9x - 12 + \sqrt{4 \times 6 + 1} = 5x + 1$
$9x - 12 + \sqrt{25} = 5x + 1$
$9x - 12 + 5 = 5x + 1$
$9x - 7 = 5x + 1$
$4x = 8$
$x = 2$

⑤ Divide. Express answers as mixed numbers where appropriate.

$\dfrac{9}{14} \div \dfrac{3}{35} = \dfrac{\cancel{9}^3}{\cancel{14}_2} \times \dfrac{\cancel{35}^5}{\cancel{3}_1} = \dfrac{15}{2} = 7\dfrac{1}{2}$

$7\dfrac{1}{5} \div 4\dfrac{1}{2} = \dfrac{36}{5} \div \dfrac{9}{2} = \dfrac{\cancel{36}^4}{5} \times \dfrac{2}{\cancel{9}_1} = \dfrac{8}{5} = 1\dfrac{3}{5}$

$\dfrac{18}{25} \div \dfrac{27}{35} = \dfrac{\cancel{18}^2}{\cancel{25}_5} \times \dfrac{\cancel{35}^7}{\cancel{27}_3} = \dfrac{14}{15}$

$9\dfrac{1}{11} \div 1\dfrac{31}{44} = \dfrac{100}{11} \div \dfrac{75}{44} = \dfrac{\cancel{100}^4}{\cancel{11}_1} \times \dfrac{\cancel{44}^4}{\cancel{75}_3} = \dfrac{16}{3} = 5\dfrac{1}{3}$

$\dfrac{27}{32} \div \dfrac{9}{16} = \dfrac{\cancel{27}^3}{\cancel{32}_2} \times \dfrac{\cancel{16}^1}{\cancel{9}_1} = \dfrac{3}{2} = 1\dfrac{1}{2}$

$1\dfrac{8}{15} \div 6\dfrac{9}{10} = \dfrac{23}{15} \div \dfrac{69}{10} = \dfrac{\cancel{23}^1}{\cancel{15}_3} \times \dfrac{\cancel{10}^2}{\cancel{69}_3} = \dfrac{2}{9}$

$\dfrac{35}{36} \div \dfrac{25}{27} = \dfrac{\cancel{35}^7}{\cancel{36}_4} \times \dfrac{\cancel{27}^3}{\cancel{25}_5} = \dfrac{21}{20} = 1\dfrac{1}{20}$

$4\dfrac{4}{15} \div \dfrac{12}{45} = \dfrac{64}{15} \div \dfrac{12}{45} = \dfrac{\cancel{64}^{16}}{\cancel{15}_1} \times \dfrac{\cancel{45}^4}{\cancel{12}_3} = 16$

⑥ Complete the chart to reflect simple interest.

Principal	Interest rate	Time, in years	Amount of interest	Total amount paid
$5000	8.2%	5	$i = \$5000(0.082)(5) = \$2050$	$5000 + $2050 = $7050
$10,000	6.125%	10	$i = \$10,000(0.06125)(10) = \$6125$	$10,000 + $6125 = $16,125
$12,500	7%	9	$i = \$12,500(0.07)(9) = \$7875$	$12,500 + $7875 = $20,375
$15,000	10%	6	$i = \$15,000(0.1)(6) = \$9000$	$15,000 + $9000 = $24,000
$18,000	0.9%	7	$i = \$18,000(0.009)(7) = \$1134$	$18,000 + $1134 = $19,134

Discount and Mark-up   Worksheet 28

① Calculate the sale price, given the percent discount.

Original Price	Percent Discount	Sale Price
$10	25%	$10(1 − 0.25) = $10(0.75) = $7.50
$20	30%	$20(1 − 0.3) = $20(0.7) = $14
$25	20%	$25(1 − 0.2) = $25(0.8) = $20
$30	66.$\overline{6}$%	$30(1 − 0.$\overline{6}$) = $30(1 − $\frac{2}{3}$) = $30($\frac{1}{3}$) = $10
$40	15%	$40(1 − 0.15) = $40(0.85) = $34
$50	40%	$50(1 − 0.4) = $50(0.6) = $30

② Calculate the new price, given the percent mark-up.

Original Price	Percent Mark-up	New Price
$10	25%	$10(1 + 0.25) = $10(1.25) = $12.50
$20	30%	$20(1 + 0.3) = $20(1.3) = $26
$25	20%	$25(1 + 0.2) = $25(1.2) = $30
$30	66.$\overline{6}$%	$30(1 + 0.$\overline{6}$) = $30(1 + $\frac{2}{3}$) = $30($\frac{5}{3}$) = $50
$40	15%	$40(1 + 0.15) = $40(1.15) = $46
$50	40%	$50(1 + 0.4) = $50(1.4) = $70

Teaching Tips, Cont.

➤ Teach the definition of commission and ask the students what occupations might pay a commission. (Real estate agent, car salesman, general sales)

➤ Teach how to find the amount of commission on a sale.

➤ Complete the Classwork exercises. Have some students work the problems on the board for the class and explain their answers. All students should work the problems in their books.

Assignments

- Complete Lesson 55, assignment 2-6.
- Bring a scientific calculator beginning in Lesson 58.

Lesson 56

Concepts
- Percents less than 1
- One-variable inequalities
- Multiplying fractions
- Multiplying mixed numbers
- Dividing fractions
- Dividing mixed numbers
- Percents
- Math in the real world

Learning Objectives
The student will be able to:
- Write percents less than 1 using the proper format
- Convert percents less than one to decimal format
- Apply percents less than 1 to real life scenarios

Materials Needed
- Student Book, Lesson 56

Teaching Tips
- Review percent-decimal conversion. (See Lesson 47.)

- Ask students what 1% of 100 is. (1) Ask students what 1% of 1000 is. (10) Ask students what half of 10 is. (5) Explain that this represents half of 1% of 1000.

- Ask students how to write $\frac{1}{2}$ as a decimal. (0.5) Show the students that 5 out of 1000 is written as 0.5% of 1000.

- Ask students how to convert 0.5% to a decimal. (Move the decimal point two places to the left to get 0.005)

Percents Less Than 1

Percents less than 1 indicate a very small amount when compared to the whole. They will always have a leading zero, as in 0.9%. Pay careful attention to the number of zeros when converting to a decimal. Insert two zeros between the decimal point and the first non-zero digit.

0.9% = 0.009   0.004% = 0.00004

Staplers comprise 0.3% of the total items in Denny's current inventory. How many staplers are in Denny's current inventory if he has a total of 10,000 items in his inventory?

10,000 × 0.003 = 30 staplers

① Classwork
Solve.

Denny has 25 packs of markers in the office supply section of his store. The markers comprise 0.4% of the office supply inventory. How many items does Denny have in his office supply inventory?
Let x = the number of items
25 = 0.004x
x = 25 ÷ 0.004
x = 6250

Activities
② Solve.
Denny offers free local delivery for his customers and delivers to 0.5% of his monthly customers each day. How many customers does Denny have each month if he makes 15 deliveries each day?
Let x = the number of customers Denny has each month.
15 = 0.005x
15 ÷ 0.005 = x
x = 3000

Denny's store is open 20 days each month. How many customers does he have each day?
Let x = the number of customers Denny has each day.
x = 3000 ÷ 20
x = 150

How many deliveries does Denny make each month?
Let x = the number of deliveries Denny has each month.
x = 15 × 20
x = 300

Denny has 10 hours each day to complete his deliveries. How much time does he have for each delivery?
Let x = the amount of time Denny has for each delivery.
x = 10 ÷ 15
$x = \frac{2}{3}$ of an hour
$\frac{2}{3} = \frac{x}{60}$
3x = 120
x = 40 minutes

③ Solve.

$7x + (6-9)^2 > 3(x+4)$
$7x + (-3)^2 > 3x + 12$
$7x + 9 > 3x + 12$
$4x > 3$
$x > \dfrac{3}{4}$

$8x + 2(5-3x) < 3x - (3^3 \div 3^2)$
$8x + 10 - 6x < 3x - 3$
$2x + 10 < 3x - 3$
$-x < -13$
$x > 13$

$4(2x-5) + \sqrt{3^2 + 2^2 + 3} < 2(x+1)$
$8x - 20 + \sqrt{9 + 4 + 3} < 2x + 2$
$8x - 20 + \sqrt{16} < 2x + 2$
$8x - 20 + 4 < 2x + 2$
$8x - 16 < 2x + 2$
$6x < 18$
$x < 3$

④ Multiply or divide as indicated.

$\dfrac{36}{49} \times \dfrac{35}{54} = \dfrac{\overset{2}{\cancel{36}}}{\underset{7}{\cancel{49}}} \times \dfrac{\overset{5}{\cancel{35}}}{\underset{3}{\cancel{54}}} = \dfrac{10}{21}$

$\dfrac{25}{63} \times \dfrac{56}{75} = \dfrac{\overset{1}{\cancel{25}}}{\underset{9}{\cancel{63}}} \times \dfrac{\overset{8}{\cancel{56}}}{\underset{3}{\cancel{75}}} = \dfrac{8}{27}$

$1\dfrac{15}{21} \times 4\dfrac{1}{12} = \dfrac{\overset{3}{\cancel{36}}}{\underset{7}{\cancel{21}}} \times \dfrac{\overset{7}{\cancel{49}}}{\underset{1}{\cancel{12}}} = 7$

$3\dfrac{2}{11} \times 3\dfrac{17}{20} = \dfrac{\overset{7}{\cancel{35}}}{\underset{1}{\cancel{11}}} \times \dfrac{\overset{7}{\cancel{77}}}{\underset{4}{\cancel{20}}} = \dfrac{49}{4} = 12\dfrac{1}{4}$

$\dfrac{35}{72} \div \dfrac{28}{45} = \dfrac{\overset{5}{\cancel{35}}}{\underset{8}{\cancel{72}}} \times \dfrac{\overset{5}{\cancel{45}}}{\underset{4}{\cancel{28}}} = \dfrac{25}{32}$

$\dfrac{54}{55} \div \dfrac{18}{25} = \dfrac{\overset{3}{\cancel{54}}}{\underset{11}{\cancel{55}}} \times \dfrac{\overset{5}{\cancel{25}}}{\underset{1}{\cancel{18}}} = \dfrac{15}{11} = 1\dfrac{4}{11}$

$6\dfrac{1}{20} \div 6\dfrac{3}{5} = \dfrac{121}{20} \div \dfrac{33}{5} = \dfrac{\overset{11}{\cancel{121}}}{\underset{4}{\cancel{20}}} \times \dfrac{\overset{1}{\cancel{5}}}{\underset{3}{\cancel{33}}} = \dfrac{11}{12}$

$4\dfrac{4}{15} \div 1\dfrac{7}{9} = \dfrac{64}{15} \div \dfrac{16}{9} = \dfrac{\overset{4}{\cancel{64}}}{\underset{5}{\cancel{15}}} \times \dfrac{\overset{3}{\cancel{9}}}{\underset{1}{\cancel{16}}} = \dfrac{12}{5} = 2\dfrac{2}{5}$

⑤ Solve.

What is 95% of 280?
$x = 0.95(280)$
$x = 266$

What is 0.3% of 60?
$x = 0.003(60)$
$x = 0.18$

What is 254% of 500?
$x = 2.54(500)$
$x = 1270$

16 is what percent of 64?
$16 = 64x$
$x = \dfrac{16}{64}$
$x = \dfrac{1}{4} = 25\%$

5 is what percent of 950?
Round to the nearest tenth of a percent.
$5 = 950x$
$x = \dfrac{5}{950}$
$x = \dfrac{1}{190} = 0.005 = 0.5\%$

225 is what percent of 50?
$225 = 50x$
$x = \dfrac{225}{50}$
$x = \dfrac{45}{10} = 4.5 = 450\%$

24 is 72% of what number?
$24 = 0.72x$
$x = 24 \div 0.72$
$x = 33.\overline{3}$ or $x = 33\dfrac{1}{3}$

3 is 0.02% of what number?
$3 = 0.0002x$
$x = 3 \div 0.0002$
$x = 15,000$

132 is 150% of what number?
$132 = 1.5x$
$x = 132 \div 1.5$
$x = 88$

Teaching Tips, Cont.

➢ Emphasize the importance of writing the leading zero before the decimal point for numbers less than 1. This will help eliminate errors from not noticing the decimal point in small numbers.

➢ Teach how to use percents less than 1 from the teaching box.

➢ Show students how to set up an equation from a word problem involving percents less than 1.

➢ Complete the Classwork exercises. Have one student work the problem on the board for the class and explain the answer. All students should work the problem in their books.

Assignments

- Complete Lesson 56, Activities 2-5.
- Bring a scientific calculator beginning in Lesson 58.
- Bring a compass and protractor beginning in Lesson 61.

Horizons Pre-Algebra, Teacher's Guide

Lesson 57

Concepts
- Profits and royalties
- Fraction-decimal-percent conversion
- Simple interest
- Powers of 10
- Metric conversions
- Math in the real world

Learning Objectives
The student will be able to:
- Define *profit*
- Define *royalties*
- Calculate profit
- Calculate royalties
- Apply principles of profit and royalties to real life scenarios

Materials Needed
- Student Book, Lesson 57

Teaching Tips
- Review commission. Ask students how some occupations might pay if they do not pay based on commission. (Salary, hourly wage, piece work, royalties)

- Define *profit*. Tell students that this can be applied to piece work pay when the worker must purchase the materials to make each piece, and then gets paid per piece completed or sold.

- Explain that profit takes into account all expenses incurred, not just the cost of the materials for the specific items sold.

Profits and Royalties

Profit is the difference between an item's selling price and the costs incurred to sell the item. These costs can include the expenses to get the item, salaries for employees to sell the item, and costs associated with the building and day-to-day business operations (rent or mortgage payment, utilities, etc.).

Royalties are payment for the use of property. Often, musicians and authors are paid royalties based on the number of albums or books sold. Royalties may be paid as a percent of the total sales or as a set amount per item.

① Classwork

A gospel quartet pays $20,000 to record a new CD. If they charge $15 per CD, how many CDs will they have to sell to earn back their initial investment?

$20,000 ÷ $15 = 1333.\overline{3}$

They must sell 1334 CDs.

What will be their profit after selling 2500 CDs?

$2500 \times \$15 = \$37,500$
$\$37,500 - \$20,000 = \$17,500$ profit.

Activities

② Solve.

A parent is selling hand-made gifts for teachers in Denny's store. Denny pays the parent 60% of the selling price for each gift sold. If the gifts cost the parent 78 cents each to make and Denny sells them for $3.95 each, how much profit is the parent making on the sale of each gift?

Denny pays the parent $3.95 × 0.6 = $2.37
The parent's profit on the sale of each gift is $2.37 - $0.78 = $1.59

If the parent made 50 gifts for Denny's store but only sold 41 gifts, how much profit did the parent make?

Cost to make 50 gifts is $0.78 × 50 = $39.00
Denny pays the parent $2.37 × 41 = $97.17
Profit is $97.17 - $39.00 = $58.17

The author of several novels is paid $7,000 for writing a book, plus royalties based on the book sales as follows: 5% of the cover price for each of the first 5000 books sold, 10% of the cover price for each of the next 5000 books sold, and 15% of the cover price for each book over 10,000 copies. If the cover price of a hardback is $24.95, how much money does the author make from selling 4000 books? 7500 books? 10,250 books?

4000 books: $7000 + 4000(0.05)(24.95) = $7000 + $4990 = $11,990

7500 books: $7000 + 5000(0.05)(24.95) + 2500(0.1)(24.95) = $7000 + $6237.50 + $6237.50 = $19,475

10,250 books: $7000 + 5000(0.05)(24.95) + 5000(0.1)(24.95) + 250(0.15)(24.95) = $7000 + $6237.50 + $12,475 + $935.63 = $26,648.13

---

③ Complete the chart to show proper fraction-decimal-percent conversion.

Fraction	Decimal	Percent
$\frac{1}{2}$	0.5	50%
$\frac{5}{8}$	0.625	62.5%
$\frac{1}{3}$	$0.\overline{3}$	$33.\overline{3}\%$
$\frac{9}{10}$	0.9	90%
$\frac{3}{4}$	0.75	75%

Fraction	Decimal	Percent
$\frac{1}{10}$	0.1	10%
$\frac{2}{3}$	$0.\overline{6}$	$66.\overline{6}\%$
$\frac{5}{6}$	$0.8\overline{3}$	$83.\overline{3}\%$
$\frac{1}{8}$	0.125	12.5%
$\frac{7}{8}$	0.875	87.5%

④ Complete the chart to reflect simple interest.

Principal	Interest rate	Time, in years	Amount of interest	Total amount paid
$5000	3.5%	4	$i = \$5000(0.035)(4) = \$700$	$\$5000 + \$700 = \$5700$
$10,000	5.875%	7	$i = \$10,000(0.05875)(7) = \$4112.50$	$\$10,000 + \$4112.50 = \$14,112.50$
$12,500	8%	5	$i = \$12,500(0.08)(5) = \$5000$	$\$12,500 + \$5000 = \$17,500$
$15,000	20%	8	$i = \$15,000(0.2)(8) = \$24,000$	$\$15,000 + \$24,000 = \$39,000$
$18,000	0.8%	10	$i = \$18,000(0.008)(10) = \$1440$	$\$18,000 + \$1440 = \$19,440$

⑤ Multiply or divide by the correct powers of 10 to convert the metric measurements.

13 m = __13,000__ mm   33,000 cm = ___330___ m

0.17 L = ___170___ mL   2943 mL = ___2.943__ L

3.7 g = ___370___ cg   755 cW = ___7.55___ W

94.27 W = ___94,270___ mW   8.11 mg = ___0.00811___ g

Pay method pros and cons

Commission: An aggressive salesperson may do well, especially if the commission rate is good. If the salesperson is not aggressive, if the economy is in a downturn, or if the commission rate is low, the salesperson will not get paid very much.

Salary: Guaranteed amount of pay. However, a hard-working employee can earn the same as a lazy employee. Salaried employees are not always paid extra for having to work extra hours.

Hourly: Guaranteed amount of pay for each hour worked, and most companies pay hourly workers time-and-a-half for anything over 40 hours in a week. Hourly employees are often the first to be let go when the work load eases.

Royalties: If a book or song is a hit, the writer can make a lot of money. If it does not sell well, the writer does not get paid.

Teaching Tips, Cont.

➢ Point out the second word problem in section 2, where the parent made 50 gifts but only sold 41 gifts. Make sure students understand that the parent had the expense of making 50 gifts, even though only 41 were sold, so the expense of making all 50 gifts must be taken into consideration when determining profit.

➢ Define *royalties*. Tell students that a very small percent of people are paid based on royalties.

➢ If time permits, have a class discussion on the pros and cons of the various ways pay may be determined. (See list at left for ideas.)

➢ Complete the Classwork exercises. Have some students work the problems on the board for the class and explain their answers. All students should work the problems in their books.

Assignments
- Complete Lesson 57, Activities 2-5.
- Bring a scientific calculator every day beginning with the next lesson.
- Bring a compass and protractor beginning in Lesson 61.

Lesson 58

Concepts
- Compound interest
- Adding mixed numbers
- Subtracting mixed numbers
- Divisibility tests
- Prime/composite numbers
- Math in the real world

Learning Objectives
The student will be able to:
- Define *compound interest*
- Explain the difference between simple and compound interest
- Calculate compound interest

Materials Needed
- Student Book, Lesson 58
- Worksheet 29
- Scientific calculator

Teaching Tips
> Have students complete Worksheet 29 in class. This may be for added practice of earlier topics, or graded as a quiz, if desired.

> Review the definition of simple interest. Tell the students that there is another way of calculating interest that will yield a different amount of interest.

> Teach the definition of compound interest. Ask the students to identify the big difference between simple and compound interest. (Simple interest is on the principal amount only; compound interest is on the principal and accrued interest)

> Introduce the formula for compound interest.

Compound Interest

Compound interest is similar to simple interest, except that interest is earned (or paid) on the principal *and* the previously earned interest. When interest is calculated, the amount of interest is added to the principal. The next time interest is calculated, it is based on the sum of the principal plus the interest that has been added. If you have money in a savings account, you want to earn compound interest. If you have a loan, you want to pay simple interest.

To calculate the amount of compound interest, use the formula $A = P(1 + r)^t$, where A is the amount after time t has passed, P is the original amount of principal, r is the interest rate for each compounding period (given as a percent), and t is the number of times the interest is compounded.

Note that in the compound interest formula, the answer is the total balance, including all accrued interest. In the simple interest formula, the answer is just the amount of interest accrued.

How much compound interest will be earned on a $25,000 investment with a 6% interest rate that is compounded annually for 5 years? (Use a calculator and round answers to the nearest cent.)

A = the amount after 5 years
$P = \$25,000$
$r = 6\% = 0.06$
$t = 5$
Use the formula $A = P(1 + r)^t$.

$A = \$25,000(1 + 0.06)^5$

$A = \$25,000(1.06)^5$

$A = \$25,000(1.3382255776)$

$A = \$33,455.64$

① Classwork
Solve.

Denny has arranged for a retirement plan for his employees. If the plan pays a guaranteed 10% interest each year, compounded annually, what will be the balance at the end of 5 years if the initial balance was $10,000 and no additional deposits were made? (Round answers to the nearest cent.)
$P = \$10,000$
$r = 0.1$
$t = 5$
$A = \$10,000(1 + 0.1)^5$
$A = \$10,000(1.1)^5$
$A = \$10,000(1.61051)$
$A = \$16,105.10$
What would be the balance at the end of one year?
$P = \$10,000$
$r = 0.1$
$t = 1$
$A = \$10,000(1 + 0.1)^1$
$A = \$10,000(1.1)^1$
$A = \$11,000$
What would be the balance at the end of one year if the interest were compounded quarterly instead of annually?
$P = \$10,000$
$r = 0.1 \div 4 = 0.025$
$t = 1 \times 4 = 4$
$A = \$10,000(1 + 0.025)^4$
$A = \$10,000(1.025)^4$
$A = \$11,038.13$

Activities
② Solve.
What is the balance of a saving account paying 3% interest compounded annually if the initial balance of $750 was invested for 2 years?
$A = \$750(1.03)^2 = \$795.68$

---

③ Complete the table to show compound interest.

Initial principal	Interest rate	Time, in years	Total compounded annually	Total compounded quarterly
$1000	3%	3	$A = \$1000(1 + .03)^3$ = $1092.73	$A = \$1000(1 + 0.03 \div 4)^{3 \times 4}$ = $1093.81
$5000	7%	3	$A = \$5000(1.07)^3$ = $6125.22	$A = \$5000(1 + 0.07 \div 4)^{3 \times 4}$ = $6157.20
$7500	10%	5	$A = \$7500(1.1)^5$ = $12,078.83	$A = \$7500(1 + 0.1 \div 4)^{5 \times 4}$ = $12,289.62
$12,000	15%	10	$A = \$12,000(1.15)^{10}$ = $48,546.69	$A = \$12,000(1 + 0.15 \div 4)^{10 \times 4}$ = $52,324.55
$25,000	24%	10	$A = \$25,000(1.24)^{10}$ = $214,860.64	$A = \$25,000(1 + 0.24 \div 4)^{10 \times 4}$ = $257,142.95

④ Add or subtract as indicated. Express answers as mixed numbers where appropriate.

$7\frac{5}{12} + 9\frac{5}{6} = (7 + 9) + \left(\frac{5}{12} + \frac{5}{6}\right) = 16 + \frac{5}{12} + \frac{10}{12} = 16 + \frac{15}{12} = 16 + 1\frac{3}{12} = 17\frac{3}{12} = 17\frac{1}{4}$

$8\frac{14}{25} + 5\frac{4}{15} = (8 + 5) + \left(\frac{14}{25} + \frac{4}{15}\right) = 13 + \frac{42}{75} + \frac{20}{75} = 13 + \frac{62}{75} = 13\frac{62}{75}$

$15\frac{3}{4} - 11\frac{2}{3} = (15 - 11) + \left(\frac{3}{4} - \frac{2}{3}\right) = 4 + \left(\frac{9}{12} - \frac{8}{12}\right) = 4\frac{1}{12}$

$10\frac{7}{10} - 8\frac{11}{12} = (10 - 8) + \left(\frac{7}{10} - \frac{11}{12}\right) = 2 + \left(\frac{42}{60} - \frac{55}{60}\right) = 1 + \left(\frac{60 + 42}{60} - \frac{55}{60}\right) = 1 + \left(\frac{102}{60} - \frac{55}{60}\right) = 1\frac{47}{60}$

⑤ Use the divisibility tests to identify each number as prime or composite.

311   Prime
313   Prime
315   Composite (3, 5, 9)

317   Prime
321   Composite (3)
325   Composite (5)

⑥ Solve.
If you deposit $100 in a savings account that pays 6% annual interest compounded monthly, what will be your balance at the end of 1 month?

$A = \$100\left(1 + \frac{0.06}{12}\right)^1 = \$100(1 + 0.005)^1 = \$100(1.005) = \$100.50$

If you deposit an additional $100 at the end of the first month, what will be the balance at the end of the second month?
Beginning balance of second month = $100.50 + $100 = $200.50
$A = \$200.50(1.005) = \$201.50$

Simple Interest

① Identify what each variable represents in the formula $i = Prt$.

i ___interest___

P ___principal___

r ___rate___

t ___time___

② Complete the chart to reflect simple interest.

Principal	Interest rate	Time, in years	Amount of interest
$100	4.5%	2	$i = \$100(0.045)(2) = \$9$
$500	7%	4	$i = \$500(0.07)(4) = \$140$
$1000	5%	3	$i = \$1000(0.05)(3) = \$150$
$5000	8%	5	$i = \$5000(0.08)(5) = \$2000$
$10,000	6%	10	$i = \$10,000(0.06)(10) = \$6000$
$15,000	11%	9	$i = \$15,000(0.11)(9) = \$14,850$
$20,000	10%	6	$i = \$20,000(0.1)(6) = \$12,000$
$25,000	0.5%	7	$i = \$25,000(0.005)(7) = \$875$

③ For each loan in the chart above, find the total amount owed, including all interest.

Principal	Interest rate	Time, in years	Total amount owed
$100	4.5%	2	$100 + $9 = $109
$500	7%	4	$500 + $140 = $640
$1000	5%	3	$1000 + $150 = $1150
$5000	8%	5	$5000 + $2000 = $7000
$10,000	6%	10	$10,000 + $6000 = $16,000
$15,000	11%	9	$15,000 + $14,850 = $29,850
$20,000	10%	6	$20,000 + $12,000 + $32,000
$25,000	0.5%	7	$25,000 + $875 = $25,875

Teaching Tips, Cont.

➢ Have students take out their scientific calculators and find the [x^y] button.

➢ Teach students how to use a calculator to do calculations with exponents by entering the base, followed by the [x^y] button, and then entering the exponent and pressing the [=] button.

➢ Work through the example problem in the teaching box with the students, having all students using their calculators to find the answer. Make sure all students are able to use a calculator to get the correct answer before continuing.

➢ Point out that the simple interest formula gives the amount of the interest only. The amount of interest must be added to the principal to get the total balance. The compound interest formula gives the balance at the end of the time period. To get the amount of interest, the initial principal must be subtracted from the balance.

➢ Complete the Classwork exercises. Have some students work the problems on the board for the class and explain their answers. All students should work the problems in their books.

Assignments
- Complete Lesson 58, Activities 2-6
- Bring a compass and protractor beginning in Lesson 61.

Lesson 59

Concepts
- Percents greater than 100
- Greatest common factor
- Powers of 10
- Metric conversions
- Simple interest
- Compound interest
- Proportions
- Math in the real world

Learning Objectives
The student will be able to:
- Write percents greater than 100 as decimals
- Explain the value of percents greater than 100
- Apply percents greater than 100 to real life scenarios

Materials Needed
- Student Book, Lesson 59
- Scientific calculator

Teaching Tips
➤ Review percents. (See Lessons 47 – 48.)

➤ Ask the students what percent of a pizza they have if they have the entire pizza. (100%) Ask what percent of a pizza they have if they have half of a pizza. (50%) Ask what percent of a pizza they have if they have two whole pizzas. (200% -- Some students may answer 100% or not know how to answer the question.)

➤ Introduce the concept of percents greater than 100 by explaining that since 100% of something is one whole of that thing, then more than 100% is more than one of that thing.

Percents Greater Than 100

Percents greater than 100 indicate an amount that is greater than the original value. They will always have at least three digits preceding the decimal point. When written as a decimal, there will always be at least one non-zero digit to the left of the decimal point.

135.9% = 1.359   2497% = 24.97

What is 135.9% of 500?
$x = 1.359(500)$
$x = 679.5$

① Classwork
Solve.

On Black Friday (the day after Thanksgiving), Denny had 250% of the average number of customers in his store. If he averages 150 customers each day, how many customers did Denny have on Black Friday?
$x = 150(2.5) = 375$

Activities
② Solve.

What is 100.5% of 50?
$x = 1.005(50)$
$x = 50.25$

What is 105% of 50?
$x = 1.05(50)$
$x = 52.5$

What is 238% of 500?
$x = 2.38(500)$
$x = 1190$

What is 333% of 900?
$x = 3.33(900)$
$x = 2997$

What is 475% of 350?
$x = 4.75(350)$
$x = 1662.5$

What is 234.9% of 200?
$x = 2.349(200)$
$x = 469.8$

What is 521% of 40?
$x = 5.21(40)$
$x = 208.4$

What is 941% of 80?
$x = 9.41(80)$
$x = 752.8$

What is 1042% of 300?
$x = 10.42(300)$
$x = 3126$

What is 999% of 500?
$x = 9.99(500)$
$x = 4995$

What is 1423% of 700?
$x = 14.23(700)$
$x = 9961$

What is 1554% of 600?
$x = 15.54(600)$
$x = 9324$

③ Find the greatest common factor of each set of numbers.

56 and 84	126 and 189	90 and 126
$56 = ②\times②\times2\times⑦$	$126 = 2\times③\times③\times⑦$	$90 = ②\times③\times③\times5$
$84 = ②\times②\times3\times⑦$	$189 = ③\times③\times3\times⑦$	$126 = ②\times③\times③\times7$
GCF: $2^2\times7 = 28$	GCF: $3^2\times7 = 63$	GCF: $2\times3^2 = 18$

④ Multiply or divide by the correct powers of 10 to convert the metric measurements.

26.7 W = ___26,700___ mW   25,800 mm = ___25.8___ m

0.08 g = ___80___ mg   8169 cL = ___81.69___ L

0.17 m = ___17___ cm   398 mW = ___0.398___ W

5.381 L = ___5381___ mL   0.55 cg = ___0.0055___ g

⑤ Complete the chart.

Principal	Interest rate	Time, in years	Total amount of simple interest	Balance, compounded annually
$1000	5%	2	$i = \$1000(0.05)(2) = \$100$	$A = \$1000(1 + 0.05)^2$ $= \$1102.50$
$5,000	4%	4	$i = \$5000(0.04)(4) = \$800$	$A = \$5000(1 + 0.04)^4$ $= \$5849.29$
$10,000	8%	6	$i = \$10,000(0.08)(6) = \$4800$	$A = \$10,000(1 + 0.08)^6$ $= \$15,868.74$
$15,000	6%	8	$i = \$15,000(0.06)(8) = \$7200$	$A = \$15,000(1 + 0.06)^8$ $= \$23,907.72$
$20,000	10%	10	$i = \$20,000(0.1)(10) = \$20,000$	$A = \$20,000(1 + 0.1)^{10}$ $= \$51,874.85$

⑥ Complete the proportions.

$\frac{8}{15} = \frac{12}{x}$ $8x = 15(12)$ $8x = 180$ $x = 22\frac{1}{2}$ $\frac{x}{24} = \frac{45}{27}$ $27x = 24(45)$ $27x = 1080$ $x = 40$

$\frac{15}{x} = \frac{35}{7}$ $35x = 15(7)$ $35x = 105$ $x = 3$ $\frac{x}{54} = \frac{18}{45}$ $45x = 54(18)$ $45x = 972$ $x = 21\frac{3}{5}$

$\frac{24}{15} = \frac{x}{25}$ $15x = 24(25)$ $15x = 600$ $x = 40$ $\frac{16}{48} = \frac{x}{72}$ $48x = 16(72)$ $48x = 1152$ $x = 24$

Teaching Tips, Cont.

➤ Ask the students again what percent of a pizza they have if they have two whole pizzas. (200%)

➤ Show the students that when 2 is changed to a percent, the decimal point is moved two places to the right, making it 200%.

➤ Complete the Classwork exercises. Have one student work the problem on the board for the class and explain the answer. All students should work the problem in their books.

Assignments

- Complete Lesson 59, Activities 2-6.
- Bring a compass and protractor beginning in Lesson 61.

Horizons Pre-Algebra, Teacher's Guide

Lesson 60

Concepts
- Pictographs
- Divisibility tests
- Prime/composite numbers
- Roots
- Compound interest
- Multiplying fractions
- Multiplying mixed numbers
- Dividing fractions
- Dividing mixed numbers

Learning Objectives
The student will be able to:
- Define *pictograph*
- Read and interpret information on a pictograph
- Draw a pictograph to represent a set of data

Materials Needed
- Student Book, Lesson 60
- Worksheet 30
- Scientific calculator

Teaching Tips
➤ Ask students to imagine they are store owners trying to manage inventory. Ask them how they would keep up with the number of each item the store had on hand. (Most students will probably suggest using a computer.) Suggest to the students that a computer print-out with a list of items and numbers is not very useful for knowing at a glance what items are running low.

➤ Introduce the pictograph. Show students that looking at a row of pictures gives a better idea of the inventory levels than just looking at a long list of numbers.

Pictographs

A **pictograph** (sometimes referred to as a pictogram or pictogramme) uses pictures or symbols to represent data on a graph. A pictograph will always have a title to tell what information is on the graph, and a key to tell exactly what each picture or symbol represents.

Use the following pictograph to answer the questions below.

Copy Paper in Denny's Store

20-lb	
24-lb	
28-lb	
67-lb	
80-lb	

= 10 reams of paper
= 1 ream of paper

How many reams of paper does Denny have in stock of each weight?

20-lb: 5(10) + 3 = 50 + 3 = 53
24-lb: 3(10) + 6 = 30 + 6 = 36
28-lb: 4(10) + 7 = 40 + 7 = 47
67-lb: 2(10) + 3 = 20 + 3 = 23
80-lb: 1(10) + 2 = 10 + 2 = 12

① **Classwork**
Solve.

Use the following pictograph to answer the questions below.

Rolls of Bulletin Board Border in Denny's Store

Red	
Yellow	
Blue	
Green	
Orange	

= 4 rolls of bulletin board border
= 1 roll of bulletin board border

How many rolls of each color does Denny have in stock?

Red: 4(4) + 1 = 16 + 1 = 17
Yellow: 3(4) + 2 = 12 + 2 = 14
Blue: 2(4) + 2 = 8 + 2 = 10
Green: 5(4) + 1 = 20 + 1 = 21
Orange: 1(4) + 3 = 4 + 3 = 7

Activities
② Draw a pictograph to represent the following data.

Denny sells hanging storage bags in his store. He sells the bags individually as well as in 5-bag packs. He currently has 3 extra small, 7 small, 14 medium, 9 large, and 6 extra large bags on hand. Draw a pictograph, including the title and key.
Answers may vary. A sample pictograph is shown.

Hanging Storage Bags in Denny's Store

Extra small	
Small	
Medium	
Large	
Extra Large	

= 5 hanging bags
= 1 hanging bag

---

③ Use the divisibility tests to identify each number as prime or composite.

331 Prime
333 Composite (3,9)
335 Composite (5)

337 Prime
339 Composite (3)
345 Composite (3, 5)

④ Simplify the roots.

$\sqrt{32} + 5\sqrt{8} = \sqrt{2 \times 4 \times 4} + 5\sqrt{2 \times 2 \times 2} = 4\sqrt{2} + 5(2)\sqrt{2} = 4\sqrt{2} + 10\sqrt{2} = 14\sqrt{2}$

$2\sqrt{45} - \sqrt{80} = 2\sqrt{3 \times 3 \times 5} - \sqrt{4 \times 4 \times 5} = 2(3)\sqrt{5} - 4\sqrt{5} = 6\sqrt{5} - 4\sqrt{5} = 2\sqrt{5}$

$6\sqrt[3]{54}\left(2\sqrt[3]{24}\right) = 6\sqrt[3]{2 \times 3 \times 3 \times 3}\left(2\sqrt[3]{2 \times 2 \times 2 \times 3}\right) = 6(3)\sqrt[3]{2}\left(2(2)\sqrt[3]{3}\right) = 18\sqrt[3]{2}\left(4\sqrt[3]{3}\right) = 72\sqrt[3]{6}$

$5\sqrt[3]{48} \div \sqrt[3]{250} = 5\sqrt[3]{2 \times 2 \times 2 \times 2 \times 3} \div \sqrt[3]{2 \times 5 \times 5 \times 5} = 5(2)\sqrt[3]{2 \times 3} \div 5\sqrt[3]{2} = 10\sqrt[3]{6} \div 5\sqrt[3]{2} = 2\sqrt[3]{3}$

⑤ Complete the chart to show compound interest.

Initial principal	Interest rate	Time, in years	Total compounded annually	Total compounded quarterly
$1000	5%	2	$A = \$1000(1 + .05)^2$ $= \$1102.50$	$A = \$1000(1 + 0.05 \div 4)^{2 \cdot 4}$ $= \$1104.49$
$5000	8%	4	$A = \$5000(1.08)^4$ $= \$6802.44$	$A = \$5000(1 + 0.08 \div 4)^{4 \cdot 4}$ $= \$6863.93$
$7500	15%	6	$A = \$7500(1.15)^6$ $= \$17,347.96$	$A = \$7500(1 + 0.15 \div 4)^{6 \cdot 4}$ $= \$18,145.79$
$12,000	20%	8	$A = \$12,000(1.2)^8$ $= \$51,597.80$	$A = \$12,000(1 + 0.2 \div 4)^{8 \cdot 4}$ $= \$57,179.30$
$25,000	25%	10	$A = \$25,000(1.25)^{10}$ $= \$232,830.64$	$A = \$25,000(1 + 0.25 \div 4)^{10 \cdot 4}$ $= \$282,551.46$

⑥ Multiply or divide as indicated.

$\dfrac{42}{25} \times \dfrac{45}{56} = \dfrac{\overset{3}{\cancel{42}}}{\underset{5}{\cancel{25}}} \times \dfrac{\overset{9}{\cancel{45}}}{\underset{4}{\cancel{56}}} = \dfrac{27}{20} = 1\dfrac{7}{20}$

$\dfrac{27}{42} \times \dfrac{49}{63} = \dfrac{\overset{3}{\cancel{27}}}{\underset{6}{\cancel{42}}} \times \dfrac{\overset{7}{\cancel{49}}}{\underset{7}{\cancel{63}}} = \dfrac{3}{6} = \dfrac{1}{2}$

$3\dfrac{2}{11} \times 6\dfrac{2}{7} = \dfrac{\overset{5}{\cancel{35}}}{\underset{1}{\cancel{11}}} \times \dfrac{\overset{4}{\cancel{44}}}{\underset{1}{\cancel{7}}} = 20$

$4\dfrac{4}{15} \times 2\dfrac{7}{24} = \dfrac{\overset{8}{\cancel{64}}}{\underset{3}{\cancel{15}}} \times \dfrac{\overset{11}{\cancel{55}}}{\underset{3}{\cancel{24}}} = \dfrac{88}{9} = 9\dfrac{7}{9}$

$\dfrac{51}{55} \div \dfrac{17}{35} = \dfrac{\overset{3}{\cancel{51}}}{\underset{11}{\cancel{55}}} \times \dfrac{\overset{7}{\cancel{35}}}{\underset{1}{\cancel{17}}} = \dfrac{21}{11} = 1\dfrac{10}{11}$

$\dfrac{28}{81} \div \dfrac{32}{63} = \dfrac{\overset{7}{\cancel{28}}}{\underset{9}{\cancel{81}}} \times \dfrac{\overset{7}{\cancel{63}}}{\underset{8}{\cancel{32}}} = \dfrac{49}{72}$

$4\dfrac{7}{12} \div 2\dfrac{4}{9} = \dfrac{55}{12} \div \dfrac{22}{9} = \dfrac{\overset{5}{\cancel{55}}}{\underset{4}{\cancel{12}}} \times \dfrac{\overset{3}{\cancel{9}}}{\underset{2}{\cancel{22}}} = \dfrac{15}{8} = 1\dfrac{7}{8}$

$7\dfrac{7}{12} \div 3\dfrac{9}{10} = \dfrac{91}{12} \div \dfrac{39}{10} = \dfrac{\overset{7}{\cancel{91}}}{\underset{6}{\cancel{12}}} \times \dfrac{\overset{5}{\cancel{10}}}{\underset{3}{\cancel{39}}} = \dfrac{35}{18} = 1\dfrac{17}{18}$

Pictographs

① Complete the chart to show the number of brothers and sisters each classmate has. If you have more than 10 classmates, choose any 10 for this project.

Name	Brothers	Sisters	Name	Brothers	Sisters

② Draw a pictograph to show the information collected in the charts above.

Answers will vary. A sample pictograph is shown below for reference. Students should include a title at the top and a key at the bottom of the pictograph.

Numbers of Siblings of my Classmates

Abbie	♦ ♦
Charis	♦ ♦
Emilie	♦ ♦
Eric	♦ ♦
Ethan	♦
Jeb	♦
John	♦
Joshua	♦ ♦
Levi	♦
Nathan	♦ ♦

♦ = 1 brother
♦ = 1 sister

Teaching Tips, Cont.

➢ Have students look at the pictograph in the teaching box. Point out that there are two different icons used in each row. One represents 10 reams of paper, and the other represents 1 ream of paper. Have students look at the graph and tell as quickly as possible which weight of paper has the least in stock. (80-pound) Ask students which has the most in stock, telling them to pay careful attention to the number of 10-ream icons in each row. (20-pound)

➢ Take a survey of the class to find out how many brothers and sisters each student has. Have the students record this information on Worksheet 30. For homeschools and classes with fewer than 10 students, have the students use their own siblings, cousins, friends, etc. to get a total of 10 people.

➢ Complete the Classwork exercises. Have some students work the problems on the board for the class and explain their answers. All students should work the problems in their books.

Assignments

- Complete Lesson 60, Activities 2-5.
- Worksheet 30
- Study for Test 6 (Lessons 48-57)
- Bring a compass and protractor beginning in Lesson 61.

Test 6

Testing Objectives

The student will:

- Solve problems involving percents
- Convert fractions to percents
- Convert percents to fractions
- Calculate the percent discount
- Calculate sale prices
- Calculate the percent mark-up
- Calculate mark-up prices
- Use the simple interest formula to calculate simple interest
- Calculate commission
- Calculate profit
- Calculate royalties

Materials Needed

- Test 6
- *It's College Test Prep Time!* from Student Book
- *A Math Minute with…* Duane L. from Student Book

Teaching Tips

➤ Administer Test 6, allowing the students 30-40 minutes to complete the test.

➤ When all students are finished taking the test, introduce *It's College Test Prep Time* from the student book. This page may be completed in class or assigned as homework.

➤ Have students read the Math Minute interview for Lessons 61-70.

---

① Solve.   **6 points**

What is 45% of 80?
$x = 0.45(80)$
$x = 36$

32 is 40% of what number?
$32 = 0.4x$
$32 \div 0.4 = x$
$x = 80$

75 is what percent of 125?
$75 = 125x$
$75 \div 125 = x$
$0.6 = x$
$x = 60\%$

What is 0.36% of 600?
$x = 0.0036(600)$
$x = 2.16$

33 is 0.55% of what number?
$33 = 0.0055x$
$33 \div 0.0055 = x$
$x = 6000$

5 is what percent of 1250?
$5 = 1250x$
$5 \div 1250 = x$
$0.004 = x$
$x = 0.4\%$

② Complete the fraction-percent conversions.   **16 points**

Fraction	Percent	Percent	Fraction
$\frac{1}{4}$	25%	$66.\overline{6}\%$	$\frac{2}{3}$
$\frac{1}{3}$	$33.\overline{3}\%$	40%	$\frac{2}{5}$
$\frac{1}{5}$	20%	$16.\overline{6}\%$	$\frac{1}{6}$
$\frac{1}{10}$	10%	12.5%	$\frac{1}{8}$
$\frac{3}{5}$	60%	75%	$\frac{3}{4}$
$\frac{5}{6}$	$83.\overline{3}\%$	30%	$\frac{3}{10}$
$\frac{5}{8}$	62.5%	70%	$\frac{7}{10}$
$\frac{7}{8}$	87.5%	37.5%	$\frac{3}{8}$

③ Complete the chart.   **6 points**

Original price	Discount	Sale price
$50	70%	$50(1 - 0.7) = \$50(0.3) = \$15$
$120	$\frac{120 - 75}{120} = \frac{\overset{3}{\cancel{45}}}{\underset{8}{\cancel{120}}} = \frac{3}{8} = 0.375 = 37.5\%$	$75
$90	40%	$90(1 - 0.4) = \$90(0.6) = \$54$
$144	$\frac{144 - 120}{144} = \frac{\overset{1}{\cancel{24}}}{\underset{6}{\cancel{144}}} = \frac{1}{6} = 0.1\overline{6} = 16.\overline{6}\%$	$120
$45	30%	$45(1 - 0.3) = \$45(0.7) = \$31.5$
$75	$\frac{75 - 50}{75} = \frac{\overset{1}{\cancel{25}}}{\underset{3}{\cancel{75}}} = \frac{1}{3} = 0.\overline{3} = 33.\overline{3}\%$	$50

---

④ Complete the chart.   **6 points**

Original price	Mark-up	New price
$50	50%	$50(1 + 0.5) = \$50(1.5) = \$75$
$120	$\frac{150 - 120}{120} = \frac{\overset{1}{\cancel{30}}}{\underset{4}{\cancel{120}}} = \frac{1}{4} = 0.25 = 25\%$	$150
$90	30%	$90(1 + 0.3) = \$90(1.3) = \$117$
$144	$\frac{168 - 144}{144} = \frac{\overset{1}{\cancel{24}}}{\underset{6}{\cancel{144}}} = \frac{1}{6} = 0.1\overline{6} = 16.\overline{6}\%$	$168
$45	80%	$45(1 + 0.8) = \$45(1.8) = \$81$
$75	$\frac{100 - 75}{75} = \frac{\overset{1}{\cancel{25}}}{\underset{3}{\cancel{75}}} = \frac{1}{3} = 0.\overline{3} = 33.\overline{3}\%$	$100

⑤ Complete the chart to reflect simple interest.   **10 points**

Principal	Interest rate	Time, in years	Amount of interest	Total amount paid
$1000	4%	3	$i = \$1000(0.04)(3) = \$120$	$1000 + \$120 = \$1120$
$5000	6%	5	$i = \$5000(0.06)(5) = \$1500$	$5000 + \$1500 = \$6500$
$10,000	8%	7	$i = \$10,000(0.08)(7) = \$5600$	$10,000 + \$5600 = \$15,600$
$15,000	10%	9	$i = \$15,000(0.1)(9) = \$13,500$	$15,000 + \$13,500 = \$28,500$
$20,000	12%	11	$i = \$20,000(0.12)(11) = \$26,400$	$20,000 + \$26,400 = \$46,400$

⑥ Solve.   **5 points**

A real estate agent charges 7% commission for selling a house. If you offer a $5000 reward to the person who refers a buyer for you to sell your house yourself, what percent are you paying as a reward if you sell your house for $125,000? What would the real estate agent have charged you had you listed the house with the agent? How much money would you save by selling the house yourself? $\$5000 \div \$125,000 = 0.04 = 4\%$
Agent would have charged $\$125,000(0.07) = \$8750$
You would save $\$8750 - \$5000 = \$3750$

If you purchased the home for $99,500 and sold it for $125,000, how much profit did you make if you paid a $5000 reward to the person finding a buyer for your house?
$\$125,000 - \$99,500 - \$5000 = \$20,500$

A musician is paid royalties as follows: 10% of the selling price of a CD for each of the first 10,000 CDs sold; 20% of the selling price for each of the next 10,000 CDs sold, and 30% of the selling price for each CD sold over 20,000. If a musician sells 50,000 CDs for $15 each, what will the musician earn in royalties?
$(0.1)(\$15)(10,000) + (0.2)(\$15)(10,000) + (0.3)(\$15)(30,000) =$
$\$15,000 + \$30,000 + \$135,000 = \$180,000$

49 points total

It's College Test Prep Time!

1. A library has reference, fiction, and non-fiction books in the ratio 3 to 5 to 7. What fraction of the books in the library are fiction?

   A. $\frac{1}{2}$

   B. $\frac{1}{3}$ The ratio of the fiction books to the entire library is

   C. $\frac{1}{5}$ $\frac{5}{3+5+7} = \frac{5}{15} = \frac{1}{3}$

   D. $\frac{3}{5}$

   E. $\frac{5}{7}$

2. Given $r^{\frac{1}{3}}\left(r^{\frac{1}{3}}\right)\left(r^{\frac{1}{3}}\right)\left(r^{\frac{1}{3}}\right) = 1$, find the value of p^r.

   A. p Add the exponents when multiplying. This gives

   B. r $r^{\frac{3}{3}} = 1$ so that $r = 1$.

   C. p^5 If $r = 1$, then $p^r = p^1$.

   D. r^5

   E. 1

3. The formula $A = p(1.05)^t$ shows the value of an amount p deposited in a savings account for t years. If \$1500 is deposited on January 2, 2013, what will be its value on January 2, 2015?

   A. \$1575

   B. $\underline{\$1653.75}$ $p = \$1500$ and $t = 2$

   C. \$1736.44 $A = \$1500(1.05)^2 = \$1653.75$

   D. \$3150

   E. \$2,480,625

4. It takes 20 pounds of propane to operate a 24,000 BTU gas grill for 15 hours. How many pounds of propane would it take to operate 6 of these grills for 3 hours?

   A. 3

   B. 4   6 grills operating for 3 hours is 18 grilling hours

   C. 9 $\frac{20 \text{ pounds}}{15 \text{ hours}} = \frac{x \text{ pounds}}{18 \text{ hours}}$

   D. 18 $15x = 20(18)$

   E. $\underline{24}$ $x = \frac{20\left(\overset{4}{\cancel{18}}\,^6\right)}{\cancel{15}_{\,1}} = 24$

A Math Minute with . . .

Duane L. – Professional Illusionist

What is your occupation? I am a professional illusionist.

Where do you work? I work at a variety of local, regional and worldwide events. I have performed on five continents, in eighteen countries, and in forty-seven of the fifty states in the U.S.

Did you attend college? If so, what was your major? I have a three year degree in Bible and Pastoral Studies.

What parts of your job require the use of math? Some people have said that two thirds of "show business" is business. I need to calculate my travel costs to determine how much to charge clients for a show. I plan my equipment investments based on how much money I might make versus the amount of money I will spend. As you can see, adding and subtracting are important in my job.

Also, some of my illusions are based on math. Because I know the number of cards in a stack and what happens when the number of cards changes, I know how a trick will work. At times when I am on stage, I need to remember special numbers and do addition in my head. Remembering and using these numbers is part of the presentation I am making.

More than that, I build many of my illusions. Building always requires math. I measure, multiply and figure percentages when I build. I must check the numbers to make sure I have what I need and make the items correctly.

What is the biggest "problem" you have faced that required the use of math to solve? The biggest math problems come when I am building an illusion. I do not want to waste money or materials. I carefully calculate how to get the most for my investment. I also design the prop on paper before I work out exact sizes and measurements. This process involves addition, multiplication, division, proportions, percentages, and geometry.

Are there any other interesting math uses you have experienced? Many tricks are based on math.

Assignments

- Complete *It's College Test Prep Time!*
- Read *A Math Minute with…* Duane L. – Professional Illusionist
- Bring a compass and protractor for the next lesson.

Lesson 61

Concepts
- Circle graphs
- Natural numbers
- Factors
- Greatest common factor
- English measurement conversion
- Proportions
- Math in the real world

Learning Objectives
The student will be able to:
- Define *circle graph*
- Draw a circle graph to represent a given data set
- Use a protractor to draw angles of given measures

Materials Needed
- Student Book, Lesson 61
- Compass
- Protractor

Teaching Tips
➤ Review pictographs. (See Lesson 60.)

➤ Introduce circle graphs as another way to represent data so that the information is easily readable.

➤ Explain that while pictographs give the exact number of each item, the circle graph gives a visual comparison of the relative amounts. It is easy to tell which item has the greatest value, but it does not give any indication of the exact value.

➤ Ask students when a circle graph might be useful. (Survey results, marketing, opinions, etc.)

Circle Graphs

Circle graphs, also known as pie charts, are visual representations of the percent each part is of the whole.

To draw a circle graph, first calculate the total value of the whole, and the fraction of each part. Because there are 360° in a circle, multiply each fraction by 360° to get the number of degrees for that sector, or piece of the pie. Use a protractor to measure the angle at the center of the circle. Make a key to identify each sector, and give the chart a title.

Duane did a magic show at a magicians' conference where some families from the public were invited to attend. Draw a pie chart to show the breakdown of the attendance at Duane's show if there were 75 professional magicians, 25 amateur magicians, and 50 attendees from the public.

Total number of attendees: $75 + 25 + 50 = 150$

Professional: $\frac{75}{150}(360°) = \frac{1}{2}(360°) = 180°$

Amateur: $\frac{25}{150}(360°) = \frac{1}{6}(360°) = 60°$

Public: $\frac{50}{150}(360°) = \frac{1}{3}(360°) = 120°$

Show Attendees

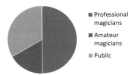

- ■ Professional magicians
- ■ Amateur magicians
- ■ Public

① Classwork
Make a pie chart.

Duane designs and sells props and illusions for professional magicians. At the magicians' conference, he sold 70 stage props, 20 stage illusions, and 110 close-up illusions. Draw a pie chart to show the breakdown of the types of items Duane sold at the conference.

Total number of items sold:
$70 + 20 + 110 = 200$

Stage props: $\frac{70}{200}(360°) = \frac{35}{100}(360°) = 126°$

Stage illusions: $\frac{20}{200}(360°) = \frac{10}{100}(360°) = 36°$

Close-up illusions:
$\frac{110}{200}(360°) = \frac{55}{100}(360°) = 198°$

Items Sold

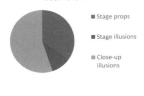

- ■ Stage props
- ■ Stage illusions
- ■ Close-up illusions

Activities
② Make a pie chart.
Duane did a gospel magic show for a church's basketball awards program. There were 8 teams of 4- and 5-year-olds, 6 teams of first and second graders, 6 teams of third and fourth graders, and 10 teams of fifth and sixth graders. Make a pie chart showing the percentage of the teams that were in each age group.

Basketball Teams

- ■ 4-5 Years -- 96°
- ■ 1st - 2nd -- 72°
- ■ 3rd - 4th -- 72°
- ■ 5th - 6th -- 120°

③ List all natural number factors for each of the following numbers.

72 1, 2, 3, 4, 6, 8, 9, 12, 18, 24, 36, 72	175 1, 5, 7, 25, 35, 175
100 1, 2, 4, 5, 10, 20, 25, 50, 100	250 1, 2, 5, 10, 25, 50, 125, 250
144 1, 2, 3, 4, 6, 8, 9, 12, 16, 18, 24, 36, 48, 72, 144	333 1, 3, 9, 37, 111, 333

④ Find the greatest common factor of each number.

$$72 \text{ and } 96 \qquad\qquad 132 \text{ and } 144 \qquad\qquad 125 \text{ and } 175$$

$$72 = ②\times②\times②\times③\times 3 \qquad 132 = ②\times②\times③\times 11 \qquad 125 = ⑤\times⑤\times 5$$
$$96 = ②\times②\times②\times 2\times 2\times ③ \qquad 144 = ②\times②\times 2\times 2\times ③\times 3 \qquad 175 = ⑤\times⑤\times 7$$
$$\text{GCF: } 2^3 \times 3 = 24 \qquad\qquad \text{GCF: } 2^2 \times 3 = 12 \qquad\qquad \text{GCF: } 5^2 = 25$$

⑤ Complete the chart to show proper measurement conversion. (See Lesson 40.)

15 miles	$15 \text{ miles}\left(\frac{1760 \text{ yards}}{1 \text{ mile}}\right) = 26,400$ yards
8 miles	$8 \text{ miles}\left(\frac{5280 \text{ feet}}{1 \text{ mile}}\right) = 42,240$ feet
20 yards	$20 \text{ yards}\left(\frac{36 \text{ inches}}{1 \text{ yards}}\right) = 720$ inches
75 feet	$_{25}75 \text{ feet}\left(\frac{1 \text{ yard}}{3 \text{ feet}}\right) = 25$ yards
10 yards	$10 \text{ yards}\left(\frac{3 \text{ feet}}{1 \text{ yards}}\right) = 30$ feet
47,520 feet	$_9 47,520 \text{ feet}\left(\frac{1 \text{ mile}}{5280 \text{ feet}}\right) = 9$ miles
24,640 yards	$_{14}24,640 \text{ yards}\left(\frac{1 \text{ mile}}{1760 \text{ yards}}\right) = 14$ miles
11 feet	$11 \text{ feet}\left(\frac{12 \text{ inches}}{1 \text{ feet}}\right) = 132$ inches
96 inches	$_8 96 \text{ inches}\left(\frac{1 \text{ foot}}{12 \text{ inches}}\right) = 8$ feet
504 inches	$_{14}504 \text{ inches}\left(\frac{1 \text{ yard}}{36 \text{ inches}}\right) = 14$ yards

⑥ Solve the following proportions. Leave answers as improper fractions where necessary.

$$\frac{12}{25} = \frac{x}{35} \qquad\qquad \frac{x}{14} = \frac{18}{35} \qquad\qquad \frac{15}{x} = \frac{40}{48}$$
$$25x = 12(35) \qquad\qquad 35x = 14(18) \qquad\qquad 40x = 15(48)$$
$$x = \frac{12\left(35^7\right)}{25_5} = \frac{84}{5} \qquad x = \frac{\overset{2}{14}(18)}{35_5} = \frac{36}{5} \qquad x = \frac{\overset{3}{15}\left(48^6\right)}{40_{8_1}} = 18$$

$$\frac{24}{55} = \frac{40}{x} \qquad\qquad \frac{25}{63} = \frac{x}{81} \qquad\qquad \frac{x}{48} = \frac{17}{51}$$
$$24x = 55(40) \qquad\qquad 63x = 25(81) \qquad\qquad 51x = 48(17)$$
$$x = \frac{55\left(40^5\right)}{24_3} = \frac{275}{3} \qquad x = \frac{25\left(81^9\right)}{63_7} = \frac{225}{7} \qquad x = \frac{\overset{16}{48}\left(17^1\right)}{51_{17_1}} = 16$$

Teaching Tips, Cont.

➢ Teach students how to draw a circle graph. See the information at the left for details.

➢ Complete the first part of the Classwork exercises. Have a student calculate the number of degrees for each of the three categories on the board and explain the answers. All students should work the problems on their own paper.

➢ Have all students draw the circle graphs in their books. Assist individual students as needed. Check to see that students are using their protractors correctly to draw central angles.

Assignment

• Complete Lesson 61, Activities 2-6.

Steps for Drawing a Circle Graph

1. Calculate the number of degrees for each section. The total number of degrees for all sections must be 360.
2. Use a compass to draw a circle. The hole left by the compass is the center of the circle.
3. Draw a radius (a line segment from the center of the circle to the edge of the circle) in the circle.
4. Beginning at the radius, use a protractor to draw adjacent central angles (angles whose vertex is at the center of the circle) that have the same number of degrees as the sections calculated in Step 1. There should be one angle for each section. The last angle should end where the first angle started.
5. Shade each section a different color and make a key.

Lesson 62

Concepts
- Mean
- Least common multiple
- Roots
- Compound interest
- Scale drawings
- Ratios

Learning Objectives
The student will be able to:
- Define *mean*
- Calculate the mean of a set of numbers

Materials Needed
- Student Book, Lesson 62
- Worksheet 31
- Scientific calculator

Teaching Tips
➢ Have students use their calculators to complete Worksheet 31 in class. This may be for added practice of earlier topics, or graded as a quiz, if desired.

➢ Ask students the following series of questions: If you had a 100 as your only grade for the quarter, what would your grade be? (100) If you had a 100 and a 90, what would your grade be? (95) If you had a 100, 95, and 90, what would your grade be? (95)

➢ Ask students to explain how they arrived at their answers. (Most students understand the concept of averaging grades at this point. If not, forego the student explanations and proceed directly to the lesson.)

Mean

The **mean**, or **arithmetic mean**, of a set of numbers is the average of that set of numbers. The mean is calculated by dividing the sum of the values by the number of values in the set.

$$\text{mean} = \frac{\text{sum of values}}{\text{number of values}}$$

The mean may or may not be one of the values in the given set.

The attendance at 6 of Duane's shows one week was 147, 144, 153, 147, 152, and 149. Find the mean attendance at Duane's shows for the week. Round your answer to the nearest whole number.

The sum of the values is:
147 + 144 + 153 + 147 + 152 + 149 = 892
The number of values is 6.
$\text{mean} = \frac{892}{6} = 148.\overline{6}$
To the nearest whole number, the mean is 149.

① **Classwork**
Find the mean of each set of numbers. Round answers to the nearest whole number.

53, 84, 61, 32, 45
Sum: 53 + 84 + 61 + 32 + 45 = 275
Number of values: 5
Mean = 275 ÷ 5 = 55

549, 315, 278, 101, 492
Sum: 549 + 315 + 278 + 101 + 492 = 1735
Number of values: 5
Mean = 1735 ÷ 5 = 347

97, 106, 138, 84
Sum: 97 + 106 + 138 + 84 = 425
Number of values: 4
Mean = 425 ÷ 4 = 106.25
To the nearest whole, mean = 106.

Activities
② Find the mean of each set of numbers. Round answers to the nearest whole number.

487, 329, 617
Sum: 487 + 329 + 617
Sum = 1433
Mean = 1433 ÷ 3 = 477.6̄
Mean = 478

21, 49, 73, 95
Sum: 21 + 49 + 73 + 95
Sum = 238
Mean = 238 ÷ 4 = 59.5
Mean = 60

132, 519, 642, 311
Sum: 132 + 519 + 642 + 311
Sum = 1604
Mean = 1604 ÷ 4 = 401

87, 45, 92, 66, 71
Sum: 87 + 45 + 92 + 66 + 71
Sum = 361
Mean = 361 ÷ 5 = 72.2
Mean = 72

345, 612, 398, 753, 192
Sum: 345 + 612 + 398 + 753 + 192
Sum = 2300
Mean = 2300 ÷ 5 = 460

99, 78, 84, 72, 65, 85
Sum: 99 + 78 + 84 + 72 + 65 + 85
Sum = 483
Mean = 483 ÷ 6 = 80.5
Mean = 81

③ Find the least common multiple of each set of numbers.

6, 10, and 15
$6 = \boxed{2} \times 3$
$10 = 2 \times \boxed{5}$
$15 = \boxed{3} \times 5$
LCM: $2 \times 3 \times 5 = 30$

10, 12, and 15
$10 = 2 \times \boxed{5}$
$12 = 2 \times 2 \times 3 = \boxed{2^2} \times 3$
$15 = \boxed{3} \times 5$
LCM: $2^2 \times 3 \times 5 = 60$

12, 15, and 20
$12 = 2 \times 2 \times 3 = \boxed{2^2} \times 3$
$15 = \boxed{3} \times 5 =$
$20 = 2 \times 2 \times 5 = 2^2 \times \boxed{5}$
LCM: $2^2 \times 3 \times 5 = 60$

④ Simplify the following roots.

$\sqrt[3]{16} + 5\sqrt[3]{54} = \sqrt[3]{2 \times 2 \times 2 \times 2} + 5\sqrt[3]{2 \times 3 \times 3 \times 3} = 2\sqrt[3]{2} + 5(3)\sqrt[3]{2} = 2\sqrt[3]{2} + 15\sqrt[3]{2} = 17\sqrt[3]{2}$

$6\sqrt{45} - \sqrt{125} = 6\sqrt{3 \times 3 \times 5} - \sqrt{5 \times 5 \times 5} = 6(3)\sqrt{5} - 5\sqrt{5} = 18\sqrt{5} - 5\sqrt{5} = 13\sqrt{5}$

$3\sqrt[3]{32}\left(3\sqrt[4]{128}\right) = 3\sqrt[3]{2 \times 2 \times 2 \times 2 \times 2}\left(3\sqrt[4]{2 \times 2 \times 2 \times 2 \times 2 \times 2 \times 2}\right) =$
$3(2)\sqrt[3]{2}\left(3(2)\sqrt[4]{8}\right) = 6\sqrt[3]{2}\left(6\sqrt[4]{8}\right) = 36\sqrt[12]{16} = 36\sqrt[12]{2 \times 2 \times 2 \times 2} = 36(2) = 72$

$4\sqrt[3]{162} \div 3\sqrt[3]{24} = 4\sqrt[3]{2 \times 3 \times 3 \times 3 \times 3} \div 3\sqrt[3]{2 \times 2 \times 2 \times 3} =$
$4(3)\sqrt[3]{2 \times 3} \div 3(2)\sqrt[3]{3} = 12\sqrt[3]{6} \div 6\sqrt[3]{3} = \frac{\overset{2}{\cancel{12}}\sqrt[3]{\overset{2}{\cancel{6}}}}{\underset{1}{\cancel{6}}\sqrt[3]{\underset{1}{\cancel{3}}}} = 2\sqrt[3]{2}$

⑤ Complete the chart to show compound interest.

Initial principal	Interest rate	Time, in years	Total compounded annually	Total compounded quarterly
$1000	3.5%	2	$A = \$1000(1 + .035)^2$ $= \$1071.23$	$A = \$1000\left(1 + 0.035 \div 4\right)^{2 \times 4}$ $= \$1072.18$
$5000	7.75%	4	$A = \$5000(1.0775)^4$ $= \$6739.68$	$A = \$5000\left(1 + 0.0775 \div 4\right)^{4 \times 4}$ $= \$6796.94$
$7500	10.125%	6	$A = \$7500(1.10125)^6$ $= \$13,377.56$	$A = \$7500\left(1 + 0.10125 \div 4\right)^{6 \times 4}$ $= \$13,665.05$

⑥ Label the scale drawing to show a ratio of 2:5.

The small rocket is $5\frac{3}{5}$ inches wide and 20 inches tall.

14 inches wide
50 inches tall

Compound Interest

① Identify what each variable represents in the formula $A = P(1+r)^t$.

A _amount at the end of the time_

P _____principal_____

r _____rate_____

t _____time_____

② Complete the chart to reflect interest compounded annually. You may use your calculator. Round all answers to the nearest cent.

Principal	Interest rate	Time, in years	Interest compounded annually
$100	0.5%	2	$A = \$100(1+0.005)^2 = \$101.00$
$500	2.5%	4	$A = \$500(1+0.025)^4 = \$551.91$
$1000	5%	3	$A = \$1000(1+0.05)^3 = \$1157.63$
$5000	6%	5	$A = \$5000(1+0.06)^5 = \$6691.13$
$10,000	8%	10	$A = \$10,000(1+0.08)^{10} = \$21,589.25$
$15,000	10%	9	$A = \$15,000(1+0.1)^9 = \$35,369.22$
$20,000	11%	6	$A = \$20,000(1+0.11)^6 = \$37,408.29$
$25,000	15%	7	$A = \$25,000(1+0.15)^7 = \$66,500.50$

③ Complete the chart to reflect interest compounded quarterly. You may use your calculator. Round all answers to the nearest cent.

Principal	Interest rate	Time, in years	Interest compounded quarterly
$100	0.5%	2	$A = \$100(1+0.005 \div 4)^{2 \cdot 4} = \$101.00$
$500	2.5%	4	$A = \$500(1+0.025 \div 4)^{4 \cdot 4} = \$552.41$
$1000	5%	3	$A = \$1000(1+0.05 \div 4)^{3 \cdot 4} = \$1160.75$
$5000	6%	5	$A = \$5000(1+0.06 \div 4)^{5 \cdot 4} = \$6734.28$
$10,000	8%	10	$A = \$10,000(1+0.08 \div 4)^{10 \cdot 4} = \$22,080.40$
$15,000	10%	9	$A = \$15,000(1+0.1 \div 4)^{9 \cdot 4} = \$36,488.03$
$20,000	11%	6	$A = \$20,000(1+0.11 \div 4)^{6 \cdot 4} = \$38,352.52$
$25,000	15%	7	$A = \$25,000(1+0.15 \div 4)^{7 \cdot 4} = \$70,082.08$

Significant Figures

Significant figures, referred to as sig figs in upper-level science courses, are an important element of mathematical calculations. They control the precision of calculations made from various measurements and ensure that the answer is not more precise than any one numerical value used in the calculation. While it is not important to teach sig figs prior to high school, it is important that the students understand that you cannot increase precision by doing calculations.

For example, if you measure several lengths to the nearest tenth of an inch, it would not be accurate to give the average length to the nearest thousandth of an inch. The answer should be rounded to the nearest tenth of an inch.

Teaching Tips, Cont.

➤ Teach the definition of *mean*, emphasizing the fact that *mean* and *average* are the same thing.

➤ Teach the formula for calculating the mean of a set of numbers. Demonstrate this using the hypothetical grades from the previous questions.

➤ Explain that the mean is rounded to the same place value as the numbers in the data set, unless instructed otherwise. If the data set is whole numbers, the mean should be rounded to the nearest whole number. If the data set includes decimals, round the answer to the decimal place of the least precise decimal. For example, if some numbers are given to the tenths and other numbers are given to the hundredths, round the answer to the tenths, since tenths are less precise than hundredths. (See the note on significant figures to the left.)

➤ Complete the Classwork exercises. Have some students work the problems on the board for the class and explain their answers. All students should work the problems in their books.

Assignment
- Complete Lesson 62, Activities 2-6.

Lesson 63

Concepts
- Median
- Mean
- Single-variable equations
- Least common multiple
- Powers of 10
- Metric measurement conversions
- Circle graphs
- Math in the real world

Learning Objectives
The student will be able to:
- Define *median*
- Find the median of a set of values
- Apply the concept of mean to the median of an even number of values

Materials Needed
- Student Book, Lesson 63
- Worksheet 32

Teaching Tips
➤ Review mean. (See Lesson 62.) Ask the students if the mean is always one of the numbers in the list. (No.) Ask the students if the mean is always in the exact middle of the list. (No.)

➤ Ask the students to describe a divided highway. (Lanes going in opposite directions are not right next to each other.) If the students have not mentioned it, point out that the lanes may be divided by a painted striped area, grass, concrete, etc.

➤ Ask the students what the region that divides the lanes is called. (Median.)

Median

The **median** of a set of numbers is the middle value when all numbers are listed in order from smallest to largest or largest to smallest. If there is an odd number of values, there will be one median that corresponds to one of the given values. If there is an even number of values, there will be one median that is the mean of the two middle numbers.

The median may or may not correspond to the mean, but it will *always* be one or two of the given values.

The attendance at 6 of Duane's shows one week was 147, 144, 153, 147, 152, and 149. Find the median attendance at Duane's shows for the week.

List the numbers from smallest to largest.
144, 147, 147, 149, 152, 153

Cross off one number from each end until you have exactly one or two numbers left.
~~144~~, ~~147~~, 147, 149, ~~152~~, ~~153~~

If there is only one number remaining, that number is the median. If there are two numbers remaining, find the mean of those two numbers.
$\frac{147+149}{2} = \frac{296}{2} = 148$
148 is the median of the given list of numbers. Notice that this is close to, but not equal, to the mean of the same list of numbers calculated in Lesson 62.

① **Classwork**
Find the median of each set of numbers. Round answers to the nearest tenth where necessary.

53, 84, 61, 32, 45
Order from smallest to largest:
32, 45, 53, 61, 84
Cross off numbers from the ends:
~~32~~, ~~45~~, 53, ~~61~~, ~~84~~
Median = 53

549, 315, 278, 101, 492
Order from smallest to largest:
101, 278, 315, 492, 549
Cross off numbers from the ends:
~~101~~, ~~278~~, 315, ~~492~~, ~~549~~
Median = 315

97, 106, 138, 84
Order from smallest to largest:
84, 97, 106, 138
Cross off numbers from the ends:
~~84~~, 97, 106, ~~138~~
Median = $\frac{97+106}{2} = 101.5$

Activities
② Find the mean and median of each set of numbers. Round answers to the nearest tenth.

784, 923, 716
Sum: 2423
Mean: $2423 \div 3 = 807.7$
Median: 784

52, 94, 87, 69
Sum: 302
Mean: $302 \div 4 = 75.5$
Median: $(69 + 87) \div 2 = 78$

231, 159, 426, 131
Sum: 947
Mean: $947 \div 4 = 236.8$
Median: $(231 + 159) \div 2 = 195$

78, 54, 69, 55, 72
Sum: 328
Mean: $328 \div 5 = 65.6$
Median: 69

542, 621, 838, 573, 291
Sum: 2865
Mean: $2865 \div 5 = 573$
Median: 573

88, 87, 78, 74, 56, 68
Sum: 451
Mean: $451 \div 6 = 75.2$
Median: $(78 + 74) \div 2 = 76$

---

③ Solve.

$$\frac{3x}{4} - 1 = -7$$
$$\frac{3x}{4} = -6$$
$$\cancel{4}\left(\frac{3x}{\cancel{4}}\right) = 4(-6)$$
$$3x = -24$$
$$x = -8$$

$$\frac{5x}{3} + 5 = 2x - 3$$
$$\frac{5x}{3} = 2x - 8$$
$$\cancel{3}\left(\frac{5x}{\cancel{3}}\right) = 3(2x - 8)$$
$$5x = 6x - 24$$
$$-x = -24$$
$$x = 24$$

$$\frac{3x+1}{2} - 3 = 2x - 5$$
$$\frac{3x+1}{2} = 2x - 2$$
$$\cancel{2}\left(\frac{3x+1}{\cancel{2}}\right) = 2(2x - 2)$$
$$3x + 1 = 4x - 4$$
$$-x = -5$$
$$x = 5$$

④ Find the least common multiple of each set of numbers.

15, 18, and 20
$15 = 3 \times \boxed{5} =$
$18 = 2 \times 3 \times 3 = 2 \times \boxed{3^2}$
$20 = 2 \times 2 \times 5 = \boxed{2^2} \times 5$
LCM: $2^2 \times 3^2 \times 5 = 180$

15, 20, and 25
$15 = \boxed{3} \times 5 =$
$20 = 2 \times 2 \times 5 = \boxed{2^2} \times 5$
$25 = 5 \times 5 = \boxed{5^2}$
LCM: $2^2 \times 3 \times 5^2 = 300$

18, 20, and 25
$18 = 2 \times 3 \times 3 = 2 \times \boxed{3^2}$
$20 = 2 \times 2 \times 5 = \boxed{2^2} \times 5$
$25 = 5 \times 5 = \boxed{5^2}$
LCM: $2^2 \times 3^2 \times 5^2 = 900$

⑤ Multiply or divide by the correct power of 10 to complete the metric conversions.

23.4 m = ___23,400___ mm

40,000 cm = ___400___ m

0.07 L = ___70___ mL

2035 mL = ___2.035___ L

0.5 g = ___50___ cg

901 cW = ___9.01___ W

86.03 W = ___86,030___ mW

4.01 mg = ___0.00401___ g

⑥ Draw a circle graph.

Duane has done 350 shows in Tennessee, 200 shows in the rest of North America, 200 shows in Europe, 50 shows in Asia, and 35 shows in Africa. Draw a circle graph to show what fraction of the shows was done in each location.

Total number of shows:
$350 + 200 + 200 + 50 + 35 = 835$

The degrees are provided in the graph key for grading convenience.

Duane's Shows

- ■ Tennessee (150.9°)
- ■ North America (86.2°)
- ■ Europe (86.2°)
- ■ Asia (21.6°)
- ■ Africa (15.1°)

Mean, Median

① Complete the chart.

Given values	Values from smallest to largest	Sum	Mean	Median
10, 24, 26, 14, 17, 20, 21	10, 14, 17, 20, 21, 24, 26	132	19	20
10.7, 24.5, 26.1, 37.1, 19.7	10.7, 19.7, 24.5, 26.1, 37.1	118.1	23.6	24.5
51, 37, 44, 33, 45, 35	33, 35, 37, 44, 45, 51	245	41	40.5
51.2, 37.4, 44.2, 45.3	37.4, 44.2, 45.3, 51.2	178.1	44.5	44.75
98, 85, 75, 92	75, 85, 92, 98	350	88	88.5
89, 64, 57, 58, 46	46, 57, 58, 64, 89	314	63	58
79, 82, 54, 94	54, 79, 82, 94	309	77	80.5
37.24, 44.21, 33.23	33.23, 37.24, 44.21	114.68	38.23	37.24
17.13, 7.30, 23.37, 6.28	6.28, 7.30, 17.13, 23.37	54.08	13.52	12.215

② Find the grade point average.

To calculate grade point averages, first assign a numerical value to each letter grade as follows: an A is worth 4.000, a B is worth 3.000, a C is worth 2.000, and a D is worth 1.000 on a 4-point scale. Then find the mean of the numerical values of the letter grades.

What is your grade point average if you have 5 A's and 2 B's?

5(4.000) + 2(3.000) = 20.000 + 6.000 = 26.000
26.000 ÷ 7 = 3.714

What is your grade point average if you have 2 A's and 3 B's and 1 C?
2(4.000) + 3(3.000) + 2.000 = 8.000 + 9.000 + 2.000 = 19.000
19.000 ÷ 6 = 3.167

Teaching Tips, Cont.

➤ Ask the students where the median is found. (In the middle of the road.)

➤ Teach the definition of *median*, emphasizing that it is the number in the middle when the values are arranged from smallest to greatest. In the case of an even number of values, the median is the mean of the two middle values since there is not one value that falls in the middle.

➤ When finding the mean of the two middle values, it is appropriate to write the answer with one additional decimal point when the final digits of the two numbers have one odd and one even number. For example, if the two middle numbers are 37 and 38, the median would be 37.5. If the two middle numbers are 37.4 and 37.5, then the median would be 37.45.

➤ Complete the Classwork exercises. Have some students work the problems on the board for the class and explain their answers. All students should work the problems in their books.

Assignments
- Complete Lesson 63, Activities 2-6.
- Worksheet 32

Lesson 64

Concepts
- Frequency distribution
- Pictographs
- Adding mixed numbers
- Subtracting mixed numbers
- Math in the real world

Learning Objectives
The student will be able to:
- Define *frequency distribution*
- Make a frequency distribution of a given set of data

Materials Needed
- Student Book, Lesson 64
- Students' quiz grades for the year

Teaching Tips
➤ Review finding the mean and median of a set of numbers. (See Lessons 62-63.)

➤ Ask students what information about a data set could be useful besides knowing the average and the middle number. If they do not think of it, suggest that knowing how many times each value appears can be useful.

➤ Introduce the frequency distribution. Ask the students to think of times when a frequency distribution would be helpful. (Knowing most common group sizes for ticket sales and seating arrangements, how many items customers purchase at one time to plan number of registers and express lanes for check-out, etc.)

Frequency Distribution

A **frequency distribution** is a table listing the number of times each value appears in a set.

To make a frequency distribution, first list each unique value from smallest to largest. Then list all inclusive values (including those values that do not appear in the set but are within the range of the given values) in a column. Next to each value, place a tally mark for each time that value appears in the set. Finally, write the total number of times that value appears in a column after the tally marks.

The number of people sitting in each row of the center section at one of Duane's shows is as follows: 25, 24, 25, 23, 22, 24, 23, 24, 25, 25, 22, 20, 23, 22, 24. Make a chart showing the frequency distribution of the seating at Duane's show.

People	Tally	Number
20	/	1
21		0
22	///	3
23	///	3
24	////	4
25	////	4

Notice that the number 21 was included, even though that number did not appear in the set.

① Classwork
Make a chart showing the frequency distribution of the results of the roll of a game die. 1, 1, 3, 5, 2, 6, 3, 4, 3, 4, 5, 3, 3, 1, 6, 5, 4, 1, 4, 3

Die Roll	Tally	Number
1	////	4
2	/	1
3	ЖН /	6
4	////	4
5	///	3
6	//	2

Make a chart showing the frequency distribution of your grades on math quizzes this year.

Answers will vary, but should appear similar to the chart above.

Activities
② Find the mean, median, and frequency distribution.

When two game dice are rolled, the sum of the numbers is between 2 (double 1's) and 12 (double 6's) inclusive. Make a frequency table showing the results of 20 rolls of two dice. Then find the mean and the median of the rolls. Round answers to the nearest whole number.
5, 6, 5, 5, 2, 8, 9, 8, 9, 12,
5, 5, 9, 3, 8, 9, 9, 6, 11, 4
Sum: 138
Mean: 138 ÷ 20 = 6.9=7
Median: 2̶, 3̶, 4̶, 5̶, 5̶, 5̶, 5̶, 5̶, 6̶, 6,
8, 8̶, 8̶, 9̶, 9̶, 9̶, 9̶, 9̶, 1̶1̶, 1̶2̶
Median: (6 + 8) ÷ 2 = 7

Dice Roll	Tally	Number
2	/	1
3	/	1
4	/	1
5	ЖН	5
6	//	2
7		0
8	///	3
9	ЖН	5
10		0
11	/	1
12	/	1

---

③ Draw a pictograph.

When Duane does a 2-hour theater show, he usually does 10 grand illusions, 10 small illusions, and 10 silk tricks. When he does a banquet or awards show, he usually does 12 small illusions and 10 silk tricks. Draw a pictograph showing the number of each type of trick Duane does at theaters and banquets.

Illusions at Duane's Shows

| Theater Shows | 🖐🖐🖐🖐🖐 ☺☺☺☺☺ ✌✌✌✌✌ |
| Banquet or Awards Shows | ☺☺☺☺☺☺ ✌✌✌✌✌ |

🖐 = 2 grand illusions

☺ = 2 small illusions

✌ = 2 silk tricks

④ Add or subtract as indicated.

$$8\frac{4}{11} + 6\frac{2}{3} = (8+6) + \left(\frac{4}{11} + \frac{2}{3}\right) = 14 + \frac{12}{33} + \frac{22}{33} = 14 + \frac{34}{33} = 14 + 1\frac{1}{33} = 15\frac{1}{33}$$

$$7\frac{8}{9} + 10\frac{5}{6} = (7+10) + \left(\frac{8}{9} + \frac{5}{6}\right) = 17 + \frac{16}{18} + \frac{15}{18} = 17 + \frac{31}{18} = 17 + 1\frac{13}{18} = 18\frac{13}{18}$$

$$12\frac{5}{6} - 8\frac{2}{3} = (12-8) + \left(\frac{5}{6} - \frac{2}{3}\right) = 4 + \left(\frac{5}{6} - \frac{4}{6}\right) = 4 + \frac{1}{6} = 4\frac{1}{6}$$

$$11\frac{2}{3} - 7\frac{3}{4} = (11-7) + \left(\frac{2}{3} - \frac{3}{4}\right) = 4 + \left(\frac{8}{12} - \frac{9}{12}\right) = 3 + \frac{12}{12} + \frac{8}{12} - \frac{9}{12} = 3\frac{11}{12}$$

⑤ Solve.

Duane charges adults $29.98 at the door and $28.19 if they purchase tickets in advance online. He allows one child to attend free per paying adult. Additional children are $8.95 each. How much will he charge a group of 9 adults and 7 children at the door if 11.75% sales tax is added to the price of the tickets? How much will they save as a group if they purchase tickets in advance?

The 7 children are free.

The adult tickets at the door cost (9)($29.98)(1.1175) = $301.52

The adult tickets in advance cost (9)($28.19)(1.1175) = $283.52

Savings: $18

How much will Duane charge a group of 7 adults and 9 children at the door? How much will they save as a group if they purchase tickets in advance?

7 children are free. The other two children are $8.95 each.

At the door, the tickets cost (7)($29.98)(1.1175) + (2)($8.95)(1.1175) = $254.52

In advance, the tickets cost (7)($28.19)(1.1175) + (2)($8.95)(1.1175) = $240.52

Savings: $14

Teaching Tips, Cont.

➢ Teach how to make a frequency distribution. Emphasize the importance of including all potential values, even if they do not appear in the data set.

➢ Ask the students why all values should be included, even if they do not appear in the data set. (Just because the value does not appear in the given data set, it does not mean that the value does not exist. It can be just as helpful to know what values do not appear as it is to know the values that appear frequently.)

➢ Give each student a list of his quiz grades for this year to use in the Classwork exercises. This list should be saved for use in Lessons 65 and 66.

➢ Complete the Classwork exercises. Have one student work the first problem on the board for the class and explain the answer. All students should work both problems in their books.

Assignment

- Complete Lesson 64, Activities 2-5.

Lesson 65

Concepts
- Mode
- Single-variable equations
- Multiplying decimals
- Multiplying mixed numbers
- Dividing mixed numbers
- Roots
- Scientific notation
- Math in the real world

Learning Objectives
The student will be able to:
- Define *mode*
- Use a frequency distribution to find the mode
- Identify a set of data as having no mode, one mode, or more than one mode

Materials Needed
- Student Book, Lesson 65
- Worksheet 33
- Compass
- Protractor
- Students' quiz grades from Lesson 64

Teaching Tips
➢ Have students complete Worksheet 33 in class. This may be for added practice of earlier topics or graded as a quiz, if desired. Students will need a compass and protractor to complete this Worksheet. You may wish to have students place a stack of paper under their Worksheet to avoid poking a hole in the desktop with the compass.

➢ Review mean and median as needed. (See Lessons 62-63.)

➢ Review frequency distributions. (See Lesson 64.)

Mode

The **mode** is the value or values that appear the most number of times in the set. There may be one mode, more than one mode, or no mode in a given set of numbers, but any mode will *always* be a member of the given set.

To find the mode, make a frequency distribution of the values in the set.

If every value in the set appears the same number of times, there is no mode. If one unique value appears more than any other value, that value is the only mode. If two or more values appear the same number of times, and more times than at least one other value, there is more than one mode, and each of the values that appears the most number of times is a mode.

The number of people sitting in each row of the center section at one of Duane's shows is as follows: 25, 24, 25, 23, 22, 24, 23, 24, 25, 25, 22, 20, 23, 22, 24. What is the mode?

Make a chart showing the frequency distribution of the seating at Duane's show. (See Lesson 64.)

People	Tally	Number
20	/	1
21		0
22	////	3
23	////	3
24	////	4
25	////	4

24 and 25 are the modes because they each occur 4 times.

① **Classwork**
The results of 20 rolls of a game die are 1, 1, 3, 5, 2, 6, 3, 4, 3, 4, 5, 3, 3, 1, 6, 5, 4, 1, 4, and 3. What is the mode?

Die Roll	Tally	Number
1	////	4
2	/	1
3	////-/	6
4	////	4
5	///	3
6	//	2

The mode is 3.

Using the list of grades from Lesson 64, what is the mode of your math quiz grades?

Answers will vary. Students may have no mode, one mode, or more than one mode, depending on individual grades.

Activities
② Solve.
The number of points scored in a series of football games is 31, 3, 29, 15, 13, 12, 13, 10, 30, and 21. Find the mean, median, and mode of the scores.
Sum: 177, Mean: $177 \div 10 = 17.7$
Median: 3, 10, 12, 13, 13, 15, 21, 29, 30, 31 $(13 + 15) \div 2 = 14$
Mode: 13

---

③ Solve.

$2(3x - 2) + 5 = 4 + 15 \div 3 - 2x$
$6x - 4 + 5 = 4 + 5 - 2x$
$6x + 1 = 9 - 2x$
$8x = 8$
$x = 1$

$6x \div 3 + 14 \div 2 + 6 = 4(x - 2) + x$
$2x + 7 + 6 = 4x - 8 + x$
$2x + 13 = 5x - 8$
$-3x = -21$
$x = 7$

$3(5 - 2x) - 4(1 - x) = 2x + 3$
$15 - 6x - 4 + 4x = 2x + 3$
$-2x + 11 = 2x + 3$
$-4x = -8$
$x = 2$

④ Multiply.

32.085	80.06	91.324	0.025
× 10.4	× 2.07	× 78.06	×0.709
128340	56042	547944	225
+3208500	+1601200	73059200	+17500
333.6840	165.7242	+639268000	0.017725
		7128.75144	

⑤ Multiply or divide as indicated.

$2\frac{2}{5} \times 1\frac{7}{9} = \frac{\overset{4}{\cancel{12}}}{5} \times \frac{16}{\cancel{15}_3} = \frac{64}{15} = 4\frac{4}{15}$

$7\frac{7}{9} \times 5\frac{2}{5} = \frac{\overset{14}{\cancel{70}}}{\cancel{9}_1} \times \frac{27^3}{\cancel{5}_1} = \frac{42}{1} = 42$

$5\frac{5}{7} \times 8\frac{2}{5} = \frac{\overset{8}{\cancel{40}}}{\cancel{7}_1} \times \frac{\cancel{42}^6}{\cancel{5}_1} = \frac{48}{1} = 48$

$\frac{\sqrt{18}}{2} \times \frac{4\sqrt{2}}{3} = \frac{\overset{2}{\cancel{4}}\sqrt{36}}{\cancel{2} \times 3} = \frac{2 \times \cancel{6}^2}{\cancel{3}_1} = 4$

$\frac{\sqrt{2}}{5} \times \frac{5\sqrt{32}}{8} = \frac{\cancel{5}\sqrt{2 \times 32}}{\cancel{5} \times 8} = \frac{\sqrt{64}}{8} = \frac{8}{8} = 1$

$3\frac{1}{3} \times \frac{3\sqrt{32}}{4} = \frac{\overset{5}{\cancel{10}}}{\cancel{3}_1} \times \frac{\cancel{3}\sqrt{32}}{\cancel{4}_2} =$

$\frac{5}{1} \times \frac{\overset{2}{\cancel{4}}\sqrt{2}}{\cancel{2}} = 5(2\sqrt{2}) = 10\sqrt{2}$

$31\frac{1}{2} \div 5\frac{1}{7} = \frac{63}{2} \div \frac{36}{7} = \frac{\overset{7}{\cancel{63}}}{2} \times \frac{7}{\cancel{36}_4} = \frac{49}{8} = 6\frac{1}{8}$

$5\frac{9}{11} \div 3\frac{1}{5} = \frac{64}{11} \div \frac{16}{5} = \frac{\overset{4}{\cancel{64}}}{11} \times \frac{5}{\cancel{16}_1} = \frac{20}{11} = 1\frac{9}{11}$

$7\frac{1}{5} \div 3\frac{3}{7} = \frac{36}{5} \div \frac{24}{7} = \frac{\overset{3}{\cancel{36}}}{5} \times \frac{7}{\cancel{24}_2} = \frac{21}{10} = 2\frac{1}{10}$

$\frac{\sqrt{8}}{15} \div \frac{\sqrt{2}}{9} = \frac{2\sqrt{2}}{15} \div \frac{\sqrt{2}}{9} = \frac{2\cancel{\sqrt{2}}}{\cancel{5}\cancel{15}} \times \frac{\cancel{9}^3}{\cancel{\sqrt{2}}} = \frac{6}{5} = 1\frac{1}{5}$

$\frac{\sqrt{18}}{8} \div 3\frac{1}{2} = \frac{3\sqrt{2}}{8} \div \frac{7}{2} = \frac{3\sqrt{2}}{\cancel{8}_4} \times \frac{\cancel{2}^1}{7} = \frac{3\sqrt{2}}{28}$

$\frac{\sqrt{24}}{72} \div \frac{\sqrt{3}}{45} = \frac{\sqrt{24}^8}{\cancel{72}_8} \times \frac{\cancel{45}^5}{\sqrt{3}} =$

$\frac{\sqrt{8}}{8} \times \frac{5}{1} = \frac{5(2\sqrt{2})}{\cancel{8}_4} = \frac{5\sqrt{2}}{4}$

⑥ Complete the chart to show proper conversion between scientific notation and standard form.

Scientific notation	Standard form		Standard form	Scientific notation
2.005×10^8	200,500,000		63,020,000,000	6.302×10^{10}
7.0001×10^{-8}	0.000000070001		0.0000000090007	9.0007×10^{-9}

Pictographs, Circle Graphs
Worksheet 33

① Follow the directions.

Duane has made 5 videos about doing magic tricks with silks, 4 videos about doing magic tricks with various items, 8 videos about using magic tricks to teach biblical truths, and 1 video of magic tricks for kids. Draw a pictograph to show how many of each type of video Duane has made.

Magic Trick Videos Duane has Made

Silks	⊙ ⊙ ⊙ ⊙ ⊙
Various Items	⊙ ⊙ ⊙ ⊙
Biblical Truths	⊙ ⊙ ⊙ ⊙ ⊙ ⊙ ⊙ ⊙
For Kids	⊙

⊙ = 1 video

Ensure all pictographs have a title and a key. Some students may use a different symbol to represent more than one video. This is fine as long as the total number of videos represented on each row is accurate.

Make a circle graph showing the distribution of the types of videos Duane has made.

Total numbers of videos = 5 + 4 + 8 + 1 = 18 videos
Set up the ratios to get the number of degrees:

$\frac{5}{18}(360°) = 100°$ $\frac{4}{18}(360°) = 80°$

$\frac{8}{18}(360°) = 160°$ $\frac{1}{18}(360°) = 20°$

Magic Trick Videos Duane has Made

■ Silks
■ Various Items
■ Biblical Truths
■ Kids

Make sure the circle graph has a title and a key, and that the angle of each section is accurate.

Teaching Tips, Cont.

➢ Have students look at the frequency distribution in the teaching box. This is the same frequency distribution from Lesson 64. Ask the students which value or values appear the most number of times. (24 and 25 each appear 4 times.)

➢ Define *mode*. Emphasize the beginning sound of MOde and MOst. The auditory cues will help most students to remember the definition.

➢ Explain that a data set can have one mode, more than one mode, or no mode. If exactly one value appears more than any other value, that value is the only mode. If multiple values appear the same number of times, but more than other values, there is more than one mode. This is the case in the example in the teaching box. If every value appears the same number of times, there is no mode. Do not list every value in the list as a mode because the word *mode*, or *most*, implies that something appears more than another thing.

➢ Make sure all students have their quiz grades from Lesson 64. They should save these for use in Lesson 66.

➢ Complete the Classwork exercises. Have one student work the first problem on the board for the class and explain the answer. All students should work both problems in their books.

Assignment

• Complete Lesson 65, Activities 2-6.

Lesson 66

Concepts
- Range
- Mean
- Median
- Mode
- Single-variable equations
- Single-variable inequalities
- Roots
- Dividing decimals
- Math in the real world

Learning Objectives
The student will be able to:
- Define *range*
- Find the range of a given set of numbers

Materials Needed
- Student Book, Lesson 66
- Students' quiz grades from Lesson 64

Teaching Tips
➢ Review how to find the mean, median, and mode of a set of numbers.

➢ Ask students what information about a data set could be useful besides knowing the mean, median, and mode. If they do not think of it, suggest that knowing the smallest and largest values can be useful.

➢ Introduce the range and give its definition. Explain that the range is simply the difference between the largest and smallest values. It is not a list of the largest and smallest values in a data set, but the *difference*.

Range

The **range** is the difference between the largest and smallest values in a set of numbers.

To find the range, list the values in the set in order from smallest to largest or from largest to smallest. Then subtract the smallest value from the largest value. The difference is the range.

The number of people sitting in each row of the center section at one of Duane's shows is as follows: 25, 24, 25, 23, 22, 24, 23, 24, 25, 25, 22, 20, 23, 22, 24. What is the range?

Order the unique values from smallest to largest. 20, 22, 23, 24, 25

Now subtract the smallest value from the largest value. 25 – 20 = 5
The range is 5.

① Classwork
The results of 20 rolls of a game die are 1, 1, 3, 5, 2, 6, 3, 4, 3, 4, 5, 3, 3, 1, 6, 5, 4, 1, 4, and 3. What is the range?

Smallest to largest: 1, 2, 3, 4, 5, 6
Range: 6 – 1 = 5
The range is 5.

Using the list of grades from Lesson 64, what is the range of your math quiz grades?

Answers will vary. The answer should be the difference between the highest grade and the lowest grade.

Activities
② Find the mean, median, mode, and range of each set of numbers. Round answers to the nearest tenth when necessary.

65, 75, 74, 72, 50, 60, 52, 44, 17, 27
Sum: 536
Mean: 536 ÷ 10 = 53.6

Median:
17, 27, 44, 50, 52, 60, 65, 72, 74, 75
(52 + 60) ÷ 2 = 56
The median is 56.

Mode: No Mode

Range: 75 – 17 = 58

795, 847, 749, 901, 847, 892, 749
Sum: 5780
Mean: 5780 ÷ 7 = 825.7

Median:
749, 749, 795, 847, 847, 892, 901
The median is 847.

Mode: 749 and 847

Range: 901 – 749 = 152

67, 77, 77, 74, 54, 48, 60
Sum: 457
Mean: 457 ÷ 7 = 65.3

Median: 48, 54, 60, 67, 74, 77, 77
The median is 67.

Mode: 77

Range: 77 – 48 = 29

142, 287, 179, 198, 217, 287
Sum: 1310
Mean: 1310 ÷ 6 = 218.3

Median: 142, 179, 198, 217, 287, 287
(198 + 217) ÷ 2 = 207.5
The median is 207.5.

Mode: 287

Range: 287 – 142 = 145

---

③ Solve.

$6x + (3+4)^2 = 5(x+7)$
$6x + 7^2 = 5x + 35$
$6x + 49 = 5x + 35$
$x = -14$

$8x + 3(5-2x) + 2 = 5x - (3^3 - 2^3)$
$8x + 15 - 6x + 2 = 5x - (27 - 8)$
$2x + 17 = 5x - 19$
$-3x = -36$
$x = 12$

$4(2x-3) + \sqrt{2^3 \times 6 + 1} = 3x + 2$
$8x - 12 + \sqrt{8 \times 6 + 1} = 3x + 2$
$8x - 12 + \sqrt{49} = 3x + 2$
$8x - 12 + 7 = 3x + 2$
$8x - 5 = 3x + 2$
$5x = 7$
$x = \dfrac{7}{5}$

$6x + (5-9)^2 > 4(x+3)$
$6x + (-4)^2 > 4x + 12$
$6x + 16 > 4x + 12$
$2x > -4$
$x > -2$

$7x + 3(4-x) < 3x - (2^3 \div 2^2)$
$7x + 12 - 3x < 3x - 2$
$4x + 12 < 3x - 2$
$x < -14$

$5(2x-3) + \sqrt{3^2 + 2^3 - 1} < 3(x+2)$
$10x - 15 + \sqrt{9 + 8 - 1} < 3x + 6$
$10x - 15 + \sqrt{16} < 3x + 6$
$10x - 15 + 4 < 3x + 6$
$10x - 11 < 3x + 6$
$7x < 17$
$x < \dfrac{17}{7}$

④ Divide.

$\begin{array}{r} 0.475 \\ 0.23\overline{)0.10925} \\ \underline{92} \\ 172 \\ \underline{161} \\ 115 \\ \underline{115} \end{array}$

$\begin{array}{r} 38.4 \\ 2.7\overline{)103.68} \\ \underline{81} \\ 226 \\ \underline{216} \\ 108 \\ \underline{108} \end{array}$

$\begin{array}{r} 6.8 \\ 0.76\overline{)5.168} \\ \underline{456} \\ 608 \\ \underline{608} \end{array}$

$\begin{array}{r} 0.068 \\ 0.82\overline{)0.05576} \\ \underline{492} \\ 656 \\ \underline{656} \end{array}$

⑤ Solve.

Duane does 10 short tricks in the first three minutes of an illusion show. After that, he averages one trick every three minutes for the duration of the show. How many tricks does Duane do in a 45-minute show?

First 3 minutes: 10 tricks
Remaining 42 minutes: 42 ÷ 3 = 14
Total number of tricks in a 45-minute show: 10 + 14 = 24

Teaching Tips, Cont.

➢ Teach how to find the range of a set of numbers. Emphasize that subtraction *must* be done to properly give the range. Many students, especially at first, are tempted to list the highest and lowest values as the range and never do the subtraction.

➢ Make sure students remember to list all values in the data set in order from smallest to largest. If they get in the habit of doing this as a first step, it will simplify many statistical calculations they may be asked to do.

➢ All students should have their quiz grades from Lesson 64 before beginning the Classwork exercises.

➢ Complete the Classwork exercises. Have one student work the first problem on the board for the class and explain the answer. All students should work both problems in their books.

Assignment
• Complete Lesson 66, Activities 2-5.

Lesson 67

Concepts
- Stem-and-leaf plots
- Median
- Mode
- Prime factorization
- Exponents
- Single-variable inequalities
- Roots
- Ratios
- Math in the real world

Learning Objectives
The student will be able to:
- Describe a stem-and-leaf plot
- Draw a stem-and-leaf plot to represent a given set of data
- Use a stem-and-leaf plot to find the median and mode of a given set of data

Materials Needed
- Student Book, Lesson 67

Teaching Tips
- Review median and mode. (See Lessons 63 and 65.)

- Introduce stem-and-leaf plots as a way to see trends in data clusters.

- Teach stem-and-leaf plots from the teaching box. Make sure students understand that stem-and-leaf plots are not limited to two-digit numbers, but that they will not be asked to make a stem-and-leaf plot with anything larger than a two-digit number.

Lesson 67

Stem-and-Leaf Plots

A **stem-and-leaf plot** shows groups of value frequencies within a set of data.

This book will focus on stem-and-leaf plots of two-digit numbers. In this case, the tens digits are the stems, and the ones digits are the leaves.

To make a stem-and-leaf plot of a set of two-digit numbers, begin by writing the numbers in order from smallest to largest. Then make a two-column chart, with the stems (digits 0 – 9) in the left column and the leaves (ones digits in the given values) in the corresponding right column. The stems will always have exactly one number per row. The leaves may have zero, one, or more than one number per row.

Make a stem-and-leaf plot showing the distribution of the numbers 92, 84, 64, 60, 64, 61, 72, 66, 57, 56, 25, 28, 97, 98, 99.

Begin by writing the numbers in numerical order. 25, 28, 56, 57, 60, 61, 64, 64, 66, 72, 84, 92, 97, 98, 99

Now make a two-column chart. Label the left column "Stems" and the right column "Leaves." Write the digits 0 – 9 in the left column. In the right column, write the ones digits that correspond to the tens digits in the left column.

Stems	Leaves
0	
1	
2	5, 8
3	
4	
5	6, 7
6	0, 1, 4, 4, 6
7	2
8	4
9	2, 7, 8, 9

① Classwork
Make a stem-and-leaf plot.

Show the distribution of the following numbers: 43, 50, 26, 36, 70, 65, 48, 78, 80, 63, 65, 69, 80, 69, 28, 34, 33, 45, 57, 94, 69, 80.

Write the numbers in numerical order: 26, 28, 33, 34, 36, 43, 45, 48, 50, 57, 63, 65, 65, 69, 69, 69, 70, 78, 80, 80, 80, 94

Divide the stems (tens digits) from the leaves (ones digits).

Stems	Leaves
0	
1	
2	6, 8
3	3, 4, 6
4	3, 5, 8
5	0, 7
6	3, 5, 5, 9, 9, 9
7	0, 8
8	0, 0, 0
9	4

Activities

② Make a stem-and-leaf plot, and find the median and mode of each set of numbers.

60, 63, 74, 79, 80, 63, 34, 28, 57, 94, 80, 69, 30, 46, 48, 78, 35, 59

70, 58, 33, 75, 58, 64, 56, 86, 76, 49, 58, 70, 72, 53, 88, 66, 42, 70, 72, 52, 61, 69, 87, 62, 93

Stems	Leaves
0	
1	
2	8
3	0, 4, 5
4	6, 8
5	7, 9
6	0, 3, 3, 9
7	4, 8, 9
8	0, 0
9	4

Median: (60 + 63) ÷ 2 = 61.5
Mode: 63, 80

Stems	Leaves
0	
1	
2	
3	3
4	2, 9
5	2, 3, 6, 8, 8, 8
6	1, 2, 4, 6, 9
7	0, 0, 0, 2, 2, 5, 6
8	6, 7, 8
9	3

Median: 66
Mode: 58, 70

③ Give the prime factorization of each number, using exponents where appropriate.

$$135$$
$$135 = 3 \times 3 \times 3 \times 5$$
$$135 = 3^3 \times 5$$

$$136$$
$$136 = 2 \times 2 \times 2 \times 17$$
$$136 = 2^3 \times 17$$

$$138$$
$$138 = 2 \times 3 \times 23$$

④ Solve.

$$7x + (10-6)^2 > 3(4-x)$$
$$7x + (4)^2 > 12 - 3x$$
$$7x + 16 > 12 - 3x$$
$$10x > -4$$
$$x > \frac{-2}{5}$$

$$11x + 3(3-2x) < 14x - (3^3 - 3^2)$$
$$11x + 9 - 6x < 14x - 18$$
$$5x + 9 < 14x - 18$$
$$-9x < -27$$
$$x > 3$$

$$6(2x-3) + \sqrt{3^3 - 2^2 + 2} < 5(x+1)$$
$$12x - 18 + \sqrt{27 - 4 + 2} < 5x + 5$$
$$12x - 18 + \sqrt{25} < 5x + 5$$
$$12x - 18 + 5 < 5x + 5$$
$$12x - 13 < 5x + 5$$
$$7x < 18$$
$$x < \frac{18}{7}$$

⑤ Solve.

Duane is designing an illusion that he will market in two sizes. The smaller table top version is 3 inches wide, 5 inches long, and 8 inches tall. If the ratio of the table top version to the stage version is 3:32, what are the dimensions of the stage version?

$$\frac{3}{32} = \frac{3}{x}$$
$$3x = 96$$
$$x = 32 \text{ inches wide}$$

$$\frac{3}{32} = \frac{5}{x}$$
$$3x = 160$$
$$x = 53\frac{1}{3} \text{ inches long}$$

$$\frac{3}{32} = \frac{8}{x}$$
$$3x = 256$$
$$x = 85\frac{1}{3} \text{ inches tall}$$

Teaching Tips, Cont.

➢ Teach how to make a stem and leaf plot by separating the stems (tens digits) from the leaves (ones digits) and making a chart.

➢ Remind students to put data values in order from smallest to largest before beginning any statistical calculations.

➢ Complete the Classwork exercises. Have one student work the problem on the board for the class and explain the answer. All students should work the problem in their books.

Assignment

• Complete Lesson 67, Activities 2-5.

Lesson 68

Concepts
- Histograms
- Stem-and-leaf plots
- Percents
- Percents less than 1
- Percents greater than 100
- Math in the real world

Learning Objectives
The student will be able to:
- Define *histogram*
- Use a stem-and-leaf plot to draw a histogram

Materials Needed
- Student Book, Lesson 68
- Worksheet 34

Teaching Tips
➤ Have students complete Worksheet 34 in class. This may be for added practice of earlier topics, or graded as a quiz, if desired.

➤ Review stem-and-leaf plots. (See Lesson 67.)

➤ Introduce histograms as another way to see trends in data clusters.

➤ Teach histograms from the teaching box. Explain that each bar on a histogram represents the number of values in a specific range. It does not show what the individual values are, or if any one value appears multiple times.

Histograms

A **histogram** is a graph made from a stem-and-leaf plot. Each interval on the stem-and-leaf plot is represented by a vertical bar on the histogram. The height of the bar represents the number of values in that range. A histogram looks similar to a stem-and-leaf plot turned sideways.

When drawing a histogram, make all bars adjacent, non-overlapping, and equal in width.

Make a histogram showing the distribution of the numbers 92, 84, 64, 60, 64, 61, 72, 66, 57, 56, 25, 28, 97, 98, 99.

Begin by making a stem-and-leaf plot.

Stems	Leaves
0	
1	
2	5, 8
3	
4	
5	6, 7
6	0, 1, 4, 4, 6
7	2
8	4
9	2, 7, 8, 9

To make the histogram, make a graph with the stem ranges across the bottom. The number of leaves gives the height of the corresponding bar on the histogram.

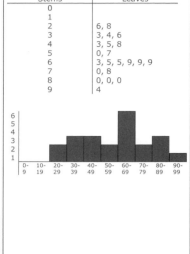

Notice that the values on the bottom of the histogram give the ranges of the stems. A stem of 6 represents all values from 60 – 69. The range of 60 – 69 is written on the histogram, not the number 6.

① Classwork
Make a histogram.

Show the distribution of the following numbers: 43, 50, 26, 36, 70, 65, 48, 78, 80, 63, 65, 69, 80, 69, 28, 34, 33, 45, 57, 94, 69, 80.

Stems	Leaves
0	
1	
2	6, 8
3	3, 4, 6
4	3, 5, 8
5	0, 7
6	3, 5, 5, 9, 9, 9
7	0, 8
8	0, 0, 0
9	4

Activities

② Draw a histogram to represent each set of data.

60, 63, 74, 79, 80, 63, 34, 28, 57, 94, 80, 69, 30, 46, 48, 78, 35, 59

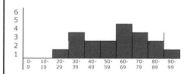

70, 58, 33, 75, 58, 64, 56, 86, 76, 49, 58, 70, 72, 53, 88, 66, 42, 70, 72, 52, 61, 69, 87, 62, 93

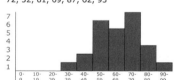

③ Solve.

What is 85% of 320?
$x = 0.85(320)$
$x = 272$

What is 0.5% of 280?
$x = 0.005(280)$
$x = 1.4$

What is 152% of 500?
$x = 1.52(500)$
$x = 760$

15 is what percent of 90?
$15 = 90x$
$x = \frac{15}{90}$
$x = \frac{1}{6} = 16.\overline{6}\%$

16 is what percent of 800?
$16 = 800x$
$x = \frac{16}{800}$
$x = \frac{1}{50} = 0.02 = 2\%$

210 is what percent of 60?
$210 = 60x$
$x = \frac{210}{60}$
$x = \frac{7}{2} = 3.5 = 350\%$

36 is 18% of what number?
$36 = 0.18x$
$x = 36 \div 0.18$
$x = 200$

4 is 0.09% of what number?
$4 = 0.0009x$
$x = 4 \div 0.0009$
$x = 4444.\overline{4}$ or $4444\frac{4}{9}$

256 is 150% of what number?
$256 = 1.5x$
$x = 256 \div 1.5$
$x = 170.\overline{6}$ or $170\frac{2}{3}$

④ Solve.
Duane charges for his hotel expenses plus 75 cents per mile that he drives for a show to cover travel expenses. Duane drove 234 miles each way to a show and got a hotel room for $89 plus 12% tax for one night. What did Duane charge for his travel expenses?

Hotel expenses: $89(1.12) = $99.68
Mileage expenses: (234 + 234)($0.75) = $351
Total travel expenses: $99.68 + $351 = $450.68

① For each set of numbers, make a frequency distribution and find the mean, median, and mode. Round answers to the nearest tenth where necessary.

6, 1, 5, 6, 3, 6, 4, 4, 3, 4, 2, 5, 4, 4, 1, 1, 4, 3, 2, 3, 6

Number	Tally	Total
1	//	2
2	//	2
3	////	4
4	ЖНТ /	6
5	//	2
6	////	4

Mean: Sum = 76; Mean = 76 ÷ 20 = 3.8
Median: 1, 1, 2, 2, 3, 3, 3, 3, 4, 4, 4, 4, 4, 4, 5, 5, 6, 6, 6, 6
The median is 4.
The mode is 4.

3, 1, 3, 3, 6, 2, 3, 4, 3, 4, 1, 6, 4, 5, 1, 6, 3, 6, 2, 1

Number	Tally	Total
1	////	4
2	//	2
3	ЖНТ /	6
4	///	3
5	/	1
6	////	4

Mean: Sum = 67; Mean = 67 ÷ 20 = 3.4
Median: 1, 1, 1, 1, 2, 2, 3, 3, 3, 3, 3, 3, 4, 4, 4, 4, 5, 6, 6, 6, 6
The median is 3.
The mode is 3.

Teaching Tips, Cont.

➤ Teach how to make a histogram. Emphasize the fact that all bars on a histogram are joined with no space between.

➤ Show students that the bars on a histogram correspond to the leaves on a stem-and-leaf plot. The stems with the most leaves also have the tallest bars.

➤ Some students might prefer to use graph paper for making histograms.

➤ Complete the Classwork exercises. Have one student work the problem on the board for the class and explain the answer. All students should work the problem in their books. Make sure all students are drawing the histogram correctly.

Assignment

• Complete Lesson 68, Activities 2-4.

Lesson 69

Concepts
- Box-and-whisker plots
- 5-number summary
- Prime factorization
- Exponents
- Mean
- Median
- Mode
- Range

Learning Objectives
The student will be able to:
- Describe a box-and-whisker plot
- List the 5 components of the 5-number summary
- Calculate quartiles
- Draw a box-and-whisker plot using a 5-number summary
- Identify skew in a data set

Materials Needed
- Student Book, Lesson 69
- Standard 6-sided game die

Teaching Tips
➢ Review how to find the median. (See Lesson 63.)

➢ Have the students make a list of all the statistical calculations they have learned so far. (Mean, median, frequency distribution, mode, range). Introduce the box-and-whisker plot as another way of summarizing a group of data. Explain that this diagram allows you to quickly see the median of a group of numbers, but also shows you how the other values are grouped around the median.

➢ Teach how to find the 5-number summary of a group of values from the teaching box.

Box-and-Whisker Plots

A **box-and-whisker plot**, also called a box plot, is a graphical representation of the 5-number summary of a group of data. The **5-number summary** is the minimum value, maximum value, median, median of the lower half (also called the **first quartile**), and the median of the upper half (also called the **third quartile**). The median of the entire group of data is the **second quartile**. A box-and-whisker plot allows you to quickly see how well distributed the data is in a group. The box will "bunch up" where there are many values close together, and stretch out where the data values are farther apart.

To draw a box-and-whisker plot, first write all values in order from smallest to largest. Identify the minimum and maximum values, and find the median of the whole group. If there is an odd number of values, there will be one median. Use this number as the second quartile. If there is an even number of values, there will be two medians. Use the average of the medians as the second quartile.

Next, find the median of each half. If the whole group of data has an odd number of values, you have already used one of the values in the 5-number summary. Therefore, do not use the median in calculating the median of each half. If the whole group of data has an even number of values, you have used an average for the second quartile an not one of the values. Use exactly half of the original data group to calculate the median of each half. If there is an even number of values in each half, take the average of the two medians in each half to get the first and third quartile values.

Finally, draw a number line, making vertical lines to mark the points of the 5 numbers you have just calculated. Draw a box with ends on the first and third quartiles. Draw a horizontal line from the left side of the box to the vertical line representing the minimum value, and a horizontal line from the right side of the box to the vertical line representing the maximum value. The vertical line representing the median of the whole group should appear inside the larger box, dividing it into two sections.

① **Classwork**
Make a box-and-whisker plot.

List the 5-number summary and draw a box-and-whisker plot to show the distribution of the following numbers: 43, 50, 26, 36, 70, 65, 48, 78, 80, 63, 65, 69, 80, 69, 28, 34, 33, 45, 57, 94, 69, 80.

5-number summary:
Minimum value: 26
Maximum value: 94
Median: The two middle numbers are 63 and 65, so the median is $(63 + 65) \div 2 = 64$
First quartile: Find the median of the numbers in the range 26 – 63. The first quartile is 43
Third quartile: Find the median of the numbers in the range 65 – 94. The third quartile is 70.

The 5 number summary is 26, 43, 64, 70, and 94.

Additional Information about Skew

- When looking at a box-and-whisker plot, if the median is centered in the box and the box is centered in the whiskers, the plot is said to be symmetric and has no skew.

- If the median is closer to the right side of the box so the box appears larger on the left side, the plot is said to be skewed left, or have negative skew.

- If the median is closer to the left side of the box so the box appears larger on the right side, the plot is said to be skewed right, or have positive skew.

60, 63, 74, 79, 80, 63, 34, 28, 57, 94, 80, 69, 30, 46, 48, 78, 35, 59

5-number summary:
Minimum value: 28
Maximum value: 94
Median: The two middle numbers are 60 and 63, so the median is (60 + 63) ÷ 2 = 61.5
First quartile: Find the median of the numbers in the range 28 – 60. The first quartile is 46
Third quartile: Find the median of the numbers in the range 63 – 94. The third quartile is 78.

The 5 number summary is 28, 46, 61.5, 78, and 94.

70, 58, 33, 75, 58, 64, 56, 86, 76, 49, 58, 70, 72, 53, 88, 66, 42, 70, 72, 52, 61, 69, 87, 62, 93

5-number summary:
Minimum value: 33
Maximum value: 93
Median: The median is 66.
First quartile: Find the median of the numbers in the range 33 – 64. The two middle numbers are 56 and 58, so the first quartile is 57.
Third quartile: Find the median of the numbers in the range 69 – 93. The two middle numbers are 72 and 75, so the third quartile is (72 + 75) ÷ 2 = 73.5.

The 5 number summary is 33, 57, 66, 73.5, and 93.

③ Give the prime factorization of each number, using exponents where appropriate.

140	144	147
$140 = 2 \times 2 \times 5 \times 7$	$144 = 2 \times 2 \times 2 \times 2 \times 3 \times 3$	$147 = 3 \times 7 \times 7$
$140 = 2^2 \times 5 \times 7$	$144 = 2^4 \times 3^2$	$147 = 3 \times 7^2$

④ Give the mean, median, mode, and range of each set of data.
Roll a standard game die 10 times and record the results. Find the mean, median, mode, and range of the set of numbers you have generated.

Answers will vary.

Roll a standard game die 20 times and record the results. Find the mean, median, mode, and range of the set of numbers you have generated.

Answers will vary.

How do the means, medians, modes, and ranges compare between the two sets? Which are the same for both sets? Which are different?

Answers will vary. For most students, the range will be the same for both sets and should be 6 – 1 = 5.

Additional Teacher Information

When drawing box-and-whisker plots in upper level statistics, outliers should be calculated and excluded from the whiskers. Outliers are defined as any value that is more than 1.5 times the interquartile range. (The interquartile range is the difference between the third quartile and the first quartile, or the values at the ends of the box.) By definition, any values that are more than 1.5 times this range away from the box are not considered statistically significant in the data set and are called outliers.

For the purpose of this book, and to simplify the learning process, we are not calculating outliers. All given values in a problem will be used in drawing a box-and-whisker plot. The concept of outliers will be introduced in a statistics course.

Teaching Tips, Cont.

➢ Teach the concept of quartiles. Ask the students what fraction of a dollar a quarter is worth. $\left(\frac{1}{4}\right)$ Ask the students what fraction of a gallon a quart is. $\left(\frac{1}{4}\right)$ Ask the students what fraction of the total number of values a quartile is. $\left(\frac{1}{4}\right)$

➢ Explain that quartiles simply divide the number of values into four parts with an equal number of values in each part. The easiest way to do this is to find the median of the set. This is the second quartile, and divides the set in half. If there is an odd number of values in the set, the median is the middle value, and that value is not used again in calculating the median of the separate halves. If there is an even number of values in the set, the median is the average of the two middle values. Because neither value was singled out and used as a median, both values will be used in calculating the medians of the halves – the smaller value in the lower half to find the first quartile, and the larger value in the upper half to find the third quartile.

➢ Complete the Classwork exercises. Have one student work the problem on the board for the class and explain the answer. All students should work the problem in their books.

➢ You may wish to do the die-rolling portion of Activity 4 in class and have the students record the results on their own paper.

Assignment Complete Lesson 69, Activities 2-4.

Lesson 70

Concepts
- Probability
- Powers of 10
- Metric measurement conversions
- Fraction-decimal-percent conversions
- Simple interest
- Math in the real world

Learning Objectives
The student will be able to:
- Define *probability*
- Write probabilities with proper notation
- Calculate the probability of an event occurring or not occurring

Materials Needed
- Student Book, Lesson 70
- Worksheet 35

Teaching Tips
➤ Review fraction-decimal conversion. (See Lesson 33.)

➤ Ask the students if they would have a good chance of winning a drawing if they were entered 9 times and there were only 10 entries total. (Yes.) Ask if they would have a good chance of winning if they had 5 of the 10 entries. (Maybe.) Ask if they would have a good chance of winning if they had 1 of the 10 entries. (No.)

➤ Tell the students there is a branch of mathematics that calculates how good your chance is to win in situations like this. That branch of math is called *probability*.

Lesson 70

Probability

Probability is the area of math that describes the chance or likelihood that something (called an **event**) will happen, when compared to all possible results. All the possible results, whether desired or not, are called **outcomes**. The probability of event E occurring is written P(E).

Probabilities are usually expressed as a percent from 0% to 100%, although it is also acceptable to express probabilities as a number from 0 to 1. (Notice that the latter is the decimal representation of the percentages.)

To calculate the probability of an event occurring, divide the number of possible ways the event can occur by the total number of possible outcomes.

$$P(E) = \frac{\text{The number of ways E can occur}}{\text{The total number of possible outcomes}}$$

A card game has cards numbered 1 – 14 in each of 4 different colors (red, yellow, green, and black). What is the probability of drawing a red 3?

There is only 1 red 3 in the deck, so the number of ways E can occur is 1. There are 14(4) = 56 cards in the deck, so the total number of possible outcomes is 56.

$$P(\text{red 3}) = \frac{1}{56}$$

① Classwork
Use the card deck in the example at the left to find the following probabilities.

What is the probability of drawing a green card?

$$P(\text{green}) = \frac{14}{56} = \frac{1}{4}$$

What is the probability of drawing an even yellow card?

$$P(\text{even yellow}) = \frac{7}{56} = \frac{1}{8}$$

What is the probability of drawing a 7?

$$P(7) = \frac{4}{56} = \frac{1}{14}$$

What is the probability of drawing a card that is a multiple of 5?

$$P(\text{multiple of 5}) = \frac{8}{56} = \frac{1}{7}$$

Activities
② Find the probabilities.
When you flip a coin, what is the probability of getting tails?

$$P(\text{tails}) = \frac{1}{2}$$

When you roll a die, what is the probability of rolling a 2?

$$P(2) = \frac{1}{6}$$

When you roll a die, what is the probability of rolling an even number?

$$P(\text{even}) = \frac{3}{6} = \frac{1}{2}$$

When you roll a die, what is the probability of rolling a number less than 10?

$$P(\text{less than 10}) = \frac{6}{6} = 1$$

---

③ Multiply or divide by the proper powers of 10 to complete the metric conversions.

6.2 m = __6,200__ mm   32 cm = __0.32__ m

0.08 L = __80__ mL   94 mL = __0.094__ L

12.4 g = __1240__ cg   88.5 cW = __0.885__ W

3.09 W = __3,090__ mW   57.1 mg = __0.0571__ g

④ Complete the chart to show proper fraction-decimal-percent conversion.

Fraction	Decimal	Percent		Fraction	Decimal	Percent
$\frac{1}{3}$	$0.\bar{3}$	$33.\bar{3}\%$		$\frac{3}{4}$	0.75	75%
$\frac{3}{8}$	0.375	37.5%		$\frac{3}{5}$	0.6	60%
$\frac{1}{2}$	0.5	50%		$\frac{1}{6}$	$0.1\bar{6}$	$16.\bar{6}\%$
$\frac{7}{10}$	0.7	70%		$\frac{7}{8}$	0.875	87.5%
$\frac{5}{6}$	$0.8\bar{3}$	$83.\bar{3}\%$		$\frac{2}{3}$	$0.\bar{6}$	$66.\bar{6}\%$

⑤ Complete the chart to show simple interest.

Principal	Interest rate	Time, in years	Amount of interest	Total amount paid
$5000	6.5%	3	$i = \$5000(0.065)(3) = \$975$	$5000 + $975 = $5975
$10,000	7.75%	6	$i = \$10{,}000(0.0775)(6) = \$4650$	$10,000 + $4650 = $14,650
$15,000	9%	8	$i = \$15{,}000(0.09)(8) = \$10{,}800$	$15,000 + $10,800 = $25,800
$20,000	18%	10	$i = \$20{,}000(0.18)(10) = \$36{,}000$	$20,000 + $36,000 = $56,000
$25,000	21.5%	15	$i = \$25{,}000(0.215)(15) = \$80{,}625$	$25,000 + $80,625 = $105,625

⑥ Solve.
Duane uses a standard deck of 52 playing cards for some of his tricks. What is the probability that he will correctly guess a card selected by a volunteer?

$$P(\text{1 unique card}) = \frac{1}{52}$$

Probabilities

Probabilities Worksheet 35

① Find the probabilities.
A card game has cards numbered 1-14 in each of 4 different colors (red, yellow, green, and black). Find each of the following probabilities assuming the entire deck is used for each problem.

What is the probability of drawing a black card?

$P(black) = \frac{14}{56} = \frac{1}{4}$

What is the probability of drawing an odd red card?

$P(odd\ red) = \frac{7}{56} = \frac{1}{8}$

What is the probability of drawing a 10?

$P(10) = \frac{4}{56} = \frac{1}{14}$

What is the probability of drawing a card that is a multiple of 3?

$P(multiple\ of\ 3) = \frac{16}{56} = \frac{2}{7}$

What is the probability of drawing a blue card?

$P(blue) = \frac{0}{56} = 0$

What is the probability of drawing the green 7 card?

$P(green\ 7) = \frac{1}{56}$

You have drawn 14 cards and do not have the black 11. What is the probability that the next card will be the black 11?

$P(black\ 11) = \frac{1}{56 - 14} = \frac{1}{42}$

You have drawn 12 cards and have 2 cards that are green. What is the probability that the next card will be green?

$P(green) = \frac{14 - 2}{56 - 12} = \frac{12}{44} = \frac{3}{11}$

Teaching Tips, Cont.

➤ Teach probability from the teaching box. Make sure the students are very familiar with the terms *event* and *outcome*, as these will appear throughout the book in various probability problems.

➤ Show students how to set up a probability problem using the formula. Tell them that it is generally best to leave probability answers in fractional form, but they should reduce all fractions to lowest terms.

➤ Complete the Classwork exercises. Have some students work the problems on the board for the class and explain their answers. All students should work the problems in their books.

Assignments

- Complete Lesson 70, Activities 2-6.
- Worksheet 35
- Study for Test 7 (Lessons 58-67)

Horizons Pre-Algebra, Teacher's Guide

Test 7

Testing Objectives
The student will:
- Calculate compound interest
- Solve percents greater than 100
- Draw a pictograph
- Draw a circle graph
- Make a frequency diagram
- Find the mean
- Find the median
- Find the mode
- Make a stem-and-leaf plot
- Find the range

Materials Needed
- Test 7
- Compass
- Protractor
- *It's College Test Prep Time!* from Student Book
- *A Math Minute with...* Andy H. from Student Book

Teaching Tips
➤ Administer Test 7, allowing the students 30-40 minutes to complete the test.

➤ When all students are finished taking the test, introduce *It's College Test Prep Time* from the student book. This page may be completed in class or assigned as homework.

---

① Use the formula $A = P(1 + r)^t$ to calculate compound interest. **10 points**

Initial principal	Interest rate	Time, in years	Total compounded annually	Total compounded quarterly
$100	3%	3	$A = \$100(1 + .03)^3$ = \$109.27	$A = \$100(1 + 0.03 \div 4)^{3 \cdot 4}$ = \$109.38
$500	7%	3	$A = \$500(1.07)^3$ = \$612.52	$A = \$500(1 + 0.07 \div 4)^{3 \cdot 4}$ = \$615.72
$1000	10%	5	$A = \$1000(1.1)^5$ = \$1610.51	$A = \$1000(1 + 0.1 \div 4)^{5 \cdot 4}$ = \$1638.62
$5000	15%	10	$A = \$5000(1.15)^{10}$ = \$20,227.79	$A = \$5000(1 + 0.15 \div 4)^{10 \cdot 4}$ = \$21,801.89
$10,000	24%	10	$A = \$10,000(1.24)^{10}$ = \$85,944.26	$A = \$10,000(1 + 0.24 \div 4)^{10 \cdot 4}$ = \$102,857.18

② Solve. **3 points**

What is 350% of 700?
$x = 3.50(700)$
$x = 2450$

What is 375% of 450?
$x = 3.75(450)$
$x = 1687.5$

What is 248.9% of 400?
$x = 2.489(400)$
$x = 995.6$

③ Draw a pictograph to show the number of rows for each number of seats. **6 points**
The theater Duane performs in has 12 rows with 14 seats each, 27 rows with 8 seats each, 8 rows with 7 seats each, and 7 rows with 6 seats each.
Answers may vary. A sample pictograph is shown. Graphs must have a title and a key.

Seating Rows in Duane's Theater

14 seats	🖐🖐✋✊✊ or ✊✊✊✊✊✊✊✊✊✊✊✊
8 seats	🖐🖐🖐🖐🖐✊✊ or ✊✊✊✊✊✊✊✊✊✊✊✊✊✊✊✊✊✊✊✊✊✊✊✊✊✊✊
7 seats	🖐✊✊✊ or ✊✊✊✊✊✊✊✊
6 seats	🖐✊✊ or ✊✊✊✊✊✊✊

🖐 = 5 rows
✊ = 1 row

---

④ Draw a circle graph. **6 points**
The theater Duane performs in has 12 rows with 14 seats each, 27 rows with 8 seats each, 8 rows with 7 seats each, and 7 rows with 6 seats each.
Answers may vary. A sample circle graph is shown. Graphs must have a title and a key.

Row Configuration in Duane's Theater

- ■ 14 seats
- ■ 8 seats
- ■ 7 seats
- ■ 6 seats

⑤ Make a frequency distribution and find the mean, median, and mode. **15 points**

The results of 20 rolls of a die are 1, 3, 6, 2, 3, 1, 2, 6, 1, 1, 5, 2, 5, 2, 5, 6, 2, 4, 4, 2
Round answers to the nearest tenth where appropriate.

Die Roll	Tally	Number
1	////	4
2	⊮ /	6
3	//	2
4	//	2
5	///	3
6	///	3

Mean: Sum = 63; Mean = 63 ÷ 20 = 3.2
Median: (2 + 3) ÷ 2 = 5 ÷ 2 = 2.5
Mode: 2

⑥ Make a stem-and-leaf plot and find the range. **11 points**

The points scored by 30 college football teams in bowl games are as follows: 35, 28, 45, 24, 42, 32, 45, 10, 17, 21, 21, 13, 44, 20, 21, 30, 43, 42, 47, 20, 13, 35, 14, 13, 38, 35, 17, 20, 41, 31.

Stems	Leaves
0	
1	0, 3, 3, 3, 4, 7, 7
2	0, 0, 0, 1, 1, 1, 4, 8
3	0, 1, 2, 5, 5, 5, 8
4	1, 2, 2, 3, 4, 5, 5, 7
5	
6	
7	
8	
9	

Range: 47 − 10 = 37

51 points total

It's College Test Prep Time!

1. A store keeps its merchandise at the regular price for 6 weeks. At that time, the merchandise goes on clearance for 15% off. Every two weeks, the percent discount increases as follows: 30%, 50%, 75%, and 90%. When the merchandise reaches 90% off, the price remains the same until it is sold. Which of the following graphs shows the price of a $200 item over an eighteen-week period?

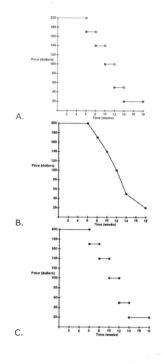

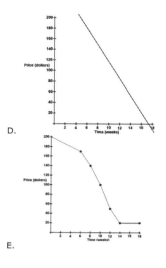

A is the correct answer because there is no gradual decrease in price, as pictured in B, D, and E. Choice C has solid dots as the endpoints of the segments, indicating there were two prices in effect at the same time. Choice A shows a step down in price in two-week increments.

A Math Minute with . . .

Andy H. – Electrician

What is your occupation? I am an electrician.

Where do you work? I am self-employed with my own electric company.

Did you attend college? If so, what was your major? No. I worked as an apprentice for five years.

What parts of your job require the use of math? I use math to calculate the correct size for wires, breakers, and conduit. I also use math to calculate the proper amperage.

What is the biggest "problem" you have faced that required the use of math to solve? While working at a large construction site, I was given papers with the electrical needs of the building. No information was given about the building's transformers. I needed to take the known electrical load requirements and calculate the transformer sizes.

Are there any other interesting math uses you have experienced? One interesting way I have used math is in calculating the lighting loads of different styles of lights. Some configurations can handle a maximum of 40 watt light bulbs. Other configurations can use 100 watt bulbs. I also rely on math to figure out what electrical requirements a house has if it uses gas or electric to run the stove, dryer, furnace, and water heater.

Teaching Tips, Cont.
> Have students read the Math Minute interview for Lessons 71-80.

Assignments
- Complete *It's College Test Prep Time!*
- Read *A Math Minute with…* Andy H.

Lesson 71

Concepts
- Bar graphs
- Divisibility tests
- Prime/composite numbers
- Measurement conversions
- Dividing fractions
- Roots
- Math in the real world

Learning Objectives
The student will be able to:
- Define *bar graph*
- Draw a bar graph to represent a given set of data

Materials Needed
- Student Book, Lesson 71
- Formula strip, Lesson 71

Teaching Tips
➢ Review pictographs and histograms. (See Lessons 60 and 68.)

➢ Introduce the bar graph as another method of showing different values in a set of data.

➢ Explain that while the pictograph uses a certain number of pictures to represent a given amount, a bar graph uses lines, or bars, of varying lengths to represent the different amounts.

➢ Have the students look at the picture of the bar graph in the teaching box and compare it with the histogram in Lesson 68. Ask them to identify similarities and differences between the two graphs.

Bar Graphs

A **bar graph**, also known as a **bar chart**, shows a comparison between two or more values. It uses rectangular bars whose lengths are proportional to the values of the data they represent. The bars may be displayed vertically or horizontally with space between each bar.

Make a bar graph to show that Andy did electrical work in 157 houses, 45 office buildings, and 73 retail locations.

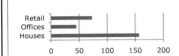

Andy's Electrical Work

Notice that the bar graph has a title to identify the information in the chart, labels to tell what specific information is included in each row, and a scale across the bottom of the graph to make the bar length more meaningful.

① **Classwork**
Make a bar graph.

Andy coaches a basketball team of first- and second-graders. Their scores in each of 8 games during the season are 14, 22, 10, 18, 16, 24, 18, 22.

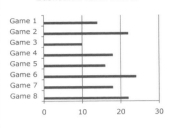

Basketball Team Scores

Activities
② Follow the directions.

The states having the largest number of electoral votes in the 2008 presidential election were California (55), Florida (27), Illinois (21), New York (31), Ohio (20), Pennsylvania (21), and Texas (34). Draw a bar graph showing the number of electoral votes each state had in the 2008 election.

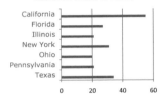

Electoral Votes in 2008

③ Use the divisibility tests to identify each number as prime or composite.

347	Prime	353	Prime
349	Prime	355	Composite (5)
351	Composite (3, 9)	357	Composite (3)

④ Complete the chart to show proper measurement conversion. (See Lesson 40.)

18 miles	18 miles $\left(\frac{1760\ yards}{1\ mile}\right) = 31,680$ yards
10 miles	10 miles $\left(\frac{5280\ feet}{1\ mile}\right) = 52,800$ feet
25 yards	25 yards $\left(\frac{36\ inches}{1\ yards}\right) = 900$ inches
78 feet	$_{26}78$ feet $\left(\frac{1\ yard}{3\ feet}\right) = 26$ yards
12 yards	12 yards $\left(\frac{3\ feet}{1\ yards}\right) = 36$ feet
63,360 feet	$_{12}63,360$ feet $\left(\frac{1\ mile}{5280\ feet}\right) = 12$ miles
15,840 yards	$_{9}15,840$ yards $\left(\frac{1\ mile}{1760\ yards}\right) = 9$ miles
15 feet	15 feet $\left(\frac{12\ inches}{1\ foot}\right) = 180$ inches
120 inches	$_{10}120$ inches $\left(\frac{1\ foot}{12\ inches}\right) = 10$ feet
576 inches	$_{16}576$ inches $\left(\frac{1\ yard}{36\ inches}\right) = 16$ yards

⑤ Divide.

$$\frac{\sqrt{32}}{18} \div \frac{\sqrt{2}}{3} = \frac{4\sqrt{2}}{18} \div \frac{\sqrt{2}}{3} = \frac{\cancel{4}^2 \cancel{\sqrt{2}}}{\cancel{18}_{3\cdot6}} \times \frac{\cancel{3}^1}{\cancel{\sqrt{2}}} = \frac{2}{3}$$

$$\frac{\sqrt{75}}{12} \div 3\frac{3}{4} = \frac{5\sqrt{3}}{12} \div \frac{15}{4} = \frac{\cancel{5}^1\sqrt{3}}{\cancel{12}_{3\cdot12}} \times \frac{\cancel{4}^1}{\cancel{15}_3} = \frac{\sqrt{3}}{9}$$

$$\frac{\sqrt{24}}{8} \div \frac{\sqrt{6}}{2} = \frac{\sqrt{24}^4}{\cancel{8}_4} \times \frac{\cancel{2}^1}{\sqrt{6}} = \frac{\sqrt{4}}{4} \times \frac{1}{1} = \frac{2}{4} = \frac{1}{2}$$

⑥ Solve the word problems.

There are 119 electricians listed in the yellow pages of the phone book. If a customer selects an electrician at random, what is the probability that Andy will be selected? What is the probability as a percent? Round to the nearest tenth of a percent.

$P(\text{Andy}) = \frac{1}{119}$

$\frac{1}{119} = 0.8\%$

Andy has one of the five ads in the electrician section of the yellow pages. If a customer selects an electrician at random from those having ads, what is the probability that Andy will be selected? What is the probability as a percent?

$P(\text{Andy}) = \frac{1}{5}$

$\frac{1}{5} = 20\%$

Teaching Tips, Cont.

➢ Emphasize that bar graphs are not histograms turned sideways. Histograms give information for a range of values, but bar graphs give information for each specific value. Histograms are vertical with the bars joined. Bar graphs may be vertical or horizontal, but there is always space between the bars. This book will always draw bar graphs in a horizontal orientation to avoid confusion. Both graphs should always have a title at the top and labels for the axes.

➢ Teach how to draw a bar graph from the teaching box. Remind students to put a space between the bars on all bar graphs.

➢ Complete the Classwork exercises. Have one student work the problem on the board for the class and explain the answer. All students should work the problem in their books.

➢ Pass out the formula strip for Lesson 71 from the *Tests and Resources* book for use in the assignment.

➢ If you plan to administer Exam 2 following Lesson 80 and Test 8, spend a few minutes reviewing for the Exam.

Assignment

• Complete Lesson 71, Activities 2-6.

Horizons Pre-Algebra, Teacher's Guide

Lesson 72

Concepts
- Line graphs
- Divisibility tests
- Prime/composite numbers
- Greatest common factor
- Simple interest
- Math in the real world

Learning Objectives
The student will be able to:
- Define *line graph*
- Draw a line graph to represent a given set of data
- Read a line graph to interpret data

Materials Needed
- Student Book, Lesson 72
- Worksheet 36

Teaching Tips
➤ Have students complete Worksheet 36 in class. This may be for added practice of earlier topics, or graded as a quiz, if desired.

➤ Review bar graphs. (See Lesson 71.)

➤ Introduce line graphs. Explain that while bar graphs show a specific value at a given time, line graphs show a trend in values over a period of time. The horizontal axis will be a unit of time, and the vertical axis will be the values.

➤ Ask the students what items must appear on every graph. (Title and labeled axes.)

Line Graphs

A **line graph**, or a **line chart**, shows trends in the given data over time. It is made by plotting points on a graph, and connecting the dots with line segments.

Make a line graph showing the average rainfall for Atlanta, Georgia. The average rainfall each month, in inches, is as follows: January: 5.02, February: 4.68, March: 5.38, April: 3.62, May: 3.95, June: 3.63, July: 5.12, August: 3.67, September: 4.09, October: 3.11, November: 4.10, December: 3.82

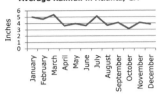
Average Rainfall in Atlanta, GA

Like other charts, the line graph should include a title. Also, the axes should be labeled if it is not clear what is being represented. In this case, the vertical axis is labeled "Inches" so the reader will know the units being reported in the graph.

① **Classwork**
Use the graph at the left to answer the following questions.

What is the wettest month in Atlanta?
March

What is the driest month in Atlanta?
October

Draw a line graph showing the average high temperatures in Atlanta. The average degrees Fahrenheit for each month is as follows: January: 51.9, February: 56.8, March: 65.0, April: 72.9, May: 80.0, June: 86.5, July: 89.4, August: 87.9, September: 82.3, October: 72.9, November: 63.3, December: 54.6

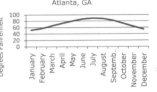
Average High Temperatures in Atlanta, GA

Activities
② Draw a line graph.
Draw a line graph showing the average high and low temperatures in Atlanta. The average low temperature, in degrees Fahrenheit, for each month is as follows: January: 33.5, February: 36.5, March: 43.6, April: 50.4, May: 59.5, June: 67.1, July: 70.6, August: 69.9, September: 64.3, October: 62.8, November: 43.5, December: 36.2. Use the average high temperatures from the Classwork section.

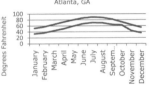
Average High and Low Temperatures in Atlanta, GA

---

③ Use the divisibility tests to identify each number as prime or composite.

359	Prime	367	Prime
363	Composite (3)	369	Composite (3, 9)
365	Composite (5)	373	Prime

④ Find the greatest common factor of each set of numbers.

56, 84, and 168
$56 = ②×②×2×⑦$
$84 = ②×②×3×⑦$
$168 = ②×②×2×3×⑦$
GCF: $2^2 × 7 = 28$

84, 126, and 189
$84 = 2×2×③×⑦$
$126 = 2×③×3×⑦$
$189 = ③×3×3×⑦$
GCF: $3 × 7 = 21$

90, 108, and 126
$90 = ②×③×③×5$
$108 = ②×2×③×③×3$
$126 = ②×③×③×7$
GCF: $2 × 3^2 = 18$

⑤ Complete the chart to show simple interest.

Principal	Interest rate	Time, in years	Amount of interest	Total amount paid
$4000	6.5%	2	$i = \$4000(0.065)(2) = \$520$	$4000 + $520 = $4520
$8000	7.75%	5	$i = \$8000(0.0775)(5) = \$3100$	$8000 + $3100 = $11,100
$12,000	9%	8	$i = \$12{,}000(0.09)(8) = \$8640$	$12,000 + $8640 = $20,640
$16,000	18%	11	$i = \$16{,}000(0.18)(11) = \$31{,}680$	$16,000 + $31,680 = $47,680
$20,000	21.5%	14	$i = \$20{,}000(0.215)(14) = \$60{,}200$	$25,000 + $60,200 = $85,200

⑥ Solve.
To cover materials and labor, Andy charges $1.50 per square foot of heated living space to wire a home's living space. He charges an additional $1 per square foot of unheated space to wire any unheated rooms, such as a garage. If a home has 1855 square feet of heated living space and 300 square feet of unheated space, what will Andy charge to wire the entire home?

$\$1.50(1855) + \$1(300) = \$2782.50 + \$300 = \$3082.50$

When wiring a building, Andy uses the formula $P = I(E)$, where P is the wattage, I is the amperage, and E is the voltage on the circuit. If Andy is installing a 15-amp breaker on a 120-volt circuit, how many 60-watt light bulb sockets can be safely wired into the breaker?

$P = IE$
$P = 15(120)$
$P = 1800$
The circuit can handle up to 1800 watts.
$1800 ÷ 60 = 30$
Andy can safely wire 30 sockets into the breaker.

Stem-and-Leaf Plot, Histogram   Worksheet 36

① Find the median, mode(s), and range; make a stem-and-leaf plot, and draw a histogram.

The basketball scores for the most recent games of the NCAA top 25 teams were 72, 72, 89, 82, 72, 64, 90, 73, 71, 71, 77, 87, 71, 68, 63, 51, 91, 73, 73, 82, 76, 91, 69, 83, and 63.

Median: 73
Mode: There are 3 modes – 71, 72, and 73
Range: 91 – 51 = 40

Stems	Leaves
0	
1	
2	
3	
4	
5	1
6	3, 3, 4, 8, 9
7	1, 1, 1, 2, 2, 2, 3, 3, 3, 6, 7
8	2, 2, 3, 7, 9
9	0, 1, 1

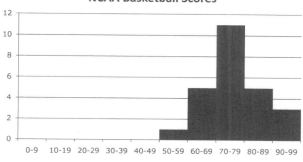

NCAA Basketball Scores

Teaching Tips, Cont.

➢ Teach how to draw a line graph from the teaching box. Make sure students understand that this is a continuous line, not just a sequence of points. It may help to suggest that students think of a line graph as a dot-to-dot activity once they have plotted all of the points.

➢ Complete the Classwork exercises. Have some students work the problems on the board for the class and explain their answers. All students should work the problems in their books.

➢ If you plan to administer Exam 2 following Lesson 80 and Test 8, spend a few minutes reviewing for the Exam.

Assignment
• Complete Lesson 72, Activities 2-6.

Lesson 73

Concepts
- Probability
- Odds in favor
- Odds against
- Roots
- Math in the real world

Learning Objectives
The student will be able to:
- Define *odds*
- Calculate the odds of an event occurring
- Calculate the odds of an event not occurring

Materials Needed
- Student Book, Lesson 73
- Worksheet 37
- Game or sweepstakes rules using the word *odds*

Teaching Tips
➤ Review probability. (See Lesson 70.)

➤ Explain that there is another way of describing the likelihood of an event occurring. Instead of just comparing the number of ways that an event can occur with the total number of possible outcomes, you can compare the number of ways an event can occur with the number of ways the event cannot occur.

➤ Teach how to calculate odds, pointing out the similarities and differences to probability.

➤ Ask students where they are likely to see the word *odds*. (Rules for sweepstakes, drawings, games of chance, etc.)

Probability and Odds

Recall from Lesson 70 that probability describes the chance or likelihood that an event will happen, when compared to all possible outcomes.

Odds described the chance or likelihood that an event will happen, when compared to all possible ways that it will not happen.

Compare the two formulas.

Probability (E) =
$$\frac{\text{The number of ways E can occur}}{\text{The total number of possible outcomes}}$$

Odds (E) =
$$\frac{\text{The number of ways E can occur}}{\text{The number of ways E cannot occur}}$$

While probabilities are generally expressed as percents, odds are generally expressed as ratios.

Find the probability and the odds of rolling a 3 on a standard six-sided die.

The event (E) is rolling a 3.
The number of ways E can occur: 1
The number of possible outcomes: 6 (1, 2, 3, 4, 5, and 6)
The number of ways E cannot occur: 5 (1, 2, 4, 5, and 6)

Probability (E) = $\frac{1}{6}$ or $16.\overline{6}\%$
Odds (E) = $\frac{1}{5}$, or 1:5, read "one *to* five," not "one *out of* five."

① **Classwork**
Solve.

A set of double-six dominoes has 28 dominoes. If you draw 1 domino, what is the probability that you will draw the double six?

Probability (Double 6) = $\frac{1}{28}$

What are the odds in favor of you drawing the double six?

Odds (double 6) = $\frac{1}{27}$ or 1:27

What are the odds against you drawing the double six?

Odds (not double 6) = $\frac{27}{1}$ or 27:1

If a game states that there is one winning piece and the odds of winning are 1:5000, how many total game pieces are available?

1 winning game piece + 5000 losing game pieces = 5001 total game pieces

Activities
② Calculate the probability of each scenario.

Using a standard 6-sided game die, find the probability of rolling each of the following:

6	even number	odd number	number less than 5
P(6) = $\frac{1}{6}$	P(even) = $\frac{3}{6}$ = $\frac{1}{2}$	P(odd) = $\frac{3}{6}$ = $\frac{1}{2}$	P(less than 5) = $\frac{4}{6}$ = $\frac{2}{3}$
or $16.\overline{6}\%$	or 50%	or 50%	or $66.\overline{6}\%$

---

③ Calculate the odds in favor.
Using a standard 6-sided game die, find the odds in favor of rolling each of the following:

6	even number	odd number	number less than 5
Odds(6) = $\frac{1}{5}$	Odds(even) = $\frac{3}{3}$ = $\frac{1}{1}$	Odds(odd) = $\frac{3}{3}$ = $\frac{1}{1}$	Odds(less than 5) = $\frac{4}{2}$ = $\frac{2}{1}$
or 1:5	or 1:1	or 1:1	or 2:1

④ Calculate the odds against.
Using a standard 6-sided game die, find the odds against rolling each of the following:

6	even number	odd number	number less than 5
Odds(not 6) = $\frac{5}{1}$	Odds(not even) = $\frac{3}{3}$ = $\frac{1}{1}$	Odds(not odd) = $\frac{3}{3}$ = $\frac{1}{1}$	Odds(not less than 5) = $\frac{2}{4}$ = $\frac{1}{2}$
or 5:1	or 1:1	or 1:1	or 1:2

⑤ Simplify the following roots.

$$\frac{\sqrt[3]{16}}{2} + \frac{5\sqrt[3]{54}}{3} = \frac{\sqrt[3]{2\times2\times2\times2}}{2} + \frac{5\sqrt[3]{2\times3\times3\times3}}{3} = \frac{2\sqrt[3]{2}}{2} + \frac{5(3)\sqrt[3]{2}}{3} = \sqrt[3]{2} + 5\sqrt[3]{2} = 6\sqrt[3]{2}$$

$$\frac{5\sqrt{45}}{2} - \frac{\sqrt{125}}{2} = \frac{5\sqrt{3\times3\times5}}{2} - \frac{\sqrt{5\times5\times5}}{2} = \frac{5(3)\sqrt{5}}{2} - \frac{5\sqrt{5}}{2} = \frac{15\sqrt{5}}{2} - \frac{5\sqrt{5}}{2} = \frac{10\sqrt{5}}{2} = 5\sqrt{5}$$

$$\frac{3\sqrt[3]{32}}{4}\left(\frac{3\sqrt[4]{128}}{8}\right) = \frac{3\sqrt[3]{2\times2\times2\times2\times2}}{4}\left(\frac{3\sqrt[4]{2\times2\times2\times2\times2\times2\times2}}{8}\right) =$$
$$\frac{3(2)\sqrt[3]{2}}{4}\left(\frac{3(2)\sqrt[4]{8}}{8}\right) = \frac{3\sqrt[3]{2}}{2}\left(\frac{3\sqrt[4]{8}}{4}\right) = \frac{9\sqrt[12]{16}}{8} = \frac{9\sqrt[12]{2\times2\times2\times2}}{8} = \frac{9\left(2\right)}{8} = \frac{9}{4}$$

$$\frac{4\sqrt[3]{162}}{3} \div \frac{3\sqrt[3]{250}}{5} = \frac{4\sqrt[3]{2\times3\times3\times3\times3}}{3} \div \frac{3\sqrt[3]{2\times5\times5\times5}}{5} =$$
$$\frac{4(3)\sqrt[3]{2\times3}}{3} \div \frac{3(5)\sqrt[3]{2}}{5} = 4\sqrt[3]{6} \div 3\sqrt[3]{2} = \frac{4\sqrt[3]{6}}{3\sqrt[3]{2}} = \frac{4\sqrt[3]{3}}{3}$$

⑥ Solve.
When wiring a building, Andy uses the formula $P = I(E)$, where P is the wattage, I is the amperage, and E is the voltage on the circuit. If Andy is installing a 4400-watt electric dryer on a 240-volt circuit, will a standard 15-amp breaker be big enough?
$P = IE$
$4400 = I(240)$
$I = \frac{4400}{240} = 18.\overline{3}$
A 15-amp breaker is not big enough.

① Complete the chart to show probability and odds.

Scenario	Number of Possible Outcomes	Desired Event (E)	P(E)	Odds (in favor of E)	Odds (Against E)
Flipping a coin once	2	Heads	$P(E) = \frac{1}{2}$	1:1	1:1
Rolling a 6-sided die once	6	5	$P(E) = \frac{1}{6}$	1:5	5:1
Rolling a 6-sided die once	6	Even number	$P(E) = \frac{3}{6} = \frac{1}{2}$	3:3 = 1:1	3:3 = 1:1
Rolling a 6-sided die once	6	Multiple of 3	$P(E) = \frac{2}{6} = \frac{1}{3}$	2:4 = 1:2	4:2 = 2:1
Choosing an integer from 1 to 25	25	7	$P(E) = \frac{1}{25}$	1:24	24:1
Choosing an integer from 1 to 25	25	Even number	$P(E) = \frac{12}{25}$	12:13	13:12
Choosing an integer from 1 to 25	25	Multiple of 3	$P(E) = \frac{8}{25}$	8:17	17:8
Choosing an integer from 1 to 25	25	Multiple of 5	$P(E) = \frac{5}{25} = \frac{1}{5}$	5:20 = 1:4	20:5 = 4:1

Teaching Tips, Cont.

➤ Ask the students what it means when a game lists the odds of winning as 1:2. (There is 1 winner for every 2 non-winners.)

➤ Show students that this is not a 50% chance of winning, but rather a 33.3% chance of winning.

➤ Ask the students how many game pieces have been distributed if there is one grand prize, and the odds of winning the grand prize are 1:1,000,000. (1,000,001)

➤ Complete the Classwork exercises. Have some students work the problems on the board for the class and explain their answers. All students should work the problems in their books.

➤ If you plan to administer Exam 2 following Lesson 80 and Test 8, spend a few minutes reviewing for the Exam.

Assignments
- Complete Lesson 73, Activities 2-6.
- Worksheet 37

Lesson 74

Concepts
- Multiplication principle of counting
- Measurement conversions
- Proportions
- Improper fractions
- Compound interest
- Math in the real world

Learning Objectives
The student will be able to:
- Explain the multiplication principle of counting
- Apply the multiplication principle of counting to real life scenarios

Materials Needed
- Student Book, Lesson 74
- Scientific calculator
- Several coins
- Standard 6-sided game die
- Formula strip, Lesson 74

Teaching Tips
➤ Review probability. (See Lesson 70.)

➤ Show the students a coin, identifying the two sides as heads (H) and tails (T). Ask them how many possible outcomes there are with one flip of the coin. (2: H and T)

➤ Show the students two coins. Ask them how many possible combinations there are when two coins are flipped. (4: HH, HT, TH, TT)

➤ Show the students three coins. Ask them how many possible combinations there are when three coins are flipped. (8: HHH, HHT, HTH, HTT, TTT, TTH, THT, THH)

Multiplication Principle of Counting

The **multiplication principle of counting** provides a quick way to calculate the total number of possible outcomes when there are multiple steps or combinations of events involved. To use the multiplication principle of counting, multiply the number of possible outcome for each individual event to get the total number of possible outcomes for the combination of events.

Andy has 6 colors of wire that come in 11 different sizes each. How many combinations of color and size does Andy have?

Possible outcomes for color: 6
Possible outcomes for size: 11
Use the multiplication principle of counting:
6 × 11 = 66 possible combinations

① Classwork
Solve.
A fast food restaurant allows kids to choose one of 4 entrees, one of 3 side items, and one of 4 beverages to make a kids' meal. How many different combinations are possible for kids' meals?

Possible outcomes for entrees: 4
Possible outcomes for sides: 3
Possible outcomes for beverages: 4

4 × 3 × 4 = 48 possible combinations

Activities
② Solve.

When Andy is wiring a house, he must know if the customer has a gas or electric dryer, gas or electric furnace, and gas or electric water heater. How many different wiring combinations are possible for the dryer, furnace, and water heater?

2 × 2 × 2 = 8 different wiring combinations

In addition to the above wiring combinations, Andy's customers have 3 choices for ceiling lighting. How many wiring combinations are possible for the dryer, furnace, water heater, and ceiling lighting?

2 × 2 × 2 × 3 = 24 different wiring combinations

Andy's customers can choose from incandescent, compact fluorescent, and LED lights in the kitchen, and incandescent, compact fluorescent, LED, and halogen in the dining room. How many lighting combinations are possible for the kitchen and dining room?

3 × 4 = 12 possible lighting combinations

---

③ Complete the chart to show conversion between the metric and English systems.

14 inches	$14 \text{ inches} \left(\frac{2.54 \text{ cm}}{1 \text{ inch}}\right) = 35.56$ cm
42 inches	$42 \text{ inches} \left(\frac{25.4 \text{ mm}}{1 \text{ inch}}\right) = 1066.8$ mm
24 yards	$24 \text{ yards} \left(\frac{0.91 \text{ meter}}{1 \text{ yard}}\right) = 21.84$ meters
16 miles	$16 \text{ miles} \left(\frac{1.61 \text{ km}}{1 \text{ mile}}\right) = 25.76$ km
60 cm	$60 \text{ cm} \left(\frac{0.39 \text{ in.}}{1 \text{ cm}}\right) = 23.4$ inches
8 meters	$8 \text{ meters} \left(\frac{1.09 \text{ yd.}}{1 \text{ meter}}\right) = 8.72$ yards
28 km	$28 \text{ km} \left(\frac{0.62 \text{ mi.}}{1 \text{ km}}\right) = 17.36$ miles

④ Solve the proportions. Leave answers as improper fractions where necessary.

$$\frac{45}{x} = \frac{55}{90}$$
$$55x = 45(90)$$
$$x = \frac{\overset{9}{\cancel{45}}(90)}{\cancel{55}_{11}} = \frac{810}{11}$$

$$\frac{45}{100} = \frac{80}{x}$$
$$45x = 100(80)$$
$$x = \frac{\overset{20}{\cancel{100}}(80)}{\cancel{45}_{9}} = \frac{1600}{9}$$

$$\frac{48}{105} = \frac{x}{123}$$
$$105x = 48(123)$$
$$x = \frac{\overset{16}{\cancel{48}}(123)}{\cancel{105}_{35}} = \frac{1968}{35}$$

⑤ Complete the chart to show compound interest.

Initial principal	Interest rate	Time, in years	Total compounded annually	Total compounded quarterly
$1000	4.75%	2	$A = \$1000(1 + .0475)^2$ $= \$1097.27$	$A = \$1000(1 + 0.0475 \div 4)^{2 \cdot 4}$ $= \$1099.04$
$5000	8.5%	5	$A = \$5000(1 + 0.085)^5$ $= \$7518.28$	$A = \$5000(1 + 0.085 \div 4)^{5 \cdot 4}$ $= \$7613.97$
$7500	11.25%	7	$A = \$7500(1 + 0.1125)^7$ $= \$15,818.36$	$A = \$7500(1 + 0.1125 \div 4)^{7 \cdot 4}$ $= \$16,305.98$

⑥ Solve.
Andy has 6 colors of wire that come in 11 different sizes each. If Andy grabs a spool of wire at random, what is the probability that it is the color and size he needs?

Possible outcomes for color: 6
Possible outcomes for size: 11
Use the multiplication principle of counting:
6 × 11 = 66 possible combinations

$$P(\text{correct wire and color}) = \frac{1}{66}$$

Teaching Tips, Cont.

➤ Show students the entire pile of coins and ask them how they could determine the total number of different combinations possible with one flip of each coin. (Some students may notice a pattern from the previous examples, but most will not get the formula right.)

➤ Teach the multiplication principle of counting from the teaching box. Have students calculate the answer to the pile of coins. This may require a calculator.

➤ Show the students one coin and a standard 6-sided game die. Ask them how many different combinations are possible with one flip of the coin and one roll of the die. (2 possible outcomes from the coin × 6 possible outcomes from the die = 12 possible combinations)

➤ Complete the Classwork exercises. Have one student work the problem on the board for the class and explain the answer. All students should work the problem in their books.

➤ Pass out the formula strip for Lesson 74 from the *Tests and Resources* book for use in the assignment.

➤ Students may use a scientific calculator to complete the compound interest problems in part 5.

➤ If you plan to administer Exam 2 following Lesson 80 and Test 8, spend a few minutes reviewing for the Exam.

Assignment
• Complete Lesson 74, Activities 2-6.

Lesson 75

Concepts
- Combined probabilities
- Greatest common factor
- Roots
- Simple interest
- Compound interest
- Scale drawings
- Ratios

Learning Objectives
The student will be able to:
- Define *combined probabilities*
- Calculate the combined probability of given scenarios
- Apply the multiplication principle of counting to combined probabilities

Materials Needed
- Student Book, Lesson 75
- Worksheet 38
- Scientific calculator
- Several coins
- Standard 6-sided game die

Teaching Tips
➤ Have students complete Worksheet 38 in class. This may be for added practice of earlier topics, or graded as a quiz, if desired.

➤ Review probability and the multiplication principle of counting. (See Lessons 70 and 74.)

➤ Show the students a coin, identifying the two sides as heads (H) and tails (T). Ask them to find the probability of getting heads with one flip of the coin. ($\frac{1}{2}$)

Combined Probabilities

Combined probabilities are used to find the probability of two events occurring either at the same time or one right after another. To find a combined probability, multiply the probabilities of the individual events.

If two dice are rolled, what is the probability that one die will be a 3 and the other die will be a 5?

$P(3) = \frac{1}{6}$

$P(5) = \frac{1}{6}$

$P(3)P(5) = \frac{1}{6}\left(\frac{1}{6}\right) = \frac{1}{36}$

① Classwork
Solve.

What is the probability that a die is rolled six times and gives the numbers 1 – 6 in order?

$P(1) = \frac{1}{6}$ $\quad$ $P(2) = \frac{1}{6}$ $\quad$ $P(3) = \frac{1}{6}$

$P(4) = \frac{1}{6}$ $\quad$ $P(5) = \frac{1}{6}$ $\quad$ $P(6) = \frac{1}{6}$

$P(1)P(2)P(3)P(4)P(5)P(6) =$

$\frac{1}{6}\left(\frac{1}{6}\right)\left(\frac{1}{6}\right)\left(\frac{1}{6}\right)\left(\frac{1}{6}\right)\left(\frac{1}{6}\right) = \frac{1}{46656}$

Activities
② Solve.

You roll 5 dice at one time. What is the probability that you will roll a 2 on all 5 dice?

$P(2) = \frac{1}{6}$

$P(2)P(2)P(2)P(2)P(2) = \frac{1}{6}\left(\frac{1}{6}\right)\left(\frac{1}{6}\right)\left(\frac{1}{6}\right)\left(\frac{1}{6}\right) = \frac{1}{7776}$

If you rolled a 2 on 3 of the dice in your first roll, what is the probability that you will roll a 2 with your two remaining dice in your second roll?

$P(2) = \frac{1}{6}$

$P(2)P(2) = \frac{1}{6}\left(\frac{1}{6}\right) = \frac{1}{36}$

If you rolled a 2 on one die in your second roll, what is the probability that you will roll a 2 on the last die on your third roll?

$P(2) = \frac{1}{6}$

---

③ Find the greatest common factor of each set of numbers.

84, 140, and 168	84, 126, and 189	90, 108, and 144
$84 = ②\times②\times3\times⑦$	$105 = ③\times5\times⑦$	$90 = ②\times③\times③\times5$
$140 = ②\times②\times5\times⑦$	$126 = 2\times③\times3\times⑦$	$108 = ②\times2\times③\times③\times3$
$168 = ②\times②\times2\times3\times⑦$	$189 = ③\times3\times3\times⑦$	$144 = ②\times2\times2\times2\times③\times③$
GCF: $2^2\times7 = 28$	GCF: $3\times7 = 21$	GCF: $2\times3^2 = 18$

④ Simplify the following roots.

$\frac{\sqrt[3]{40}}{2} + \frac{4\sqrt[3]{135}}{3} = \frac{\sqrt[3]{2\times2\times2\times5}}{2} + \frac{4\sqrt[3]{3\times3\times3\times5}}{3} = \frac{2\sqrt[3]{5}}{2} + \frac{4(3)\sqrt[3]{5}}{3} = \sqrt[3]{5} + 4\sqrt[3]{5} = 5\sqrt[3]{5}$

$\frac{3\sqrt{48}}{2} - \frac{\sqrt{75}}{5} = \frac{3\sqrt{3\times4\times4}}{2} - \frac{\sqrt{3\times5\times5}}{5} = \frac{3\left(4^2\right)\sqrt{3}}{2} - \frac{5\sqrt{3}}{5} = 6\sqrt{3} - \sqrt{3} = 5\sqrt{3}$

$\frac{3\sqrt[3]{48}}{2}\left(\frac{5\sqrt[3]{96}}{4}\right) = \frac{3\sqrt[3]{2\times2\times2\times2\times3}}{2}\left(\frac{5\sqrt[3]{2\times2\times2\times2\times2\times3}}{4}\right) = \frac{3\left(2^1\right)\sqrt[3]{3}}{2}\left(\frac{5\left(2^1\right)\sqrt[3]{6}}{4}\right) = 3\sqrt[3]{3}\left(\frac{5\sqrt[3]{6}}{2}\right) = \frac{15\sqrt[3]{18}}{2}$

$\frac{8\sqrt[3]{270}}{3} \div \frac{4\sqrt[3]{135}}{3} = \frac{8\sqrt[3]{2\times3\times3\times3\times5}}{3} \div \frac{4\sqrt[3]{3\times3\times3\times5}}{3} = \frac{8(3)\sqrt[3]{2\times5}}{3} \div \frac{4(3)\sqrt[3]{5}}{3} = 8\sqrt[3]{10} \div 4\sqrt[3]{5} = \frac{2\,8\sqrt[3]{10^2}}{1\,4\sqrt[3]{5}_1} = 2\sqrt[3]{2}$

⑤ Complete the chart to show simple interest and interest compounded annually.

Principal	Interest rate	Time, in years	Total amount of simple interest	Balance, compounded annually
$2500	5%	3	$i = \$2500(0.05)(3) = \$375$	$A = \$2500(1+0.05)^3$ $= \$2894.06$
$5,000	8%	5	$i = \$5000(0.08)(5) = \$2000$	$A = \$5000(1+0.08)^5$ $= \$7346.64$
$7500	10%	7	$i = \$7500(0.1)(7) = \$5250$	$A = \$7500(1+0.1)^7$ $= \$14,615.38$

⑥ Label the scale drawing to show a ratio of 3:7.
The large plane is $2\frac{4}{5}$ feet wide and 7 feet long.

$1\frac{1}{5}$ feet wide
3 feet long

$\frac{3}{7} = \frac{x}{2\frac{4}{5}} \Rightarrow 7x = 3\left(2\frac{4}{5}\right) \Rightarrow 7x = 3\left(\frac{14}{5}\right) \Rightarrow x = \frac{6}{5} = 1\frac{1}{5}$

$\frac{3}{7} = \frac{x}{7} \Rightarrow 7x = 21 \Rightarrow x = 3$

Probability, Odds

① Complete the chart to show probability and odds.

Scenario	Number of Possible Outcomes	Desired Event (E)	P(E)	Odds (in favor of E)	Odds (Against E)
Flipping a coin once	2	Tails	$P(E) = \frac{1}{2}$	1:1	1:1
Rolling a 6-sided die once	6	2	$P(E) = \frac{1}{6}$	1:5	5:1
Rolling a 6-sided die once	6	Odd number	$P(E) = \frac{3}{6} = \frac{1}{2}$	3:3 = 1:1	3:3 = 1:1
Rolling a 6-sided die once	6	Prime number (2, 3, 5)	$P(E) = \frac{3}{6} = \frac{1}{2}$	3:3 = 1:1	3:3 = 1:1
Choosing an integer from 1 to 25	25	10	$P(E) = \frac{1}{25}$	1:24	24:1
Choosing an integer from 1 to 25	25	Odd number	$P(E) = \frac{13}{25}$	13:12	12:13
Choosing an integer from 1 to 25	25	Multiple of 4	$P(E) = \frac{6}{25}$	6:19	19:6
Choosing an integer from 1 to 25	25	Prime number (2, 3, 5, 7, 11, 13, 17, 19, 23)	$P(E) = \frac{9}{25}$	9:16	16:9

Teaching Tips, Cont.

➤ Show the students two coins. Ask them to find the probability of getting heads on the first coin and tails on the second coin when the coins are each flipped once. ($\frac{1}{2} \times \frac{1}{2} = \frac{1}{4}$)

➤ Show the students three coins. Ask them to find the probability of getting heads on the first coin and tails on the other two coins when the coins are each flipped once. ($\frac{1}{2} \times \frac{1}{2} \times \frac{1}{2} = \frac{1}{8}$)

➤ Show students the entire pile of coins and ask them how they could determine the probability of getting heads on every coin with one flip of each coin. (The students should recognize the pattern from the previous examples and application of the multiplication principle of counting.)

➤ Teach finding combined probabilities from the teaching box, using the above coin problem as an example. Make sure all students understand how the multiplication principle of counting applies to this concept.

➤ Complete the Classwork exercises. Have one student work the problem on the board for the class and explain the answer. All students should work the problem in their books.

➤ Students may use a scientific calculator to complete the compound interest problems in part 5.

➤ If you plan to administer Exam 2 following Lesson 80 and Test 8, spend a few minutes reviewing for the Exam.

Assignment
• Complete Lesson 75, Activities 2-6.

203   Horizons Pre-Algebra, Teacher's Guide

Lesson 76

Concepts
- Permutations
- Least common multiple
- Single-variable equations
- Powers of 10
- Metric conversions
- Line graphs
- Math in the real world

Learning Objectives
The student will be able to:
- Define *permutation*
- Define *factorial*
- Calculate the factorial of a number
- Find the number of permutations possible from a given set of elements

Materials Needed
- Student Book, Lesson 76
- 1 each: penny, nickel, dime, quarter

Teaching Tips

➤ Ask students to write an expression showing the product of all integers from 1 to 4, inclusive. ($1 \times 2 \times 3 \times 4 = 24$)

➤ Ask students to write an expression showing the product of all integers from 1 to 10, inclusive. ($1 \times 2 \times 3 \times 4 \times 5 \times 6 \times 7 \times 8 \times 9 \times 10 = 3,628,800$)

➤ Teach the factorial symbol (!) as a shortened way of writing these expressions.

➤ Make sure all students understand that $0! = 1$. See the column at the right for more information.

Permutations

Permutations are ordered groups of elements taken from a given set. In the case of permutations, a different arrangement of the same elements is a different permutation. For example, when making 3-digit numbers from the digits 1 – 4, the number 243 is different from the number 324, and is therefore a different permutation.

To find the number of permutations possible from a given set of elements, use the formula

$$p(n,r) = \frac{n!}{(n-r)!}$$, where n is the number of elements in the set, and r is the number of elements you are arranging in each group. The symbol $n!$ is read "n factorial." This means to find the product of every number from 1 to n. Note: $0! = 1$.

How many different ways are there to arrange 4 of the digits 1 – 9?
$r = 4$; $n = 9$

$$p(9,4) = \frac{9!}{(9-4)!} = \frac{9 \times 8 \times 7 \times 6 \times 5!}{5!} = 3024$$

① Classwork
Solve.

How many different ways are there for Andy to arrange 3 of the 6 colors of wire?

$$p(6,3) = \frac{6!}{(6-3)!} = \frac{6 \times 5 \times 4 \times 3!}{3!} = 120$$

Andy has 11 sizes of wire. How many different ways are there for Andy to arrange the 11 sizes?

$$p(11,11) = \frac{11!}{(11-11)!} = \frac{11!}{0!} =$$

$$\frac{11!}{1} = 39,916,800$$

Activities
② Find the following permutations.

How many different ways are there to arrange 2 of 4 different colors?

$$p(4,2) = \frac{4!}{(4-2)!} = \frac{4!}{2!} = \frac{4 \times 3 \times 2!}{2!} = 12$$

A kitchen has a blender, toaster, mixer, coffee maker, and food processer on the counter. How many different ways can two of the appliances be plugged into a pair of outlets?

$$p(5,2) = \frac{5!}{(5-2)!} = \frac{5!}{3!} = \frac{5 \times 4 \times 3!}{3!} = 20$$

A slow cooker is added to the kitchen above. How many different ways can two of the six appliances be plugged into a pair of outlets?

$$p(6,2) = \frac{6!}{(6-2)!} = \frac{6!}{4!} = \frac{6 \times 5 \times 4!}{4!} = 30$$

Why does $0! = 1$?

Consider that $4! = 4 \times 3!$

Following this example, we can write an equation to say that $n! = n(n-1)!$

Since this equation is valid for all integers, let $n = 1$:
$1! = 1(1-1)!$
$1! = 1(0!)$
$1! = 0!$ Therefore $0! = 1$

Consider the problem P(3,3). Applying the formula for permutations, this gives the following equation:

$$P(3,3) = \frac{3!}{(3-3)!} = \frac{3!}{0!}$$

It is a mathematical fact that you cannot divide by zero. If $0! = 0$, this problem would not have a solution. However, we know that three items, such as the digits 1, 2, and 3, can be arranged as follows: 123, 132, 231, 213, 312, 321 for a total of 6 possible arrangements.

③ Find the least common multiple of each set of numbers.

20, 24, and 25

$20 = 2 \times 2 \times 5 = 2^2 \times 5$
$24 = 2 \times 2 \times 2 \times 3 = \boxed{2^3} \times \boxed{3}$
$25 = 5 \times 5 = \boxed{5^2}$
LCM: $2^3 \times 3 \times 5^2 = 600$

20, 25, and 30

$20 = 2 \times 2 \times 5 = \boxed{2^2} \times 5$
$25 = 5 \times 5 = \boxed{5^2}$
$30 = 2 \times \boxed{3} \times 5$
LCM: $2^2 \times 3 \times 5^2 = 300$

24, 25, and 30

$24 = 2 \times 2 \times 2 \times 3 = \boxed{2^3} \times 3$
$25 = 5 \times 5 = \boxed{5^2}$
$30 = 2 \times \boxed{3} \times 5$
LCM: $2^3 \times 3 \times 5^2 = 600$

④ Solve.

$8x + (11-8)^2 = 4(5-x)$
$8x + (3)^2 = 20 - 4x$
$8x + 9 = 20 - 4x$
$12x = 11$
$x = \dfrac{11}{12}$

$5x + 4(3-2x) = 4x - (3^3 - 2^2)$
$5x + 12 - 8x = 4x - 23$
$-3x + 12 = 4x - 23$
$-7x = -35$
$x = 5$

$4(3x-5) + \sqrt{2^3 + 3^2 - 1} = 5(2x+3)$
$12x - 20 + \sqrt{8+9-1} = 10x + 15$
$12x - 20 + \sqrt{16} = 10x + 15$
$12x - 20 + 4 = 10x + 15$
$12x - 16 = 10x + 15$
$2x = 31$
$x = \dfrac{31}{2}$

⑤ Multiply or divide by the correct power of 10 to complete the metric conversions.

23.4 mm = __0.0234__ m

0.07 mL = __0.00007__ L

0.5 cg = __0.005__ g

86.03 mW = __0.08603__ W

40,000 m = __4,000,000__ cm

2035 L = __2,035,000__ mL

901 W = __90,100__ cW

4.01 g = __4010__ mg

⑥ Draw a line graph.

The lake levels for Lake Travis in Texas were recorded on the same day each month for a year. The number of feet over 600 feet is: January: 55.27, February: 54.30, March: 54.36, April: 52.88, May: 52.9, June: 46.96, July: 39.03, August: 33.78, September: 30.44, October: 32.17, November: 48.62, December: 54.72.

Combinations of three of four coins.

There are 24: PND, PNQ, PDN, PDQ, PQN, PQD, NDQ, NDP, NQD, NQP, NPD, NPQ, DQP, DQN, DPN, DPQ, DNQ, DNP, QPN, QPD, QNP, QND, QDP, QDN

Teaching Tips, Cont.

➢ Have the students rewrite the above expressions using the factorial symbol. (4! = 24 and 10! = 3,628,800)

➢ Give a student the four coins and have them find all the different ways that three of the four coins can be arranged from left to right. (See the list at the left)

➢ Teach permutations from the teaching box. Introduce the formula for finding permutations as an application of the factorial.

➢ Write the following problem on the board: 10! ÷ 8! =
Ask students how to solve the above problem. (Some students may suggest 3,628,800 ÷ 40,320 = 90.) Show them that writing the problem as a fraction and canceling makes the problem much easier.
$\dfrac{10!}{8!} = \dfrac{10 \times 9 \times \cancel{8!}}{\cancel{8!}} = 10 \times 9 = 90$

➢ Show students how to apply this shortcut to the formula for permutations using the coin problem above.
$P(4,3) = \dfrac{4!}{(4-3)!} = \dfrac{4!}{1!} = 4! =$
$4 \times 3 \times 2 \times 1 = 24$

➢ Complete the Classwork exercises. Have some students work the problems on the board for the class and explain their answers. All students should work the problems in their books.

➢ If you plan to administer Exam 2 following Lesson 80 and Test 8, spend a few minutes reviewing for the Exam.

Assignment
• Complete Lesson 76, Activities 2-6.

Lesson 77

Concepts
- Combinations
- Divisibility tests
- Prime/composite numbers
- Single-variable equations
- Mean
- Median
- Mode
- Range
- Histogram
- Box-and-whisker plot
- Math in the real world

Learning Objectives
The student will be able to:
- Define *combination*
- Explain the difference between combinations and permutations
- Calculate the number of combinations from a given set of data

Materials Needed
- Student Book, Lesson 77

Teaching Tips
➤ Review permutations. (See Lesson 76.)

➤ Remind students that changing the order of the items produces a different permutation. Ask the students to think of situations in which the order does not matter. (Examples include ordering a meal at a restaurant, making change, items in a tossed salad, etc.)

➤ Point out that ordering a hamburger, fries, and a drink will give you the same meal as ordering fries, a hamburger, and a drink.

Combinations

Combinations are groups of elements taken from a given set. Recall that in the case of permutations, a different arrangement of the same elements is a different permutation. For combinations, the order makes no difference. The combination 243 is the same as the combination 324. Making a combination is simply choosing a number of elements from a set without regard to the order they are chosen.

To find the number of combinations possible from a given set of elements, use the formula

$C(n,k) = \dfrac{n!}{k!(n-k)!}$, where n is the number of elements in the set, and k is the number of elements you are choosing in each group.

How many different ways are there to choose 4 of the digits 1 – 9?
$k = 4$; $n = 9$

$C(9,4) = \dfrac{9!}{4!(9-4)!} = \dfrac{9 \times 8^2 \times 7 \times 6 \times 5!}{(4 \times 3 \times 2 \times 1)5!} =$

$9 \times 2 \times 7 = 644$

Notice that this is significantly less than the number of permutations calculated in Lesson 76.

① Classwork
Solve.

How many different ways are there for Andy to choose 3 of the 6 colors of wire?

$C(6,3) = \dfrac{6!}{3!(6-3)!} = \dfrac{6 \times 5 \times 4 \times 3!}{(3 \times 2 \times 1)3!} = 20$

Andy has 11 sizes of wire. How many different ways are there for Andy to choose 2 sizes?

$C(11,2) = \dfrac{11!}{2!(11-2)!} = \dfrac{11 \times 10^5 \times 9!}{2 \times 1(9!)} = 55$

Activities
② Find the following combinations.

How many different ways are there to choose 2 of 4 different colors?

$C(4,2) = \dfrac{4!}{2!(4-2)!} = \dfrac{4!}{2!(2!)} = \dfrac{4^2 \times 3 \times 2!}{2 \times 1(2!)} = 6$

A kitchen has a blender, toaster, mixer, coffee maker, and food processer on the counter. How many different combinations of two appliances can be plugged into a pair of outlets?

$C(5,2) = \dfrac{5!}{2!(5-2)!} = \dfrac{5 \times 4^2 \times 3!}{2 \times 1(3!)} = 10$

A slow cooker is added to the kitchen above. How many different combinations of two of the six appliances can be plugged into a pair of outlets?

$C(6,2) = \dfrac{6!}{2!(6-2)!} = \dfrac{6!}{2 \times 1(4!)} = \dfrac{6^3 \times 5 \times 4!}{2 \times 1(4!)} = 15$

③ Use the divisibility tests to identify each number as prime or composite.

375　Composite (5)　　　　383　Prime
379　Prime　　　　　　　385　Composite (5)
381　Composite (3)　　　　387　Composite (3, 9)

④ Solve.

$$\frac{4x}{5}+1=-7$$

$$\frac{4x}{5}=-8$$

$$\cancel{5}\left(\frac{4x}{\cancel{5}}\right)=5(-8)$$

$$4x=-40$$

$$x=-10$$

$$\frac{2x}{7}+1=3x+4$$

$$\frac{2x}{7}=3x+3$$

$$\cancel{7}\left(\frac{2x}{\cancel{7}}\right)=7(3x+3)$$

$$2x=21x+21$$

$$-19x=21$$

$$x=-\frac{21}{19}=-1\frac{2}{19}$$

$$\frac{3x-1}{4}-6=5x-2$$

$$\frac{3x-1}{4}=5x+4$$

$$\cancel{4}\left(\frac{3x-1}{\cancel{4}}\right)=4(5x+4)$$

$$3x-1=20x+16$$

$$-17x=17$$

$$x=-1$$

⑤ Find the mean, median, mode, and range. Then draw a histogram and a box-and-whisker plot.

Football scores one Saturday were 14, 0, 7, 26, 13, 27, 36, 37, 24, 7, 7, 31, 20, 19, 24, 27, 17, 10, 31, 24, 24, 27, 41, 34, 16, 13.

Mean: 556 ÷ 26 = 21.4　　　　Minimum: 0
Median: 24　　　　　　　　Maximum: 41
Mode: 24　　　　　　　　　First quartile: 13
Range: 41 − 0 = 41　　　　Third quartile: 27

Football Scores

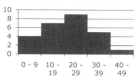

Teaching Tips, Cont.

> Teach combinations from the teaching box. Emphasize that combinations are for situations when the order does not matter—just the particular combination. Refer to the example of the hamburger, fries, and drink. Permutations are used when the order is important, such as numbers for addresses. The house at 123 Baker Street is different from the house at 132 Baker Street.

> Teach the formula for calculating combinations. Point out the similarities and differences between this formula and the formula for finding permutations.

> Complete the Classwork exercises. Have some students work the problems on the board for the class and explain their answers. All students should work the problems in their books.

> If you plan to administer Exam 2 following Lesson 80 and Test 8, spend a few minutes reviewing for the Exam.

Assignment

• Complete Lesson 77, Activities 2-5

Lesson 78

Concepts
- Mutually exclusive events
- Least common multiple
- Scientific notation
- Permutations
- Combinations
- Math in the real world

Learning Objectives
The student will be able to:
- Define *mutually exclusive events*
- Identify mutually exclusive events in a given scenario
- Write probability expressions for mutually exclusive events
- Calculate the probability of one of two mutually exclusive events occurring

Materials Needed
- Student Book, Lesson 78
- Worksheet 39

Teaching Tips
➤ Have students complete Worksheet 39 in class. This may be for added practice of earlier topics, or graded as a quiz, if desired.

➤ Review probability. (See Lesson 70.)

➤ Give students the following scenario: You are rolling 5 dice in a game. After two tries, you have two 4's and two 5's. You need a 4 or a 5 on your third roll to score a full house (2 of one number and 3 of a different number). What is the probability of rolling a 4 on your next turn? ($\frac{1}{6}$) What is the probability of rolling a 5 on your next turn? ($\frac{1}{6}$)

Mutually Exclusive Events

Mutually exclusive events are events that cannot happen at the same time, such as a die landing on both 4 and 5. The probability of one of two mutually exclusive events X and Y occurring is given by the formula $P(X \cup Y) = P(X) + P(Y)$, where $P(X \cup Y)$ means, "the probability of X or Y occurring."

After rolling 5 dice in a game, you have two 4's and two 5's and one die to roll again. What is the probability that you will roll a 4 or a 5 on your next roll?
$P(4 \cup 5) = P(4) + P(5)$

$P(4) = \frac{1}{6}$ $\qquad P(5) = \frac{1}{6}$

$P(4 \cup 5) = \frac{1}{6} + \frac{1}{6} = \frac{2}{6} = \frac{1}{3}$

If the two events can happen at the same time, such as being a 7th grader and a girl, the events are not mutually exclusive. In this case, the formula is $P(X \cup Y) = P(X) + P(Y) - P(X \cap Y)$, where $P(X \cap Y)$ is the probability of X and Y both occurring at the same time.

The math club has 12 7th graders and 13 8th graders. There are 15 boys and 10 girls in the club, and 4 of the girls are in the 7th grade. If all 25 students are entered into a random drawing, what is the probability that the winner will be in 7th grade or a girl?

$P(\text{7th grade} \cup \text{girl}) = \frac{12}{25} + \frac{10}{25} - \frac{4}{25} = \frac{18}{25}$

① Classwork
Solve.

Andy has red, white, black, green, orange, and brown wire in his truck. What is the probability that a color chosen at random will be white?

$P(\text{white}) = \frac{1}{6}$

What is the probability that a color chosen at random will be black?

$P(\text{black}) = \frac{1}{6}$

What is the probability a color chosen at random will be white or black?

$P(\text{white} \cup \text{black}) = \frac{1}{6} + \frac{1}{6} = \frac{2}{6} = \frac{1}{3}$

Activities
② Solve.
A school band has 40 woodwind players, 50 brass players, and 10 percussion players. There are 15 8th graders playing woodwind instruments, 25 8th graders playing brass instruments, and 8 8th graders playing percussion instruments. The remaining players are 7th graders. What is the probability that a player chosen at random is in 8th grade or plays a woodwind instrument?

$P(\text{8th grade} \cup \text{woodwind}) = \frac{48}{100} + \frac{40}{100} - \frac{15}{100} = \frac{73}{100}$

③ Find the least common multiple of each set of numbers.

25, 28, and 30
$25 = 5 \times 5 = \boxed{5^2}$
$28 = 2 \times 2 \times 7 = \boxed{2^2} \times \boxed{7}$
$30 = 2 \times \boxed{3} \times 5$
LCM: $2^2 \times 3 \times 5^2 \times 7 = 2100$

25, 30, and 35
$25 = 5 \times 5 = \boxed{5^2}$
$30 = \boxed{2} \times \boxed{3} \times 5$
$35 = 5 \times \boxed{7}$
LCM: $2 \times 3 \times 5^2 \times 7 = 1050$

28, 30, and 35
$28 = 2 \times 2 \times 7 = \boxed{2^2} \times \boxed{7}$
$30 = 2 \times \boxed{3} \times 5$
$35 = \boxed{5} \times 7$
LCM: $2^2 \times 3 \times 5 \times 7 = 420$

④ Complete the chart to show proper conversion between scientific notation and standard form.

Scientific notation	Standard form
2.87×10^6	2,870,000
5.06019×10^{-7}	0.000000506019

Standard form	Scientific notation
384,210,000,000	3.8421×10^{11}
0.0000000006108	6.108×10^{-10}

⑤ Calculate the permutations and combinations.

$p(5,2) = \frac{5!}{(5-2)!} = \frac{5 \times 4 \times 3!}{3!} = 20$

$p(5,3) = \frac{5!}{(5-3)!} = \frac{5 \times 4 \times 3 \times 2!}{2!} = 60$

$p(5,4) = \frac{5!}{(5-4)!} = \frac{5 \times 4 \times 3 \times 2 \times 1!}{1!} = 120$

$p(6,2) = \frac{6!}{(6-2)!} = \frac{6 \times 5 \times 4!}{4!} = 30$

$p(6,3) = \frac{6!}{(6-3)!} = \frac{6 \times 5 \times 4 \times 3!}{3!} = 120$

$p(6,4) = \frac{6!}{(6-4)!} = \frac{6 \times 5 \times 4 \times 3 \times 2!}{2!} = 360$

$p(6,5) = \frac{6!}{(6-5)!} = \frac{6 \times 5 \times 4 \times 3 \times 2 \times 1!}{1!} = 720$

$C(5,2) = \frac{5!}{(5-2)!} = \frac{5 \times 4 \times 3!}{2!(3!)} = \frac{5 \times 4^2 \times 3!}{2 \times 1 (3!)} = 10$

$C(5,3) = \frac{5!}{3!(5-3)!} = \frac{5 \times 4 \times 3 \times 2!}{3!(2!)} = \frac{5 \times 4^2 \times 3 \times 2!}{3 \times 2 \times 1 (2!)} = 10$

$C(5,4) = \frac{5!}{4!(5-4)!} = \frac{5 \times 4 \times 3 \times 2 \times 1!}{4 \times 3 \times 2 \times 1 (1!)} = 5$

$C(6,2) = \frac{6!}{2!(6-2)!} = \frac{6 \times 5 \times 4!}{2!(4!)} = \frac{{}^3 6 \times 5 \times 4!}{2 \times 1 (4!)} = 15$

$C(6,3) = \frac{6!}{3!(6-3)!} = \frac{6 \times 5 \times 4 \times 3!}{3!(3!)} = \frac{6 \times 5 \times 4 \times 3!}{3 \times 2 \times 1 (3!)} = 20$

$C(6,4) = \frac{6!}{4!(6-4)!} = \frac{6 \times 5 \times 4 \times 3 \times 2!}{4!(2!)} = \frac{6 \times 5 \times 4 \times 3 \times 2!}{4 \times 3 \times 2 \times 1 (2!)} = 15$

$C(6,5) = \frac{6!}{5!(6-5)!} = \frac{6 \times 5!}{5!(1!)} = 6$

⑥ Solve.
A basketball team has ten players. How many different combinations are there for a 5-player starting line-up?

$C(10,5) = \frac{10!}{5!(10-5)!} = \frac{10!}{5!(5!)} = \frac{{}^2 10 \times 9 \times 8^2 \times 7 \times 6 \times 5!}{5 \times 4 \times 3 \times 2 \times 1 (5!)} = 252$

① Find the probabilities.
In each of the following questions, game dice refer to standard 6-sided game dice.

What is the probability of rolling a 4 on one roll of one die?

$P(4) = \frac{1}{6}$

What is the probability of rolling two 4's on one roll of two dice?

$P(\text{two 4's}) = \frac{1}{6} \times \frac{1}{6} = \frac{1}{36}$

What is the probability of rolling all odd numbers on one roll of 3 dice?

$P(\text{all odd}) = \frac{3}{6} \times \frac{3}{6} \times \frac{3}{6} = \frac{1}{2} \times \frac{1}{2} \times \frac{1}{2} = \frac{1}{8}$

What is the probability of rolling five 3's on one roll of five dice?

$P(\text{all 3's}) = \frac{1}{6} \times \frac{1}{6} \times \frac{1}{6} \times \frac{1}{6} \times \frac{1}{6} = \frac{1}{7776}$

If you roll a 2, 3, 4, and 5 with four dice, what is the probability that a fifth die will be a 1 or 6?

$P(1 \text{ or } 6) = \frac{2}{6} = \frac{1}{3}$

What is the probability of rolling 5 dice and getting numbers whose sum is 3?

$P(\text{sum of 3}) = 0$ (The minimum sum of 5 dice is $1 + 1 + 1 + 1 + 1 = 5$.)

What is the probability of rolling a single die three times and getting an odd number on the first roll, an even number on the second roll, and a prime number on the third roll?

$P(\text{odd, even, prime}) = \frac{3}{6} \times \frac{3}{6} \times \frac{3}{6} = \frac{1}{2} \times \frac{1}{2} \times \frac{1}{2} = \frac{1}{8}$

If you roll two dice, what is the probability of getting numbers whose sum is 7?
There are 36 possible combinations (6 × 6). The combinations whose sum is 7 are $1 + 6$, $2 + 5$, $3 + 4$, $4 + 3$, $5 + 2$, and $6 + 1$.
$P(\text{sum of 7}) = \frac{6}{36} = \frac{1}{6}$

Teaching Tips, Cont.

➢ Ask the students if it is possible to roll both a 4 and a 5 on the next roll of 1 die. (No.)

➢ Explain that rolling a 4 and rolling a 5 are mutually exclusive events since it is impossible for both events to happen at the same time. In this case, the probability of getting a full house is not $\frac{1}{6}$.

➢ Teach how to find the probability of mutually exclusive events. The teaching box solves the dice-rolling problem you have presented to the students.

➢ Complete the Classwork exercises. Have some students work the problems on the board for the class and explain their answers. All students should work the problems in their books.

➢ If you plan to administer Exam 2 following Lesson 80 and Test 8, spend a few minutes reviewing for the Exam.

Assignment
• Complete Lesson 78, Activities 2-6.

Lesson 79

Concepts
- Independent events
- Dependent events
- Single-variable inequalities
- Probability
- Odds
- Permutations
- Combinations
- Math in the real world

Learning Objectives
The student will be able to:
- Define *independent events*
- Define *dependent events*
- Identify scenarios as independent or dependent
- Calculate probabilities of dependent events

Materials Needed
- Student Book, Lesson 79
- Set of double-6 dominoes

Teaching Tips
➤ Review probabilities. (See Lesson 70.)

➤ Review mutually exclusive events. (See Lesson 78.)

➤ Refer students to the full house dice-rolling example in Lesson 78. Ask the students if the outcome of the roll of one die affects the outcome of a re-roll of that die or the roll of a different die. (No.) Explain that this is an example of independent events.

➤ Show the students the set of dominoes. Ask them what the probability is of drawing the double 6. ($\frac{1}{28}$)

Independent and Dependent Events

Lesson 75 dealt with the combined probabilities of **independent events** – events whose outcomes do not depend on the outcome of a different event. When the outcome of an event is affected by the outcome of a different event, it is called a **dependent event**. The probability of the second event must be adjusted to reflect the outcome of the prior event.

A set of double-six dominoes has 28 dominoes. If you randomly select two dominoes, what is the probability of drawing the double 6 and the double 5?

$$P(\text{double 6} \cup \text{double 5}) = \frac{1}{28} + \frac{1}{28} = \frac{1}{14}$$

$$P(\text{the remaining double}) = \frac{1}{27}$$

$$P(\text{double 6})P(\text{double 5}) = \frac{1}{14}\left(\frac{1}{27}\right) = \frac{1}{378}$$

Notice that for the first draw, there are two possible acceptable outcomes. For the second draw, the denominator changed from 28 to 27. After the first domino has been chosen, there are only 27 dominos left from which to choose.

① Classwork.
Identify each scenario as independent or dependent and solve.

Andy has red, white, black, green, orange, and brown wire in his truck. What is the probability that two colors chosen at random will be white and black?
Dependent
$$P(\text{white} \cup \text{black})P(\text{the other color}) =$$
$$\left(\frac{1}{6} + \frac{1}{6}\right)\left(\frac{1}{5}\right) = \frac{1}{3}\left(\frac{1}{5}\right) = \frac{1}{15}$$

Andy has red, white, black, green, orange, and brown wire in his truck. He needs black wire, but accidentally grabs red wire. If he puts the red wire back, what is the probability that he will pull the black wire on the second try?
Independent
$$P(\text{black}) = \frac{1}{6}$$
All 6 colors are available for the second pull, so it is an independent event.

Activities
② Identify each scenario as independent or dependent and solve.

Andy has red, white, black, green, orange, and brown wire in his truck. If he needs red, white, and black for his current project, what is the probability that three colors chosen at random will be the three correct colors?
Dependent
$$P(\text{red} \cup \text{white} \cup \text{black})P(\text{remaining 2})P(\text{remaining 1}) = \frac{3}{6}\left(\frac{2}{5}\right)\left(\frac{1}{4}\right) = \frac{1}{20}$$

A standard game die is rolled 3 times. What is the probability that the first roll will be an even number, the second roll will be an odd number, and the third roll will be a 4?
Independent
$$P(\text{even}) = \frac{3}{6} = \frac{1}{2} \qquad P(\text{odd}) = \frac{3}{6} = \frac{1}{2} \qquad P(4) = \frac{1}{6}$$
$$P(\text{even})P(\text{odd})P(4) = \frac{1}{2}\left(\frac{1}{2}\right)\left(\frac{1}{6}\right) = \frac{1}{24}$$

---

③ Solve.

$$\frac{3x}{5} + 1 < -8$$

$$\frac{3x}{5} < -9$$

$$\not{5}\left(\frac{3x}{\not{5}}\right) < 5(-9)$$

$$3x < -45$$

$$x < -15$$

$$\frac{3x}{7} + 2 < 5x + 4$$

$$\frac{3x}{7} < 5x + 2$$

$$\not{7}\left(\frac{3x}{\not{7}}\right) < 7(5x + 2)$$

$$3x < 35x + 14$$

$$-32x < 14$$

$$-x < \frac{14}{32}$$

$$x > -\frac{7}{16}$$

$$\frac{5x-4}{2} - 7 > 4x - 3$$

$$\frac{5x-4}{2} > 4x + 4$$

$$\not{2}\left(\frac{5x-4}{\not{2}}\right) > 2(4x+4)$$

$$5x - 4 > 8x + 8$$

$$-3x > 12$$

$$-x > 4$$

$$x < -4$$

④ Calculate the probabilities and odds.
A board game rule states that if you roll doubles three times in a row, you will lose a turn. What is the probability that you will roll doubles three times in a row using standard game dice? What are the odds?

$$p(\text{doubles}) = \frac{6}{36} = \frac{1}{6}$$

$$p(\text{doubles})\,p(\text{doubles})\,p(\text{doubles}) = \frac{1}{6}\left(\frac{1}{6}\right)\left(\frac{1}{6}\right) = \frac{1}{216}$$

Odds of rolling doubles 3 times in a row are 1:215

⑤ Calculate the permutations and combinations.
A basketball team has ten players. How many different ways are there to announce a 5-player starting line-up?

$$p(10,5) = \frac{10!}{(10-5)!} = \frac{10!}{(5!)} = \frac{10 \times 9 \times 8 \times 7 \times 6 \times \not{5!}}{\not{5!}} = 30,240$$

Andy has 15 electrical projects to complete this week. If he completes three projects each day, how many different combinations of three projects will he have on each day, Monday – Friday?

$$C(15,3) = \frac{15!}{3!(15-3)!} = \frac{15!}{3!(12!)} = \frac{\overset{5}{\not{15}} \times \overset{7}{\not{14}} \times 13 \times \not{12!}}{\not{3} \times \not{2} \times 1(\not{12!})} = 5 \times 7 \times 13 = 455 \text{ on Monday.}$$

$$C(12,3) = \frac{12!}{3!(12-3)!} = \frac{12!}{3!(9!)} = \frac{\overset{2}{\not{12}} \times 11 \times 10 \times \not{9!}}{\not{3} \times \not{2} \times 1(\not{9!})} = 2 \times 11 \times 10 = 220 \text{ on Tuesday.}$$

$$C(9,3) = \frac{9!}{3!(9-3)!} = \frac{9!}{3!(6!)} = \frac{\overset{3}{\not{9}} \times \overset{4}{\not{8}} \times 7 \times \not{6!}}{\not{3} \times \not{2} \times 1(\not{6!})} = 3 \times 4 \times 7 = 84 \text{ on Wednesday.}$$

$$C(6,3) = \frac{6!}{3!(6-3)!} = \frac{6!}{3!(3!)} = \frac{\not{6} \times 5 \times 4 \times \not{3!}}{\not{3} \times \not{2} \times 1(\not{3!})} = 5 \times 4 = 20 \text{ on Thursday.}$$

$$C(3,3) = \frac{3!}{3!(3-3)!} = \frac{3!}{3!(0!)} = \frac{\not{3!}}{\not{3!}(1)} = \frac{1}{0} = 1 \text{ on Friday.}$$

Teaching Tips, Cont.

➢ Ask the students to find the probability of drawing the double 6 OR the double 5 on the first draw. ($\frac{1}{28} + \frac{1}{28} = \frac{1}{14}$) Make sure students understand that these are independent events on the first draw.

➢ Ask the students how many dominoes remain after the first domino is drawn. (27) Have the students find the probability of drawing the double 5 as the second domino if the double 6 is drawn first. ($\frac{1}{27}$) Ask the students if this is an independent or dependent event. (Dependent: It depends on the double 6 being drawn first.) Explain to the students that the probability of the double 6 and double 5 dominoes both being drawn as the first two dominoes is a dependent event.

➢ Teach finding the probability of dependent events from the teaching box. The teaching box solves the domino problem you have presented to the students.

➢ Complete the Classwork exercises. Have some students work the problems on the board for the class and explain their answers. All students should work the problems in their books.

➢ If you plan to administer Exam 2 following Lesson 80 and Test 8, spend a few minutes reviewing for the Exam.

Assignment
• Complete Lesson 79, Activities 2-5.

Lesson 80

Concepts
- Expected value
- Percent
- Simple interest
- Compound interest
- Probability
- Math in the real world

Learning Objectives
The student will be able to:
- Define *expected value*
- Calculate the expected value of a given scenario
- Apply expected value to real life situations
- Use expected value to make good stewardship decisions

Materials Needed
- Student Book, Lesson 80
- Worksheet 40
- Scientific calculator

Teaching Tips
➤ Review probability and independent/dependent events. (See Lessons 70, 75, and 79.)

➤ Explain that while probability gives information about each specific possible outcome, sometimes it is more helpful to know what outcome to expect.

➤ Introduce expected value. Explain that expected value is not a probability, but the average of all probable outcomes after several repetitions of the same experiment.

➤ Teach how to calculate the expected value.

Expected Value

The **expected value** of a random variable is the weighted average of the possible outcomes. It is an indication of what you could expect the average outcome to be after performing the same experiment numerous times.

To calculate the expected value, make an expected value chart. List the possible outcomes, x, in the first column, the probability of each of the possible outcomes, $P(x)$, in the second column, and the product of the possible outcomes and their respective probabilities in the third column. Add the values in the last column to get the expected value.

Find the expected value of rolling a standard game die.

x	$P(x)$	$xP(x)$
1	$\frac{1}{6}$	$1\left(\frac{1}{6}\right)=\frac{1}{6}$
2	$\frac{1}{6}$	$2\left(\frac{1}{6}\right)=\frac{1}{3}$
3	$\frac{1}{6}$	$3\left(\frac{1}{6}\right)=\frac{1}{2}$
4	$\frac{1}{6}$	$4\left(\frac{1}{6}\right)=\frac{2}{3}$
5	$\frac{1}{6}$	$5\left(\frac{1}{6}\right)=\frac{5}{6}$
6	$\frac{1}{6}$	$6\left(\frac{1}{6}\right)=1$

Add the values in the last column, looking for fractions that add to whole numbers to simplify the addition.

$\frac{1}{6}+\frac{1}{3}+\frac{1}{2}+\frac{2}{3}+\frac{5}{6}+1=3\frac{1}{2}$

The does not mean that you can expect to roll a 3.5 on the die. This number does not exist! This means that the *average* of all the numbers you roll, after many rolls, will be about 3.5.

① Classwork
Find the expected value.

A game of chance costs $1 to play. A player selects three numbers, each of which must be from the set 0 – 9, and the same number may be used more than once. If a player matches all three numbers, he wins $100, otherwise he loses his dollar. What is the expected value of the winnings from repeated playing? Is it a wise idea to play this game? Why or why not?

x	$P(x)$	$xP(x)$
Win: $100	$\frac{1}{10}\left(\frac{1}{10}\right)\left(\frac{1}{10}\right)=\frac{1}{1000}$	$\$100\left(\frac{1}{1000}\right)=\$0.10$
Lose: -$1	$1-\frac{1}{1000}=\frac{999}{1000}$	$-\$1\left(\frac{999}{1000}\right)=-\$0.999$

The expected value is ($0.10) – ($0.999) = -$0.899 = -$0.90

A player can expect to average a loss of 90¢ each time he plays this game. Any time the expected value is negative, the game is not considered fair. A fair game is one whose expected value is zero, which means neither side has an unfair advantage.

Activities
② Calculate the expected value.
The school basketball team plays 0, 1, 2, or 3 games in a week. The probability of playing no games is 10%, the probability of playing 1 game is 25%, the probability of playing 2 games is 60%, and the probability of playing 3 games is 5%. What is the expected value of the number of games played each week?

x	$P(x)$	$xP(x)$
0	0.10	0
1	0.25	0.25
2	0.60	1.2
3	0.05	0.15

0 + 0.25 + 1.2 + 0.15 = 1.6
The average number of games is 1.6.

---

③ Solve.

What is 35% of 400?
$x = 0.35(400)$
$x = 140$

What is 0.6% of 300?
$x = 0.006(300)$
$x = 1.8$

What is 224% of 500?
$x = 2.24(500)$
$x = 1120$

17 is what percent of 85?
$17 = 85x$
$x = \frac{17}{85}$
$x = \frac{1}{5} = 20\%$

20 is what percent of 740?
$20 = 740x$
$x = \frac{20}{740}$
$x = \frac{1}{37} = 0.\overline{027} = 2.\overline{702}\%$

336 is what percent of 42?
$336 = 42x$
$x = \frac{336}{42}$
$x = 8 = 800\%$

27 is 90% of what number?
$27 = 0.9x$
$x = 27 \div 0.9$
$x = 30$

6 is 0.08% of what number?
$6 = 0.0008x$
$x = 6 \div 0.0008$
$x = 7500$

138 is 150% of what number?
$138 = 1.5x$
$x = 138 \div 1.5$
$x = 92$

④ Complete the chart to show simple interest and interest compounded annually.

Principal	Interest rate	Time, in years	Total amount of simple interest	Balance, compounded annually
$3000	6%	4	$i = \$3000(0.06)(4) = \$720$	$A = \$3000(1+0.06)^4$ $= \$3787.43$
$7,000	9%	7	$I = \$7000(0.09)(7) = \$4410$	$A = \$7000(1+0.09)^7$ $= \$12,796.27$
$9000	12%	10	$i = \$9000(0.12)(10) = \$10,800$	$A = \$9000(1+0.12)^{10}$ $= \$27,952.63$

⑤ Solve.
When Andy teaches Children's Church, he gives each child one crayon from a box of crayons. If the box has 10 each of 4 different colors, what is the probability that each of the 8 children in Andy's class will receive a red crayon if all crayons are pulled at random?
Number of red crayons: 10   Number of crayons in the box: 40
p(8 children receiving red crayons) =

$\frac{10}{40}\left(\frac{9}{39}\right)\left(\frac{8}{38}\right)\left(\frac{7}{37}\right)\left(\frac{6}{36}\right)\left(\frac{5}{35}\right)\left(\frac{4}{34}\right)\left(\frac{3}{33}\right) = \frac{1}{4}\left(\frac{3}{13}\right)\left(\frac{4}{19}\right)\left(\frac{7}{37}\right)\left(\frac{1}{6}\right)\left(\frac{1}{7}\right)\left(\frac{2}{17}\right)\left(\frac{1}{11}\right) = \frac{1}{1,708,993}$

① Complete the charts to find the expected value.

A game of chance costs $1 to play. A player selects five unique numbers from the set 1 – 39. If a player matches two to five of the selected numbers, he wins according to the chart below. Otherwise he loses his dollar. What is the expected value of the winnings? Is it a wise idea to play this game? Why or why not? (Keep in mind that multiple players matching all 5 numbers must split the highest prize amount.)

x	$P(x)$	$xP(x)$
Match 5: $50,000	$\left(\frac{5}{39}\right)\left(\frac{4}{38}\right)\left(\frac{3}{37}\right)\left(\frac{2}{36}\right)\left(\frac{1}{35}\right) = \frac{1}{575,757}$	$50,000\left(\frac{1}{575,757}\right) = \$0.09$
Match 4: $128	$\left(\frac{5}{39}\right)\left(\frac{4}{38}\right)\left(\frac{3}{37}\right)\left(\frac{2}{36}\right) = \frac{5}{82,251} = \frac{35}{575,757}$	$128\left(\frac{5}{82,251}\right) = \$0.01$
Match 3: $8	$\left(\frac{5}{39}\right)\left(\frac{4}{38}\right)\left(\frac{3}{37}\right) = \frac{10}{9139} = \frac{630}{575,757}$	$8\left(\frac{10}{9139}\right) = \$0.01$
Match 2: $1	$\left(\frac{5}{39}\right)\left(\frac{4}{38}\right) = \frac{10}{741} = \frac{7770}{575,757}$	$1\left(\frac{10}{741}\right) = \$0.01$
Lose: -$1	$1 - \left(\frac{1}{575,757} + \frac{35}{575,757} + \frac{630}{575,757} + \frac{7770}{575,757}\right) = \frac{567,321}{575,757}$	$-\$1\left(\frac{567,321}{575,757}\right) = -\$0.99$

The expected value is $0.09 + $0.01 + $0.01 + $0.01 – $0.99 = -$0.87
A player can expect to average a loss of 87¢ each time he plays this game. Therefore, it is not a wise idea to play this game.

When there is no winner for a drawing, the prize values increase. After 5 consecutive days of no winners, the prize values had increased according to the chart below. Find the expected value of the current drawing. Is it a wise idea to play this game now? Why or why not? (Keep in mind that multiple players matching all 5 numbers must split the highest prize amount.)

x	$P(x)$	$xP(x)$
Match 5: $750,000	$\left(\frac{5}{39}\right)\left(\frac{4}{38}\right)\left(\frac{3}{37}\right)\left(\frac{2}{36}\right)\left(\frac{1}{35}\right) = \frac{1}{575,757}$	$750,000\left(\frac{1}{575,757}\right) = \$1.30$
Match 4: $181	$\left(\frac{5}{39}\right)\left(\frac{4}{38}\right)\left(\frac{3}{37}\right)\left(\frac{2}{36}\right) = \frac{5}{82,251} = \frac{35}{575,757}$	$181\left(\frac{5}{82,251}\right) = \$0.01$
Match 3: $9	$\left(\frac{5}{39}\right)\left(\frac{4}{38}\right)\left(\frac{3}{37}\right) = \frac{10}{9139} = \frac{630}{575,757}$	$9\left(\frac{10}{9139}\right) = \$0.01$
Match 2: $1	$\left(\frac{5}{39}\right)\left(\frac{4}{38}\right) = \frac{10}{741} = \frac{7770}{575,757}$	$1\left(\frac{10}{741}\right) = \$0.01$
Lose: -$1	$1 - \left(\frac{1}{575,757} + \frac{35}{575,757} + \frac{630}{575,757} + \frac{7770}{575,757}\right) = \frac{567,321}{575,757}$	$-\$1\left(\frac{567,321}{575,757}\right) = -\$0.99$

The expected value is $1.30 + $0.01 + $0.01 + $0.01 – $0.99 = $0.34
A player can expect to average a gain of 34¢ each time he plays this game. However, it is still not a wise idea to play. Note that a player who spent $575,757 to purchase one ticket of every possible number combination would be guaranteed to win the highest payout amount, in addition to the other winning combinations. Also, a player will only win the highest amount if he is the only winner for the drawing. Multiple winners must split the highest amount. This makes purchasing 575,757 tickets a bad idea because your actual winnings may be much lower.

Note Regarding Lottery Examples

The lottery examples are not given to promote the lottery, but rather to teach the students that playing the lottery is poor stewardship. Take this opportunity to teach the students about using the resources God has given them in a way that would be honoring and pleasing to Him. This does not just include their money and financial matters, but every aspect of their lives. Encourage the students to think of other areas of their lives that God expects good stewardship. (Talents and abilities – including academic, athletic, musical – and spiritual gifts)

So whether you eat or drink or whatever you do, do it all for the glory of God.

1 Corinthians 10:31

Teaching Tips, Cont.

➢ Explain that expected value is useful in determining whether or not a game is fair. When money must be paid for a chance at winning, the game is only considered fair if the expected value is 0. If the expected value is negative, then you can expect to lose, even after repeated plays. If the expected value is positive, you can expect to win after repeated plays. Any time the expected value is negative, it is not good stewardship to play.

➢ Explain that lottery games have a negative expected value. The games are rigged in favor of the lottery company. This is how states that fund scholarships through a lottery know they will have money to pay for them. While there is almost always a winner in every lottery, the amount of money lost by the non-winners far exceeds the amount won by the winners.

➢ Complete the Classwork exercise. Have one student work the problem on the board for the class and explain the answer. All students should work the problem in their books.

➢ Students may use a scientific calculator to complete the compound interest problems in part 5 as well as Worksheet 40.

➢ Draw students' attention to Worksheet 40. Point out that these problems involve the probability of dependent events.

➢ If you plan to administer Exam 2, spend a few minutes reviewing.

Assignments
- Complete Lesson 80, Activities 2-5.
- Worksheet 40
- Study for Test 8 (Lessons 68-77)

Test 8

Testing Objectives
The student will:
- Draw histograms
- List 5-number summaries
- Draw box-and-whisker plots
- Draw a line graph
- Calculate probability
- Calculate odds in favor
- Calculate odds against
- Calculate permutations
- Calculate combinations
- Calculate combined probabilities
- Draw a bar graph

Materials Needed
- Test 8
- *It's College Test Prep Time!* from the Student Book
- *A Math Minute with…* Mike L. from the Student Book

Teaching Tips
➢ Administer Test 8, allowing the students 30-40 minutes to complete the test.

➢ When all students are finished taking the test, introduce *It's College Test Prep Time* from the student book. This page may be completed in class or assigned as homework.

---

① For each set of numbers, draw a histogram, list the 5-number summary, and draw a box-and-whisker plot.   **14 points**

50, 53, 64, 69, 90, 52, 24, 18, 47, 16, 84, 70, 69, 20, 36, 38, 68, 26, 49, 88

60, 58, 23, 65, 48, 54, 46, 76, 66, 39, 48, 60, 63, 43, 78, 56, 12, 60, 62, 42, 51, 59, 77, 52, 83

Minimum value: 16
Maximum value: 90
Median: 51
First quartile: 31
Third quartile: 69
The 5-number summary is 16, 31, 51, 69, and 90.

Minimum value: 12
Maximum value: 83
Median: 58
First quartile: 47
Third quartile: 64
The 5-number summary is 12, 47, 58, 64, and 83.

② Draw a line graph.   **14 points**
Draw a line graph showing the average low temperatures in Honolulu. The average low temperature, in degrees Fahrenheit, for each month is as follows:
January: 66, February: 65, March: 67, April: 70, May: 70, June: 72, July: 74, August: 75, September: 74, October: 73, November: 71, December: 68.
Graphs must have a title, labels on both axes, and all 12 months plotted.

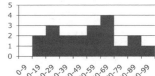

③ Complete the chart to show probability and odds.   **12 points**

Scenario	Number of Possible Outcomes	Desired Event (E)	P(E)	Odds (in favor of E)	Odds (Against E)
Flip a coin once	2	Heads	$P(E) = \frac{1}{2}$	1:1	1:1
Roll a 6-sided die once	6	Odd number	$P(E) = \frac{3}{6} = \frac{1}{2}$	1:1	1:1
Choose an integer from 1 to 10	10	Prime number (2, 3, 5, 7)	$P(E) = \frac{4}{10} = \frac{2}{5}$	2:3	3:2

---

④ Calculate the permutations and combinations.   **8 points**

$p(7,3) = \frac{7!}{(7-3)!} = \frac{7 \times 6 \times 5 \times 4!}{4!} = 210$

$C(7,3) = \frac{7!}{3!(7-3)!} = \frac{7 \times 6 \times 5 \times 4!}{(3 \times 2 \times 1)(4!)} = 35$

$p(4,2) = \frac{4!}{(4-2)!} = \frac{4 \times 3 \times 2!}{2!} = 12$

$C(4,2) = \frac{4!}{2!(4-2)!} = \frac{4^2 \times 3 \times 2!}{(2 \times 1)(2!)} = 6$

$p(6,3) = \frac{6!}{(6-3)!} = \frac{6 \times 5 \times 4 \times 3!}{3!} = 120$

$C(6,3) = \frac{6!}{3!(6-3)!} = \frac{6 \times 5 \times 4 \times 3!}{(3 \times 2 \times 1)(3!)} = 20$

$p(8,2) = \frac{8!}{(8-2)!} = \frac{8 \times 7 \times 6!}{6!} = 56$

$C(8,2) = \frac{8!}{2!(8-2)!} = \frac{8^4 \times 7 \times 6!}{(2 \times 1)(6!)} = 28$

⑤ Solve.   **4 points**
A card game has 4 different colors of cards and 14 different numbers on the cards. How many combinations are possible with one color and one number?
4 × 14 = 56 different color-number combinations
A school has 3 different choices for shirt color, 2 different choices for pant color, and 3 different choices for sweater color for the school uniform. How many different uniform combinations are possible?
3 × 2 × 3 = 18 different uniform combinations
You roll 5 dice at one time. What is the probability that you will roll a 4 on all 5 dice?

$P(4) = \frac{1}{6}$ $P(4)P(4)P(4)P(4)P(4) = \frac{1}{6}\left(\frac{1}{6}\right)\left(\frac{1}{6}\right)\left(\frac{1}{6}\right)\left(\frac{1}{6}\right) = \frac{1}{7776}$

If you rolled a 6 on two of the dice in your first roll, what is the probability that you will roll a 6 with your three remaining dice in your second roll?

$P(6) = \frac{1}{6}$ $P(6)P(6)P(6) = \frac{1}{6}\left(\frac{1}{6}\right)\left(\frac{1}{6}\right) = \frac{1}{216}$

⑥ Follow the directions.   **9 points**
It takes a minimum of 270 electoral votes to win the presidency. Draw a bar graph showing the number of electoral votes each of the past 7 presidents won. If a president won a second term, only the electoral votes for his second term are listed.
Barack Obama: 365
George W. Bush: 286
Bill Clinton: 379
George H.W. Bush: 426
Ronald Reagan: 525
Jimmy Carter: 297
Richard Nixon: 301

Electoral Votes of Presidents

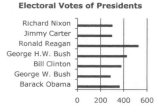

Graph must include a title, labeled axes, and 7 bars of appropriate length.

61 points total

It's College Test Prep Time!

Number of Hurricanes

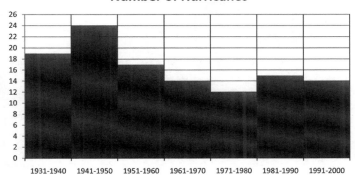

The graph above shows the number of hurricanes that hit the United States mainland each decade from 1931 to 2000. Use this graph to answer questions 1 and 2.

1. How many hurricanes hit the United States mainland from 1931 to 2000?
   A. 112
   B. <u>115</u> $19 + 24 + 17 + 14 + 12 + 15 + 14 = 115$
   C. 118
   D. 120
   E. 122

2. During what 2-decade period was the average (arithmetic mean) hurricane hits equal to 13 per decade?
   A. 1981-2000
   B. 1971-1990
   C. <u>1961-1980</u> $(14 + 12) \div 2 = 26 \div 2 = 13$
   D. 1951-1970
   E. 1941-1960

A Math Minute with . . .

Mike L. – Professional Landscaper

Where do you work? I own my own landscaping business.

Did you attend college? If so, what was your major? No.

What parts of your job require the use of math? I calculate the square footage of lots. I make precise measurements for sod installations and landscape design. I also do my own invoicing and billing.

What is the biggest "problem" you have faced that required the use of math to solve? The most difficult problems involve designing and building walls out of landscape block. I begin by measuring the desired length and height of the walls. I also measure the length and height of the landscape blocks. I use these measurements to calculate the number of landscape block needed to build the wall, taking into consideration the space between the blocks. The problem becomes more challenging if the wall is curved instead of straight.

Are there any other interesting math uses you have experienced? In my job I often use estimations. When bidding for a job, I estimate the area of the lot, determine the number of visits needed to complete the job, and give an estimate of the total price. For landscape maintenance jobs I will make multiple trips over several months to mow, trim, etc. Additionally I calculate the average cost per month over a one-year period. This allows the customer to pay less during the months when they have many services done. It also provides me with an income during the winter months when little landscaping takes place.

Teaching Tips, Cont.

➢ Have students read the Math Minute interview for Lessons 81-90.

➢ If you plan to administer Exam 2, review as time permits when all students have finished Test 8.

Assignments

- Complete *It's College Test Prep Time!*
- Read *A Math Minute with…* Mike L. – Professional Landscaper
- Study for Exam 2 (Lessons 1-77)

Exam 2

Testing Objectives

The student will:

- Use divisibility tests to identify factors
- Find the prime factorization of numbers
- Express factors using exponents
- Follow proper order of operations
- Solve square roots
- Solve single-variable equations
- Add mixed numbers
- Subtract mixed numbers
- Multiply mixed numbers
- Divide mixed numbers
- Express numbers in scientific notation
- Solve percents
- Calculate simple interest
- Convert lengths in the English measurement system
- Calculate interest compounded annually and quarterly
- Find the mean, median, mode, and range of a set of data
- Make a stem-and-leaf plot
- Find the 5-number summary of a set of data
- Draw a box-and-whisker plot
- Draw a histogram
- Calculate probability and odds
- Calculate permutations
- Calculate combinations
- Solve real world scenarios

Materials Needed

- Exam 2
- Calculator
- Formula strip, Exam 2

Teaching Tips

➤ Administer Exam 2, allowing the students 75-90 minutes to complete the test. Give students the strip labeled "For use on Exam 2" from the formula strip page.

Exam 2

① Use the divisibility tests to tell if 2, 3, 4, 5, 6, and 9 are factors of each number. **12 points**

	2	3	4	5	6	9
172	X		X			
174	X	X			X	
175				X		
180	X	X	X	X	X	X

② Express the prime factorization of each number using exponents. **3 points**

$$76 = 2 \times 2 \times 19 = 2^2 \times 19 \qquad 99 = 3 \times 3 \times 11 = 3^2 \times 11 \qquad 125 = 5 \times 5 \times 5 = 5^3$$

③ Solve, following the order of operations. **2 points**

$$\sqrt{2 \times (3^3 - 2) - 1} = \sqrt{2 \times (27 - 2) - 1} = \sqrt{2 \times 25 - 1} = \sqrt{50 - 1} = \sqrt{49} = 7$$

$$4 \times 5 - \sqrt{3^2 + 2^3 - 1} = 4 \times 5 - \sqrt{9 + 8 - 1} = 4 \times 5 - \sqrt{17 - 1} = 4 \times 5 - \sqrt{16} = 20 - 4 = 16$$

④ Solve. **3 points**

$$7x + 15 - 6 = 44$$
$$7x + 9 = 44$$
$$7x = 35$$
$$x = 5$$

$$\frac{3x}{2} + 4 + 7 = 26$$
$$\frac{3x}{2} + 11 = 26$$
$$\frac{3x}{2} = 15$$
$$3x = 30$$
$$x = 10$$

$$3x + 4(x - 1) + 11 < 24$$
$$3x + 4x - 4 + 11 < 24$$
$$7x + 7 < 24$$
$$7x < 17$$
$$x < \frac{17}{7}$$

⑤ Add, subtract, multiply, or divide as indicated. **4 points**

$$1\frac{2}{3} + 2\frac{1}{4} = \frac{5}{3} + \frac{9}{4} = \frac{5 \times 4}{3 \times 4} + \frac{9 \times 3}{4 \times 3} = \frac{20}{12} + \frac{27}{12} = \frac{47}{12} = 3\frac{11}{12}$$

$$3\frac{7}{10} - 1\frac{2}{3} = \frac{37}{10} - \frac{5}{3} = \frac{37 \times 3}{10 \times 3} - \frac{5 \times 10}{3 \times 10} = \frac{111}{30} - \frac{50}{30} = \frac{61}{30} = 2\frac{1}{30}$$

$$1\frac{2}{3} \times 2\frac{1}{10} = \frac{5}{3} \times \frac{21}{10} = \frac{1 \times 7}{1 \times 2} = \frac{7}{2} = 3\frac{1}{2}$$

$$2\frac{1}{5} \div 1\frac{1}{10} = \frac{11}{5} \div \frac{11}{10} = \frac{11}{5} \times \frac{10}{11} = \frac{2}{1} = 2$$

⑥ Write each number in scientific notation. **4 points**

490,000,000 4.9×10^8 0.000000218 2.18×10^{-7}

34,000,000 3.4×10^7 0.00043 4.3×10^{-4}

Exam 2

⑦ Solve. **3 points**

What is 65% of 80?
$$x = 0.65(80)$$
$$x = 52$$

42 is 70% of what number?
$$42 = 0.7x$$
$$42 \div 0.7 = x$$
$$x = 60$$

35 is what percent of 140?
$$35 = 140x$$
$$35 \div 140 = x$$
$$0.25 = x$$
$$x = 25\%$$

⑧ Complete the chart to reflect simple interest. **6 points**

Principal	Interest rate	Time, in years	Amount of interest	Total amount paid
$1000	5%	4	$i = \$1000(0.05)(4) = \$200$	$\$1000 + \$200 = \$1200$
$5000	7%	6	$i = \$5000(0.07)(6) = \$2100$	$\$5000 + \$2100 = \$7100$
$10,000	9%	8	$i = \$10,000(0.09)(8) = \$7200$	$\$10,000 + \$7200 = \$17,200$

⑨ Calculate the equivalent length for each given length. **8 points**

7 miles	$7 \text{ miles}\left(\frac{1760 \text{ yards}}{1 \text{ mile}}\right) = 12,320$	yards
8 miles	$8 \text{ miles}\left(\frac{5280 \text{ feet}}{1 \text{ mile}}\right) = 42,240$	feet
11 yards	$11 \text{ yards}\left(\frac{36 \text{ inches}}{1 \text{ yard}}\right) = 396$	inches
51 feet	$51 \text{ feet}\left(\frac{1 \text{ yard}}{3 \text{ feet}}\right) = 17$	yards
15 inches	$15 \text{ inches}\left(\frac{2.54 \text{ cm}}{1 \text{ inch}}\right) = 38.1$	cm
8 inches	$8 \text{ inches}\left(\frac{25.4 \text{ mm}}{1 \text{ inch}}\right) = 203.2$	mm
9 yards	$9 \text{ yards}\left(\frac{0.91 \text{ meter}}{1 \text{ yard}}\right) = 8.19$	meters
7 miles	$7 \text{ miles}\left(\frac{1.61 \text{ km}}{1 \text{ mile}}\right) = 11.27$	km

⑩ Use the formula $A = P(1 + r)^t$ to calculate compound interest. **6 points**

Initial principal	Interest rate	Time, in years	Total compounded annually	Total compounded quarterly
$1000	5%	4	$A = \$1000(1 + .05)^4 = \$1215.51$	$A = \$1000(1 + 0.05 \div 4)^{4 \times 4} = \$1219.89$
$5000	7%	6	$A = \$5000(1.07)^6 = \$7503.65$	$A = \$5000(1 + 0.07 \div 4)^{6 \times 4} = \$7582.21$
$10,000	9%	8	$A = \$10,000(1.09)^8 = \$19,925.63$	$A = \$10,000(1 + 0.09 \div 4)^{8 \times 4} = \$20,381.03$

⑪ Find the mean, median, and mode.   **3 points**

The results of 20 rolls of a die are 2, 5, 6, 2, 3, 1, 2, 6, 1, 1, 5, 2, 3, 1, 5, 6, 2, 4, 4, 2.
Round answers to the nearest tenth where appropriate.

Mean: Sum = 63; Mean = 63 ÷ 20 = 3.2
Median: (2 + 3) ÷ 2 = 5 ÷ 2 = 2.5
Mode: 2

⑫ Make a stem-and-leaf plot and find the range.   **11 points**

The points scored by the top 25 NCAA men's basketball teams are as follows: 85, 81, 90,
59, 57, 95, 70, 77, 77, 82, 89, 60, 79, 76, 77, 57, 63, 75, 68, 84, 69, 98, 85, 65, 55.

Stems	Leaves
0	
1	
2	
3	
4	
5	5, 7, 7, 9
6	0, 3, 5, 8, 9
7	0, 5, 6, 7, 7, 7, 9
8	1, 2, 4, 5, 5, 9
9	0, 5, 8

Range: 98 – 55 = 43

⑬ Draw a histogram, list the 5-number summary, and draw a box-and-whisker plot.   **7 points**

The points scored by the top 25 NCAA men's basketball teams are as follows: 85, 81, 90,
59, 57, 95, 70, 77, 77, 82, 89, 60, 79, 76, 77, 57, 63, 75, 68, 84, 69, 98, 85, 65, 55.

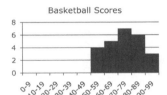
Basketball Scores

Minimum value: 55
Maximum value: 98
Median: 77
First quartile: 64
Third quartile: 84.5
The 5-number summary is 55, 64, 77, 84.5, and 98.

---

⑭ Complete the chart to show probability and odds.   **12 points**

Scenario	Number of Possible Outcomes	Desired Event (E)	P(E)	Odds (in favor of E)	Odds (Against E)
Flip a coin once	2	Tails	$P(E) = \frac{1}{2}$	1:1	1:1
Roll a 6-sided die once	6	Even number	$P(E) = \frac{3}{6} = \frac{1}{2}$	1:1	1:1
Choosing an integer from 1 to 10	10	Prime number (2, 3, 5, 7)	$P(E) = \frac{4}{10} = \frac{2}{5}$	2:3	3:2

⑮ Calculate the permutations and combinations.   **8 points**

$p(8,2) = \frac{8!}{(8-2)!} = \frac{8 \times 7 \times \cancel{6!}}{\cancel{6!}} = 56$

$C(8,2) = \frac{8!}{2!(8-2)!} = \frac{\overset{4}{\cancel{8}} \times 7 \times \cancel{6!}}{(\cancel{2} \times 1)(\cancel{6!})} = 28$

$p(5,3) = \frac{5!}{(5-3)!} = \frac{5 \times 4 \times 3 \times \cancel{2!}}{\cancel{2!}} = 60$

$C(5,3) = \frac{5!}{3!(5-3)!} = \frac{5 \times \overset{2}{\cancel{4}} \times \cancel{3} \times \cancel{2!}}{(\cancel{3} \times \cancel{2} \times 1)(\cancel{2!})} = 10$

$p(6,4) = \frac{6!}{(6-4)!} = \frac{6 \times 5 \times 4 \times 3 \times \cancel{2!}}{\cancel{2!}} = 360$

$C(6,4) = \frac{6!}{4!(6-4)!} = \frac{\overset{3}{\cancel{6}} \times 5 \times \cancel{4!}}{(\cancel{4!})(\cancel{2} \times 1)} = 15$

$p(8,3) = \frac{8!}{(8-3)!} = \frac{8 \times 7 \times 6 \times \cancel{5!}}{\cancel{5!}} = 336$

$C(8,3) = \frac{8!}{3!(8-3)!} = \frac{\overset{4}{\cancel{8}} \times 7 \times \overset{2}{\cancel{6}} \times \cancel{5!}}{(\cancel{3} \times \cancel{2} \times 1)(\cancel{5!})} = 56$

⑯ Solve.   **4 points**

A card game has 4 different colors of cards and 13 different numbers on the cards. How
many combinations are possible with one color and one number?
4 × 13 = 52 different color-number combinations
A school has 3 different choices for shirts, 4 different choices for pants, and 3 different
choices for sweaters for the school uniform. How many different uniform combinations
are possible?
3 × 4 × 3 = 36 different uniform combinations
You roll 5 dice at one time. What is the probability that you will roll a 2 on all five
dice?

$P(2) = \frac{1}{6}$ $P(2)P(2)P(2)P(2)P(2) = \frac{1}{6}\left(\frac{1}{6}\right)\left(\frac{1}{6}\right)\left(\frac{1}{6}\right)\left(\frac{1}{6}\right) = \frac{1}{7776}$

If you rolled a 3 on three of the dice on your first roll, what is the probability that
you will roll a 3 with your two remaining dice on your second roll?

$P(3) = \frac{1}{6}$ $P(3)P(3) = \frac{1}{6}\left(\frac{1}{6}\right) = \frac{1}{36}$

96 points total

➤ Calculator use is permitted on Section 10 (compound interest).

Assignment
• There is no assignment for this day.

Lesson 81

Concepts
- Plane geometry terms
- Order of operations
- Absolute value
- Mean, median, mode, range
- Dividing fractions
- Dividing mixed numbers

Learning Objectives
The student will be able to:
- Define *point*, *plane*, *line*, *segment*, *ray*, *angle*, *vertex*, *parallel*, and *congruent*
- Draw points, lines, segments, rays, angles, parallel lines, congruent segments, and congruent angles
- Write the mathematical symbol for point, line, segment, angle, parallel, and congruent

Materials Needed
- Student Book, Lesson 81
- Ruler or straightedge

Teaching Tips
- ➢ Introduce the plane geometry terms from the teaching box. Emphasize the fact that a point has no dimensions. Some students may draw their dots very large, making it appear that a point has a length or width. Show them that a line or segment drawn between two points (dots) always goes through the center of the dot.

- ➢ Have students compare and contrast lines, segments, and rays. Make sure they notice the difference in the number of endpoints each has.

Plane Geometry Terms

A **point** is a location in space. It is represented by a dot, and has no length, width, or height.

Point *A* is drawn as •ᴬ and is written as *A*.

A **plane** is a 2-dimensional flat surface that extends infinitely in all directions. Any three non-collinear (not on a straight line) points make a plane.

A **line** is the set of all points between and including two given points and extends infinitely in both directions. Line *AB* is drawn as a line with arrows and is written as $\overleftrightarrow{AB}$.

A **line segment** is the set of all points between and including two given points. Segment *AB* is drawn as a segment and is written as $\overline{AB}$.

A **ray** is the set of all points between and including two given points and extends infinitely in one direction. Ray *AB* is drawn as a ray and is written as $\overrightarrow{AB}$.

An **angle** is formed when two rays share a common endpoint. The common endpoint is the **vertex** of the angle. When a single angle is drawn at a vertex, such as an angle, the angle may be named angle *ABC*, angle *CBA*, or angle *B* and written $\angle ABC$, $\angle CBA$, or $\angle B$. If more than one angle shares a common vertex, the three-letter designation must be used. The middle letter is always the vertex, and the other two letters indicate a point on each of the two rays.

Parallel lines are two coplanar (in the same plane) lines that never intersect. Parallel lines *a* and *b* are drawn as ═ and are written as $a \parallel b$.

Congruent figures have the exact same size and shape. Congruent angles have the same measure. Congruent segments have the same length. The symbol for congruent is $\cong$.

① Classwork
Draw the figures.

D

$\overline{EF}$

$\overline{GH}$

$\overline{BC}$

$\angle XYZ$

$f \parallel g$

$\overline{MN} \cong \overline{PQ}$

$\angle A \cong \angle D$

Activities

② Complete the chart.

Figure	Drawing	Symbol
Point H		H
Line TV		$\overleftrightarrow{TV}$
Segment RT		$\overline{RT}$
Ray WX		$\overrightarrow{WX}$
Angle P		$\angle P$
Parallel lines m and n		$m \parallel n$

③ Solve.

$9 - (11 - 18) + |3 - 7| = 9 - (-7) + |-4| = 9 + 7 + 4 = 16 + 4 = 20$

$9 - (11 - 18) - |3 - 7| = 9 - (-7) - |-4| = 9 + 7 - 4 = 16 - 4 = 12$

$9 + (11 - 18) + |3 - 7| = 9 + (-7) + |-4| = 9 - 7 + 4 = 2 + 4 = 6$

$9 + (11 - 18) - |3 - 7| = 9 + (-7) - |-4| = 9 - 7 - 4 = 2 - 4 = -2$

④ Find the mean, median, mode, and range of the set of numbers.

46, 35, 53, 42, 41, 53, 49, 57, 43, 57

Mean: $(46 + 35 + 53 + 42 + 41 + 53 + 49 + 57 + 43 + 57) \div 10 = 476 \div 10 = 47.6$

Median: $(46 + 49) \div 2 = 47.5$

Mode: 53 and 57

Range: $57 - 35 = 22$

⑤ Divide.

$\dfrac{14}{27} \div \dfrac{35}{36} = \dfrac{\overset{2}{\cancel{14}}}{\cancel{27}_3} \times \dfrac{\cancel{36}^{4}}{\cancel{35}_5} = \dfrac{8}{15}$

$\dfrac{15}{16} \div \dfrac{3}{4} = \dfrac{\overset{5}{\cancel{15}}}{\cancel{16}_4} \times \dfrac{\cancel{4}}{\cancel{3}} = \dfrac{5}{4} = 1\dfrac{1}{4}$

$6\dfrac{3}{5} \div 3\dfrac{2}{3} = \dfrac{33}{5} \div \dfrac{11}{3} = \dfrac{\overset{3}{\cancel{33}}}{5} \times \dfrac{3}{\cancel{11}} = \dfrac{9}{5} = 1\dfrac{4}{5}$

$7\dfrac{7}{8} \div 3\dfrac{5}{12} = \dfrac{63}{8} \div \dfrac{41}{12} = \dfrac{63}{\cancel{8}_2} \times \dfrac{\cancel{12}^{3}}{41} = \dfrac{189}{82} = 2\dfrac{25}{82}$

Teaching Tips, Cont.

➢ Teach the concept of congruent. Ask the students if two lines can be congruent. (No.) Why not? (Lines go on infinitely and therefore have no measure.) Ask the students if two rays can be congruent. (No.) Why not? (Rays have a definite starting point, but no ending point, so they cannot be measured.)

➢ Point out that angles and segments may be congruent. Polygons may also be congruent if all the corresponding sides and angles are congruent.

➢ Teach the concept of parallel. Explain that two segments are parallel if and only if the lines that they are a portion of are also parallel. Just because two coplanar segments do not intersect does not automatically make them parallel.

➢ Tell the students to use a ruler or other straightedge whenever they draw lines, segments, rays, or angles.

➢ Complete the Classwork exercises. Have some students work the problems on the board for the class and explain their answers. All students should work the problems in their books.

Assignment

• Complete Lesson 81, Activities 2-5.

Lesson 82

Concepts
- Perimeter and area of parallelograms
- Perimeter and area of rhombuses
- Order of operations
- Absolute value
- Multiplying fractions
- Multiplying mixed numbers

Learning Objectives
The student will be able to:
- Define *polygon* and *quadrilateral*
- Define *parallelogram* and *rhombus*
- Calculate the perimeter and area of a parallelogram
- Calculate the perimeter and area of a rhombus

Materials Needed
- Student Book, Lesson 82
- Worksheet 41

Teaching Tips
➢ Have students complete Worksheet 41 in class. This may be for added practice of earlier topics or graded as a quiz, if desired.

➢ Define *polygon* and *quadrilateral* from the teaching box. Explain that all the sides on a polygon are straight. There are no curves and no gaps. Explain that the only requirement for a polygon to be a quadrilateral is that it has four sides. There is no stipulation on the relationships among the sides or the angles.

➢ Review parallel lines. (See Lesson 81.)

Parallelograms and Rhombuses

A **polygon** is a closed figure with three or more sides.

A **quadrilateral** is a polygon with exactly four sides. The sum of the interior angles of a quadrilateral is 360°.

A **parallelogram** is a quadrilateral with two pairs of parallel sides. In the figure below, $\overline{AB} \parallel \overline{DC}$ and $\overline{AD} \parallel \overline{BC}$.

Notice that the opposite sides are equal in length, but the adjacent sides are not. All parallelograms have opposite sides that are parallel and congruent. Adjacent sides may be congruent or unequal.

A **rhombus** is a parallelogram with four congruent sides. Because a rhombus is a parallelogram, the opposite sides are parallel.

All rhombuses are parallelograms, but not all parallelograms are rhombuses.

To find the perimeter of a parallelogram, find the sum of the lengths of the four sides. $P = 2\ell + 2w$, where ℓ is the length, and w is the width.

To find the area of a parallelogram, find the product of the base and the height. $A = bh$, where b is the base and h is the height. Area is always given in square units.

List everything you know to be true about the diagram below. Find the perimeter and the area.

Given: $\square ABCD$; $AB = 5$; $BC = 3$; $h = 2$
What you know:
It is a parallelogram, $\overline{AB} \parallel \overline{DC}$, $\overline{AD} \parallel \overline{BC}$, $\overline{AB} \cong \overline{DC}$, $\overline{AD} \cong \overline{BC}$
Perimeter is $2(5) + 2(3) = 10 + 6 = 16$ units.
The area is $5(2) = 10$ square units.

① **Classwork**
List everything you know to be true about the diagram below. Include the perimeter and area.

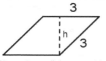

Given: A parallelogram with height 2.5

The figure is a parallelogram.

The figure is a rhombus.

The opposite sides are parallel.

The opposite sides are congruent.

All four sides are equal to 3.

The perimeter is $2(3) + 2(3) = 6 + 6 = 12$ units.

The area is $3(2.5) = 7.5$ square units.

Explain the statement, "All rhombuses are parallelograms, but not all parallelograms are rhombuses."

A rhombus is a quadrilateral with opposite sides parallel. By definition, this makes it a parallelogram. A rhombus also has all four sides congruent. A parallelogram has opposite sides congruent, but not necessarily adjacent sides congruent. For this reason, the rhombus is a parallelogram, but it is possible to have a parallelogram that is not a rhombus.

Activities
② List everything you know to be true about the diagrams below. Include the perimeter and area.

Given: $\square ABCD$; $AB = 10$; $BC = 5$; $h = 3$

$ABCD$ is a parallelogram.
$\overline{AB} \parallel \overline{DC}$
$\overline{AD} \parallel \overline{BC}$
$\overline{AB} \cong \overline{DC}$
$\overline{AD} \cong \overline{BC}$
The perimeter is $2(10) + 2(5) = 30$ units.
The area is $10(3) = 30$ square units.

Given: $\square GHJK$; $\overline{GH} \cong \overline{HJ}$; $GH = 4$; $h = 3$

$GHJK$ is a parallelogram and a rhombus.
$\overline{GH} \parallel \overline{KJ}$
$\overline{HJ} \parallel \overline{GK}$
$\overline{GH} \cong \overline{HJ} \cong \overline{JK} \cong \overline{KG}$
The perimeter is $4(4) = 16$ units.
The area is $4(3) = 12$ square units.

③ Solve.

$$3(2x-3) < 5|7-10|$$
$$6x - 9 < 5|-3|$$
$$6x - 9 < 5(3)$$
$$6x - 9 < 15$$
$$6x < 24$$
$$x < 4$$

$$3(2x-3) < (-5)|7-10|$$
$$6x - 9 < (-5)|-3|$$
$$6x - 9 < (-5)(3)$$
$$6x - 9 < -15$$
$$6x < -6$$
$$x < -1$$

$$(-3)(2x-3) < 5|7-10|$$
$$-6x + 9 < 5|-3|$$
$$-6x + 9 < 5(3)$$
$$-6x + 9 < 15$$
$$-6x < 6$$
$$x > -1$$

④ Multiply.

$$\frac{14}{27} \times \frac{15}{28} = \frac{\overset{1}{14}}{\underset{9}{27}} \times \frac{\overset{5}{15}}{\underset{2}{28}} = \frac{5}{18}$$

$$\frac{14}{15} \times \frac{3}{4} = \frac{\overset{7}{14}}{\underset{5}{15}} \times \frac{\overset{}{3}}{\underset{2}{4}} = \frac{7}{10} =$$

$$6\frac{3}{5} \times 3\frac{2}{3} = \frac{33}{5} \times \frac{11}{3} = \frac{\overset{11}{33}}{5} \times \frac{11}{3} = \frac{121}{5} = 24\frac{1}{5}$$

$$7\frac{1}{5} \times 2\frac{1}{12} = \frac{36}{5} \times \frac{25}{12} = \frac{\overset{3}{36}}{5} \times \frac{\overset{5}{25}}{12} = \frac{15}{1} = 15$$

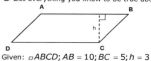

① Find the probabilities.

The pep band has 16 seventh graders and 20 eighth graders. There are 18 boys and 18 girls in the pep band, and 6 of the girls are in seventh grade. If a student is selected at random, what is the probability that the student will be in seventh grade or a girl?

$$P(\text{7th grade} \cup \text{girl}) = \frac{16}{36} + \frac{18}{36} - \frac{6}{36} = \frac{28}{36} = \frac{7}{9}$$

What is the probability that the student will be in eighth grade or a girl?

$$P(\text{8th grade} \cup \text{girl}) = \frac{20}{36} + \frac{18}{36} - \frac{12}{36} = \frac{26}{36} = \frac{13}{18}$$

When rolling a standard 6-sided game die, what is the probability of rolling a 2 or a 3?

$$P(2 \cup 3) = P(2) + P(3)$$

$$P(2) = \frac{1}{6} \qquad P(3) = \frac{1}{6}$$

$$P(2 \cup 3) = \frac{1}{6} + \frac{1}{6} = \frac{2}{6} = \frac{1}{3}$$

What is the probability of rolling a 4 or an odd number?

$$P(4 \cup \text{odd}) = P(4) + P(\text{odd})$$

$$P(4) = \frac{1}{6} \qquad P(\text{odd}) = \frac{3}{6} = \frac{1}{2}$$

$$P(4 \cup \text{odd}) = \frac{1}{6} + \frac{3}{6} = \frac{4}{6} = \frac{2}{3}$$

A pile of coins contains 7 each of pennies, nickels, dime, and quarters. If two coins are selected at random, what is the probability they will be worth a total of 26 cents?

$$P(\text{quarter} \cup \text{penny}) = \frac{7}{28} + \frac{7}{28} = \frac{1}{2}$$

$$P(\text{the remaining coin}) = \frac{7}{27}$$

$$P(\text{quarter})P(\text{penny}) = \frac{1}{2}\left(\frac{7}{27}\right) = \frac{7}{54}$$

If two coins are selected at random, what is the probability they will be worth a total of 50 cents?

$$P(\text{quarter}) = \frac{7}{28} = \frac{1}{4}$$

$$P(\text{the second quarter}) = \frac{6}{27} = \frac{2}{9}$$

$$P(\text{quarter})P(\text{quarter}) = \frac{1}{4}\left(\frac{2}{9}\right) = \frac{2}{36} = \frac{1}{18}$$

Teaching Tips, Cont.

➢ Teach parallelograms and rhombuses. Make sure all students understand that all rhombuses are parallelograms, but not all parallelograms are rhombuses.

➢ Teach the formulas for finding perimeter and area of parallelograms and rhombuses. Emphasize that the height is always perpendicular to the base and is not necessarily the length of a side.

➢ Complete the Classwork exercises. Have some students work the problems on the board for the class and explain their answers. All students should work the problems in their books.

Assignment

- Complete Lesson 82, Activities 2-4.

Lesson 83

Concepts
- Perimeter and area of rectangles
- Perimeter and area of squares
- Simple interest
- Probability and odds
- Math in the real world

Learning Objectives
The student will be able to:
- Define *rectangle* and *square*
- Calculate the perimeter and area of rectangle
- Calculate the perimeter and area of a square

Materials Needed
- Student Book, Lesson 83
- Worksheet 42

Teaching Tips
➤ Review parallelograms and rhombuses. (See Lesson 82.)

➤ Teach rectangles and squares from the teaching box. Ask students if rectangles are parallelograms. (Yes.) Why? (The opposite sides are parallel.) Ask students if squares are parallelograms. (Yes.) Why? (The opposite sides are parallel.)

➤ Ask students if rectangles are rhombuses. (Sometimes.) Why or why not? (The opposite sides are not always equal.) Ask students if squares are rhombuses. (Yes.) Why? (They are parallelograms and the opposite sides are equal.)

Rectangles and Squares

A **rectangle** is a parallelogram with four congruent angles. Because a rectangle is a parallelogram, the formulas for perimeter and area remain the same.

A **square** is a rectangle with four congruent sides. Because a square has four congruent angles and four congruent sides, the formulas for perimeter and area can be simplified as follows:
$P = 4s$, where s is the length of a side
$A = s^2$, where s is the length of a side

List everything you know to be true about the diagram below. Find the perimeter and area.

Given: $\square DCBA$; $DC = 7$; $CB = 4$
What you know:
It is a parallelogram. It is rectangle.
$\overline{AB} \parallel \overline{DC}$, $\overline{AD} \parallel \overline{BC}$, $\overline{AB} \cong \overline{DC}$, $\overline{AD} \cong \overline{BC}$
Each of the angles is equal to $360° \div 4 = 90°$.
Perimeter is $2(7) + 2(4) = 14 + 8 = 22$ units.
The area is $7(4) = 28$ square units.

① Classwork
List everything you know to be true about the diagram below. Include the perimeter and area.

Given: $\square DCBA$; $DC = 5$; $CB = 5$

The figure is a parallelogram.
The figure is a rhombus.
The figure is a rectangle.
The figure is a square.
The opposite sides are parallel.
The opposite sides are congruent.
Each of the four angles is equal to $360° \div 4 = 90°$.
Each of the four sides is equal to 5.
The perimeter is $4(5) = 20$ units.
The area is $5(5) = 25$ square units.

Activities

② List everything you know to be true about the diagrams below. Include the perimeter and area.

Given: $\square WXYZ$; $WX = 4\frac{1}{2}$; $XY = 2\frac{1}{4}$

WXYZ is a parallelogram and a rectangle.
$\overline{WX} \parallel \overline{ZY}$, $\overline{WZ} \parallel \overline{XY}$, $\overline{WZ} \cong \overline{XY}$, $\overline{WX} \cong \overline{ZY}$
Each of the angles is $360° \div 4 = 90°$.
The perimeter is
$2\left(4\frac{1}{2}\right) + 2\left(2\frac{1}{4}\right) = 9 + 4\frac{1}{2} = 13\frac{1}{2}$ units.
The area is $\left(4\frac{1}{2}\right)\left(2\frac{1}{4}\right) = \frac{9}{2} \times \frac{9}{4} = \frac{81}{8} = 10\frac{1}{8}$ square units.

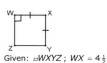

Given: $\square WXYZ$; $WX = 4\frac{1}{2}$

The figure is a parallelogram, a rhombus, a rectangle, and a square.
$\overline{WX} \parallel \overline{ZY}$, $\overline{WZ} \parallel \overline{XY}$, $\overline{WZ} \cong \overline{XY} \cong \overline{WX} \cong \overline{ZY}$

Each angle is 90°; each side is $4\frac{1}{2}$.

The perimeter is $4\left(4\frac{1}{2}\right) = \cancel{4}^{2}\left(\frac{9}{2}\right) = 18$ units.

The area is $\left(4\frac{1}{2}\right)\left(4\frac{1}{2}\right) = \left(\frac{9}{2}\right)\left(\frac{9}{2}\right) = \frac{81}{4} = 20\frac{1}{4}$ square units.

---

③ Complete the chart to show simple interest.

Principal	Interest Rate	Time, in Years	Amount of Interest
$1500	6.9%	3	$i = \$1500(0.069)(3) = \$310.50$
$3900	4.5%	5	$i = \$3900(0.045)(5) = \$877.50$
$5200	9.9%	8	$i = \$5200(0.099)(8) = \$4118.40$

④ Complete the chart to show probability and odds.

Scenario	Number of Possible Outcomes	Desired Event (E)	P(E)	Odds (in favor of E)	Odds (Against E)
Choosing an integer from 1 to 50	50	Multiple of 7 (7, 14, 21, 28, 35, 42, 49)	$P(E) = \frac{7}{50}$	7:43	43:7
Choosing an integer from 1 to 100	100	Multiple of 11 (11,22,33,44,55, 66,77,88,99)	$P(E) = \frac{9}{100}$	9:91	91:9

⑤ Solve.
Mike offers his customers an annual lawn care plan. He charges $0.01 per square foot of grass per month for 12 months to cover mowing, edging, and blowing. What should Mike charge each month for the rectangular yard pictured below? What is the total cost of an annual contract for this lawn? If Mike's contract includes 20 lawn care visits, what is the average cost per visit? (All measurements are given in feet.)

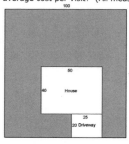

Area of lot: $100 \times 108 = 10,800$ sq. ft.
Area of house: $40 \times 50 = 2000$ sq. ft.
Area of driveway: $20 \times 25 = 500$ sq. ft.
Area of grass: $10,800 - (2000 + 500) = 10,800 - 2500 = 8300$ sq. ft.

Cost per month of an annual contract is
$8300 \times \$0.01 = \$83$

Cost per year for an annual contract is
$\$83 \times 12 = \$996$

Average cost for each of 20 visits is
$\$996 \div 20 = \$49.80$

What percent of the above lot is covered with grass? Round your answer to the nearest tenth of a percent.
$8300 \div 10,800 = 0.7685 = 76.9\%$

Perimeter and Area of Rectangles and Squares

① Complete the chart for rectangles.

Short side	Long side	Perimeter	Area
8 cm	10 cm	36 cm	80 cm^2
7 ft.	11 ft.	36 ft.	77 sq. ft.
1.5 in.	4.1 in.	11.2 in.	6.15 sq. in.
3.3 km	6.9 km	20.4 km	22.77 km^2
$3\frac{1}{2}$ m	$4\frac{3}{4}$ m	$16\frac{1}{2}$ m	$\frac{7}{2} \times \frac{19}{4} = \frac{133}{8} = 16\frac{5}{8}$ m^2
$2\frac{1}{4}$ yd.	$5\frac{1}{3}$ yd.	$(2)(\frac{9}{4} + \frac{16}{3}) = (2)(\frac{27}{12} + \frac{64}{12}) =$ $(2)\frac{91}{12} = 15\frac{1}{6}$	$\frac{9}{4} \times \frac{16}{3} = 12$ sq. yd.

② Complete the chart for squares.

Side	Perimeter	Area
8 cm	32 cm	64 cm^2
7 ft.	28 ft.	49 sq. ft.
1.5 in.	6 in.	2.25 sq. in.
3.3 km	13.2 km	10.89 km^2
$3\frac{1}{2}$ m	14 m	$12\frac{1}{4}$ m^2
$2\frac{1}{4}$ yd.	9 yd.	$\frac{9}{4} \times \frac{9}{4} = \frac{81}{16} = 5\frac{1}{16}$ sq. yd.

Teaching Tips, Cont.

➤ Teach the formulas for finding the perimeter and area of rectangles and squares. Show students that these are essentially the same formulas as those for rectangles and rhombuses.

➤ Ask the students why the lengths of the sides are used in the area formulas for rectangles and squares but not in the area formulas for parallelograms and rhombuses. (The sides are perpendicular, so the side is also the height.)

➤ Complete the Classwork exercises. Have some students work the problems on the board for the class and explain their answers. All students should work the problems in their books.

Assignments
- Complete Lesson 83, Activities 2-5.
- Worksheet 42

Lesson 84

Concepts

- Perimeter and area of triangles
- Perimeter and area of parallelograms
- Area of rectangles
- Probability
- Expected outcome
- Math in the real world

Learning Objectives

The student will be able to:

- Calculate the perimeter of a triangle
- Calculate the area of a triangle

Materials Needed

- Student Book, Lesson 84

Teaching Tips

➢ Review perimeter and area of parallelograms and rectangles. (See Lessons 82 and 83.)

➢ Teach finding the perimeter of a triangle from the teaching box. Show students that the formula for finding the perimeter is simply finding the sum of the three sides. The formula is modified for shapes that have congruent sides, such as parallelograms, rhombuses, rectangles, and squares.

➢ Draw a parallelogram on the board. Ask the students what the formula for finding the area of a parallelogram is. ($A = bh$) Draw a diagonal on the parallelogram to form two triangles. Ask students how they could find the area of half of a parallelogram. ($A = \frac{1}{2}bh$)

Triangles

A **triangle** is a polygon having exactly three sides. To find the perimeter of a triangle, find the sum of the lengths of the three sides. $P = a + b + c$, where a, b, and c are the three sides.

To find the area of a triangle, find half the product of the base and the height. $A = \frac{1}{2}bh$, where b is the base and h is the height.

List everything you know to be true about the diagram below. Find the perimeter and area.

The figure is a triangle.
Perimeter is 3 + 4 + 5 = 12 units.
Area is $\frac{1}{2}(3)(4) = 6$ square units.

① Classwork
List everything you know to be true about the diagram below. Find the perimeter and area.

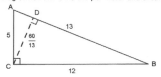

The figure is a triangle.
The perimeter is 5 + 12 + 13 = 30 units.
The area is $\frac{1}{2}(5)(12) = 30$ square units.
Some students may calculate the area as follows: $\frac{1}{2}(13)\left(\frac{60}{13}\right) = 30$ square units.

Activities
② Complete the chart with the perimeter and area of each triangle.

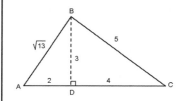

Triangle	Perimeter	Area
△ABD	$3 + 2 + \sqrt{13} =$ $5 + \sqrt{13}$ units	$\frac{1}{2}(2)(3) = 3$ square units
△BDC	$5 + 4 + 3 =$ 12 units	$\frac{1}{2}(4)(3) = 6$ square units
△ABC	$5 + 4 + 2 + \sqrt{13} =$ $11 + \sqrt{13}$ units	$\frac{1}{2}(2 + 4)(3) =$ $\frac{1}{2}(6)(3) = 9$ square units

③ Complete the chart with the perimeter and area of each figure.

Given: Parallelogram JKLM with height JN.
All measurements are given in centimeters.

Figure	Perimeter	Area
⬜JKLM	$2(5) + 2\sqrt{5} =$ $10 + 2\sqrt{5}$ cm	$(5)(2) = 10$ cm²
△JLM	$2\sqrt{5} + 5 + \sqrt{5} =$ $5 + 3\sqrt{5}$ cm	$\frac{1}{2}(5)(2) = 5$ cm²
△JLN	$2\sqrt{5} + 4 + 2 =$ $6 + 2\sqrt{5}$ cm	$\frac{1}{2}(4)(2) = 4$ cm²

④ Solve.

In the game at the left, all boxes with the same color have the same dimensions. All measurements are given in inches. Use this diagram to answer the following questions.

What is the area of one blue box?
$2 \times 2 = 4$ sq. in.
What is the area of one white box?
$1 \times 2 = 2$ sq. in.
What is the area of the entire game?
$6 \times 6 = 36$ sq. in.
If a penny is randomly tossed into the game box, what is the probability that it will land in an area that is white?
Total white area: $6 \times 2 = 12$ sq. in.
$P(\text{white}) = \frac{12}{36} = \frac{1}{3}$

What is the probability that the penny will land in a blue area in the center row?
Area of two blue boxes: $2(4$ sq. in.$) = 8$ sq. in.
$P(\text{blue center row}) = \frac{8}{36} = \frac{2}{9}$

If landing on a blue area pays 25 cents and landing on a white area pays 75 cents, what is the expected outcome if each play costs 50 cents?

x	P(x)	xP(x)
Win: white = 25 cents	$P(\text{white}) = \frac{12}{36} = \frac{1}{3}$	$\$0.25\left(\frac{1}{3}\right) = \$0.08\overline{3} = \$0.08$
Lose: blue = -25 cents	$P(\text{blue}) = \frac{24}{36} = \frac{2}{3}$	$-\$0.25\left(\frac{2}{3}\right) = -\$0.1\overline{6} = -\$0.17$

The expected value is $0.08 - $0.17 = -$0.09

Teaching Tips, Cont.

➢ Ask the students what shape is formed when the diagonal is drawn in a parallelogram. (Triangle) Show the students that the area of a triangle is half the area of a parallelogram.

➢ Remind students that the height of a figure is always perpendicular to the base. In a right triangle (there will be a box in the corner to indicate a right angle) the two legs are the base and the height.

➢ Complete the Classwork exercises. Have some students work the problems on the board for the class and explain their answers. All students should work the problems in their books.

Assignment

- Complete Lesson 84, Activities 2-4.

Lesson 85

Concepts

- Definition of *trapezoid*
- Perimeter and area of trapezoids
- Isosceles trapezoids
- Perimeter and area of rectangles
- English-Metric conversion
- Scale drawings
- Math in the real world

Learning Objectives

The student will be able to:

- Define *trapezoid*
- Define *isosceles trapezoid*
- Calculate the perimeter of a trapezoid
- Calculate the area of a trapezoid

Materials Needed

- Student Book, Lesson 85
- Worksheet 43
- Formula strip, Lesson 85

Teaching Tips

➤ Have students complete Worksheet 43 in class. This may be for added practice of earlier topics, or graded as a quiz, if desired.

➤ Teach finding the perimeter of a trapezoid from the teaching box. Remind students that the perimeter is the sum of the length of all the sides.

➤ Draw the trapezoid pictured on the facing page on the board.

➤ Review how to find the area of triangles, using the diagram you have just drawn. For each small triangle, $A = \frac{1}{2}(2)(2) = 2$. For each large triangle, $A = \frac{1}{2}(4)(2) = 4$.

Trapezoids

A **trapezoid** is a quadrilateral with exactly one pair of parallel sides. To find the perimeter of a trapezoid, find the sum of the lengths of the four sides.
$P = a + b + c + d$, where a, b, c, and d are the four sides.

To find the area of a trapezoid, find the product of the height and the mean of the lengths of the parallel sides.
$A = \frac{1}{2}(b_1 + b_2)h$, where b_1 and b_2 are the parallel sides (also called the bases) and h is the height.

If the two non-parallel sides are congruent, the trapezoid is an **isosceles trapezoid**.

List everything you know to be true about the diagram below. Find the perimeter and area.

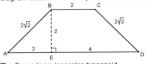

The figure is an isosceles trapezoid.
$\overline{BC} \parallel \overline{AD}$
Perimeter is $2\sqrt{2} + 2 + 2\sqrt{2} + 4 + 2 = 8 + 4\sqrt{2}$ units.
Area is $\frac{1}{2}(2 + 6)(2) = 8$ square units.

① Classwork
List everything you know to be true about the diagram below. Find the perimeter and area.

The figure is a trapezoid.
$\overline{BC} \parallel \overline{AD}$
The perimeter is
$2\sqrt{2} + 2 + 2\sqrt{10} + 6 + 2 = 10 + 2\sqrt{2} + 2\sqrt{10}$ units.
The area is $\frac{1}{2}(2 + 8)(2) = 10$ square units.

Activities

② List everything you know to be true about the diagram below. Find the perimeter and area.

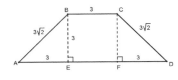

The figure is an isosceles trapezoid.
$\overline{BC} \parallel \overline{AD}$
The perimeter is
$3\sqrt{2} + 3 + 3\sqrt{2} + 9 = 12 + 6\sqrt{2}$ units.
The area is $\frac{1}{2}(3 + 9)(3) = \frac{1}{2}(12)(3) = 18$ square units.

---

③ Use the diagram of the trapezoidal lot to answer the following questions. All measurements are given in feet.

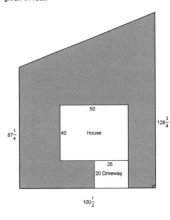

Find the area of the grass.
Total area of lot:
$\frac{1}{2}(87\frac{1}{4} + 128\frac{3}{4})(100\frac{1}{2}) =$
$\frac{1}{2}(216)(100\frac{1}{2}) =$
$108^{54}(\frac{201}{2}) = 10,854$ sq. ft.

Area of house: $40 \times 50 = 2000$ sq. ft.
Area of driveway: $20 \times 25 = 500$ sq. ft.
Area of grass: $10,854 - (2000 + 500) = 10,854 - 2500 = 8354$ sq. ft.

Find each dimension in meters. Round all answers to the nearest hundredth. (Hint: convert to yards first.)

$128.75 \text{ feet} \left(\frac{1 \text{ yard}}{3 \text{ feet}}\right)\left(\frac{0.91 \text{ meter}}{1 \text{ yard}}\right) = 39.05$ meters

$100.5 \text{ feet} \left(\frac{1 \text{ yard}}{3 \text{ feet}}\right)\left(\frac{0.91 \text{ meter}}{1 \text{ yard}}\right) = 30.49$ meters

$87.25 \text{ feet} \left(\frac{1 \text{ yard}}{3 \text{ feet}}\right)\left(\frac{0.91 \text{ meter}}{1 \text{ yard}}\right) = 26.47$ meters

$50 \text{ feet} \left(\frac{1 \text{ yard}}{3 \text{ feet}}\right)\left(\frac{0.91 \text{ meter}}{1 \text{ yard}}\right) = 15.17$ meters

$40 \text{ feet} \left(\frac{1 \text{ yard}}{3 \text{ feet}}\right)\left(\frac{0.91 \text{ meter}}{1 \text{ yard}}\right) = 12.13$ meters

$25 \text{ feet} \left(\frac{1 \text{ yard}}{3 \text{ feet}}\right)\left(\frac{0.91 \text{ meter}}{1 \text{ yard}}\right) = 7.58$ meters

$20 \text{ feet} \left(\frac{1 \text{ yard}}{3 \text{ feet}}\right)\left(\frac{0.91 \text{ meter}}{1 \text{ yard}}\right) = 6.07$ meters

If Mike edges the grass along the driveway and uses the weed eater on the grass around the house, how many feet does Mike edge? How many feet does Mike weed eat?
Mike edges $20 + 20 = 40$ feet.
Mike weed eats $40 + 50 + 40 + (50 - 25) = 40 + 50 + 40 + 25 = 155$ feet.
Mike wants to make a scale drawing of the lot to plan a landscape design for the homeowner. If the ratio of his drawing to the actual lot is $\frac{1}{4}$ in. : 1 ft., what will be the dimensions of his scale drawing?

$\frac{\frac{1}{4} \text{ in.}}{1 \text{ ft.}} = \frac{x}{128\frac{3}{4} \text{ ft.}} \Rightarrow x \text{ ft.} = \frac{1}{4} \text{ in.}\left(\frac{515}{4} \text{ ft.}\right) \Rightarrow$
$x = \frac{515}{16}$ in. $\Rightarrow x = 32\frac{3}{16}$ in.

$\frac{\frac{1}{4} \text{ in.}}{1 \text{ ft.}} = \frac{x}{100\frac{1}{2} \text{ ft.}} \Rightarrow x \text{ ft.} = \frac{1}{4} \text{ in.}\left(\frac{201}{2} \text{ ft.}\right) \Rightarrow$
$x = \frac{201}{8}$ in. $= 25\frac{1}{8}$ in.

$\frac{\frac{1}{4} \text{ in.}}{1 \text{ ft.}} = \frac{x}{87\frac{1}{4} \text{ ft.}} \Rightarrow x \text{ ft.} = \frac{1}{4} \text{ in.}\left(\frac{349}{4} \text{ ft.}\right) \Rightarrow$
$x = \frac{349}{16}$ in. $= 21\frac{13}{16}$ in.

$\frac{\frac{1}{4} \text{ in.}}{1 \text{ ft.}} = \frac{x}{50 \text{ ft.}} \Rightarrow x \text{ ft.} = \frac{1}{4} \text{ in.}(50 \text{ ft.}) \Rightarrow x = 12\frac{1}{2}$ in.

$\frac{\frac{1}{4} \text{ in.}}{1 \text{ ft.}} = \frac{x}{40 \text{ ft.}} \Rightarrow x \text{ ft.} = \frac{1}{4} \text{ in.}(40 \text{ ft.}) \Rightarrow x = 10$ in.

$\frac{\frac{1}{4} \text{ in.}}{1 \text{ ft.}} = \frac{x}{25 \text{ ft.}} \Rightarrow x \text{ ft.} = \frac{1}{4} \text{ in.}(25 \text{ ft.}) \Rightarrow x = 6\frac{1}{4}$ in.

$\frac{\frac{1}{4} \text{ in.}}{1 \text{ ft.}} = \frac{x}{20 \text{ ft.}} \Rightarrow x \text{ ft.} = \frac{1}{4} \text{ in.}(20 \text{ ft.}) \Rightarrow x = 5$ in.

① Complete the chart.

Figure	Drawing	Symbol
Point H		H
Line TV		$\overleftrightarrow{TV}$
Segment RT		$\overline{RT}$
Ray WX		$\overrightarrow{WX}$
Angle P		$\angle P$
Parallel lines m and n		$m \parallel n$

② Find the perimeter and area of each figure.

P = 2(20) + 2(10) = 40 + 20 = 60 units
A = 20(6) = 120 square units

Given:
▱ABCD; AB = 20; BC = 10; h = 6

P = 4(8) = 32 units
A = 8(6) = 48 square units

Given:
▱GHJK; $\overline{GH} \cong \overline{HJ}$; GH = 8; h = 6

P = 2(9) + 2(5) = 18 + 10 = 28 units
A = 9(5) = 45 square units

Given: ▱ABCD; DC = 9; CB = 5

P = 4(11) = 44 units
A = 11(11) = 121 square units

Given: ▱ABCD; DC = 11; CB = 11

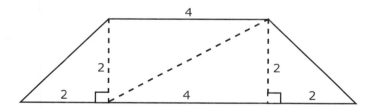

Teaching Tips, Cont.

➢ Ask students to find the area of the trapezoid from the calculations they have just done. A = 2 + 4 + 4 + 2 = 12

➢ Teach the formula for finding the area of a trapezoid, showing the students how the formula is made up of the individual formulas for the four triangles. The height is the same for each of the four triangles. Two triangles have the base equal to 2, and the other two triangles have the base equal to 4. Because one triangle has its base on the top of the trapezoid, the formula for finding the area of a trapezoid is

$$A = \left[\tfrac{1}{2}bh\right] + \left[\tfrac{1}{2}bh\right] + \left[\tfrac{1}{2}bh\right] + \tfrac{1}{2}\left[\tfrac{1}{2}(\text{top base})h\right] = A = \tfrac{1}{2}(b_1 + b_2)h$$

➢ Complete the Classwork exercises. Have some students work the problems on the board for the class and explain their answers. All students should work the problems in their books.

➢ Give the students the formula strip for Lesson 85 from the *Tests and Resources* book.

Assignment
• Complete Lesson 85, Activities 2-3.

Lesson 86

Concepts
- Circumference and area of circles
- Area of rectangles
- Math in the real world

Learning Objectives
The student will be able to:
- Define *circle*
- Calculate the radius or diameter when given the measurement of the other
- Calculate the circumference of a circle
- Calculate the diameter of a circle

Materials Needed
- Student Book, Lesson 86

Teaching Tips
➢ Review area of rectangles as necessary. (See Lesson 83.)

➢ Teach the definitions of *circle*, *diameter*, and *radius* from the teaching box.

➢ Teach the formula for finding the circumference of a circle. Explain that π is an irrational constant whose value is defined as the ratio of a circle's circumference to its diameter.

➢ The first 100 digits of pi: 3.14159265358979323846264338327950288419716939937510582097494459230781640628620899862803482534211706.... (Neither you nor the students are expected to know or memorize this. Often, students will ask, just to see if you know!) This information is repeated from Lesson 1.

Circles

A **circle** is the set of all points in a plane that are equidistant from a given point, called the **center**. The distance across the circle through the center is the **diameter**. The distance from the center to the edge of the circle is called the **radius**. The radius is exactly half the length of the diameter.

$d = 2r$ and $r = \frac{1}{2}d$

A circle does not have a perimeter because there are no sides to add up. Instead, a circle has a circumference, which is the distance around the circle. To find the circumference of a circle, find the product of the diameter and pi.

$C = \pi d$ or $C = 2\pi r$

The symbol π is left in the answer since it is an irrational number.

To find the area of a circle, find the product of pi and the square of the radius.

$A = \pi r^2$

List everything you know to be true about the diagram below. Find the circumference and area.

Given: *A* is the center; *BC* = 10
The figure is a circle. $\overline{BC}$ is the diameter; $\overline{AB}$, $\overline{AD}$, and $\overline{AC}$ are radii.
The diameter is 10 and each radius is 5.
The circumference is 10π units.
The area is $\pi\left(5^2\right) = 25\pi$ square units.

① Classwork
List everything you know to be true about the diagram below. Find the circumference and area.

Given: *A* is the center; *AD* = 7

The figure is a circle. $\overline{BC}$ is the diameter; $\overline{AB}$, $\overline{AD}$, and $\overline{AC}$ are radii.
The diameter is 14 and each radius is 7.
The circumference is 14π units.
The area is $\pi\left(7^2\right) = 49\pi$ square units.

Given a circle with radius 1 inscribed in a square, find the area of the shaded region.

The square has each side equal to 2.
The area of the square is $2^2 = 4$ sq. units.
The area of the circle is $\pi\left(1^2\right) = \pi$ sq. units.

To find the area of the shaded region, subtract the white area (the circle) from the area of the square: $4 - \pi$ square units.

Activities
② Solve.
What is the area of a circle with a radius of 8 inches?
$A = \pi\left(8^2\right) = 64\pi$ sq. in.
What is the area of a circle with a diameter of 5 cm?
$A = \pi\left(2.5^2\right) = 6.25\pi$ or $6\frac{1}{4}\pi$ or $\frac{25\pi}{4}$ cm²

③ Solve.

Each circle in the square at the left has a diameter of 4 inches. What is the area of one circle?
Radius = 4 ÷ 2 = 2 inches
$A = \pi(2^2) = 4\pi$ sq. in.

What is the area of one of the smaller squares?
Side of square = 4 inches
$A = 4^2 = 16$ sq. in.

What is the area of the large square?
Side of square = 4(3) = 12 inches
$A = 12^2 = 144$ sq. in.

What is the area of the region shaded in purple?
Area of entire square = 144 sq. in.
Area of 9 circles = $9(4\pi) = 36\pi$ sq. in.
Area of purple region =
$144 - 36\pi$ sq. in.

④ Solve.
Mike must calculate the number of square feet of grass to determine how much he charges a customer for lawn care. Find the area of the grass in the rectangular lot pictured below if the circular area has a radius of 8 feet. All measurements are given in feet. Use 3.14 as the value for pi.

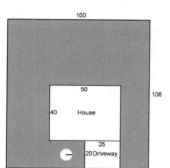

Area of lot: 100 × 108 = 10,800 sq. ft.

Area of house: 40 × 50 = 2000 sq. ft.
Area of driveway: 20 × 25 = 500 sq. ft.
Area of circle: $\pi(8^2) = 64\pi$ sq. ft.
64 × 3.14 = 200.96 sq. ft.

Area of grass:
10,800 − (2000 + 500 + 200.96) =
10,800 − 2700.96 = 8099.04 sq. ft.

Teaching Tips, Cont.

➢ Teach the formula for finding the area of a circle. Ask students how they could find the area of a circle if they are given the diameter. (Divide the diameter by 2 to find the radius.)

➢ Show the students that the formula for area can be rewritten using the diameter rather than the radius.
$$A = \pi r^2$$
$$A = \pi \left(\frac{d}{2}\right)^2$$
$$A = \frac{\pi d^2}{4}$$

➢ Complete the Classwork exercises. Have some students work the problems on the board for the class and explain their answers. All students should work the problems in their books.

Assignment

• Complete Lesson 86, Activities 2-4.

Lesson 87

Concepts
- Congruent polygons
- Area of a circle
- Area of a rectangle
- Percent
- Math in the real world

Learning Objectives
The student will be able to:
- Define *congruent polygons*
- Draw and label congruent polygons

Materials Needed
- Student Book, Lesson 87
- Ruler
- Protractor (may also be used as the ruler)
- Formula strip, Lesson 87

Teaching Tips
- ➢ Review the definition of congruent. (See Lesson 81.)

- ➢ Teach the definition of congruent polygons, emphasizing the importance of the corresponding sides and corresponding angles.

- ➢ Refer students to the figures in the teaching box. Show them how the markings are used to indicate congruent sides and congruent angles.

- ➢ If necessary, teach the students how to use a protractor to draw angles. Make sure all students are placing the center of the protractor straightedge on the vertex of the angle and are reading the angle measure beginning at 0° rather than 180°.

Congruent Polygons

Congruent polygons have all corresponding angles equal and all corresponding sides congruent. The two polygons could be stacked on top of each other and line up perfectly.

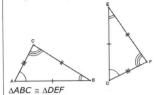

$\triangle ABC \cong \triangle DEF$

When labeling two figures as congruent, the order of the letters is important. When the two figures are traced in letter order, the order of the side lengths and angle measures must be identical. In the figures above, notice that the *A* on the first figure has the same angle markings as the *D* in the second figure. The same is true with *B* and *E*, as well as *C* and *F*. Also notice how the side markings match in the same direction. This pattern will be true for every instance of congruent polygons.

Draw and label two quadrilaterals to show that Quad *ABCD* ≅ Quad *EFGH*

There are several possibilities. One is shown below.

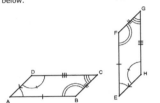

① **Classwork**
Draw and label a figure congruent to the given figure. The first side has been drawn for you.

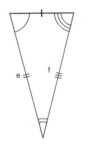

Activities

② Draw and label two congruent trapezoids.
Answers may vary. An example is shown below.

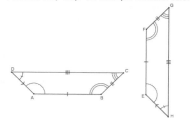

③ Solve.

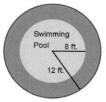

Mike is installing paving stones in a circle 4 feet wide around a swimming pool according to the diagram at the left. How many square feet will be covered with paving stones? Use 3.14 as the value for pi, and express your answer to the nearest hundredth.

$A = \pi(12^2) - \pi(8^2)$

$A = 144\pi - 64\pi = 80\pi$

$A = 80(3.14) = 251.20$ sq. ft.

Each paving stone is a rectangle that is 9 inches long and 6 inches wide. How many paving stones will Mike need?

Each paving stone is $\frac{9}{12} = \frac{3}{4}$ ft. long and $\frac{6}{12} = \frac{1}{2}$ ft. wide. The area is $\frac{3}{4} \times \frac{1}{2} = \frac{3}{8}$ sq. ft.

Convert to a decimal and divide: $251.20 \div 0.375 = 669.87$ pavers. Round to 670 pavers because you cannot buy a partial paver.

If Mike purchases 10% more paving stones than the measurements require, how many paving stones will he purchase?

$670 \times 110\% = 670 \times 1.1 = 737$ pavers

④ Solve.

The playing area of a football field is $53\frac{1}{3}$ yards wide and 120 yards long, including the end zones. If one pallet of Bermuda sod covers 504 square feet, how many pallets of sod should be ordered to cover the playing area of a football field?

The area of the football field is $53\frac{1}{3}(120) = \frac{160}{3}(120) = 6400$ square yards.

Each pallet covers $504 \div 9 = 56$ square yards

$6400 \div 56 = 114.3$ pallets. You cannot purchase a partial pallet, so order 115 pallets.

Teaching Tips, Cont.

➢ Teach the students how to draw congruent figures from the teaching box. Emphasize that the letters must be written in the correct order when identifying two polygons as congruent.

➢ Write the following on the board: $\triangle ABC \cong \triangle DEF$. Ask the students to identify all the pairs of congruent angles and congruent sides based on how the letters are ordered.

$$\begin{pmatrix} \angle A \cong \angle D;\ \angle B \cong \angle E;\ \angle C \cong \angle F \\ \overline{AB} \cong \overline{DE} \text{ or } \overline{BA} \cong \overline{ED}; \\ \overline{BC} \cong \overline{EF} \text{ or } \overline{CB} \cong \overline{FE}; \\ \overline{AC} \cong \overline{DF} \text{ or } \overline{CA} \cong \overline{FD} \end{pmatrix}$$

➢ Complete the Classwork exercises. Have one student work the problem on the board for the class and explain the answer. All students should work the problem in their books.

➢ Give the students the formula strip for Lesson 87 from the *Tests and Resources* book.

Assignment

• Complete Lesson 87, Activities 2-4.

Lesson 88

Concepts
- Symmetry
- Compound interest
- Scale drawings
- Area of trapezoids
- Math in the real world

Learning Objectives
The student will be able to:
- Define *symmetry*
- Draw lines of symmetry for a given figure

Materials Needed
- Student Book, Lesson 88
- Worksheet 44
- Calculator
- Formula strip, Lesson 88

Teaching Tips
➢ Have students complete Worksheet 44 in class. This may be for added practice of earlier topics, or graded as a quiz, if desired.

➢ Review the characteristics of parallelograms. (See Lesson 82.)

➢ Teach symmetry from the teaching box. Explain that polygons having an even number of sides with opposite sides congruent will have lines of symmetry drawn at the diagonals as well as through the midpoints of the opposite sides. Regular polygons having an odd number of sides will have lines of symmetry drawn from the midpoint of a side to the vertex of the opposite angle.

Symmetry

A polygon has **symmetry** when one half of the polygon is congruent to the other half. The line that divides a polygon into two congruent parts is the **line of symmetry**.

A polygon may have zero, one, or more than one line of symmetry.

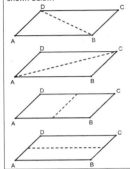

A parallelogram has four lines of symmetry, as shown below.

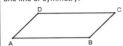

① **Classwork**
Draw all the lines of symmetry.

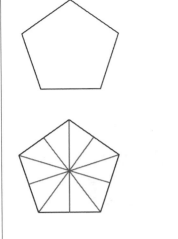

Activities
② For each of the digits 1-9, draw the lines of symmetry, if any.

The digits 1, 2, 4, 5, 6, 7, and 9 have no lines of symmetry in this font. Students may draw the number 1 as a single stick with lines of symmetry. Also, the number 8 may have one or two lines of symmetry, depending on whether or not the two circles are congruent.

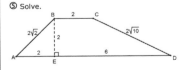

---

③ Identify the number of lines of symmetry.
For each capital letter, identify the number of lines of symmetry.

A	B	C	D	E	F	G	H	I	J	K	L	M	N	O	P	Q	R	S	T	U	V	W	X	Y	Z
1	0	1	1	1	0	0	2	2	0	0	0	1	2	2	0	0	0	2	1	1	1	1	2	1	2

④ Complete the chart to reflect interest compounded annually. You may use your calculator. Round all answers to the nearest cent.

Principal	Interest rate	Time, in years	Balance, compounded annually
$1500	0.9%	3	$A = \$1500(1 + 0.009)^3 = \$1540.87$
$2500	3.5%	5	$A = \$2500(1 + 0.035)^5 = \$2969.22$
$5800	7%	4	$A = \$5800(1 + 0.07)^4 = \$7602.62$
$9400	4.3%	6	$A = \$9400(1 + 0.043)^6 = \$12,101.35$

⑤ Solve.

Mike is installing a sandbox on the side of a play area. The diagram at the left is a scale drawing of the sandbox, with a ratio of 2:5, and all measurement given in meters.

What is the area of the sandbox? Convert the measurements to yards and round your answer to the nearest hundredth.

Base measurements are 5 meters and 20 meters; the height is 5 meters.
Convert to yards: 5(1.09) = 5.45 yards; 20(1.09) = 21.8 yards
$A = \frac{1}{2}(5.45 + 21.8)(5.45) = 74.26$ square yards

If one 50-pound bag of play sand will cover 1 square foot, what is the minimum number of bags Mike will need to cover the sandbox?

1 square yard = 9 square feet.
9 bags cover 1 square yard.
74.26 × 9 = 668.34 bags. Mike will need 669 bags of sand.

① Find the perimeter and area of each figure.

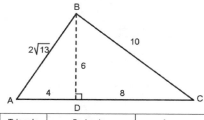

Triangle	Perimeter	Area
$\triangle ABD$	$6 + 4 + 2\sqrt{13} =$ $10 + 2\sqrt{13}$ units	$\frac{1}{2}(4)(6) = 12$ square units
$\triangle BDC$	$10 + 8 + 6 =$ 24 units	$\frac{1}{2}(8)(6) = 24$ square units
$\triangle ABC$	$10 + 8 + 4 + 2\sqrt{13} =$ $22 + 2\sqrt{13}$ units	$\frac{1}{2}(4 + 8)(6) =$ $\frac{1}{2}(12)(6) = 36$ square units

Perimeter:

$4\sqrt{3} + 4\sqrt{15} + 12\sqrt{3} + 4\sqrt{3} + 4\sqrt{6} = 20\sqrt{3} + 4\sqrt{6} + 4\sqrt{15}$ yds.

Area:

$\frac{1}{2}\left(4\sqrt{3} + 4\sqrt{3} + 12\sqrt{3}\right)\left(4\sqrt{3}\right) = \frac{1}{2}\left(20\sqrt{3}\right)\left(4\sqrt{3}\right) =$

$\left(10\sqrt{3}\right)\left(4\sqrt{3}\right) = 40(3) = 120$ square yds.

Teaching Tips, Cont.

➤ Complete the Classwork exercises. Have one student work the problem on the board for the class and explain the answer. All students should work the problem in their books.

➤ Give the students the formula strip for Lesson 88 from the *Tests and Resources* book.

Assignment

- Complete Lesson 88, Activities 2-5.

Lesson 89

Concepts

- Congruent triangles
- Perimeter and area of squares
- Perimeter and area of rectangles
- Area of triangles
- Circumference and area of circles

Learning Objectives

The student will be able to:

- Name four ways of showing whether triangles are congruent
- Identify whether or not two triangles are congruent
- Identify the SSS, SAS, ASA, and AAS patterns of congruence in triangles

Materials Needed

- Student Book, Lesson 89
- Protractor with ruler on straightedge
- 2 identical sets of three items of varying lengths (e.g.: 2 rulers, 2 pencils the same length, 2 yard sticks, etc.)

Teaching Tips

➤ Review congruent polygons. (See Lesson 87.)

➤ Teach the patterns of congruent triangles from the teaching box.

➤ Use the two sets of three items to build triangles according to each of the four patterns. Have students use a protractor to measure the angles to show that all corresponding angles are congruent.

Congruent Triangles

There are several ways of determining if two triangles are congruent.

Side-side-side: Two triangles are congruent if the sides of one triangle are congruent to the corresponding sides of the other triangle. (**SSS**)

Side-angle-side: Two triangles are congruent if two sides and their included angle on one triangle are congruent to the corresponding two sides and their included angle of the other triangle. (**SAS**)

Angle-side-angle: Two triangles are congruent if two angles and their included side on one triangle are congruent to the corresponding two angles and their included side of the other triangle. (**ASA**)

Angle-angle-side: Two triangles are congruent if two angles and an excluded side on one triangle are congruent to the corresponding two angles and excluded side of the other triangle. (**AAS**)

Identify whether or not the pair of triangles is congruent based on the information given.

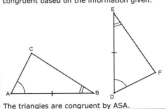

The triangles are congruent by ASA.

① **Classwork.**
Identify whether or not the pair of triangles is congruent based on the information given.

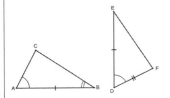

The triangles are not congruent because the first one shows the ASA pattern, and the second one shows the SAS pattern.

Activities

② Identify whether or not the pair of triangles is congruent based on the information given.

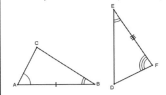

The triangles are not congruent based on the information given. Although both triangles have the ASA pattern marked, the angles and sides marked are not corresponding angles and sides.

③ Draw and label a pair of congruent triangles for each of the congruence patterns. Answers may vary. Sample answers are given.

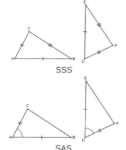

SSS

ASA

SAS

AAS

④ Draw a picture and solve.

What is the length of each side of a square if the area is 121 square feet?

$A = s^2$

121 sq. ft. $= s^2$

$\sqrt{121}$ sq. ft. $= \sqrt{s^2}$

11 ft. $= s$

What is the width of a rectangle if the perimeter is 28 cm and the length is 9 cm?

$P = 2l + 2w$

28 cm $= 2(9)$ cm $+ 2w$

28 cm $= 18$ cm $+ 2w$

10 cm $= 2w$

5 cm $= w$

What is the height of a triangle if the base is 3 inches and the area is 15 square inches?

$A = \frac{1}{2}bh$

15 sq. in. $= \frac{1}{2}(3)h$ in.

30 in. $= 3h$

10 in. $= h$

What is the circumference and radius of a circle if the area is 144π mm²?

$A = \pi r^2$

144π mm² $= \pi r^2$

$\sqrt{144}$ mm² $= \sqrt{r^2}$

12 mm $= r$

$C = 2\pi r$

$C = 2\pi(12$ mm$)$

$C = 24\pi$ mm

Teaching Tips, Cont.

> Give a pair of students the two rulers and two yardsticks but have them use their own pencils. (Make sure their pencils are different lengths for this exercise.) Ask the students to work together to build triangles following the side-side-angle pattern.

> Have the students measure the angles in the triangles they have just built. Ask them if the triangles are congruent. (No.)

> Show the students that SSA is not a valid pattern for proving triangle congruence.

> Complete the Classwork exercise. Have one student work the problem on the board for the class and explain the answer. All students should work the problem in their books.

Assignment

- Complete Lesson 89, Activities 2-4.

Lesson 90

Concepts
- Solid geometry terms
- Faces, edges, and vertices on a prism
- Faces, edges, and vertices on a pyramid
- Divisibility tests
- Prime/composite numbers
- Prime factorization
- Exponents
- Permutations
- Combinations
- Area of trapezoids

Learning Objectives
The student will be able to:
- Define *face*, *edge*, and *vertex*
- Define *prism*
- Define *pyramid*
- Calculate the number of faces, edges, and vertices on a prism
- Calculate the number of faces, edges, and vertices on a pyramid

Materials Needed
- Student Book, Lesson 90
- Worksheet 45

Teaching Tips
➢ Teach the solid geometry terms from the teaching box.

➢ Explain that prisms always have two parallel bases with parallelograms as the sides. If the sides of the prism are all rectangles, the prism is a right prism and the height of the prism is equal to the length of the side.

➢ Explain that a pyramid has exactly one base, and the faces are always triangles. It is impossible for the sides to all be perpendicular to the base.

Lesson 90

Solid Geometry Terms

A **face** is a polygon that forms a flat surface of a solid figure.

An **edge** is a line segment that forms one side of a face.

A **vertex** is a single point shared by more than one endpoint. Multiple faces on a solid meet to form a vertex, or point.

A **prism** is a solid figure that has two congruent parallel polygons as bases. The bases are joined by rectangles at each edge.

The number of faces is equal to 2 more than the number of sides on a base. In this case, it is 5 + 2 = 7. The number of edges is equal to 3 times the number of sides on a base. In this case, it is 3(5) = 15. The number of vertices is equal to 2 times the number of sides on a base. In this case, it is 2(5) = 10.

A **pyramid** is a solid with a single polygon as its base; a triangular face joins each edge and meets at a point to form the vertex.

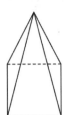

The number of faces is equal to 1 more than the number of sides on the base. In this case, it is 4 + 1 = 5 faces. The number of edges is equal to 2 times the number of sides on the base. In this case, it is 2(4) = 8 edges. The number of vertices is equal to 1 more than the number of sides on the base. In this case, it is 1 + 4 = 5.

① Classwork
Give the number of faces, edges, and vertices for each of the following figures.

Prism with hexagons as bases.

A hexagon has 6 sides.
The number of faces is 6 + 2 = 8.
The number of edges is 3(6) = 18.
The number of vertices is 2(6) = 12.

Pyramid with a hexagon as the base.

A hexagon has 6 sides.
The number of faces is 6 + 1 = 7.
The number of edges is 2(6) = 12.
The number of vertices is 6 + 1 = 7.

Activities
② Complete the chart to show the number of faces, edges, and vertices in each solid figure.

Sides on a base	Number of bases	Faces	Edges	Vertices
3	1	3 + 1 = 4	2(3) = 6	3 + 1 = 4
3	2	3 + 2 = 5	3(3) = 9	2(3) = 6
4	1	4 + 1 = 5	2(4) = 8	4 + 1 = 5
4	2	4 + 2 = 6	3(4) = 12	2(4) = 8
8	1	8 + 1 = 9	2(8) = 16	8 + 1 = 9
8	2	8 + 2 = 10	3(8) = 24	2(8) = 16

③ Use the divisibility tests to identify each number as prime or composite.

389 Prime   397 Prime
393 Composite (3)   399 Composite (3)
395 Composite (5)   401 Prime

④ Give the prime factorization of each number, using exponents where appropriate.

140   144   147
$140 = 2 \times 2 \times 5 \times 7$ $144 = 2 \times 2 \times 2 \times 2 \times 3 \times 3$ $147 = 3 \times 7 \times 7$
$140 = 2^2 \times 5 \times 7$ $144 = 2^4 \times 3^2$ $147 = 3 \times 7^2$

⑤ Calculate the permutations and combinations.

$p(7,2) = \dfrac{7!}{(7-2)!} = \dfrac{7 \times 6 \times \cancel{5!}}{\cancel{5!}} = 42$

$C(7,2) = \dfrac{7!}{2!(7-2)!} = \dfrac{7 \times 6 \times \cancel{5!}}{2!(\cancel{5!})} = \dfrac{7 \times \cancel{6}^3}{\cancel{2} \times 1} = 21$

$p(8,4) = \dfrac{8!}{(8-4)!} = \dfrac{8 \times 7 \times 6 \times 5 \times \cancel{4!}}{\cancel{4!}} = 1680$

$C(8,4) = \dfrac{8!}{4!(8-4)!} = \dfrac{8 \times 7 \times 6 \times 5 \times \cancel{4!}}{4!(\cancel{4!})} = \dfrac{\cancel{8} \times 7 \times \cancel{6}^2 \times 5}{\cancel{4} \times \cancel{3} \times \cancel{2} \times 1} = 70$

⑤ Draw a picture and solve.

What is the height of a trapezoid if the bases are $4\frac{1}{2}$ inches and $7\frac{1}{2}$ inches, and the area is 45 square inches?

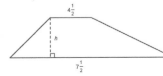

$A = \frac{1}{2}(b_1 + b_2)h$

45 sq. in. $= \frac{1}{2}(4\frac{1}{2}$ in. $+ 7\frac{1}{2}$ in.$)h$

45 sq. in. $= \frac{1}{2}(12$ in.$)h$

45 sq. in. $= (6$ in.$)h$

$\frac{45 \text{ sq. in.}}{6 \text{ in.}} = h$

$7\frac{1}{2}$ in. $= h$

① Identify whether or not each pair of triangles is congruent based on the information given. If they are congruent, write the congruence statement, paying careful attention to the order of the letters. Tell which congruence pattern applies.

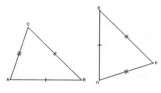

$\triangle ABC \cong \triangle DEF$
The triangles are congruent by the SSS congruence pattern.

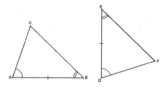

$\triangle ABC \cong \triangle DEF$
The triangles are congruent by the ASA congruence pattern.

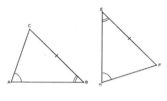

$\triangle ABC \cong \triangle DEF$
The triangles are congruent by the AAS congruence pattern.

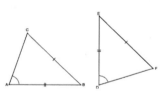

These triangles are not congruent based on the information given because SSA is not a congruence pattern.

Teaching Tips, Cont.

➤ Teach the formulas for calculating the number of faces, edges, and vertices of a prism.

➤ Teach the formulas for calculating the number of faces, edges, and vertices of a pyramid.

➤ Complete the Classwork exercises. Have some students work the problems on the board for the class and explain their answers. All students should work the problems in their books.

Assignments

- Complete Lesson 90, Activities 2-6.
- Worksheet 45
- Study for Test 9 (Lessons 78-87)

Test 9

Testing Objectives
The student will:
- Draw and label points, lines, and planes
- Find the perimeter of rectangles
- Find the perimeter of squares
- Find the perimeter of parallelograms
- Find the perimeter of trapezoids
- Calculate the area of rectangles
- Calculate the area of squares
- Calculate the area of parallelograms
- Calculate the area of trapezoids
- Calculate the circumference and area of circles
- Identify congruent figures
- Identify congruent angles and segments
- Calculate probabilities of mutually exclusive events
- Calculate probabilities of independent and dependent events

Materials Needed
- Test 9
- Formula strip, Test 9
- *It's College Test Prep Time!* from the Student Book
- *A Math Minute with…* Scott M. from the Student Book

Teaching Tips
➢ Give the students the formula strip for Test 9 from the *Tests and Resources* book.

➢ Administer Test 9, allowing the students 30-40 minutes to complete the test.

---

① Complete the chart.　　**12 points**

Figure	Drawing	Symbol
Point *T*	•T	*T*
Line *PQ*	←•——•→ P　Q	$\overleftrightarrow{PQ}$
Segment *JK*	•——• J　　K	$\overline{JK}$
Ray *AB*	•——•—→ A　　B	$\overrightarrow{AB}$
Angle *F*	(angle)	$\angle F$
Parallel lines *m* and *n*	← m → ← n →	$m \parallel n$

② Find the perimeter and area of each figure in the chart below.　　**8 points**

Figure	Perimeter	Area
$3\frac{1}{3}$ in. by $1\frac{3}{4}$ in.	$P = 2\left(3\frac{1}{3}\right) + 2\left(1\frac{3}{4}\right)$ $P = 2\left(\frac{10}{3}\right) + 2\left(\frac{7}{4}\right)$ $P = \frac{20}{3} + \frac{7}{2}$ $P = \frac{40}{6} + \frac{21}{6} = \frac{61}{6} = 10\frac{1}{6}$ in.	$A = bh$ $A = \left(3\frac{1}{3} \text{ in.}\right)\left(1\frac{3}{4} \text{ in.}\right)$ $A = \left(\frac{10}{3} \text{ in.}\right)\left(\frac{7}{4} \text{ in.}\right)$ $A = \frac{35}{6} = 5\frac{5}{6}$ sq. in.
2.1 cm square	$P = 4(2.1)$ $P = 8.4$ cm	$A = s^2$ $A = (2.1 \text{ cm})^2$ $A = 4.41 \text{ cm}^2$
4.3 m, 6.1 m, 10.2 m parallelogram	$P = 2(10.2) + 2(6.1)$ $P = 20.4 + 12.2$ $P = 32.6$ m	$A = bh$ $A = (10.2 \text{ m})(4.3 \text{ m})$ $A = 43.86 \text{ m}^2$
$2\sqrt{3}$ yd. trapezoid	$P = 2\sqrt{3} + 2\sqrt{15} + 6\sqrt{3} + 2\sqrt{3} + 2\sqrt{6}$ $P = 10\sqrt{3} + 2\sqrt{6} + 2\sqrt{15}$ yd.	$A = \frac{1}{2}(b_1 + b_2)h$ $A = \frac{1}{2}\left(2\sqrt{3} \text{ yd.} + 6\sqrt{3} \text{ yd.} + 2\sqrt{3} \text{ yd.}\right)\left(2\sqrt{3} \text{ yd.}\right)$ $A = \frac{1}{2}\left(10\sqrt{3} \text{ yd.}\right)\left(2\sqrt{3} \text{ yd.}\right)$ $A = \left(5\sqrt{3} \text{ yd.}\right)\left(2\sqrt{3} \text{ yd.}\right)$ $A = 30$ sq. yd.

---

③ Complete the chart for circles.　　**15 points**

Radius	Diameter	Circumference	Area
5 inches	10 inches	$C = 10\pi$ in.	$A = \pi(5)^2 = 25\pi$ sq. in.
7 cm	14 cm	$C = 14\pi$ cm	$A = \pi(7)^2 = 49\pi$ cm^2
1.5 ft.	3 ft.	$C = 3\pi$ ft.	$A = \pi(1.5)^2 = 2.25\pi$ sq. ft.
$2\frac{1}{2}$ m	5 m	$C = 5\pi$ m	$A = \pi\left(2\frac{1}{2}\right)^2 = \pi\left(\frac{5}{2}\right)^2 = \frac{25\pi}{4}$ m^2
$\sqrt{3}$ yd.	$2\sqrt{3}$ yd.	$C = 2\pi\sqrt{3}$ yd.	$A = \pi\left(\sqrt{3}\right)^2 = 3\pi$ sq. yd.

④ Answer the questions using the diagrams below.　　**7 points**

Write a congruence statement for the triangles shown above.
$\triangle ACB \cong \triangle DEF$　Other combinations are possible, as long as the congruent angles are in the same position.
List all pairs of congruent angles.
$\angle A \cong \angle D; \angle C \cong \angle E; \angle B \cong \angle F$
List all pairs of congruent sides.
$\overline{AC} \cong \overline{DE}; \overline{BC} \cong \overline{FE}; \overline{AB} \cong \overline{DF}$

⑤ Find the probabilities.　　**3 points**

When a standard six-sided game die is rolled one time, what is the probability that it will be a 2 or a 5?
$P(2 \cup 5) = \frac{1}{6} + \frac{1}{6} = \frac{2}{6} = \frac{1}{3}$

When a standard six-sided game die is rolled twice, what is the probability that the first roll will be a 2 and the second roll will be a 5?
$P(2)P(5) = \frac{1}{6}\left(\frac{1}{6}\right) = \frac{1}{36}$

A set of double-six dominoes has 28 dominoes. If you randomly select two dominoes, what is the probability of drawing the double 2 and the double 5?
$P(\text{double 2})P(\text{double 5}) = \frac{2}{28}\left(\frac{1}{27}\right) = \frac{1}{378}$

45 points total

It's College Test Prep Time!

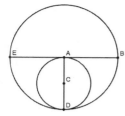

1. In the figure above, *A* is the center of the large circle and *C* is the center of the small circle. If *CD* = 3, what is the length of $\overline{EB}$?
   A. 6
   B. 9
   C. 12 $\overline{CD}$ is the radius of circle *C*, so *AD* = 6, which is the
   D. 15   radius of circle *A*. $\overline{EB}$ is the diameter of circle *A*, so it is
   E. 18   twice the radius, or 12.

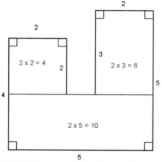

2. What is the area of the figure above?
   A. 20   Divide the figure into smaller shapes: 4 + 6 + 10 = 20.
   B. 22
   C. 23
   D. 24
   E. 25

A Math Minute with . . .

Scott M. – Crane Operator

What is your occupation? I work in crane safety operations.

Where do you work? I work at a railroad intermodal terminal.

Did you attend college? If so, what was your major? No.

What parts of your job require the use of math? One place where I use math is when lining up trains. I also use math to determine what types of cars and engines are needed for a train. Each train has a maximum total length. The individual train cars have different lengths, so the lengths of each car must be considered when designing and building a train. I am also responsible for ordering the safety equipment for the terminal. Because I must stay within a budget, I calculate the cost of different equipment in order to find the least expensive way to get the equipment we need to meet safety standards.

What is the biggest "problem" you have faced that required the use of math to solve? A train that was 7000 feet long came into the terminal. I needed to add more cars to the train. In order to do this, I had to consider the different types of cars available and the length and capacity of each car. I rearranged the train to get the maximum cargo load without exceeding the maximum train length allowed.

Are there any other interesting math uses you have experienced? The process of designing trains is interesting. We input all the available cars and train data into a computer. We use the mouse to move the cars around on the screen to design the train exactly the way we want. We then send the information to the yard to begin assembling the actual train.

Teaching Tips, Cont.

➤ When all students are finished taking the test, introduce *It's College Test Prep Time* from the student book. This page may be completed in class or assigned as homework.

➤ Have students read the Math Minute interview for lessons 91-100.

Assignments

- Complete *It's College Test Prep Time!*
- Read *A Math Minute with...* Scott M. – Crane Operator

Lesson 91

Concepts
- Volume of prisms
- Volume of cubes
- Area of polygons
- Math in the real world

Learning Objectives
The student will be able to:
- Identify the bases of a prism
- Calculate the volume of a prism
- Define *cube*
- Calculate the volume of a cube

Materials Needed
- Student Book, Lesson 91
- A pile of cubes. These may be dice, unifix cubes, the units from base 10 blocks, building blocks, etc.

Teaching Tips
➢ Review prisms. (See Lesson 90.)

➢ Arrange 6 cubes to form a 2×3 rectangle. Ask students what the area of the rectangle is. (6)

➢ Add 6 more cubes to form a second layer. Have students identify the figure you have formed as a prism. Ask the students how many units are in the prism. (12) Ask the students how they found the total number of units. (Multiply the number of units in a layer by the number of layers.)

➢ Teach how to find the volume of a prism from the teaching box.

Prisms

Recall from Lesson 90 that a prism is a solid figure that has two congruent parallel polygons as bases. The bases are joined by rectangles at each edge.

To find the volume of a prism, use the formula $V = Bh$, where B is the area of the base and h is the height of the prism.
Volume is expressed in cubic units. For metric measurements, the exponent is 3, such as cm^3.

Find the volume of the prism pictured below.

$$V = Bh$$
$$V = 5\tfrac{3}{4}(6)$$
$$V = \tfrac{23}{2}\left(\cancel{6}^{3}\right)$$
$$V = \tfrac{69}{2} = 34\tfrac{1}{2} \text{ cubic units}$$

A **cube** is a prism whose length, width, and height are equal and has six square faces. To find the volume of a cube, use the formula $V = e^3$, where e is the length of an edge.

Find the volume of the prism pictured below.

$$V = e^3$$
$$V = 5^3$$
$$V = 125 \text{ cubic units}$$

① Classwork
Find the volume of the rectangular prism. All measurements are given in feet.

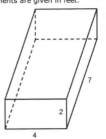

$$V = Bh$$
$$V = (4 \times 7)(2)$$
$$V = 28(2)$$
$$V = 56 \text{ cubic feet}$$

Activities
② Find the volume. All measurements are given in meters.

$$V = Bh$$
$$V = \left[\tfrac{1}{2}(3 \text{ m} \times 4 \text{ m})\right](5 \text{ m})$$
$$V = \left[\tfrac{1}{2}(12 \text{ m}^2)\right](5 \text{ m})$$
$$V = (6 \text{ m}^2)(5 \text{ m})$$
$$V = 30 \text{ m}^3$$

③ Find the area of each base, and the volume of a prism having the indicated height.

Base of Prism	Area of Base	Prism Height	Volume of Prism
$3\frac{1}{3}$ in. $1\frac{3}{4}$ in.	$A = bh$ $A = \left(3\frac{1}{3} \text{ in.}\right)\left(1\frac{3}{4} \text{ in.}\right)$ $A = \left(\frac{10}{3} \text{ in.}\right)\left(\frac{7}{4} \text{ in.}\right)$ $A = \frac{35}{6} = 5\frac{5}{6}$ sq. in.	$2\frac{2}{5}$ in.	$V = Bh$ $V = \left(5\frac{5}{6} \text{ sq. in.}\right)\left(2\frac{2}{5} \text{ in.}\right)$ $V = \left(\frac{35}{6} \text{ sq. in.}\right)\left(\frac{12}{5} \text{ in.}\right)$ $V = 14$ cubic in.
2.1 cm, 2.1 cm	$A = s^2$ $A = (2.1 \text{ cm})^2$ $A = 4.41 \text{ cm}^2$	2.1 cm	$V = s^3$ $V = (2.1 \text{ cm})^3$ $V = 9.261 \text{ cm}^3$
$3\sqrt{2}$ ft. $2\sqrt{2}$ft. $4\sqrt{2}$ft.	$A = \frac{1}{2}bh$ $A = \frac{1}{2}\left(2\sqrt{2} \text{ ft.} + 4\sqrt{2} \text{ ft.}\right)\left(3\sqrt{2} \text{ ft.}\right)$ $A = \frac{1}{2}\left(6\sqrt{2} \text{ ft.}\right)\left(3\sqrt{2} \text{ ft.}\right)$ $A = \left(3\sqrt{2} \text{ ft.}\right)\left(3\sqrt{2} \text{ ft.}\right)$ $A = 18$ sq. ft.	$3\sqrt{5}$ ft.	$V = Bh$ $V = (18 \text{ sq. ft.})\left(3\sqrt{5} \text{ ft.}\right)$ $V = 54\sqrt{5}$ cubic ft.
4.3 m, 6.1 m, 10.2 m	$A = bh$ $A = (10.2 \text{ m})(4.3 \text{ m})$ $A = 43.86 \text{ m}^2$	6.02 m	$V = Bh$ $V = (43.86 \text{ m}^2)(6.02 \text{ m})$ $V = 264.0372 \text{ m}^3$
$2\sqrt{3}$yd. $2\sqrt{6}$yd. $2\sqrt{3}$yd. $2\sqrt{15}$yd. $2\sqrt{3}$yd. $6\sqrt{3}$yd.	$A = \frac{1}{2}(b_1 + b_2)h$ $A = \frac{1}{2}\left(2\sqrt{3} \text{ yd.} + 6\sqrt{3} \text{ yd.} - 2\sqrt{3} \text{ yd.}\right)\left(2\sqrt{3} \text{ yd.}\right)$ $A = \frac{1}{2}\left(10\sqrt{3} \text{ yd.}\right)\left(2\sqrt{3} \text{ yd.}\right)$ $A = \left(5\sqrt{3} \text{ yd.}\right)\left(2\sqrt{3} \text{ yd.}\right)$ $A = 30$ sq. yd.	$2\sqrt{3}$ yd.	$V = Bh$ $V = (30 \text{ sq. yd.})\left(2\sqrt{3} \text{ yd.}\right)$ $V = 60\sqrt{3}$ cubic yd.

④ Solve.

Scott loads 53-ft. trailers onto train cars. An articulated well car can carry two 53-ft. trailers. If the cargo space of a trailer is 630 inches long, 102 inches wide, and 94 inches high, how many cubic feet of cargo space can an articulated well car carry?

$\overset{105}{630} \text{ in.} \left(\frac{1 \text{ ft.}}{12 \text{ in.}}\right) = \frac{105}{2}$ ft. $\overset{17}{102} \text{ in.} \left(\frac{1 \text{ ft.}}{12 \text{ in.}}\right) = \frac{17}{2}$ ft. $\overset{47}{94} \text{ in.} \left(\frac{1 \text{ ft.}}{12 \text{ in.}}\right) = \frac{47}{6}$ ft.

$\left(\frac{105}{2} \text{ ft.}\right)\left(\frac{17}{2} \text{ ft.}\right)\left(\frac{47}{6} \text{ ft.}\right) = \frac{27,965}{8} = 3495\frac{5}{8}$ cubic ft. in one container

$6991\frac{1}{4}$ cubic ft. in two containers

Teaching Tips, Cont.

➤ Show the students the cubes you used in the first example. Teach the special characteristics of cubes from the teaching box.

➤ Teach the special formula for finding the volume of a cube from the teaching box.

➤ Complete the Classwork exercise. Have one student work the problem on the board for the class and explain the answer. All students should work the problem in their books.

Assignment

• Complete Lesson 91, Activities 2-4.

Lesson 92

Concepts
- Surface area of prisms
- Lateral area of prisms
- Divisibility tests
- Prime/composite numbers
- Math in the real world

Learning Objectives
The student will be able to:
- Define *surface area*
- Define *lateral area*
- Calculate the surface area of a prism
- Calculate the surface area of a cube
- Calculate the lateral area of a prism
- Calculate the lateral area of a cube

Materials Needed
- Student Book, Lesson 92
- Worksheet 46

Teaching Tips
➤ Have students complete Worksheet 46 in class. This may be for added practice of earlier topics, or graded as a quiz, if desired.

➤ Review formulas for finding the area of polygons. (See Lessons 82-85.)

➤ Teach how to find the surface area of a prism from the teaching box.

➤ Ask the students what *lateral* means. (Anything relating to the side)

Surface Area

The **surface area** of a solid figure is the total area of its faces. To find the surface area of a prism, use the formula $SA = PL + 2B$, where P is the perimeter of the base, L is the slant height of the prism (the height of one of the faces joining the two bases), and B is the area of a base. The cube is a special case, having the formula $SA = 6e^2$, where e is the length of an edge of the cube.

Lateral area is the total area of the non-base faces. To find the lateral area of a prism, use the formula $LA = PL$, where LA is the lateral area, P is the perimeter of the base and L is the slant height of the prism. The cube is a special case, having the formula $LA = 4e^2$, where e is the length of an edge of the cube.

Find the surface area and lateral area of the figure below if the area of a base is $\sqrt{25 + 10\sqrt{5}}$.

$$SA = PL + 2B$$
$$SA = (10)(7) + 2\sqrt{25 + 10\sqrt{5}}$$
$$SA = 70 + 2\sqrt{25 + 10\sqrt{5}} \text{ cm}^2$$

$$LA = (10)(7)$$
$$LA = 70 \text{ cm}^2$$

① Classwork
Find the surface area and lateral area of the cube below. All measurements are given in feet.

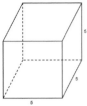

$$SA = 6e^2$$
$$SA = 6(5^2)$$
$$SA = 6(25)$$
$$SA = 150 \text{ sq. ft.}$$

$$LA = 4e^2$$
$$LA = 4(5^2)$$
$$LA = 4(25)$$
$$LA = 100 \text{ sq. ft.}$$

Activities
② Find the surface area and lateral area of each figure. All measurements are given in meters.

$$SA = PL + 2B$$
$$SA = 22(2) + 2(28)$$
$$SA = 44 + 56 = 100 \text{ m}^2$$

$$LA = PL$$
$$LA = 22(2) = 44 \text{ m}^2$$

$$SA = PL + 2B$$
$$SA = 12(5) + 2(6)$$
$$SA = 60 + 12 = 72 \text{ m}^2$$

$$LA = PL$$
$$LA = 12(5) = 60 \text{ m}^2$$

---

③ Find the surface area and lateral area of each figure.

Base of Prism	Slant Height	Lateral Area	Surface area
$3\frac{1}{3}$ in. / $1\frac{3}{4}$ in.	$2\frac{2}{5}$ in.	$LA = \left(2\left(3\frac{1}{3}\right) + 2\left(1\frac{3}{4}\right)\right)\left(2\frac{2}{5}\right)$ $LA = \left(2\left(\frac{10}{3}\right) + 2\left(\frac{7}{4}\right)\right)\left(\frac{12}{5}\right)$ $LA = \left(\frac{20}{3} + \frac{7}{2}\right)\left(\frac{12}{5}\right)$ $LA = \left(\frac{40}{6} + \frac{21}{6}\right)\left(\frac{12}{5}\right)$ $LA = \left(\frac{61}{6}\right)\left(\frac{12}{5}\right) = \frac{732}{30} = 24\frac{2}{5}$ sq. in.	$SA = 24\frac{2}{5} + 2\left(5\frac{5}{6}\right)$ $SA = \frac{122}{5} + 2\left(\frac{35}{6}\right)$ $SA = \frac{122}{5} + \frac{70}{6}$ $SA = \frac{366}{15} + \frac{175}{15} = \frac{541}{15}$ $SA = 36\frac{1}{15}$ sq. in.
2.1 cm / 2.1 cm	2.1 cm	$LA = (4(2.1))(2.1)$ $LA = (8.4)(2.1)$ $LA = 17.64 \text{ cm}^2$	$SA = 17.64 + 2(4.41)$ $SA = 17.64 + 8.82$ $SA = 26.46 \text{ cm}^2$
$\sqrt{13}$	$2\sqrt{13}$ ft.	$LA = \left(2 + 4 + 5 + \sqrt{13}\right)\left(2\sqrt{13}\right)$ $LA = \left(11 + \sqrt{13}\right)\left(2\sqrt{13}\right)$ $LA = 22\sqrt{13} + 26 \text{ sq. ft.}$	$SA = \left(22\sqrt{13} + 26\right) + 2\left(\frac{1}{2}(2 + 4)(3)\right)$ $SA = \left(22\sqrt{13} + 26\right) + 2\left(\frac{1}{2}(6)(3)\right)$ $SA = \left(22\sqrt{13} + 26\right) + 2(9)$ $SA = \left(22\sqrt{13} + 26\right) + 18$ $SA = 22\sqrt{13} + 44 \text{ sq. ft.}$
4.3 m / 6.1 m / 10.2 m	3.5 m	$LA = (2(10.2) + 2(6.1))(3.5)$ $LA = (20.4 + 12.2)(3.5)$ $LA = (32.6)(3.5)$ $LA = 114.1 \text{ m}^2$	$SA = 114.1 + 2(43.86)$ $SA = 114.1 + 87.72$ $SA = 201.82 \text{ m}^2$
$2\sqrt{3}$ yd. trapezoid	$2\sqrt{3}$ yd.	$LA = \left(2\sqrt{3} + 2\sqrt{15} + 8\sqrt{3} + 2\sqrt{6}\right)\left(2\sqrt{3}\right)$ $LA = \left(10\sqrt{3} + 2\sqrt{15} + 2\sqrt{6}\right)\left(2\sqrt{3}\right)$ $LA = 20\sqrt{9} + 4\sqrt{45} + 4\sqrt{18}$ $LA = 60 + 12\sqrt{5} + 12\sqrt{2} \text{ sq. yd.}$	$SA = \left(60 + 12\sqrt{5} + 12\sqrt{2}\right) + 2(30)$ $SA = 60 + 12\sqrt{5} + 12\sqrt{2} + 60$ $SA = 120 + 12\sqrt{5} + 12\sqrt{2} \text{ sq. yd.}$

④ Use the divisibility tests to identify each number as prime or composite.

405   Composite (3, 5, 9)   415   Composite (5)
409   Prime   417   Composite (3)
411   Composite (3)   419   Prime

⑤ Solve.
Scott has 156 containers that must be loaded in groups of 2 on a train. How many different combinations of 2 containers can Scott make on the train?

$$C(156, 2) = \frac{156!}{2!(154!)} = \frac{\overset{78}{\cancel{156}} \times 155 \times \cancel{154!}}{(\cancel{2} \times 1)(\cancel{154!})} = 12{,}090$$

Symmetry, Congruent Triangles   Worksheet 46

① Draw a line of symmetry in the figure below.

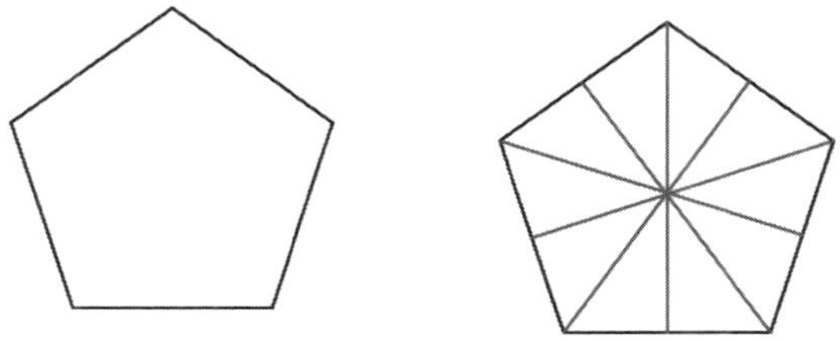

Any one of the above lines is correct.

② List the four congruence patterns for congruent triangles. For each congruence pattern, draw and label a pair of congruent triangles.

Answers may vary. A sample solution is given for each of the four congruence patterns.

SSS

ASA

SAS

AAS

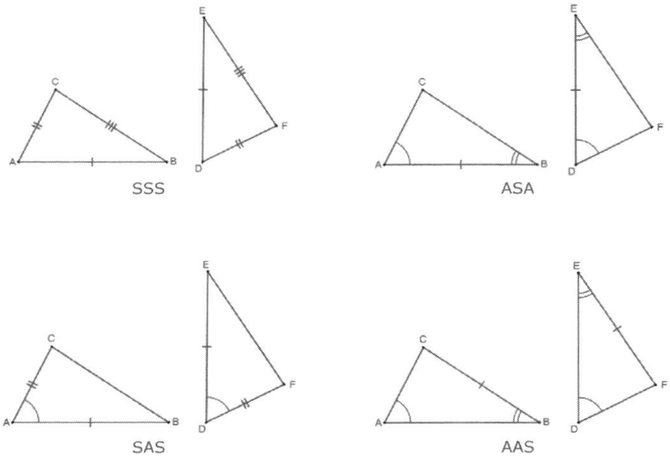

Teaching Tips, Cont.

> Ask the students for examples of the use of the word lateral. (lateral pass – pass to the side in football; lateral move in a company – new job on the same level rather than moving up or down; lateral view on a medical image – the view from the side)

> Explain that lateral area is the area of the side of a solid figure. Teach the formula for finding lateral area.

> Complete the Classwork exercises. Have some students work the problems on the board for the class and explain their answers. All students should work the problems in their books.

Assignments

- Complete Lesson 92, Activities 2-5.
- Bring scissors and tape for Lesson 97.

Lesson 93

Concepts
- Pyramids
- Volume of a pyramid
- Lateral area of a pyramid
- Surface area of a pyramid

Learning Objectives
The student will be able to:
- Define *pyramid*
- Calculate the volume of a pyramid
- Calculate the lateral area of a pyramid
- Calculate the surface area of a pyramid

Materials Needed
- Student Book, Lesson 93
- Worksheet 47

Teaching Tips
➤ Review prisms. (See Lesson 91.)

➤ Teach the definition of *pyramid* from the teaching box. Have the students compare and contrast prisms and pyramids.

➤ Teach how to find the volume of a pyramid. Tell the students that if they can find the volume of a prism, then they can easily find the volume of a pyramid with the same base and height by dividing by 3.

➤ Review the difference between surface area and lateral area. (See Lesson 92.)

Pyramids

A **pyramid** is a solid figure having a single polygonal base, and triangular lateral faces that meet at a single vertex.

To find the volume of a pyramid, use the formula $V = \frac{1}{3}Bh$, where B is the area of the base and h is the height of the pyramid.

To find the lateral area of a pyramid, use the formula $LA = \frac{1}{2}PL$, where P is the perimeter of the base, and L is the slant height of the pyramid.

To find the total surface area of a pyramid, use the formula $SA = \frac{1}{2}PL + B$, where P is the perimeter of the base, L is the slant height of the pyramid, and B is the area of the base.

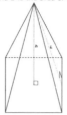

Find the volume, lateral area, and surface area of the above square pyramid if each side of the square is 10 cm, the height is 12 cm, and the slant height is 13 cm.

$V = \frac{1}{3}Bh$
$V = \frac{1}{3}(10^2)(12)$
$V = \frac{1}{3}(100)(12) = 400$ cm³
$LA = \frac{1}{2}PL$
$LA = \frac{1}{2}(4 \times 10)(13)$
$LA = \frac{1}{2}(40)(13) = 260$ cm²
$SA = \frac{1}{2}PL + B$
$SA = 260 + 100 = 360$ cm²

① Classwork
Find the volume, lateral area, and surface area.

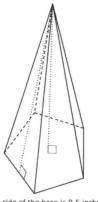

Given: Each side of the base is 9.5 inches, the height of the pyramid is 10 inches, the slant height is 12 inches, and the area of the base is 156 square inches.

$V = \frac{1}{3}Bh$
$V = \frac{1}{3}(156)(10)$
$V = (52)(10) = 520$ cubic inches

$LA = \frac{1}{2}PL$
$LA = \frac{1}{2}(5 \times 9.5)(12)$
$LA = (47.5)(6) = 285$ square inches

$SA = \frac{1}{2}PL + B$
$SA = 285 + 156 = 441$ square inches

Activities

② Calculate the volume of each pyramid.

Base of Pyramid	Height	Volume
$3\frac{1}{3}$ in. $1\frac{3}{4}$ in.	$2\frac{2}{5}$ in.	$V = \frac{1}{3}(3\frac{1}{3})(1\frac{3}{4})(2\frac{2}{5})$ $V = \frac{1}{3}\left(\frac{10}{3}\right)\left(\frac{7}{4}\right)\left(\frac{12}{5}\right)$ $V = \frac{14}{3} = 4\frac{2}{3}$ cu. in.
2.1 cm 2.1 cm	2.1 cm	$V = \frac{1}{3}(2.1)^3$ $V = \frac{1}{3}(9.261)$ $V = 3.087$ cm³
$\sqrt{13}$ 5 3 2 4	$2\sqrt{13}$ ft.	$V = \frac{1}{3}(\frac{1}{2}(6)(3))(2\sqrt{13})$ $V = \frac{1}{3}(9)(2\sqrt{13})$ $V = 3(2\sqrt{13}) = 6\sqrt{13}$ cu. ft.
4.3 m 6.1 m 10.2 m	3.5 m	$V = \frac{1}{3}(10.2)(4.3)(3.5)$ $V = \frac{1}{3}(153.51)$ $V = 51.17$ m³

③ Find the lateral area and total surface area of each pyramid.

Base of Pyramid	Slant Height	Lateral Area	Surface area
$3\frac{1}{3}$ in. $1\frac{3}{4}$ in.	$2\frac{2}{5}$ in.	$LA = \frac{1}{2}(2(3\frac{1}{3}) + 2(1\frac{3}{4}))(2\frac{2}{5})$ $LA = \frac{1}{2}(2(\frac{10}{3}) + 2(\frac{7}{4}))(\frac{12}{5})$ $LA = \frac{1}{2}(\frac{20}{3} + \frac{7}{2})(\frac{12}{5})$ $LA = \frac{1}{2}(\frac{40}{6} + \frac{21}{6})(\frac{12}{5})$ $LA = \frac{1}{2}(\frac{61}{6})(\frac{12}{5}) = \frac{61}{5} = 12\frac{1}{5}$ sq. in.	$SA = 12\frac{1}{5} + (3\frac{1}{3})(1\frac{3}{4})$ $SA = \frac{61}{5} + \frac{10}{3}\cdot(\frac{7}{4})$ $SA = \frac{61}{5} + \frac{35}{6}$ $SA = \frac{366}{30} + \frac{175}{30} = \frac{541}{30}$ $SA = 18\frac{1}{30}$ sq. in.
2.1 cm 2.1 cm	2.1 cm	$LA = \frac{1}{2}(4(2.1))(2.1)$ $LA = \frac{1}{2}(8.4)(2.1)$ $LA = 8.82$ cm²	$SA = 8.82 + (2.1)^2$ $SA = 8.82 + 4.41$ $SA = 13.23$ cm²
$\sqrt{13}$ 5 3 2 4	$2\sqrt{13}$ ft.	$LA = \frac{1}{2}(2 + 4 + 5 + \sqrt{13})(2\sqrt{13})$ $LA = \frac{1}{2}(11 + \sqrt{13})(2\sqrt{13})$ $LA = \frac{1}{2}(22\sqrt{13} + 26)$ $LA = 11\sqrt{13} + 13$ sq. ft.	$SA = (11\sqrt{13} + 13) + (\frac{1}{2}(2+4)(3))$ $SA = (11\sqrt{13} + 13) + (\frac{1}{2}(6)(3))$ $SA = (11\sqrt{13} + 13) + 9$ $SA = 11\sqrt{13} + 22$ sq. ft.

① Solve.

A prism is 12 inches tall and has a square base whose sides are each 10 inches.

What is the lateral area of the prism?
$LA = PL$

$LA = 4(10)(12)$

$LA = 480$ sq. in.

What is the surface area of the prism?
$SA = PL + 2B$

$SA = 4(10)(12) + 2(10)^2$

$SA = 480 + 200$

$SA = 680$ sq. in.

What is the volume of the prism?
$V = Bh$

$V = (10)^2(12)$

$V = 1200$ cu. in.

If a pyramid has the same base and height, what is the volume of the pyramid?
$V = \frac{1}{3}Bh$

$V = \frac{1}{3}(10)^2(12)$

$V = 400$ cu. in.

The slant height of the pyramid is 13 inches. What is the lateral area of the pyramid?
$LA = \frac{1}{2}PL$

$LA = \frac{1}{2}(40)(13)$

$LA = 260$ sq. in.

What is the surface area of the pyramid?
$SA = \frac{1}{2}PL + B$

$SA = \frac{1}{2}(40)(13) + (10)^2$

$SA = 260 + 100$

$SA = 360$ sq. in.

Teaching Tips, Cont.

➢ Teach how to find the surface area of a pyramid.

➢ Ask the students how many faces are excluded from the lateral area of a pyramid. (1) Ask the students which face is eliminated. (The base.) Teach how to find the lateral area of a pyramid.

➢ Complete the Classwork exercises. Have some students work the problems on the board for the class and explain their answers. All students should work the problems in their books.

Assignments

- Complete Lesson 93, Activities 2-3.
- Worksheet 47.
- Bring scissors and tape for Lesson 97.

Lesson 94

Concepts

- Cylinders
- Volume of a cylinder
- Lateral area of a cylinder
- Surface area of a cylinder
- Math in the real world

Learning Objectives

The student will be able to:

- Define *cylinder*
- Calculate the volume of a cylinder
- Calculate the lateral area of a cylinder
- Calculate the surface area of a cylinder

Materials Needed

- Student Book, Lesson 94
- 2 identical cans of food

Teaching Tips

➤ Prior to this lesson, empty out one can and cut the top and bottom off. Cut a slit in the side from top to bottom so the can opens to form a rectangle. Save all the pieces for use in this lesson.

➤ Review finding the area of a circle. (See Lesson 86.)

➤ Teach the definition of *cylinder* from the teaching box. Show the students the whole can you brought.

➤ Teach how to find the volume of a cylinder.

Cylinders

A **cylinder** is a solid figure having two parallel circles as bases which are joined by a curved surface.

To find the volume of a cylinder, use the formula $V = \pi r^2 h$, where r is the radius of the base, and h is the height of the cylinder. Notice that this follows the same format $V = Bh$.

To find the lateral area of a cylinder, use the formula $LA = 2\pi rL$, where L is the slant height of the cylinder. Notice that this follows the same format $LA = PL$. The circumference of a circle corresponds to the perimeter of a polygon.

To find the total surface area of a cylinder, use the formula $SA = 2\pi rL + 2\pi r^2$. Notice that this follows the same format $SA = PL + 2B$.

Find the volume, lateral area, and total surface area of the cylinder below if the radius is 3 mm and the height and slant height are both 8 mm.

$V = \pi r^2 h$
$V = \pi (3^2)(8)$
$V = \pi (9)(8) = 72\pi$ mm³

$LA = 2\pi rL$
$LA = 2\pi (3)(8)$
$LA = 2\pi (24) = 48\pi$ mm²

$SA = 2\pi rL + 2\pi r^2$
$SA = 48\pi + 2\pi (3^2)$
$SA = 48\pi + 2\pi (9)$
$SA = 48\pi + 18\pi = 66\pi$ mm²

① Classwork

Find the volume, lateral area, and total surface area of the cylinder below.

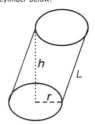

Given: A cylinder with diameter 10 yd., height 12 yd., and slant height 13 yd.

The radius is 10 ÷ 2 = 5 yd.

$V = \pi r^2 h$
$V = \pi (5^2)(12)$
$V = \pi (25)(12) = 300\pi$ cu. yd.

$LA = 2\pi rL$
$LA = 2\pi (5)(13)$
$LA = 2\pi (65) = 130\pi$ sq. yd.

$SA = 2\pi rL + 2\pi r^2$
$SA = 130\pi + 2\pi (5^2)$
$SA = 130\pi + 2\pi (25)$
$SA = 130\pi + 50\pi = 180\pi$ sq. yd.

② Complete the chart for cylinders.

Radius	Height	Slant Height	Volume	Lateral Area	Surface Area
7 mm	12 mm	12 mm	$V = \pi(7)^2(12)$ $V = \pi(49)(12)$ $V = 588\pi$ mm³	$LA = 2\pi(7)(12)$ $LA = 2\pi(84)$ $LA = 168\pi$ mm²	$SA = 168\pi + 2\pi(7)^2$ $SA = 168\pi + 2\pi(49)$ $SA = 168\pi + 98\pi = 266\pi$ mm²
5.2 in.	1.8 in.	1.8 in.	$V = \pi(5.2)^2(1.8)$ $V = \pi(27.04)(1.8)$ $V = 48.672\pi$ cu. in.	$LA = 2\pi(5.2)(1.8)$ $LA = 2\pi(9.36)$ $LA = 18.72\pi$ sq. ft.	$SA = 18.72\pi + 2\pi(5.2)^2$ $SA = 18.72\pi + 2\pi(27.04)$ $SA = 18.72\pi + 54.08\pi = 72.8\pi$ sq. in
$3\frac{1}{2}$ cm	$4\frac{1}{3}$ cm	$4\frac{1}{3}$ cm	$V = \pi\left(3\frac{1}{2}\right)^2\left(4\frac{1}{3}\right)$ $V = \pi\left(\frac{7}{2}\right)^2\left(\frac{13}{3}\right)$ $V = \pi\left(\frac{49}{4}\right)\left(\frac{13}{3}\right)$ $V = \frac{637\pi}{12}$ cm³	$LA = 2\pi\left(3\frac{1}{2}\right)\left(4\frac{1}{3}\right)$ $LA = 2\pi\left(\frac{7}{2}\right)\left(\frac{13}{3}\right)$ $LA = \frac{91\pi}{3}$ cm²	$SA = \frac{91\pi}{3} + 2\pi\left(3\frac{1}{2}\right)^2$ $SA = \frac{91\pi}{3} + 2\pi\left(\frac{7}{2}\right)^2$ $SA = \frac{91\pi}{3} + 2\pi\left(\frac{49}{4}\right)$ $SA = \frac{91\pi}{3} + \frac{49\pi}{2} = \frac{182\pi}{6} + \frac{147\pi}{6}$ $SA = \frac{229\pi}{6}$ cm²
$2\sqrt{3}$ ft.	$5\sqrt{3}$ ft.	$5\sqrt{3}$ ft.	$V = \pi\left(2\sqrt{3}\right)^2\left(5\sqrt{3}\right)$ $V = \pi(12)\left(5\sqrt{3}\right)$ $V = 60\pi\sqrt{3}$ cu. ft.	$LA = 2\pi\left(2\sqrt{3}\right)\left(5\sqrt{3}\right)$ $LA = 2\pi(30)$ $LA = 60\pi$ sq. ft.	$SA = 60\pi + 2\pi\left(2\sqrt{3}\right)^2$ $SA = 60\pi + 2\pi(12)$ $SA = 60\pi + 24\pi = 84\pi$ sq. ft.
6 m	8 m	10 m	$V = \pi(6)^2(8)$ $V = \pi(36)(8)$ $V = 288\pi$ m³	$LA = 2\pi(6)(10)$ $LA = 2\pi(60)$ $LA = 120\pi$ m²	$SA = 120\pi + 2\pi(6)^2$ $SA = 120\pi + 2\pi(36)$ $SA = 120\pi + 72\pi = 192\pi$ m²
0.5 yd.	1.2 yd.	1.3 yd.	$V = \pi(0.5)^2(1.2)$ $V = \pi(0.25)(1.2)$ $V = 0.3\pi$ cu. yd.	$LA = 2\pi(0.5)(1.3)$ $LA = 2\pi(0.65)$ $LA = 1.3\pi$ sq. yd.	$SA = 1.3\pi + 2\pi(0.5)^2$ $SA = 1.3\pi + 2\pi(0.25)$ $SA = 1.3\pi + 0.5\pi = 1.8\pi$ sq. yd.

③ Solve.

The tank portion of a tanker car on a train has a diameter of 3 meters and is 16 meters long. What is the volume of a tanker car? Use 3.14 as the value of pi.

$V = \pi r^2 h$

$V = (3.14)(1.5)^2(16)$

$V = 113.04$ m³

If 1 m³ = 264.1721 gallons, how many gallons can a tanker car hold? Round your answer to the nearest gallon.

$113.04 \times 264.1721 = 29{,}862$ gallons

Teaching Tips, Cont.

➢ Ask the students how they could find the surface area of the can. Show the top and bottom of the can you cut up. They should quickly determine they must find the area of two circles as the bases.

➢ Show the students how the lateral portion of the can opens to form a rectangle. Point out that the height of the rectangle is the same as the height of the can. Ask the students how they can find the length of the rectangle. (Many students will say to measure it with a ruler.) Curve the rectangle around to form a cylinder again. Ask the students what that distance is on the cylinder. (The circumference)

➢ Review the formula for finding circumference. (See Lesson 86.)

➢ Teach how to find the surface area and the lateral area of a cylinder.

➢ Complete the Classwork exercises. Have some students work the problems on the board for the class and explain their answers. All students should work the problems in their books.

Assignments

- Complete Lesson 94, Activities 2-3.
- Bring scissors and tape for Lesson 97.

Lesson 95

Concepts
- Cones
- Volume of a cone
- Lateral area of a cone
- Surface area of a cone
- Math in the real world

Learning Objectives
The student will be able to:
- Define *cone*
- Calculate the volume of a cone
- Calculate the lateral area of a cone
- Calculate the surface area of a cone

Materials Needed
- Student Book, Lesson 95
- Worksheet 48
- Party hat or other cone-shaped paper object

Teaching Tips
➤ Have students complete Worksheet 48 in class. This may be for added practice of earlier topics, or graded as a quiz, if desired.

➤ Review cylinders. (See Lesson 94.)

➤ Teach the definition of *cone* from the teaching box.

➤ Teach how to find the volume of a cone. Point out that the relationship between cylinders and cones is the same as the relationship between prisms and pyramids when it comes to volume.

Cones

A **cone** is a solid figure having a single circular base joining a curved surface that meets at a single vertex.

To find the volume of a cone, use the formula $V = \frac{1}{3}\pi r^2 h$, where r is the radius of the base, and h is the height of the cone.

To find the lateral area of a cone, use the formula $LA = \pi r L$, where L is the slant height of the cone.

To find the total surface area of a cone, use the formula $SA = \pi r L + \pi r^2$.

Find the volume, lateral area, and total surface area of the cone if the radius is 7 units, the height is 24 units, and the slant height is 25 units.

$V = \frac{1}{3}\pi r^2 h$
$V = \frac{1}{3}\pi (7)^2 (24^{\;8})$
$V = \pi(49)(8)$
$V = 392\pi$ cu. units

$LA = \pi r L$
$LA = \pi(7)(25)$
$LA = 175\pi$ sq. units

$SA = \pi r L + \pi r^2$
$SA = 175\pi + \pi(7)^2$
$SA = 175\pi + 49\pi = 224\pi$ sq. units

① Classwork
Find the volume, lateral area, and total surface area of the cone.

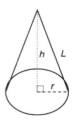

Given: A cone with radius 8 in., height 15 in., and slant height 17 in.

$V = \frac{1}{3}\pi r^2 h$
$V = \frac{1}{3}\pi (8)^2 (15^{\;5})$
$V = \pi(64)(5)$
$V = 320\pi$ cu. in.

$LA = \pi r L$
$LA = \pi(8)(17)$
$LA = 136\pi$ sq. in.

$SA = \pi r L + \pi r^2$
$SA = 136\pi + \pi(8)^2$
$SA = 136\pi + 64\pi = 200\pi$ sq. in.

Activities
② Complete the chart for cones.

Radius	Height	Slant Height	Volume	Lateral Area	Surface Area
7 mm	12 mm	12 mm	$V = \frac{1}{3}\pi (7)^2 (12)$ $V = \frac{1}{3}\pi(49)(12^{\;4})$ $V = 196\pi$ mm³	$LA = \pi(7)(12)$ $LA = \pi(84)$ $LA = 84\pi$ mm²	$SA = 84\pi + \pi(7)^2$ $SA = 84\pi + \pi(49)$ $SA = 84\pi + 49\pi = 133\pi$ mm²
5.2 in.	1.8 in.	1.8 in.	$V = \frac{1}{3}\pi (5.2)^2 (1.8)$ $V = \frac{1}{3}\pi(27.04)(1.8)$ $V = 16.224\pi$ cu. in.	$LA = \pi(5.2)(1.8)$ $LA = \pi(9.36)$ $LA = 9.36\pi$ sq. ft.	$SA = 9.36\pi + \pi(5.2)^2$ $SA = 9.36\pi + \pi(27.04)$ $SA = 9.36\pi + 27.04\pi = 36.4\pi$ sq. in.
$3\frac{1}{2}$ cm	$4\frac{1}{3}$ cm	$4\frac{1}{3}$ cm	$V = \frac{1}{3}\pi (3\frac{1}{2})^2 (4\frac{1}{3})$ $V = \frac{1}{3}\pi(\frac{7}{2})^2(\frac{13}{3})$ $V = \frac{1}{3}\pi(\frac{49}{4})(\frac{13}{3})$ $V = \frac{637\pi}{36}$ cm³	$LA = \pi(3\frac{1}{2})(4\frac{1}{3})$ $LA = \pi(\frac{7}{2})(\frac{13}{3})$ $LA = \frac{91\pi}{6}$ cm²	$SA = \frac{91\pi}{6} + \pi(3\frac{1}{2})^2$ $SA = \frac{91\pi}{6} + \pi(\frac{7}{2})^2$ $SA = \frac{91\pi}{6} + \pi(\frac{49}{4})$ $SA = \frac{91\pi}{6} + \frac{49\pi}{4} = \frac{182\pi}{12} + \frac{147\pi}{12}$ $SA = \frac{329\pi}{12}$ cm²
$2\sqrt{3}$ ft.	$5\sqrt{3}$ ft.	$5\sqrt{3}$ ft.	$V = \frac{1}{3}\pi (2\sqrt{3})^2 (5\sqrt{3})$ $V = \frac{1}{3}\pi(12^{\;4})(5\sqrt{3})$ $V = 20\sqrt{3}\pi$ cu. ft.	$LA = \pi(2\sqrt{3})(5\sqrt{3})$ $LA = \pi(30)$ $LA = 30\pi$ sq. ft.	$SA = 30\pi + \pi(2\sqrt{3})^2$ $SA = 30\pi + \pi(12)$ $SA = 30\pi + 12\pi = 42\pi$ sq. ft.
6 m	8 m	10 m	$V = \frac{1}{3}\pi (6)^2 (8)$ $V = \frac{1}{3}\pi(36^{\;12})(8)$ $V = 96\pi$ m³	$LA = \pi(6)(10)$ $LA = \pi(60)$ $LA = 60\pi$ m²	$SA = 60\pi + \pi(6)^2$ $SA = 60\pi + \pi(36)$ $SA = 60\pi + 36\pi = 96\pi$ m²
0.5 yd.	1.2 yd.	1.3 yd.	$V = \frac{1}{3}\pi (0.5)^2 (1.2)$ $V = \frac{1}{3}\pi(0.25)(1.2)$ $V = 0.1\pi$ cu. yd.	$LA = \pi(0.5)(1.3)$ $LA = \pi(0.65)$ $LA = 0.65\pi$ sq. yd.	$SA = 0.65\pi + \pi(0.5)^2$ $SA = 0.65\pi + \pi(0.25)$ $SA = 0.65\pi + 0.25\pi = 0.9\pi$ sq. yd

③ Solve.
Scott is assembling a train whose maximum length is 7000 feet. He must have 4 engines, 8 tanker cars, 12 boxcars, and the remaining cars are articulated well cars. Given the dimensions below, how many articulated well cars can Scott attach to the train?

Engine: 59' 2"   Tanker: 59' 9"   Boxcar: 58' 4.25"   Articulated well: 76' 8.75"

Convert everything to inches – Engine: 710 in.   Tanker: 717 in.   Boxcar: 700.25 in.
Articulated well: 920.75 in.   Total train: 84,000 in.
Length remaining for articulated well: 84,000 – 4(710) – 8(717) – 12(700.25) =
84,000 – 2840 – 5736 – 8403 = 67,021 inches
67,021 ÷ 920.75 = 72.8
Scott can add 72 articulated well cars to the train.

Horizons Pre-Algebra, Teacher's Guide   248

① Solve.

A prism is 4 inches tall and has a square base whose sides are each 6 inches.

What is the lateral area of the prism?
$LA = PL$
$LA = 4(6)(4)$
$LA = 96$ sq. in.

What is the surface area of the prism?
$SA = PL + 2B$
$SA = 4(6)(4) + 2(6)^2$
$SA = 96 + 72$
$SA = 168$ sq. in.

What is the volume of the prism?
$V = Bh$
$V = (6)^2(4)$
$V = 144$ cu. in.

If a pyramid has the same base and height, what is the volume of the pyramid?
$V = \frac{1}{3}Bh$
$V = \frac{1}{3}(6)^2(4)$
$V = 48$ cu. in.

The slant height of the pyramid is 5 inches. What is the lateral area of the pyramid?
$LA = \frac{1}{2}PL$
$LA = \frac{1}{2}(24)(5)$
$LA = 60$ sq. in.

What is the surface area of the pyramid?
$SA = \frac{1}{2}PL + B$
$SA = \frac{1}{2}(24)(5) + (6)^2$
$SA = 60 + 36$
$SA = 96$ sq. in.

Teaching Tips, Cont.

➢ Show students the cone you brought. Cut the side of the cone from the base to the tip to open it up. Ask the students if the side of the cone is equal to the height of the cone. (No.) Why not? (The side of the cone is at an angle to the base rather than perpendicular.)

➢ Ask the students how they can know the length of the curved side of the wedge. (Some may remember from the cylinder that it is the same as the circumference of the base.)

➢ Teach how to find the surface area and lateral area of a cone from the teaching box.

➢ Complete the Classwork exercises. Have some students work the problems on the board for the class and explain their answers. All students should work the problems in their books.

Assignments

• Complete Lesson 95, Activities 2-3.
• Bring scissors and tape for Lesson 97.

Lesson 96

Concepts
- Spheres
- Volume of a sphere
- Surface area of a sphere
- Divisibility tests
- Prime/composite numbers
- Prime factorization
- Faces, edges, and vertices of solids
- Math in the real world

Learning Objectives
The student will be able to:
- Define *sphere*
- Calculate the volume of a sphere
- Calculate the surface area of a sphere

Materials Needed
- Student Book, Lesson 96

Teaching Tips
➤ Review cylinders. (See Lesson 94.)

➤ Introduce spheres from the teaching box.

➤ Tell the students that Archimedes showed that the volume of a sphere is equal to $\frac{2}{3}$ the volume of a cylinder having the same radius and whose height is equal to the diameter of the sphere. Derive the formula for the volume of a sphere using this method. See the derivation at the right for details.

Spheres

A **sphere** is the set of all points equidistant from a single point, called the center.

To find the volume of a sphere, use the formula $V = \frac{4}{3}\pi r^3$, where r is the radius of the sphere.

A sphere has no lateral area. To find the surface area of a sphere, use the formula $SA = 4\pi r^2$, where r is the radius of the sphere.

Find the volume and surface area of the sphere below if the radius is 10 feet.

$V = \frac{4}{3}\pi r^3$
$V = \frac{4}{3}\pi (10)^3$
$V = \frac{4}{3}\pi (1000)$
$V = \frac{4000\pi}{3}$ cu. ft.

$SA = 4\pi (10)^2$
$SA = 4\pi (100)$
$SA = 400\pi$ sq. ft.

① Classwork
Find the volume and surface area of the sphere below.

Given: A sphere with diameter 8 m.

The radius is 4 m.

$V = \frac{4}{3}\pi r^3$
$V = \frac{4}{3}\pi (4)^3$
$V = \frac{4}{3}\pi (64)$
$V = \frac{256\pi}{3}$ m³

$SA = 4\pi (4)^2$
$SA = 4\pi (16)$
$SA = 64\pi$ m²

Activities
② Find the volume and surface area of the balls below.

Basketball radius = 4.75 in.	Baseball diameter = 3 in.	Volleyball diameter = 9 in.
$V = \frac{4}{3}\pi \left(4\frac{3}{4}\right)^3$	$V = \frac{4}{3}\pi r^3$	$V = \frac{4}{3}\pi r^3$
$V = \frac{4}{3}\pi \left(\frac{19}{4}\right)^3$	$V = \frac{4}{3}\pi \left(\frac{3}{2}\right)^3$	$V = \frac{4}{3}\pi \left(\frac{9}{2}\right)^3$
$V = \frac{4}{3}\pi \left(\frac{6859}{64}\right)$	$V = \frac{4}{3}\pi \left(\frac{27}{8}\right)$	$V = \frac{4}{3}\pi \left(\frac{729}{8}\right)$
$V = \frac{6859\pi}{48}$ cu. in.	$V = \frac{9\pi}{2}$ cu. in.	$V = \frac{243\pi}{2}$ cu. in.
$SA = 4\pi \left(\frac{19}{4}\right)^2$	$SA = 4\pi \left(\frac{3}{2}\right)^2$	$SA = 4\pi \left(\frac{9}{2}\right)^2$
$SA = 4\pi \left(\frac{361}{16}\right)$	$SA = 4\pi \left(\frac{9}{4}\right)$	$SA = 4\pi \left(\frac{81}{4}\right)$
$SA = \frac{361\pi}{4}$ sq. in.	$SA = 9\pi$ sq. in.	$SA = 81\pi$ sq. in.

Derivation of Formula for the Volume of a Sphere

Volume of a cylinder:
$V = \pi r^2 h$

The height is equal to the diameter of the sphere, or 2*r*.

Substitute this in the equation.
$V = \pi r^2 (2r)$
$V = 2\pi r^3$

Multiply by $\frac{2}{3}$ to get the volume of the sphere.
$V = \frac{2}{3}\left(2\pi r^3\right)$
$V = \frac{4}{3}\pi r^3$

③ Use the divisibility tests to identify each number as prime or composite.

421	Prime	429	Composite (3)
423	Composite (3, 9)	431	Prime
425	Composite (5)	433	Prime

④ Give the prime factorization of each number, using exponents where appropriate.

148	150	175
$148 = 2 \times 2 \times 37$	$150 = 2 \times 3 \times 5 \times 5$	$175 = 5 \times 5 \times 7$
$148 = 2^2 \times 37$	$150 = 2 \times 3 \times 5^2$	$175 = 5^2 \times 7$

⑤ Complete the chart to show the number of faces, edges, and vertices in each solid figure.

Sides on a base	Number of bases	Faces	Edges	Vertices
5	1	$5 + 1 = 6$	$2(5) = 10$	$5 + 1 = 6$
5	2	$5 + 2 = 7$	$3(5) = 15$	$2(5) = 10$
6	1	$6 + 1 = 7$	$2(6) = 12$	$6 + 1 = 7$
6	2	$6 + 2 = 8$	$3(6) = 18$	$2(6) = 12$
10	1	$10 + 1 = 11$	$2(10) = 20$	$10 + 1 = 11$
10	2	$10 + 2 = 12$	$3(10) = 30$	$2(10) = 20$

⑥ Solve.

Scott has room for 72 articulated well cars on the train he is assembling. Each articulated well car can carry two 53-ft. containers or one 53-ft. container and two 20-ft. containers. Scott has 125 53-ft. containers and 50 20-ft. containers to load on the train. If each articulated well car must have at least one 53-ft. container, and all 53-ft. containers have a higher priority than the 20-ft. containers, is there enough room on the train for all of the 20-ft. containers? If so, how many more 20-ft. containers will there be room for when Scott is done loading? If not, how many 20-ft. containers will be left in the train yard?

This problem requires logical thinking to solve.

Each car must have a 53-ft. container, so that leaves 125 – 72 = 53 containers to be doubled up. This leaves 72 – 53 = 19 cars with space for the 20-ft. containers.

Since each car can hold two 20-ft. trailers, there is room for 19 × 2 = 38 of the 20-ft. containers. There were 50 of these containers to begin with, so that leaves 50 – 38 = 12 containers in the train yard.

There is not enough room for all of the containers. 12 will remain in the train yard.

Teaching Tips, Cont.

➢ Teach how to find the surface area of a sphere from the teaching box.

➢ Ask the students if a sphere has a separate lateral area calculation. (No.) Why not? (It does not have any bases.)

➢ Complete the Classwork exercises. Have some students work the problems on the board for the class and explain their answers. All students should work the problems in their books.

Assignments

- Complete Lesson 96, Activities 2-6.
- Bring scissors and tape for the next lesson.

Lesson 97

Concepts
- Nets of solid figures
- Octahedrons
- Dodecahedrons
- Icosahedrons

Learning Objectives
The student will be able to:
- Define *net*
- Tell the number of faces in a octahedron, dodecahedron, and icosahedrons
- Draw nets of solid figures
- Assemble solid figures from nets

Materials Needed
- Student Book, Lesson 97
- Nets Supplements 1-3 (in back of *Tests & Resources* book)
- Scissors
- Cellophane tape

Teaching Tips
- ➤ Note to the teacher: This lesson is an exercise in spatial relations. Students with non-verbal learning disabilities or other conditions that affect skills in this area may need extra assistance. For this reason, only the names of the solid figures introduced in this lesson will be tested, not the nets themselves.

- ➤ Teach nets from the teaching box.

- ➤ Instruct the students to remove Nets Supplements 1-3 from the back of the *Tests & Resources* book. Have the students follow the directions for each net to assemble the given three-dimensional figure.

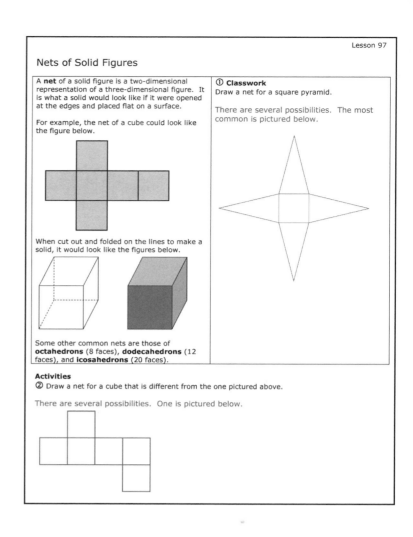

Nets of Solid Figures

A **net** of a solid figure is a two-dimensional representation of a three-dimensional figure. It is what a solid would look like if it were opened at the edges and placed flat on a surface.

For example, the net of a cube could look like the figure below.

When cut out and folded on the lines to make a solid, it would look like the figures below.

Some other common nets are those of **octahedrons** (8 faces), **dodecahedrons** (12 faces), and **icosahedrons** (20 faces).

① Classwork
Draw a net for a square pyramid.

There are several possibilities. The most common is pictured below.

Activities
② Draw a net for a cube that is different from the one pictured above.

There are several possibilities. One is pictured below.

③ Identify each net as an octahedron, dodecahedron, or icosahedron. Match each net with its 3-dimensional figure.

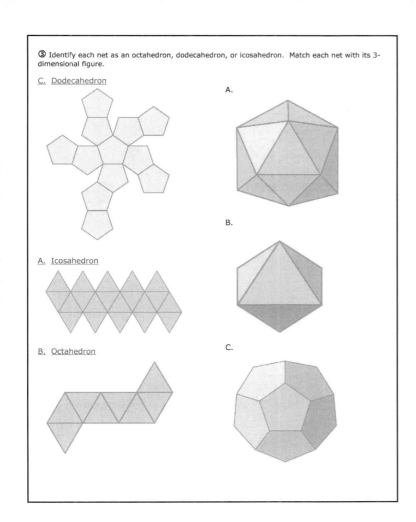

C. Dodecahedron

A. Icosahedron

B. Octahedron

A.

B.

C.

Teaching Tips, Cont.
➢ Use the shapes the students have assembled to teach the octahedron, dodecahedron, and icosahedron.

➢ Complete the Classwork exercise. Have one student work the problem on the board for the class and explain the answer. All students should work the problems in their books.

Assignment
• Complete Lesson 97, Activities 2-3.

Lesson 98

Concepts
- Mass
- Weight
- Volume of a prism
- Volume of a pyramid
- Volume of a cylinder
- Volume of a cone
- Volume of a cube
- Volume of a sphere
- Surface area of a sphere

Learning Objectives
The student will be able to:
- Define *mass* and *weight*
- Calculate mass when the weight and force of gravity are known
- Calculate weight when the mass and force of gravity are known

Materials Needed
- Student Book, Lesson 98
- Worksheet 49
- Something that is sold by weight, such as fresh produce
- A scale that gives mass in grams, if possible

Teaching Tips
➤ Have students complete Worksheet 49 in class. This may be for added practice of earlier topics, or graded as a quiz, if desired.

➤ Teach the definitions of mass and weight from the teaching box. Emphasize that the mass of an object does not change with a change in location, but the weight of an object can.

➤ Show the students the fresh produce (or whatever you brought). This example will use an apple.

Mass

Mass is the amount of matter in an object. Although mass is related to weight, it is not the same thing. **Weight** is a measure of the force of gravity on an object's mass. An object's weight will change with a change in location. This is why you weigh less at higher elevations than you do at lower elevations. Mass remains constant because it is not dependent on gravity.

The standard SI unit of mass is the kilogram.

The formula for mass is $m = \frac{w}{g}$, where m is the mass, w is the weight, and g is the force of gravity.

Find the mass of a train boxcar if its weight is 329,838.6 kg•m/s², and the force of gravity is 9.8 m/s².

$m = \frac{w}{g}$

$m = \frac{329{,}838.6 \text{ kg•m/s}^2}{9.8 \text{ m/s}^2}$

$m = 33{,}657 \text{ kg}$

① **Classwork**
Solve.

Find the mass of a hopper car if the weight is 273,380.8 kg•m/s² and the force of gravity is 9.8 m/s².

$m = \frac{w}{g}$

$m = \frac{273{,}380.8 \text{ kg•m/s}^2}{9.8 \text{ m/s}^2}$

$m = 27{,}896 \text{ kg}$

Find the weight of an empty car carrier if the mass is 67,132 kg and the force of gravity is 9.8 m/s².

$m = \frac{w}{g}$

$67{,}132 \text{ kg} = \frac{w}{9.8 \text{ m/s}^2}$

$w = 657{,}893.6 \text{ kg • m/s}^2$

Activities

② Complete the chart for each type of train car.

	Engine	Tanker	Articulated Well
Mass	$m = \frac{w}{g}$ $m = \frac{1{,}958{,}040 \text{ kg•m/s}^2}{9.8 \text{ m/s}^2}$ $m = 199{,}800 \text{ kg}$	29,801 kg	$m = \frac{w}{g}$ $m = \frac{224{,}478.8 \text{ kg•m/s}^2}{9.8 \text{ m/s}^2}$ $m = 22{,}906 \text{ kg}$
Weight	1,958,040 kg • m/s²	$29{,}801 \text{ kg} = \frac{w}{9.8 \text{ m/s}^2}$ $w = 292{,}049.8 \text{ kg • m/s}^2$	224,478.8 kg • m/s²
Gravity	9.8 m/s²	9.8 m/s²	9.8 m/s²

---

③ Find the volume of each solid.
A prism with a base that is 14 sq. in. and a height of 4.5 inches.
$V = Bh$
$V = (14 \text{ sq. in.})(4.5 \text{ in.})$
$V = 63$ cubic in.

A pyramid with a base that is 14 sq. in. and a height of 4.5 inches.
$V = \frac{1}{3}Bh$
$V = \frac{1}{3}(14 \text{ sq. in.})(4.5 \text{ in.})$
$V = \frac{1}{3}(63)$ cubic in.
$V = 21$ cubic in.

A cylinder with a radius that is 1.5 cm and a height of 9.2 cm.
$V = \pi (1.5)^2 (9.2)$
$V = \pi (2.25)(9.2)$
$V = 20.7\pi$ cm³

A cone with a radius that is 1.5 cm and a height of 9.2 cm.
$V = \frac{1}{3}\pi (1.5)^2 (9.2)$
$V = \frac{1}{3}\pi (2.25)(9.2)$
$V = 6.9\pi$ cm³

A cube with an edge equal to 12.5 m.
$V = e^3$
$V = (12.5)^3$
$V = 1953.125$ cm³

④ Solve.
Find the volume and surface area of a sphere with a 10-in. diameter.
The radius is 10 ÷ 2 = 5 in.

$V = \frac{4}{3}\pi (5)^3$ $SA = 4\pi (5)^2$
$V = \frac{4}{3}\pi (125)$ $SA = 4\pi (25)$
$V = \frac{500\pi}{3}$ cu. in. $SA = 100\pi$ sq. in.

Find the radius and volume of a sphere with a surface area of 64π mm².

$64 \text{ mm}^2 = 4\pi (r)^2$ $^{16 \text{ mm}^2}$ $V = \frac{4}{3}\pi (4)^3$
$16 \text{ mm}^2 = r^2$ $V = \frac{4}{3}\pi (64)$
$\sqrt{16 \text{ mm}^2} = \sqrt{r^2}$ $V = \frac{256\pi}{3}$ mm³
$4 \text{ mm} = r$

① Solve.

A cylinder is 12 inches tall and has a base whose diameter is 10 inches.

What is the lateral area of the cylinder?
$LA = 2\pi rL$
$LA = 2\pi(5)(12)$
$LA = 120\pi$ sq. in.

What is the surface area of the cylinder?
$SA = 2\pi rL + 2\pi r^2$
$SA = 2\pi(5)(12) + 2\pi(5)^2$
$SA = 120\pi + 2\pi(25)$
$SA = 170\pi$ sq. in.

What is the volume of the cylinder?
$V = \pi r^2 h$
$V = \pi(5)^2(12)$
$V = 300\pi$ cu. in.

If a cone has the same base and height, what is the volume of the cone?
$V = \frac{1}{3}\pi r^2 h$
$V = \frac{1}{3}\pi(5)^2(12)$
$V = 100\pi$ cu. in.

The slant height of the cone is 13 inches. What is the lateral area of the cone?
$LA = \pi rL$
$LA = \pi(5)(13)$
$LA = 65\pi$ sq. in.

What is the surface area of the cone?
$SA = \pi rL + \pi r^2$
$SA = \pi(5)(13) + \pi(5)^2$
$SA = 65\pi + 25\pi$
$SA = 90\pi$ sq. in.

Note about weight units:

The unit $kg \cdot m/s^2$ seen in this lesson is the SI unit of weight. This unit is also known as the Newton, abbreviated N.

$1 \ kg \cdot m/s^2 = 1 \ N$

One Newton is equivalent to just under a quarter pound. One pound is equivalent to just under $4\frac{1}{2}$ Newtons.

Teaching Tips, Cont.

➤ If you have a scale, find the mass of the apple in grams. Ask the students what the mass of the apple would be at the ocean. (The same as it is now.) Ask the students what the mass of the apple would be in Denver, CO. (The same as it is now.) Ask the students what would happen to the weight of the apple when it was moved from the ocean to Denver. (It would decrease. Denver's altitude is about one mile above sea level.)

➤ Teach the formula for finding mass from the teaching box. Show the students that the weight of an object can be determined when the mass is known by solving the equation for w.

➤ Complete the Classwork exercises. Have some students work the problems on the board for the class and explain their answers. All students should work the problems in their books.

Assignment
• Complete Lesson 98, Activities 2-4.

Lesson 99

Concepts
- Density
- Mass
- Math in the real world

Learning Objectives
The student will be able to:
- Define *density*
- Calculate the density of an object
- Determine if an object will sink or float in water based on its density

Materials Needed
- Student Book, Lesson 99
- 2 objects with the same mass but different sizes
- 2 objects the same size but with different masses
- Scale that measures in grams

Teaching Tips
➤ Review mass. (See Lesson 98.)

➤ Ask the students if objects having the same mass are the same size. (No.) Show the students the two objects you brought that have the same mass. Ask why the two objects are not the same size. (Most students will say it is because one object has more air in it taking up space. The correct answer is that one object is more dense than the other.)

➤ Show the students the two objects that are the same size but have different masses. Ask the students if they have the same mass. (No.) Weigh the objects to show they have different masses.

Density

Density is the amount of mass per unit of volume an object has. Two objects with the same dimensions can have different weights if their densities are different. The greater the density, the greater the weight of an object of equal size.

The formula for density is $d = \frac{m}{v}$, where d is the density, m is the mass, and v is the volume.

What is the density of water if 3 kg has a volume of 0.003 m^3?

$d = \frac{m}{v}$

$d = \frac{3 \text{ kg}}{0.003 \text{ m}^3}$

$d = 1000$ kg/m^3

This is the density of pure water at 4° Celsius (about 39° Fahrenheit). Tap water has a slightly higher density that varies by location. Temperature will also affect the density of water. Materials with a higher density will sink in water, and material with a lower density will float in water.

① **Classwork.**
Solve.

Will a piece of solid chalk sink or float in pure water if a 0.5 m^3 piece of chalk has a mass of 1249.5 kg?

$d = \frac{m}{v}$

$d = \frac{1249.5 \text{ kg}}{0.5 \text{ m}^3}$

$d = 2499$ kg/m^3

The chalk will sink because it has a higher density.

Activities
② Find the density of each substance and identify if it will float in pure water.

Substance	Mass	Volume	Density	Float: Y/N
Apples	128.2 kg	0.2 m^3	$d = \frac{m}{v}$ $d = \frac{128.2 \text{ kg}}{0.2 \text{ m}^3}$ $d = 641$ kg/m^3	Y
Ice	1314.17 kg	1.43 m^3	$d = \frac{m}{v}$ $d = \frac{1314.17 \text{ kg}}{1.43 \text{ m}^3}$ $d = 919$ kg/m^3	Y
Solid soap	5526.9 kg	6.9 m^3	$d = \frac{m}{v}$ $d = \frac{5526.9 \text{ kg}}{6.9 \text{ m}^3}$ $d = 801$ kg/m^3	Y
Silver	839.2 kg	0.08 m^3	$d = \frac{m}{v}$ $d = \frac{839.2 \text{ kg}}{0.08 \text{ m}^3}$ $d = 10490$ kg/m^3	N

---

③ Solve.

The tank portion of a train tanker car can hold 113.04 m³. If the density of sodium hydroxide is 1250 kg/m³, how many kilograms of sodium hydroxide can a tanker car hold?

$d = \frac{m}{v}$

$1250 \text{ kg/m}^3 = \frac{m}{113.04 \text{ m}^3}$

$m = \left(1250 \text{ kg/m}^3\right)\left(113.04 \text{ m}^3\right)$

$m = 141{,}300 \text{ kg}$

How many grams of sodium hydroxide can a tanker car hold?

$141{,}300 \text{ kg} = 141{,}300 \times 1000 = 141{,}300{,}000 \text{ g}$

What is the weight (in kg•m/s²) of the sodium hydroxide in a full tanker car? (The force of gravity is 9.8 m/s².)

$m = \frac{w}{g}$

$141{,}300 \text{ kg} = \frac{w}{9.8 \text{ m/s}^2}$

$w = 1{,}384{,}740 \text{ kg} \cdot \text{m/s}^2$

④ Solve.

A 0.41 m³ piece of gold has a mass of 7921.2 kg. What is the density of gold?

$d = \frac{m}{v}$

$d = \frac{7921.2 \text{ kg}}{0.41 \text{ m}^3}$

$d = 19{,}320 \text{ kg/m}^3$

A 1.52 m³ piece of pyrite (fool's gold) has a mass of 7622.8 kg. What is the density of pyrite?

$d = \frac{m}{v}$

$d = \frac{7622.8 \text{ kg}}{1.52 \text{ m}^3}$

$d = 5015 \text{ kg/m}^3$

If someone was trying to pass off fool's gold as real gold, how would you be able to tell the difference?

Use a balance or scale to find the mass of the sample. For irregular pieces, you can drop the sample in water to determine its volume. Use these figures to calculate the density of the sample. Knowing the density of gold, you would easily be able to tell whether or not the sample is real gold.

Students are not expected to know this, but 1 cm³ = 5 mL. 1,000,000 cm³ = 1 m³

Teaching Tips, Cont.

➢ Teach density from the teaching box.

➢ Tell the students that body fat has a lower density than skeletal muscle, so it is possible to gain weight when following an exercise program because the less dense fat is being replaced by the more dense muscle. You may wear a smaller size even though you weigh more!

➢ Teach the density of water from the teaching box. Explain how to determine whether or not an object will float in water based on its density.

➢ Complete the Classwork exercise. Have one student work the problem on the board for the class and explain the answer. All students should work the problem in their books.

Assignment

• Complete Lesson 99, Activities 2-4.

Horizons Pre-Algebra, Teacher's Guide

Lesson 100

Concepts
- Time
- Velocity
- Simple interest
- Compound interest
- Math in the real world

Learning Objectives
The student will be able to:
- List units of time
- Define *velocity*
- Explain the difference between velocity and speed
- Perform calculations using velocity, distance, and time

Materials Needed
- Student Book, Lesson 100
- Worksheet 50

Teaching Tips
➤ Teach time from the teaching box. Most students should already have the time equivalents memorized.

➤ Ask a student to give an example of speed. (55 miles per hour) Point out that speed always involves a unit of time. Ask a student to give an example of velocity. (Most students will give an answer similar speed, but it should include a direction, such as 55 miles per hour north.)

➤ Teach velocity from the teaching box. Most students confuse speed and velocity and think they are the exact same thing. Explain that velocity is similar to speed, but with an added component – direction.

Time and Velocity

Time is measured in days, hours, minutes, and seconds. Other units of time are based on these units. Time conversions that must be memorized are as follows:
1 day = 24 hours; 1 hour = 60 minutes; 1 minute = 60 seconds.

Velocity is closely related to speed. While speed is traveling a particular distance in a given amount of time, such as 55 miles per hour, velocity has an added component: direction.
Velocity is displacement in a straight line in a given amount of time. Think of velocity as the distance "as the crow flies" over a period of time. For example, if you travel 3 miles north, then 4 miles west, you are really just 5 miles in a straight line from where you started.

To calculate velocity, use the formula $v = \frac{d}{t}$, where v is velocity, d is displacement (or straight-line distance), and t is time. Average speed uses the same formula, without worrying about the distance being in a straight line.

Find the velocity of a freight train that travels 135 miles north in 3 hours.
$v = \frac{d}{t}$
$v = \frac{135 \text{ miles}}{3 \text{ hours}}$
$v = 45$ miles per hour

You will not be required to include the direction of travel as part of your answer in this book, but you should note that direction will be included when you reach physics-level classes.

Note: Convert the time measurements to the same unit *before* doing any math calculations.

① Classwork

Convert 60 miles per hour to feet per second.
$\frac{60 \text{ miles}}{1 \text{ hour}} \times \frac{5280 \text{ feet}}{1 \text{ mile}} \times \frac{1 \text{ hour}}{60 \text{ minutes}} \times \frac{1 \text{ minute}}{60 \text{ seconds}} =$
88 ft./sec.

The men's downhill Alpine skiing course at the 2010 Winter Olympics in Vancouver had a 1100 m vertical drop. Calculate the vertical velocity in meters per second for the three medal winners if the gold medalist finished in 1 minute 54.31 seconds, the silver medalist finished in 1 minute 54.38 seconds, and the bronze medalist finished in 1 minute 54.40 seconds. Round answers to the nearest thousandth.

Convert all times to seconds.
Gold: 60 + 54.31 = 114.31 seconds
Silver: 60 + 54.38 = 114.38 seconds
Bronze: 60 + 54.40 = 114.40 seconds

For each medalist, divide 1100 meters by the number of seconds.
Gold: 1100 ÷ 114.31 = 9.623 m/s
Silver: 1100 ÷ 114.38 = 9.617 m/s
Bronze: 1100 ÷ 114.40 = 9.615 m/s

Activities
② Complete the chart.

Velocity	Distance	Time
$v = \frac{165 \text{ miles}}{3 \text{ hours}}$ $v = 55$ miles/hour	165 miles	3 hours
48 miles per hour	$d = (48 \text{ miles/hour})(2.5 \text{ hours})$ $d = 120$ miles	2.5 hours
70 miles per hour	301 miles	$t = \frac{301 \text{ miles}}{70 \text{ miles/hour}}$ $t = 4.3$ hours

---

③ Solve.
NASA's space shuttle assembly building is 3.4 miles from the launch pad. It takes the crawler-transporter 6 hours to move the shuttle from the assembly building to the launch pad. How many feet does the crawler-transporter have to move the shuttle?

$3.4 \text{ miles} \times \frac{5280 \text{ feet}}{1 \text{ mile}} = 17{,}952$ ft.

How many minutes does it take the crawler-transporter to move the shuttle to the launch pad?

$6 \text{ hours} \times \frac{60 \text{ minutes}}{1 \text{ hour}} = 360$ min.

What is the crawler-transporter's average velocity in feet per minute? Round your answer to the nearest whole number.

$\frac{3.4 \text{ miles}}{6 \text{ hour}} \times \frac{5280 \text{ feet}}{1 \text{ mile}} \times \frac{1 \text{ hour}}{60 \text{ minutes}} = 49.86 \text{ ft./min.} \approx 50$ ft./min

④ Solve.
Two trains leave the station at the same time going in opposite directions. One train is traveling at 35 miles per hour, and the other train is traveling at 45 miles per hour. How far apart will the trains be after 2 hours 15 minutes?

Convert the time to hours. 15 minutes = .25 hours, so the total time is 2.25 hours.

The first train travels $d = (35 \text{ miles/hour})(2.25 \text{ hours}) = 78.75$ miles.
The second train travels $d = (45 \text{ miles/hour})(2.25 \text{ hours}) = 101.25$ miles.

The total distance apart is 78.75 + 101.25 = 180 miles.

⑤ Complete the chart to show simple interest and interest compounded annually.

Principal	Interest rate	Time, in years	Total amount of simple interest	Balance, compounded annually
$15,500	7%	5	$i = \$15{,}500(0.07)(5) = \$5425$	$A = \$15{,}500(1 + 0.07)^5$ $= \$21{,}739.55$
$25,000	14.9%	10	$i = \$25{,}000(0.149)(10) = \$37{,}250$	$A = \$25{,}000(1 + 0.149)^{10}$ $= \$100{,}262.91$
$75,000	5.75%	20	$i = \$75{,}000(0.0575)(20) = \$86{,}250$	$A = \$75{,}000(1 + 0.0575)^{20}$ $= \$229{,}439.82$

① Solve.

Geocaching is like a treasure hunt using a GPS (global positioning system) receiver. If a GPS receiver is accurate to within 3 meters, what is the area of the region you will have to search for a hidden geocache once the receiver has led you to the location?

$A = \pi r^2$

$A = \pi (3 \text{ m})^2$

$A = 9\pi \text{ m}^2$

A geocache is a box that contains a logbook and various treasures. If the geocache box is 3 inches wide, 12 inches long, and 8 inches tall, what is the volume of the geocache?

$V = (3 \text{ in.})(12 \text{ in.})(8 \text{ in.}) = 288 \text{ cu. in.}$

A logbook in the geocache is 4 inches wide, 6 inches tall, and ½ inch thick. What is the volume of the logbook?

$V = (4 \text{ in.})(6 \text{ in.})(\frac{1}{2} \text{ in.}) = 12 \text{ cu. in.}$

When the logbook is in the geocache, what is the volume of the remaining empty space?

288 cu. in. – 12 cu. in. = 276 cu. in.

A geocoin is a trackable coin that is moved from one geocache to another. The coin is 1 inch in diameter. What is the circumference of the geocoin? Use 3.14 as the value of π.

$C = \pi d$

$C = (3.14)(1 \text{ in.})$

$C = 3.14 \text{ in.}$

What is the area of one side of the geocoin? Use 3.14 as the value of π.

$A = \pi r^2$

$A = (3.14)(0.5 \text{ in.})^2$

$A = 0.785 \text{ sq. in.}$

The geocoin is 1/8 inch thick. Find the volume of the geocoin. Use 3.14 as the value of π. Round your answer to the nearest hundredth.

$A = \pi r^2 h$

$A = (0.785 \text{ sq. in.})(0.125 \text{ in.})$

$A = 0.098125 \text{ cu. in.}$

Rounded, $A = 0.10 \text{ cu. in.}$

Teaching Tips, Cont.

➢ Teach the formula for calculating velocity. Point out that this is the same formula for calculating speed. Students are not required to include direction as part of the answer to velocity problems in this book. However, it is important to note that direction is a required component of velocity in physics-level courses.

➢ Remind students to check all units before beginning any calculations. All distance units must be converted to the same unit prior to doing any other calculations. The same rule applies to units of time.

➢ Complete the Classwork exercises. Have some students work the problems on the board for the class and explain their answers. All students should work the problems in their books.

Assignments

- Complete Lesson 100, Activities 2-5.
- Worksheet 50
- Study for Test 10 (Lessons 88-97)

Test 10

Testing Objectives

The student will:

- Draw lines of symmetry
- Identify pairs of triangles as congruent or not congruent
- Label congruent triangles
- Identify congruence patterns
- Find the number of faces, edges, and vertices in a solid
- Calculate the lateral area, surface area, and volume of prisms, pyramids, cylinders, and cones
- Calculate the surface area and volume of spheres
- Identify dodecahedrons, icosahedrons, and octahedrons

Materials Needed

- Test 10
- *It's College Test Prep Time!* from the Student Book
- *A Math Minute with...* Ron M. from the Student Book

Teaching Tips

➢ Administer Test 10, allowing the students 30-40 minutes to complete the test.

➢ When all students are finished taking the test, introduce *It's College Test Prep Time* from the student book. This page may be completed in class or assigned as homework.

---

① Draw 6 lines of symmetry in the figure below. **6 points**

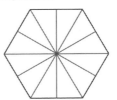

② Identify whether or not each pair of triangles is congruent based on the information given. If the triangles are congruent, write a congruence statement and tell which congruence pattern applies. **8 points**

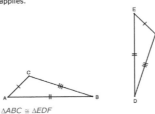

$\triangle ABC \cong \triangle EDF$
SSS

$\triangle ABC \cong \triangle EDF$
AAS

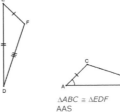

The triangles are not congruent based on the information given.

$\triangle ABC \cong \triangle EDF$
SAS

---

③ Give the number of faces, edges, and vertices in each solid figure. **18 points**

Sides on a base	Number of bases	Faces	Edges	Vertices
3	1	3 + 1 = 4	2(3) = 6	3 + 1 = 4
3	2	3 + 2 = 5	3(3) = 9	2(3) = 6
5	1	5 + 1 = 6	2(5) = 10	5 + 1 = 6
5	2	5 + 2 = 7	3(5) = 15	2(5) = 10
6	1	6 + 1 = 7	2(6) = 12	6 + 1 = 7
6	2	6 + 2 = 8	3(6) = 18	2(6) = 12

④ Find the lateral area, surface area, and volume of each solid figure. **14 points**

A prism with a height of 9 feet and a rectangular base that is 8 feet long and 3 feet wide.

$LA = PL$

$LA = 22(9) = 198$ sq. ft.

$SA = PL + 2B$

$SA = 198 + 2(24)$

$SA = 198 + 48 = 246$ sq. ft.

$V = Bh$

$V = (24)(9)$

$V = 216$ cu. ft.

A pyramid with a height of 6 meters, a slant height of 10 meters, and a square base that is 16 meters on each side.

$LA = \frac{1}{2}PL$

$LA = \frac{1}{2}(4 \times 16)(10)$

$LA = (32)(10) = 320$ m²

$SA = \frac{1}{2}PL + B$

$SA = 320 + 256$

$SA = 576$ m²

$V = \frac{1}{3}Bh$

$V = \frac{1}{3}(256)(6)$

$V = 512$ m³

A cylinder with a height of 8 inches and a base that has a diameter of 3 inches.

$LA = 2\pi rL$

$LA = 2\pi(1.5)(8)$

$LA = 24\pi$ sq. in.

$SA = 2\pi rL + 2\pi r^2$

$SA = 24\pi + 2\pi(1.5)^2$

$SA = 24\pi + 2\pi(2.25)$

$SA = 28.5\pi$ sq. in.

$V = \pi r^2 h$

$V = \pi(1.5)^2(8)$

$V = 18\pi$ cu. in.

A cone with a height of 12 yards, a slant height of 13 yards, and a base that has a diameter of 10 yards.

$LA = \pi rL$

$LA = \pi(5)(13)$

$LA = 65\pi$ sq. yd.

$SA = \pi rL + \pi r^2$

$SA = 65\pi + \pi(5)^2$

$SA = 65\pi + 25\pi = 90\pi$ sq. yd.

$V = \frac{1}{3}\pi r^2 h$

$V = \frac{1}{3}\pi(5)^2(\cancel{12}^4)$

$V = \pi(25)(4)$

$V = 100\pi$ cu. yd.

A sphere with a diameter of 12 cm.

A sphere has no lateral area.

$SA = 4\pi(6)^2$

$SA = 4\pi(36)$

$SA = 144\pi$ cm²

$V = \frac{4}{3}\pi r^3$

$V = \frac{4}{3}\pi(6)^3$

$V = \frac{4}{3}\pi(216)$

$V = 288\pi$ cm³

⑤ Tell the number of faces in each solid figure. **3 points**

Dodecahedron	12
Icosahedron	20
Octahedron	8

49 points total

It's College Test Prep Time!

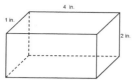

1. How many rectangular prisms pictured above can fit in a cube that is 16 inches on a side?

A. 4
B. 8   4 of the 4-inch sides will fit across one 16-inch side.
C. 16   16 of the 1-inch sides will fit across one 16-inch side.
D. 256   8 of the 2-inch sides will fit across one 16-inch side.
E. <u>512</u> $4 \times 16 \times 8 = 512$

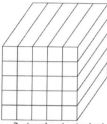

2. Lumber is stacked according to the diagram above. If 9 pieces of lumber have a total volume of 60, what is the volume of the entire stack?

A. $106\frac{2}{3}$ Set up a proportion:

B. $166\frac{2}{3}$ $\frac{9}{60} = \frac{25}{x}$

C. $\underline{540}$ Cross multiply and solve for x:

D. $1333\frac{1}{3}$ $9x = 1500$

E. 1500 $x = 166\frac{2}{3}$

A Math Minute with . . .

Ron M. – Printer

What is your occupation? I am the plant manager and owner of a print shop.

Where do you work? I work at my print shop.

Did you attend college? If so, what was your major? Yes, I attended college studying computer science for three years.

What parts of your job require the use of math? The entire printing process relies on math from the estimation of costs, to the prepress, press, and binding. I use estimation to determine what to charge a customer. I use ratios and proportions to determine the number of sheets in a stack of paper. Fractions are especially useful in the page layout and binding process.

What is the biggest "problem" you have faced that required the use of math to solve? The most difficult math problem involves calculating profitability. The print shop can only handle a certain number of projects at a time. When there is more work available than the shop can handle, I have to decide which projects to accept and which to turn down. Based on the requirements of the customer, I have to determine the profitability of the job along with the cost effectiveness. Then I decide which projects are the best to accept to maximize profit.

Are there any other interesting math uses you have experienced? Determining the formulas for ink colors involves the use of math. Each ink color has a specific formula that involves combining certain amounts, in ounces, of various colors. If I am off by even a fraction of an ounce on one of the ingredient colors, the resulting color will be wrong.

Teaching Tips, Cont.

➤ Have students read the Math Minute interview for lessons 101-110.

Assignments

- Complete *It's College Test Prep Time!*
- Read *A Math Minute with…*Ron M.

Horizons Pre-Algebra, Teacher's Guide

Lesson 101

Concepts
- Points, lines, and planes
- Proportions
- Bar graphs
- Math in the real world

Learning Objectives
The student will be able to:
- Define *point*
- Define *line*
- Define *plane*
- Draw and label points
- Draw and label lines

Materials Needed
- Student Book, Lesson 101
- A tripod
- A chair, desk, or table that does not sit square on the floor (one leg is always in the air and it rocks slightly)

Teaching Tips
➢ Define *point* from the teaching box. Emphasize that a point has no dimension, but is represented by a dot.

➢ Define *line*, or *straight line*, from the teaching box. Explain that arrow heads must be drawn at both ends of the line.

➢ Draw two large dots on the board. Ask the students what these represent. (Points) Ask the students how many lines can be drawn between two points. (1) Draw a line that passes through the center of each dot.

Points, Lines, and Planes

A **point** is a location in space. It is represented by a dot and labeled by a capital letter. A point has no size whatsoever – no length, width, or height. Notice how point *P* is drawn. •*P*

A **line** (also called a straight line) is the shortest distance between two points. It extends infinitely in both directions. Although its length is infinite, it has no width or height. A line is represented by the symbol ↔ drawn above two capital letters. The capital letters correspond to the two points that determine the line. Notice how line *PQ* is drawn and written.

$\overset{\leftrightarrow}{PQ}$

A **plane** is a flat surface defined by three non-collinear points. It extends infinitely in all directions but has no thickness. The intersection of two planes forms a line.

① **Classwork**
Draw the following figures.

Point A

•A

Line AB

A   B

Activities
② Answer the questions. Draw a picture to illustrate your answer.

How many lines can be drawn between two points?
1

How many points can be drawn on a single line?
An infinite number

How many lines can be drawn through a single point?
An infinite number

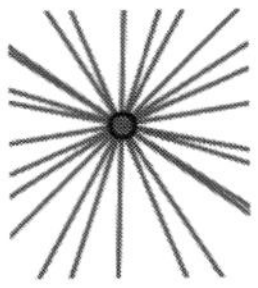

---

③ Use proportions to solve.

A stack of 1000 sheets of new 20-lb bond paper is 97 mm thick. Ron needs to print 750 copies of a document. If his stack of paper is 73 mm thick, does Ron have enough paper to complete the job?

$$\frac{1000 \text{ sheets}}{97 \text{ mm}} = \frac{750 \text{ sheets}}{x \text{ mm}}$$

$1000x = 72{,}750$

$x = 72.75$ mm

Yes, Ron has enough paper to complete the job.

Is a 3.4-inch-thick stack of paper enough to print 950 copies of a document? (1 in. = 25.4 mm)

$$3.4 \text{ inches} \times \frac{25.4 \text{ mm}}{1 \text{ in.}} = 86.36 \text{ mm}$$

$$\frac{1000 \text{ sheets}}{97 \text{ mm}} = \frac{950 \text{ sheets}}{x \text{ mm}}$$

$1000x = 92{,}150$

$x = 92.15$ mm

No, Ron does not have enough paper to complete the job.

Ron must mix 170 parts red ink, 174 parts green ink, and 60 parts blue ink to achieve the ink color he needs. If he uses 0.09 ounces of blue ink, how many ounces of red and green must he use to get the correct color?

$\frac{red}{blue} = \frac{170}{60}$

$\frac{red}{0.09 \text{ oz.}} = \frac{170^{17}}{60_6}$

$6(red) = 0.09(17)$

$6(red) = 1.53$

$red = 0.255$ oz.

$\frac{green}{blue} = \frac{174}{60}$

$\frac{green}{0.09 \text{ oz.}} = \frac{174^{29}}{60_{10}}$

$10(green) = 0.09(29)$

$10(green) = 2.61$

$green = 0.261$ oz.

④ Draw two bar graphs to show the number of vertices, edges, and faces for a rectangular prism and a rectangular pyramid.

Rectangular Prisms

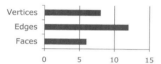

Rectangular Pyramids

Teaching Tips, Cont.

➤ Now draw additional lines that go through both dots, but not necessarily through the center. Ask the students if you have just proved that more than one line can be drawn between two points. (No.) Why not? (A point has no dimension. Just because you draw the dot with dimension does not mean multiple lines will go through a single point. The center of the dot is the location of the actual point.)

➤ Define *plane* from the teaching box.

➤ Show the students the tripod and the object that rocks slightly. Ask them which one is more stable. (The tripod.) Why? (It has three legs (points), which form an exact plane. The chair has four legs, so one of the legs can be in a different plane.)

➤ Complete the Classwork exercises. Have some students work the problems on the board for the class and explain their answers. All students should work the problems in their books.

Assignment

• Complete Lesson 101, Activities 2-4.

Horizons Pre-Algebra, Teacher's Guide

Lesson 102

Concepts
- Line segments
- Rays
- Intersecting lines
- Parallel lines
- Skew lines
- Math in the real world

Learning Objectives
The student will be able to:
- Define *line segment*
- Define *ray*
- Define *intersecting lines*
- Define *parallel lines*
- Define *skew lines*
- Identify types of lines

Materials Needed
- Student Book, Lesson 102
- Worksheet 51
- A box large enough for the class to see

Teaching Tips

➢ Have students complete Worksheet 51 in class. This may be for added practice of earlier topics, or graded as a quiz, if desired.

➢ Review points, lines, and planes. (See Lesson 101.)

➢ Teach line segments and rays from the teaching box. Have the students identify the number of endpoints on a line, line segment, and ray. (Line: 0; line segment: 2; ray: 1.)

➢ Remind students that all drawings must have an arrow whenever there is not an endpoint.

Types of Lines

A **line segment** is a portion of a line that has a definite starting point and a definite stopping point. A segment has a definite length but no width or height. A segment is represented by the symbol — drawn above two capital letters. The capital letters correspond to the two points that determine the segment. Notice how a segment is drawn and written. $\overline{PQ}$

A **ray** is a portion of a line that extends in one direction. It has one endpoint and continues infinitely in one direction. A ray is represented by the symbol → drawn above two capital letters. The first capital letter corresponds to the end point and the second to another point on the ray. Notice how a ray is drawn and written. $\overrightarrow{AB}$

Intersecting lines have exactly one point in common and are always coplanar. In the diagram below, *m* and *n* are intersecting lines.

Parallel lines are coplanar lines that do not intersect. Parallel lines are represented by the symbol ‖. In the diagram below, $\overline{PQ} \parallel \overline{RT}$.

Skew lines are non-coplanar lines. Because they are non-coplanar, they never intersect. The lines below are skew because they are in two different planes.

Look at the line formed by a wall and the floor. Now look at the line formed by an adjacent wall and the ceiling. Each wall represents a different plane. These two lines are skew lines because they are part of two different planes. You could extend them indefinitely and they would never intersect.

① Classwork
Answer the following questions based on your classroom.

Using the lines formed where walls meet the ceiling, floor, or other walls, how many parallel lines can you find?

How many intersecting lines can you find?

How many skew lines can you find?

Answers will vary, depending on the layout of the room. Intersecting lines will occur at each corner. Parallel lines will occur on opposite ends of each wall, the floor and the ceiling. Skew lines will occur on adjacent walls with one line in common with the floor and the other line in common with the ceiling. Some students may notice that the line joining two walls is skew with the line joining the opposite wall with the floor or ceiling.

Activities
② Mark the diagram according to the instructions.

Color one set of parallel lines red.
Color one set of intersecting lines blue.
Color one set of skew lines green.

③ Solve.
When Ron is printing on $8\frac{1}{2} \times 11$-inch paper to bind in a book, he leaves a 1-inch margin on both of the short sides and one long side, and a 1.25-inch margin on the other long side to have room for the binding. What is the area of the $8\frac{1}{2} \times 11$-inch piece of paper? What are the dimensions of the area available to print on? What percent of the area of the paper does Ron have to print on? Round your answer to the nearest tenth of a percent.

Area of paper: $8\frac{1}{2}$ in. $\times 11$ in. $= \frac{17}{2}$ in. $\times 11$ in. $= \frac{187}{2}$ sq. in. $= 93.5$ sq. in.

Dimensions of printing area: $(8\frac{1}{2}$ in. $- 1$ in. $- 1\frac{1}{4}$ in.$) \times (11$ in. $- 1$ in. $- 1$ in.$) = (6\frac{1}{4}$ in.$) \times (9$ in.$) = \frac{25}{4}$ in. $\times 9$ in. $= \frac{225}{4}$ sq. in. $= 56.25$ sq. in.

Percent of the paper available for print: $\frac{\frac{225}{4} \text{ sq. in.}}{\frac{187}{2} \text{ sq. in.}} = \frac{225}{4} \times \frac{2}{187} = \frac{225}{374} = 0.602 = 60.2\%$

Ron's customer submitted an image on $8\frac{1}{2} \times 14$-inch paper with a 1-inch margin on all 4 sides. If the customer wants the image printed on a poster that is 3 feet long with no margins, how wide will the poster be?

Dimensions of original image: $(8\frac{1}{2}$ in. $- 1$ in. $- 1$ in.$) \times (14$ in. $- 1$ in. $- 1$ in.$) = 6\frac{1}{2}$ in. $\times 12$ in.

3 ft. $\times \frac{12 \text{ in.}}{1 \text{ ft.}} = 36$ in.

The width is $\frac{12 \text{ in.}}{36 \text{ in.}} = \frac{6\frac{1}{2} \text{ in.}}{x}$ $x = 3(6\frac{1}{2}$ in.$) = 3(\frac{13}{2})$ in. $= \frac{39}{2}$ in. $= 19.5$ in.

What is the ratio of the length of the original to the length of the poster?

$\frac{6\frac{1}{2} \text{ in.}}{19\frac{1}{2} \text{ in.}} = \frac{\frac{13}{2}}{\frac{39}{2}} = \frac{13}{39} = \frac{1}{3}$ or 1:3

---

① Use the formula $m = \frac{w}{g}$ to find the mass or weight of each item.

	Offset duplicator	Digital printing press	Short run color printer
Mass	$m = \frac{w}{g}$ $m = \frac{7644\ kg \cdot m/s^2}{9.8\ m/s^2}$ $m = 780$ kg	7100 kg	$m = \frac{w}{g}$ $m = \frac{47{,}530\ kg \cdot m/s^2}{9.8\ m/s^2}$ $m = 4850$ kg
Weight	7644 kg • m/s²	$m = \frac{w}{g}$ $7100\ kg = \frac{w}{9.8\ m/s^2}$ $w = 69{,}580$ kg • m/s²	47,530 kg • m/s²
Gravity	9.8 m/s²	9.8 m/s²	9.8 m/s²

② Use the formula $d = \frac{m}{v}$ to find the density of each object and identify if it will float in pure water. The density of pure water is 1000 kg/m³.

Substance	Mass	Volume	Density	Float: Y/N
Crushed asphalt	504.7 kg	0.7 m³	$d = \frac{m}{v}$ $d = \frac{504.7\ kg}{0.7\ m^3}$ $d = 721$ kg/m³	Y
Baking powder	742.63 kg	1.03 m³	$d = \frac{m}{v}$ $d = \frac{742.63\ kg}{1.03\ m^3}$ $d = 721$ kg/m³	Y
Beeswax	2114.2 kg	2.2 m³	$d = \frac{m}{v}$ $d = \frac{2114.2\ kg}{2.2\ m^3}$ $d = 961$ kg/m³	Y
Window glass	206.32 kg	0.08 m³	$d = \frac{m}{v}$ $d = \frac{206.32\ kg}{0.08\ m^3}$ $d = 2579$ kg/m³	N

Teaching Tips, Cont.

➤ Teach intersecting lines and parallel lines from the teaching box. Tell them that the same rules apply to segments and rays that are intersecting or parallel.

➤ Show the students the box you brought and have them identify parallel and intersecting lines.

➤ Teach skew lines from the teaching box. Make sure the students understand that intersecting and parallel lines are coplanar, but skew lines are not.

➤ Have the students identify skew lines on the box you brought.

➤ Complete the Classwork exercises orally. Have some students explain the answers. All students should write the answers in their books.

Assignment

• Complete Lesson 102, Activities 2-3.

Lesson 103

Concepts
- Parts of a circle
- Divisibility tests
- Prime/composite numbers
- Parallel and skew lines
- Math in the real world

Learning Objectives
The student will be able to:
- Define *chord*
- Define *secant*
- Define *tangent*
- Define *central angle*
- Identify Activities of a circle

Materials Needed
- Student Book, Lesson 103
- Worksheet 52
- Chalkboard compass and straightedge

Teaching Tips
➤ Review lines and segments. (See Lessons 101-102.)

➤ Teach the parts of a circle from the teaching box. Refer the students to the circle diagram. Ask the students which parts are lines. (Tangent and secant.) Ask the students which parts are segments. (Chord, diameter, and radius.)

➤ Ask the students what the difference is between a chord and a secant. (A chord is a line segment with endpoints on the circle. A secant is a line that has a chord as a piece of the line.)

Parts of a Circle

A **chord** is a line segment whose endpoints are on a circle.

A **secant** is a line that intersects a circle in exactly two points.

A **tangent** is a line that touches a circle in exactly one point.

A **central angle** is an angle whose vertex is the center of a circle. It is formed by two radii.

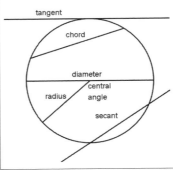

① **Classwork**
Identify each item in circle A.

Diameter
$\overline{BC}$
Radius
$\overline{AC}$, $\overline{AB}$, or $\overline{AD}$
Chord
$\overline{BC}$, $\overline{EF}$, or $\overline{BG}$
Secant
$\overleftrightarrow{BG}$
Tangent
$\overleftrightarrow{HJ}$
Central angle
$\angle CAD$ or $\angle BAD$

Activities
② Follow the directions for circle A.

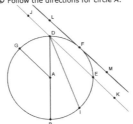

Color the radius red.
Color the diameter blue.
Color the chord green.
Color the secant orange.
Color the tangent purple.

---

③ Use the divisibility tests to identify each number as prime or composite.

435	Composite (3, 5)	443	Prime
439	Prime	445	Composite (5)
441	Composite (3, 9)	447	Composite (3)

④ Identify parallel and skew edges.

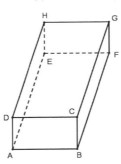

In the diagram above, all faces are parallelograms; opposite faces are parallel.

List all pairs of parallel edges.
$\overline{AB} \parallel \overline{DC}$; $\overline{AB} \parallel \overline{EF}$; $\overline{AB} \parallel \overline{HG}$; $\overline{DC} \parallel \overline{EF}$; $\overline{DC} \parallel \overline{HG}$;
$\overline{EF} \parallel \overline{HG}$; $\overline{BF} \parallel \overline{CG}$; $\overline{BF} \parallel \overline{AE}$; $\overline{BF} \parallel \overline{DH}$; $\overline{CG} \parallel \overline{AE}$;
$\overline{CG} \parallel \overline{DH}$; $\overline{AE} \parallel \overline{DH}$; $\overline{AD} \parallel \overline{BC}$; $\overline{AD} \parallel \overline{EH}$; $\overline{AD} \parallel \overline{FG}$;
$\overline{BC} \parallel \overline{EH}$; $\overline{BC} \parallel \overline{FG}$; $\overline{EH} \parallel \overline{FG}$;
For each edge, list 4 skew edges.
$\overline{AB}$ is skew to $\overline{CG}, \overline{DH}, \overline{EH}, \overline{FG}$
$\overline{DC}$ is skew to $\overline{BF}, \overline{AE}, \overline{EH}, \overline{FG}$
$\overline{AD}$ is skew to $\overline{CG}, \overline{BF}, \overline{HG}, \overline{EF}$
$\overline{BC}$ is skew to $\overline{DH}, \overline{AE}, \overline{HG}, \overline{EF}$
$\overline{BF}$ is skew to $\overline{CD}, \overline{GF}, \overline{EH}, \overline{AD}$
$\overline{CG}$ is skew to $\overline{AB}, \overline{EF}, \overline{AD}, \overline{EH}$
$\overline{AE}$ is skew to $\overline{DC}, \overline{HG}, \overline{BC}, \overline{FG}$
$\overline{DH}$ is skew to $\overline{AB}, \overline{EF}, \overline{BC}, \overline{FG}$
$\overline{EF}$ is skew to $\overline{DH}, \overline{CG}, \overline{AD}, \overline{BC}$
$\overline{HG}$ is skew to $\overline{AE}, \overline{BF}, \overline{AD}, \overline{BC}$
$\overline{HE}$ is skew to $\overline{AB}, \overline{DC}, \overline{BF}, \overline{CG}$
$\overline{GF}$ is skew to $\overline{AB}, \overline{DC}, \overline{AE}, \overline{DH}$

⑤ Solve.
Ron's customer does not want the total cost of his project to exceed $20,000. If the customer must take out a loan at 7% simple interest ($i = prt$) to pay for a $15,000 project, what is the maximum number of years the customer has to pay off the loan and stay within his budget? Give your answer as a whole number.

Use the formula $i = prt$. Substitute the maximum amount of interest he can pay ($5000) for i and change sign to show that prt must be less than i.
$i > prt$
$\$5000 > (\$15,000)(0.07)t$
$\$5000 > \$1050t$
$4.76 > t$
Ron's customer must pay his loan off in 4 years to stay within his budget.

Circle Terminology, Parallel and Skew Lines

Worksheet 52

① In the circle below, draw and label the following parts: tangent, chord, diameter, radius, central angle, and secant.

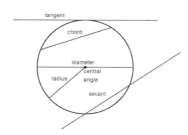

② Identify parallel and skew edges.

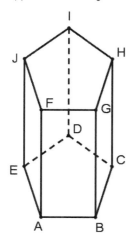

List all pairs of parallel edges.
$\overline{AF} \parallel \overline{BG}; \overline{AF} \parallel \overline{CH}; \overline{AF} \parallel \overline{DI}; \overline{AF} \parallel \overline{EJ}; \overline{BG} \parallel \overline{CH};$
$\overline{BG} \parallel \overline{DI}; \overline{BG} \parallel \overline{EJ}; \overline{CH} \parallel \overline{DI}; \overline{CH} \parallel \overline{EJ}; \overline{DI} \parallel \overline{EJ};$
$\overline{AB} \parallel \overline{FG}; \overline{BC} \parallel \overline{GH}; \overline{CD} \parallel \overline{HI}; \overline{DE} \parallel \overline{IJ}; \overline{EA} \parallel \overline{JF}$

For each edge, list all the skew lines.
$\overline{AB}$ is skew to $\overline{CH}, \overline{DI}, \overline{EJ}, \overline{FJ}, \overline{JI}, \overline{IH}, \overline{HG}$
$\overline{BC}$ is skew to $\overline{AF}, \overline{DI}, \overline{EJ}, \overline{FJ}, \overline{JI}, \overline{IH}, \overline{FG}$
$\overline{CD}$ is skew to $\overline{AF}, \overline{BG}, \overline{EJ}, \overline{FJ}, \overline{JI}, \overline{FG}, \overline{HG}$
$\overline{DE}$ is skew to $\overline{CH}, \overline{BG}, \overline{AF}, \overline{FJ}, \overline{FG}, \overline{IH}, \overline{HG}$
$\overline{EA}$ is skew to $\overline{CH}, \overline{DI}, \overline{BG}, \overline{FG}, \overline{JI}, \overline{IH}, \overline{HG}$
$\overline{FG}$ is skew to $\overline{CH}, \overline{DI}, \overline{EJ}, \overline{AE}, \overline{ED}, \overline{DC}, \overline{CB}$
$\overline{GH}$ is skew to $\overline{AF}, \overline{DI}, \overline{EJ}, \overline{AE}, \overline{ED}, \overline{DC}, \overline{BA}$
$\overline{HI}$ is skew to $\overline{AF}, \overline{BG}, \overline{EJ}, \overline{AE}, \overline{ED}, \overline{AB}, \overline{CB}$
$\overline{IJ}$ is skew to $\overline{CH}, \overline{AF}, \overline{BG}, \overline{AE}, \overline{AB}, \overline{DC}, \overline{CB}$
$\overline{JF}$ is skew to $\overline{CH}, \overline{DI}, \overline{BG}, \overline{AB}, \overline{ED}, \overline{DC}, \overline{CB}$
$\overline{AF}$ is skew to $\overline{BC}, \overline{CD}, \overline{DE}, \overline{GH}, \overline{HI}, \overline{IJ}$
$\overline{BG}$ is skew to $\overline{EA}, \overline{CD}, \overline{DE}, \overline{JF}, \overline{HI}, \overline{IJ}$
$\overline{CH}$ is skew to $\overline{AB}, \overline{EA}, \overline{DE}, \overline{FG}, \overline{JF}, \overline{IJ}$
$\overline{DI}$ is skew to $\overline{BC}, \overline{EA}, \overline{AB}, \overline{GH}, \overline{JF}, \overline{FG}$
$\overline{EJ}$ is skew to $\overline{BC}, \overline{CD}, \overline{AB}, \overline{GH}, \overline{HI}, \overline{FG}$

Teaching Tips, Cont.

➤ Ask the students what the difference is between a secant and a tangent. (A secant touches the circle in 2 places, but a tangent touches the circle in 1 place.)

➤ Ask the students what the difference is between a chord and a diameter. (A diameter is a chord that passes through the center of a circle. A generic chord does not necessarily pass through the center of a circle.)

➤ Draw a circle and two intersecting diameters. Ask the students what kind of angles you have formed. (Central angles.)

➤ Draw a circle and two intersecting chords that are not diameters. Ask the students if you have central angles. (No.) Why not? (The vertex of the angles is not in the center of the circle.)

➤ Complete the Classwork exercises. Have some students work the problems on the board for the class and explain their answers. All students should work the problems in their books.

Assignments

• Complete Lesson 103, Activities 2-5.
• Worksheet 52.

Horizons Pre-Algebra, Teacher's Guide

Lesson 104

Concepts
- Acute, right, and obtuse angles
- Adjacent angles
- Complementary angles
- Supplementary angles
- Straight angles
- Prime factorization
- Exponents
- Math in the real world

Learning Objectives
The student will be able to:
- Identify angles based on measure
- Identify types of angles based on position relative to other angles
- Calculate the measure of complementary angles
- Calculate the measure of supplementary angles

Materials Needed
- Student Book, Lesson 104
- A protractor

Teaching Tips
➤ Review rays. (See Lesson 102.)

➤ Teach angles from the teaching box. (Introduce acute, right, and obtuse angles based on their degree measures.)

➤ Ask the students where they have used right angles before. (The height of geometric figures.)

➤ Teach adjacent angles from the teaching box. Draw the angles at the right on the board and have the students identify them as adjacent or not adjacent.

Angles

An **angle** is made up of two rays sharing a common endpoint.

Angles can be classified according to their size.

An **acute** angle has a measure of less than 90°. A **right** angle has a measure of exactly 90°. An **obtuse** angle has a measure of more than 90° but less than 180°.

Angles can be classified according to their relation with other angles.

Adjacent angles share a common vertex and one common side.
Complementary angles are two angles whose measures have a sum of 90°.
Supplementary angles are two angles whose measures have a sum of 180°. Adjacent supplementary angles form a **straight angle**.

Complementary and supplementary angles may or may not be adjacent.

Given a 40° angle, what is the measure of its complementary angle? What is the measure of its supplementary angle?

Complementary angle: 90° – 40° = 50°
Supplementary angle: 180° – 40° = 140°

① Classwork
Identify each angle as acute, right, obtuse, or straight. Find the measure of the complementary and supplementary angles, if applicable, for each given angle.

30°
Acute
Complementary angle: 90° – 30° = 60°
Supplementary angle: 180° – 30° = 150°
145°
Obtuse
Complementary angle: None
Supplementary angle: 180° – 145° = 35°
88°
Acute
Complementary angle: 90° – 88° = 2°
Supplementary angle: 180° – 88° = 92°
169°
Obtuse
Complementary angle: None
Supplementary angle: 180° – 169° = 11°
90°
Right
Complementary angle: None
Supplementary angle: 180° – 90° = 90°

Activities
② Identify each angle as acute, right, obtuse, or straight. Find the measure of the complementary and supplementary angles, if applicable, for each given angle.

15°
Acute
Complementary angle: 90° – 15° = 75°
Supplementary angle: 180° – 15° = 165°
160°
Obtuse
Complementary angle: None
Supplementary angle: 180° – 160° = 20°
72°
Acute
Complementary angle: 90° – 72° = 18°
Supplementary angle: 180° – 72° = 108°

134°
Obtuse
Complementary angle: None
Supplementary angle: 180° – 134° = 46°
180°
Straight
Complementary angle: None
Supplementary angle: None
6°
Acute
Complementary angle: 90° – 6° = 84°
Supplementary angle: 180° – 6° = 174°

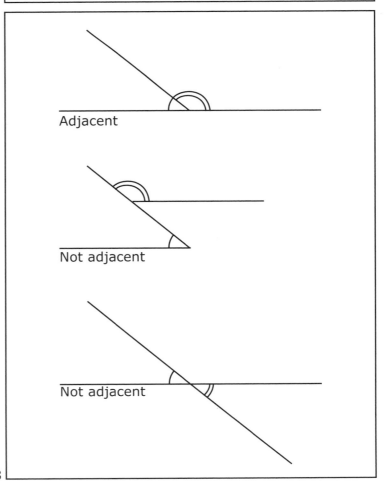

Adjacent

Not adjacent

Not adjacent

---

③ Label the measure of each angle in the diagram below. (The sum of the three interior angles of a triangle is 180°.)

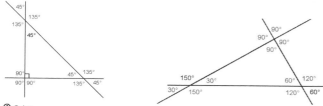

④ Solve.
Ron uses four colors in his print shop: cyan, magenta, yellow, and black. Find the number of different color combinations possible using 4 color parts per combination, where any one of the 4 colors may be in each part. (Hint: Find C(16,4).)

$$C(16,4) = \frac{16!}{12!(4!)} = \frac{\overset{2}{\cancel{16}} \times \overset{5}{\cancel{15}} \times 14 \times 13 \times \cancel{12!}}{\cancel{12!}(\cancel{4} \times \cancel{3} \times \cancel{2} \times 1)} = 1820$$

(In reality, there are an infinite number of color combinations because the different color parts do not all have to be the same size. This process has been simplified for the sake of this problem.)

When mixing a unique ink color, Ron uses from 0 to 99 hundredths of an ounce of each of four different ink colors. Use the multiplication principle of counting to find the total number of different possible colors Ron can make. (See Lesson 74.)

There are 100 different amounts possible for each color, including 0. According to the multiplication principle of counting, there are $(100)(100)(100)(100) = (100)^4 = 100,000,000$ different colors possible using this method of mixing.

If Ron's machine runs out of cyan ink, how many colors are possible?
There are 100 different amounts possible for each color except blue. According to the multiplication principle of counting, there are $(100)(100)(100) = (100)^3 = 1,000,000$ different colors possible.

⑤ Give the prime factorization of each number, using exponents where appropriate.

200	264	300
$200 = 2 \times 2 \times 2 \times 5 \times 5$	$264 = 2 \times 2 \times 2 \times 3 \times 11$	$300 = 2 \times 2 \times 3 \times 5 \times 5$
$200 = 2^3 \times 5^2$	$264 = 2^3 \times 3 \times 11$	$300 = 2^2 \times 3 \times 5^2$

Teaching Tips, Cont.

➢ Teach complementary and supplementary angles from the teaching box. Explain that complementary and supplementary angles may be adjacent, but they don't have to be.

➢ Teach straight angles from the teaching box. Show students the protractor. Ask them how many degrees are shown on a protractor. (180°) Direct their attention to the straight edge on the bottom of the protractor. Explain that adjacent angles that form a straight edge also form a straight angle.

➢ Complete the Classwork exercises. Have some students work the problems on the board for the class and explain their answers. All students should work the problems in their books.

Assignment
• Complete Lesson 104, Activities 2-5.

Lesson 105

Concepts
- Perpendicular lines
- Complementary angles
- Straight angles
- Divisibility tests
- Prime/Composite numbers
- Sum of interior angles of a polygon

Learning Objectives
The student will be able to:
- Define *perpendicular lines*
- Identify and label perpendicular lines using the ⊥ symbol
- Use perpendicular lines to find complementary angles

Materials Needed
- Student Book, Lesson 105
- Worksheet 53

Teaching Tips
➤ Have students complete Worksheet 53 in class. This may be for added practice of earlier topics, or graded as a quiz, if desired.

➤ Review right angles, complementary angles, and supplementary angles. (See Lesson 104.)

➤ Teach perpendicular lines from the teaching box. Ask the students if perpendicular lines are coplanar. (Yes.)

➤ Tell students that perpendicular lines are marked by a box in the corner.

Perpendicular Lines

Perpendicular lines are intersecting lines that form adjacent right angles. Perpendicular lines are represented by the symbol ⊥. In the diagram below, $\overline{AB} \perp \overline{CD}$.

When finding the area of a figure, the height is always perpendicular to the base. When finding the volume of a solid, the height is always perpendicular to the base.

Find all the right angles in the diagram below.

Perpendicular lines form adjacent right angles, so ∠COB, ∠BOD, ∠DOA, and ∠AOC are all right angles.

① Classwork
Identify all the pairs of supplementary angles in the diagram below.

∠COB and ∠BOD
∠COB and ∠DOA
∠COB and ∠AOC
∠BOD and ∠DOA
∠BOD and ∠AOC
∠DOA and ∠AOC

Activities
② List all pairs of complementary angles.

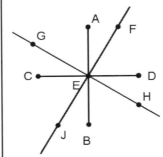

In the diagram at the left, $\overline{AB} \perp \overline{CD}$ and $\overline{GH} \perp \overline{JF}$.

∠AEF and ∠FED
∠FED and ∠DEH
∠DEH and ∠HEB
∠AEG and ∠GEC
∠GEC and ∠CEJ
∠CEJ and ∠JEB
∠JEB and ∠BEH
∠GEA and ∠AEF

When vertical angles are used, there are 8 additional pairs. However, these are not listed here because vertical angles are not introduced until Lesson 107.

---

③ Find all of the straight angles. List each angle using three letters.

∠GEH
∠AEB
∠FEJ
∠DEC

④ Use the divisibility tests to identify each number as prime or composite.

449	Prime	457	Prime
453	Composite (3)	459	Composite (3, 9)
455	Composite (5)	461	Prime

⑤ Solve.
The sum of the interior angles of a polygon having *n* sides is given by the formula $sum = (n-2)180°$. Use this formula to complete the chart.

Polygon	Number of sides	Sum of angles	Degrees per angle if all angles are equal
△	3	$sum = (3-2)180° =$ $1(180°) = 180°$	$180° \div 3 = 60°$
□	4	$sum = (4-2)180° =$ $2(180°) = 360°$	$360° \div 4 = 90°$
⬠	5	$sum = (5-2)180° =$ $3(180°) = 540°$	$540° \div 5 = 108°$
⬡	6	$sum = (6-2)180° =$ $4(180°) = 720°$	$720° \div 6 = 120°$
⯃	8	$sum = (8-2)180° =$ $6(180°) = 1080°$	$1080° \div 8 = 135°$
⬣	10	$sum = (10-2)180° =$ $8(180°) = 1440°$	$1440° \div 10 = 144°$

Can you find a formula for calculating the degrees per angle?

$degrees\ per\ angle = \dfrac{(n-2)180°}{n}$ Students may or may not see the pattern.

Points, Lines   Worksheet 53

① Answer the questions. Draw a picture to illustrate your answer.
How many lines can be drawn between two points?
1

How many points can be drawn on a single line?
An infinite number

How many lines can be drawn through a single point?
An infinite number

② Mark the diagram according to the instructions.

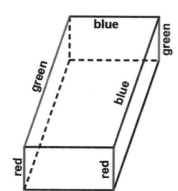

Color one set of parallel lines red.
Color one set of intersecting lines blue.
Color one set of skew lines green.

Answers will vary.

Teaching Tips, Cont.

➤ Ask the students what polygons will always have perpendicular lines. (Rectangles and squares.)

➤ Complete the Classwork exercise. Have one student work the problem on the board for the class and explain the answer. All students should work the problem in their books.

Assignment

• Complete Lesson 105, Activities 2-5.

Lesson 106

Concepts
- Parallel lines
- Perpendicular lines
- Interior angles
- Exterior angles
- Regular polygons

Learning Objectives
The student will be able to:
- Identify whether or not lines are parallel
- Draw parallel lines
- Draw perpendicular lines

Materials Needed
- Student Book, Lesson 106
- Graph paper
- Ruler

Teaching Tips
➢ Review parallel lines. (See Lesson 102.)

➢ Review perpendicular lines. (See Lesson 105.)

➢ Teach how to determine if two lines are parallel from the teaching box. Emphasize that the lines measured must both be perpendicular to the same given line. (Technically, the lines do not have to be perpendicular as long as they both form the same angle with the given line. However, it is easier to identify perpendicular lines and eliminates error from measuring angles.)

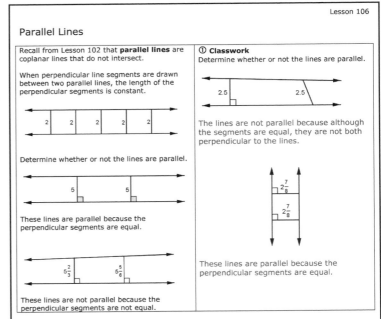

Parallel Lines

Recall from Lesson 102 that **parallel lines** are coplanar lines that do not intersect.

When perpendicular line segments are drawn between two parallel lines, the length of the perpendicular segments is constant.

Determine whether or not the lines are parallel.

These lines are parallel because the perpendicular segments are equal.

These lines are not parallel because the perpendicular segments are not equal.

① **Classwork**
Determine whether or not the lines are parallel.

The lines are not parallel because although the segments are equal, they are not both perpendicular to the lines.

These lines are parallel because the perpendicular segments are equal.

Activities
② Use graph paper and a ruler to draw the following diagrams.

Draw two parallel lines. Label two perpendicular segments that are 4 units long. Should appear similar to the second diagram in either column above.
Draw two non-parallel lines. Label two joining segments that are each one inch long. Should appear similar to the first Classwork diagram.
Draw two non-parallel lines joined by two perpendicular segments of different lengths. Label the lengths of the segments. Should appear similar to the third diagram in the left column above.
Draw two lines joined by two segments. Mark any perpendicular lines, but do not label any measurements. Exchange papers with a friend and solve each other's problems. Exchange papers back and check your friend's work. Answers will vary.

③ Solve.

For each regular polygon (all sides and angles are equal) in the chart below, find the sum of the interior angles, the measure of one interior angle, and the measure of one external angle.

Polygon	Sum of angles	Degrees per interior angle	Degrees per exterior angle
 (triangle)	sum = $(3-2)180° =$ $1(180°) = 180°$	$180° \div 3 = 60°$	$180° - 60° = 120°$
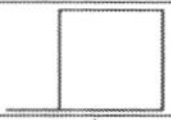 (square)	sum = $(4-2)180° =$ $2(180°) = 360°$	$360° \div 4 = 90°$	$180° - 90° = 90°$
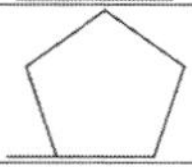 (pentagon)	sum = $(5-2)180° =$ $3(180°) = 540°$	$540° \div 5 = 108°$	$180° - 108° = 72°$
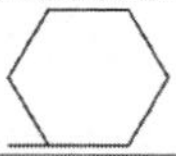 (hexagon)	sum = $(6-2)180° =$ $4(180°) = 720°$	$720° \div 6 = 120°$	$180° - 120° = 60°$
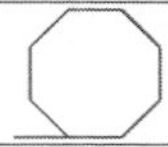 (octagon)	sum = $(8-2)180° =$ $6(180°) = 1080°$	$1080° \div 8 = 135°$	$180° - 135° = 45°$
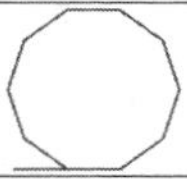 (decagon)	sum = $(10-2)180° =$ $8(180°) = 1440°$	$1440° \div 10 = 144°$	$180° - 144° = 36°$

Can you find a formula for calculating the degrees in an exterior angle of a regular polygon?

$$\text{degrees per exterior angle} = 180° - \frac{(n-2)180°}{n} = \frac{180n°}{n} - \frac{(n-2)180°}{n} = \frac{180n° - 180n° - 360°}{n} = \frac{360°}{n}$$

This is based on the formula from Lesson 106, most students should get the initial formula of $\text{degrees per exterior angle} = 180° - \frac{(n-2)180°}{n}$. If necessary, remind students how to simplify fractions with variables to get the final formula:

$$\text{degrees per exterior angle} = \frac{360°}{n}.$$

Teaching Tips, Cont.

➤ Refer students to the drawings in the teaching box. Show them that if the perpendicular segments are not congruent, then the other lines are not parallel.

➤ Complete the Classwork exercises. Have some students work the problems on the board for the class and explain their answers. All students should work the problems in their books.

Assignment

• Complete Lesson 106, Activities 2-3.

Lesson 107

Concepts

- Transversals
- Interior angles
- Exterior angles
- Vertical angles
- Corresponding angles
- Mean, median, mode, range
- 5-number summary
- Box-and-whisker plot

Learning Objectives

The student will be able to:

- Define *transversal*
- Define *interior angle*
- Define *exterior angle*
- Define *vertical angle*
- Define *corresponding angle*
- Identify types of angles on a diagram
- Calculate angle measures on a diagram

Materials Needed

- Student Book, Lesson 107

Teaching Tips

➤ Review parallel lines. (See Lesson 106.)

➤ Teach transversals from the teaching box. Tell the students that a transversal is not limited to parallel lines. Draw two intersecting lines and a transversal to form a triangle as an example.

➤ Teach the types of angles formed when two parallel lines are cut by a transversal.

➤ Teach the relationships of the angles formed when two parallel lines are cut by a transversal.

Transversals and Special Angles

A **transversal** is a line that intersects two or more lines.

Interior angles are those angles that are formed between the two lines that are cut by the transversal.

Exterior angles are those angles that are formed outside the two lines that are cut by the transversal.

Vertical angles are non-adjacent angles formed by the intersection of two lines. Vertical angles are always equal.

Corresponding angles are those angles that are in the same relative position in two intersections of a transversal.

In the above diagram, corresponding angles have the same number. In a single intersection, the odd-numbered angles are vertical angles, and the even-numbered angles are vertical angles.

When a transversal intersects parallel lines, several special cases apply.
- Alternate (on the opposite side of the transversal and adjacent to opposite parallel lines) interior angles are equal.
- Alternate exterior angles are equal.
- Corresponding angles are equal.
- Exterior angles on the same side of the transversal are supplementary.
- Interior angles on the same side of the transversal are supplementary.

① Classwork
Solve.

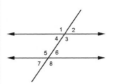

In the diagram above, there are two parallel lines cut by a transversal. If ∠2 = 45°, find the measure of the remaining angles.

∠1 = 180° – 45° = 135° because adjacent angles that form a straight line are supplementary.
∠3 = 180° – 45° = 135° because adjacent angles that form a straight line are supplementary. Also, ∠3 and ∠1 are vertical angles.
∠4 = 45° because ∠4 and ∠2 are vertical angles.
∠5 = 135° because ∠1 and ∠5 are corresponding angles.
∠6 = 45° because ∠2 and ∠6 are corresponding angles.
∠7 = 45° because ∠4 and ∠7 are corresponding angles.
∠8 = 135° because ∠3 and ∠8 are corresponding angles.

Note: ∠2 and ∠4 are vertical angles.
∠5 and ∠8 are vertical angles.
∠6 and ∠7 are vertical angles.
∠1 and ∠8 are alternate exterior angles.
∠2 and ∠7 are alternate exterior angles.
∠4 and ∠6 are alternate interior angles.
∠3 and ∠5 are alternate interior angles.
∠1 and ∠7 are supplementary angles.
∠2 and ∠8 are supplementary angles.
∠4 and ∠5 are supplementary angles.
∠3 and ∠6 are supplementary angles.

② Solve.

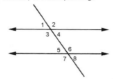

In the diagram at the left, there are two parallel lines cut by a transversal. If ∠2 = 35°, find the measure of the remaining angles.

∠1 = 180° – 35° = 145° because adjacent angles that form a straight line are supplementary. ∠3 = 180° – 35° = 145° because adjacent angles that form a straight line are supplementary. Also, ∠3 and ∠1 are vertical angles. ∠4 = 35° because ∠4 and ∠2 are vertical angles. ∠5 = 145° because ∠1 and ∠5 are corresponding angles. ∠6 = 35° because ∠2 and ∠6 are corresponding angles. ∠7 = 35° because ∠4 and ∠7 are corresponding angles. ∠8 = 145° because ∠3 and ∠8 are corresponding angles.

③ Identify the pairs of equal angles and identify each pair as alternate exterior, alternate interior, vertical, or corresponding.

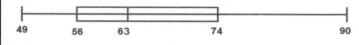

In the diagram at the left, there are two parallel lines cut by a transversal.
Alternate exterior: ∠1 = ∠8, ∠2 = ∠7
Alternate interior: ∠3 = ∠6, ∠4 = ∠5
Vertical: ∠1 = ∠4, ∠2 = ∠3, ∠5 = ∠8, ∠6 = ∠7
Corresponding: ∠1 = ∠5, ∠2 = ∠6, ∠3 = ∠7, ∠4 = ∠8

④ Find the mean, median, mode, range, and 5-number-summary.
74, 75, 61, 90, 61, 65, 52, 56, 49, 69

Mean: 652 ÷ 10 = 65.2
Median: 49, 52, 56, 61, 61, 65, 69, 74, 75, 90   61 + 65 = 126   126 ÷ 2 = 63
Mode: 61
Range: 90 – 49 = 41
5-number summary: Minimum = 49
                          First quartile = 56
                          Median = 63
                          Third quartile = 74
                          Maximum = 90

⑤ Draw a box-and-whisker plot for the 5-number summary above.

```
   |--------[------|------]--------------------|
   49     56      63     74                   90
```

Teaching Tips, Cont.

➤ Direct the students' attention to the 5 special cases at the bottom of the teaching box.

➤ Complete the Classwork exercises. Have some students work the problems on the board for the class and explain their answers. All students should work the problems in their books.

Assignment

• Complete Lesson 107, Activities 2-5.

Lesson 108

Concepts
- The coordinate plane
- Quadrants
- Graphing points
- Area of triangles
- Area of polygons

Learning Objectives
The student will be able to:
- Describe the coordinate plane
- Identify the axes and origin
- Identify the four quadrants
- Plot points given in (x, y) format

Materials Needed
- Student Book, Lesson 108
- Worksheet 54
- Graph paper

Teaching Tips
➤ Have students complete Worksheet 54 in class. This may be for added practice of earlier topics, or graded as a quiz, if desired.

➤ Review planes. (See Lesson 101.)

➤ Introduce the coordinate plane. Explain that this is the same thing as the Cartesian plane.

➤ Teach the correct labels for the axes, origin, and quadrants. Note: Many books incorrectly draw arrows on both ends of the axes. Arrows should only be drawn to show the direction the value is increasing. Do not draw arrows to show the negative side getting smaller. There are some graphs that have the axes going different directions, so the arrow location is crucial.

The Coordinate Plane

Recall from Lesson 101 that a plane is a flat surface that extends infinitely in all directions but has no thickness. Any three non-collinear points determine a plane.

If two number lines are placed on a plane perpendicular to each other and intersect at point zero, they can be used to describe the location of any point on the plane. The grid that is formed is known as the **coordinate plane** or the **Cartesian plane**.

The horizontal number line is called the **x-axis**. Negative values are on the left, and positive values are on the right.

The vertical number line is called the **y-axis**. Negative values are below the x-axis, and positive values are above the x-axis.

The point where the two axes cross (the zeros) is called the **origin**.

Points on the plane are defined by a **coordinate** in the format (x, y), where x is the value on the x-axis, and y is the value on the y-axis.

The intersecting axes divide the plane into four quadrants. The diagram below shows the location of each quadrant, as well as the values of x and y in each coordinate.

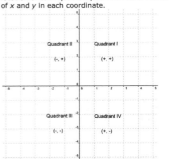

① Classwork

Graph each point and identify if it is at the origin or which quadrant it is in.

(1, 3)   Quadrant I
(2, -1)   Quadrant IV
(-3, 2)   Quadrant II
(-1, -1)   Quadrant III
(0, 0)   Origin

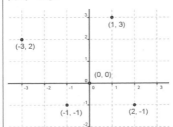

Activities

② Give the coordinates for each point and identify the quadrant.

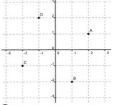

A: (2, 1)   Quadrant I
B: (1, -2)   Quadrant IV
C: (-2, -1)   Quadrant III
D: (-1, 2)   Quadrant II

③ Graph the points on your own graph paper. Draw line segments between consecutive points. Draw a segment joining point A to point K.

A: (-3, 4)
B: (-2, 1)
C: (-1, -2)
D: (0, -5)
E: (1, -2)
F: (2, 1)
G: (3, 4)
H: (-1, 1)
I: (-5, -2)
J: (5, -2)
K: (1, 1)

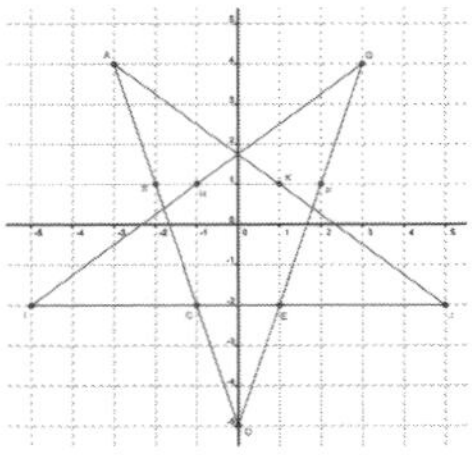

④ Find the area.

Find the area of the triangle formed by joining points C, D, and E in the graph above.
$A = \frac{1}{2}bh$
$A = \frac{1}{2}(2)(3)$
$A = 3$ sq. units

Find the area of the triangle formed by joining points B, D, and F in the graph above.
$A = \frac{1}{2}bh$
$A = \frac{1}{2}(4)(6)$
$A = 12$ sq. units

Find the area of the polygon formed by joining points C, D, E, K, and H.
Divide the area into two sections: triangle CDE and rectangle CEKH.
The area of triangle CDE has already been found to be 3 sq. units.
The area of rectangle CEKH is $A = 2(3) = 6$ sq. units.
The area of polygon CDEKH is $3 + 6 = 9$ sq. units.

Complementary, Supplementary, and Vertical Angles

Worksheet 54

① Identify each angle as acute, right, obtuse, or straight. Find the measure of the complementary and supplementary angles, if applicable, for each given angle.

19°
Acute
Complementary angle: 90° – 19° = 71°
Supplementary angle: 180° – 19° = 161°

136°
Obtuse
Complementary angle: None
Supplementary angle: 180° – 136° = 44°

167°
Obtuse
Complementary angle: None
Supplementary angle: 180° – 167° = 13°

180°
Straight
Complementary angle: None
Supplementary angle: None

71°
Acute
Complementary angle: 90° – 71° = 19°
Supplementary angle: 180° – 71° = 109°

2°
Acute
Complementary angle: 90° – 2° = 88°
Supplementary angle: 180° – 2° = 178°

② Use the diagram below to answer the questions.

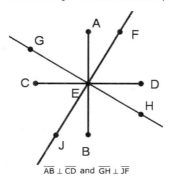

$\overline{AB} \perp \overline{CD}$ and $\overline{GH} \perp \overline{JF}$

List 8 pairs of complementary angles.
∠AEF and ∠FED
∠FED and ∠DEH
∠DEH and ∠HEB
∠AEG and ∠GEC
∠GEC and ∠CEJ
∠CEJ and ∠JEB
∠JEB and ∠BEH
∠GEA and ∠AEF

When vertical angles are used, there are 8 additional pairs. However, these are not listed here because vertical angles were not introduced until the last lesson and most students will not use these in this exercise.

List each straight angle using three letters.
∠GEH
∠AEB
∠FEJ
∠DEC

Teaching Tips, Cont.

➤ Teach how to graph points on the coordinate plane. Remind students that the positive directions on the coordinate plane are up and to the right.

➤ Have students identify the four quadrants in the coordinate plane. Make sure they all understand that Quadrant I is in the upper right corner, and the other quadrants follow in order counter-clockwise.

➤ Complete the Classwork exercises. Have some students work the problems on the board for the class and explain their answers. All students should work the problems in their books.

Assignment

• Complete Lesson 108, Activities 2-4.

Lesson 109

Concepts
- Two-variable equations
- Independent variables
- Dependent variables
- Solving two-variable equations
- Solving one-variable equations

Learning Objectives
The student will be able to:
- Identify the dependent and independent variables in a two-variable equation
- Solve two-variable equations

Materials Needed
- Student Book, Lesson 109

Teaching Tips
➢ Review how to solve one-variable equations. (See Lesson 20.) Ask the students how many solutions a one-variable equation has. (One.)

➢ Introduce two-variable equations. Explain that two-variable equations have an infinite number of solutions.

➢ Teach independent and dependent variables from the teaching box.

➢ Teach how to solve two-variable equations by using a T-chart. Explain that all solutions are expressed as coordinate points in the form (x, y). Students should be expected to supply multiple possible solutions for a two-variable equation unless otherwise instructed.

Two-Variable Equations

So far, you have learned how to solve one-variable equations. These equations have exactly one solution. Some equations have an infinite number of solutions. These are **two-variable equations**.

$2x - y = 3$ is a two-variable equation. To solve a two-variable equation, begin by rewriting the equation so that one variable is isolated on one side of the equal sign, and all other terms are on the other side of the equal sign.

$2x - y = 3$
$2x - 3 = y$

In this case, x is called the **independent variable** because you can substitute any value for x. The **dependent variable** is y because its value depends on the value you substitute for x.

Once you have identified the independent and dependent variables, you can solve for values of those variable. Make a T-chart, with one variable on each side. Choose several values for the independent variable. Substitute each value into the equation and solve for the dependent variable. Solutions are written in coordinate format (x, y) for each solution combination.

x	y
0	$y = 2(0) - 3 = -3$
1	$y = 2(1) - 3 = -1$
2	$y = 2(2) - 3 = 1$
-1	$y = 2(-1) - 3 = -5$
-2	$y = 2(-2) - 3 = -7$

Possible solutions for this equation include (0, -3), (1, -1), (2, 1), (-1, -5), and (-2, -7)

① **Classwork.**
Find 5 possible solutions for each equation.

$y = x$

x	y
0	$y = 0$
1	$y = 1$
2	$y = 2$
-1	$y = -1$
-2	$y = -2$

Possible solutions for this equation include (0, 0), (1, 1), (2, 2), (-1, -1), and (-2, -2)

$y = 3x + 1$

x	y
0	$y = 3(0) + 1 = 1$
1	$y = 3(1) + 1 = 4$
2	$y = 3(2) + 1 = 7$
-1	$y = 3(-1) + 1 = -2$
-2	$y = 3(-2) + 1 = -5$

Possible solutions for this equation include (0, 1), (1, 4), (2, 7), (-1, -2), and (-2, -5)

$y = 2(x + 1)$

x	y
0	$y = 2(0 + 1) = 2$
1	$y = 2(1 + 1) = 4$
2	$y = 2(2 + 1) = 6$
-1	$y = 2(-1 + 1) = 0$
-2	$y = 2(-2 + 1) = -2$

Possible solutions for this equation include (0, 2), (1, 4), (2, 6), (-1, 0), and (-2, -2)

Activities
② Solve each two-variable equation when $x = 5$.

$y = x + 4$	$y = 2x - 3$	$y = 5(x - 3)$
$y = 5 + 4$	$y = 2(5) - 3$	$y = 5(5 - 3)$
$y = 9$	$y = 10 - 3$	$y = 5(2)$
	$y = 7$	$y = 10$

---

③ Find 5 possible solutions for each equation.

$y = -x$

x	y
0	$y = 0$
1	$y = -1$
2	$y = -2$
-1	$y = 1$
-2	$y = 2$

Possible solutions for this equation include (0, 0), (1, -1), (2, -2), (-1, 1), and (-2, 2).

$y = x + 4$

x	y
0	$y = 0 + 4 = 4$
1	$y = 1 + 4 = 5$
2	$y = 2 + 4 = 6$
-1	$y = -1 + 4 = 3$
-2	$y = -2 + 4 = 2$

Possible solutions for this equation include (0, 4), (1, 5), (2, 6), (-1, 3), and (-2, 2).

$y = 2x - 3$

x	y
0	$y = 2(0) - 3 = -3$
1	$y = 2(1) - 3 = -1$
2	$y = 2(2) - 3 = 1$
-1	$y = 2(-1) - 3 = -5$
-2	$y = 2(-2) - 3 = -7$

Possible solutions for this equation include (0, -3), (1, -1), (2, 1), (-1, -5), and (-2, -7).

$y = 5(x - 3)$

x	y
0	$y = 5(0 - 3) = -15$
1	$y = 5(1 - 3) = -10$
2	$y = 5(2 - 3) = -5$
-1	$y = 5(-1 - 3) = -20$
-2	$y = 5(-2 - 3) = -25$

Possible solutions for this equation include (0, -15), (1, -10), (2, -5), (-1, -20), and (-2, -25).

④ Solve.

$6x - (2 - 9)^2 = -5(7 - x)$ $6x - 7^2 = -35 + 5x$ $6x - 49 = -35 + 5x$ $x = 14$	$8x - 3(5 - 2x) - 2 = 5x - (2^3 - 3^3)$ $8x - 15 + 6x - 2 = 5x - (8 - 27)$ $14x - 17 = 5x + 19$ $9x = 36$ $x = 4$	$4(3 - 2x) + \sqrt{2(3^3 + 5)} = 3x - 2$ $12 - 8x + \sqrt{2(27 + 5)} = 3x - 2$ $12 - 8x + \sqrt{2(32)} = 3x - 2$ $12 - 8x + \sqrt{64} = 3x - 2$ $12 - 8x + 8 = 3x - 2$ $20 = 11x - 2$ $22 = 11x$ $x = 2$
$7x + (6 - 11)^2 > 4(4 + x)$ $7x + (-5)^2 > 16 + 4x$ $7x + 25 > 16 + 4x$ $3x > -9$ $x > -3$	$9x + 2(5 - 2x) < 4x - (3^3 \div 3^2)$ $9x + 10 - 4x < 4x - 3$ $5x + 10 < 4x - 3$ $x < -13$	$3(2x + 3) - \sqrt{3^2 + 2^3 - 1} < 3(2 - x)$ $6x + 9 - \sqrt{9 + 8 - 1} < 6 - 3x$ $6x + 9 - \sqrt{16} < 6 - 3x$ $6x + 9 - 4 < 6 - 3x$ $6x + 5 < 6 - 3x$ $9x < 1$ $x < \dfrac{1}{9}$

Teaching Tips, Cont.

➢ Complete the Classwork exercises. Have some students work the problems on the board for the class and explain their answers. All students should work the problems in their books.

Assignment

• Complete Lesson 109, Activities 2-4.

Lesson 110

Concepts
- Graphing two-variable equations
- Area of polygons
- Percent

Learning Objectives
The student will be able to:
- Graph two-variable equations
- Identify two-variable equations as linear equations

Materials Needed
- Student Book, Lesson 110
- Worksheet 55
- Graph paper
- Straightedge

Teaching Tips
➤ Review how to solve two-variable equations. (See Lesson 109.)

➤ Review graphing points. (See Lesson 108.)

➤ Explain that the solution of a two-variable equation can be expressed as a graph. Tell students to plot the points from the solution and join them with a straight line. The line should have arrows on both ends since it is a line rather than a segment. The exception is if a condition is given for the independent variable, such as $-2 \leq x \leq 2$.

➤ Teach how to graph two-variable equations from the teaching box, using the example from Lesson 109.

Graphing Equations

Two-variable equations are also called **linear equations** because the solution coordinates can be plotted on a coordinate plane and joined to form a line.

Recall the example from Lesson 109.
$$2x - y = 3$$
$$2x - 3 = y$$

x	y
0	$y = 2(0) - 3 = -3$
1	$y = 2(1) - 3 = -1$
2	$y = 2(2) - 3 = 1$
-1	$y = 2(-1) - 3 = -5$
-2	$y = 2(-2) - 3 = -7$

Possible solutions for this equation include (0, -3), (1, -1), (2, 1), (-1, -5), and (-2, -7).

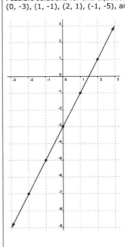

① **Classwork**
Graph these equations from Lesson 109.

$y = x$

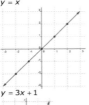

$y = 3x + 1$

$y = 2(x + 1)$

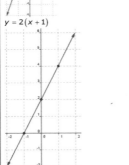

Activities
② Graph the following equations on your own graph paper.

$y = -x$ $\qquad$ $y = 2x - 3$ $\qquad$ $y = 2(x - 3)$

$y = x + 4$

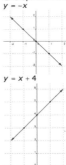 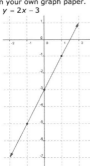 

③ Graph the following equations on the same coordinate plane.

$y = -2$

$x = -2$

$y = 2 - x$

④ Solve.
Find the area of the figure bounded by the three lines in the graph above.
$A = \frac{1}{2}(6)(6) = 18$ sq. units

What percent of the area is in Quadrant I? Round your answer to the nearest tenth.
Quadrant I area: $A = \frac{1}{2}(2)(2) = 2$ sq. units, which is $\frac{2}{18} = \frac{1}{9} = 0.\overline{1}$ or 11.1% of the total.

What percent of the area is in Quadrant II? Round your answer to the nearest tenth.
Quadrant II area: $A = \frac{1}{2}(2 + 4)(2) = 6$ sq. units, which is $\frac{6}{18} = \frac{1}{3} = 0.\overline{3}$ or 33.3% of the total.

What percent of the area is in Quadrant III? Round your answer to the nearest tenth.
Quadrant III area: $A = (2)(2) = 4$ sq. units, which is $\frac{4}{18} = \frac{2}{9} = 0.\overline{2}$ or 22.2% of the total.

What percent of the area is in Quadrant IV? Round your answer to the nearest tenth.
Quadrant IV area: $A = \frac{1}{2}(2 + 4)(2) = 6$ sq. units, which is $\frac{6}{18} = \frac{1}{3} = 0.\overline{3}$ or 33.3% of the total.

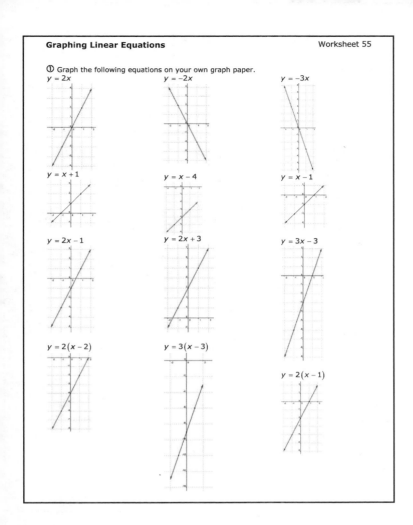

Graphing Linear Equations   Worksheet 55

① Graph the following equations on your own graph paper.

$y = 2x$ $y = -2x$ $y = -3x$

$y = x + 1$ $y = x - 4$ $y = x - 1$

$y = 2x - 1$ $y = 2x + 3$ $y = 3x - 3$

$y = 2(x - 2)$ $y = 3(x - 3)$

$y = 2(x - 1)$

Teaching Tips, Cont.

➢ Complete the Classwork exercises. Have some students work the problems on the board for the class and explain their answers. All students should work the problems in their books.

Assignments

- Complete Lesson 110, Activities 2-4.
- Worksheet 55.
- Study for Test 11. (Lessons 98-107)

Horizons Pre-Algebra, Teacher's Guide

Test 11

Testing Objectives

The student will:
- Calculate the mass of an object when given the weight
- Calculate the weight of an object when given the mass
- Calculate the density of objects when given the mass and volume
- Calculate velocity, distance, and time
- Identify types of lines in a diagram
- Identify parts of a circle
- Calculate the measure of angles formed by parallel lines, perpendicular lines, and transversals

Materials Needed
- Test 11
- *It's College Test Prep Time!* from the Student Book
- *A Math Minute with...* Amie D. from the Student Book

Teaching Tips

➤ Administer Test 11, allowing the students 30-40 minutes to complete the test.

➤ When all students are finished taking the test, introduce *It's College Test Prep Time* from the student book. This page may be completed in class or assigned as homework.

① Use the formula $m = \frac{w}{g}$ to find the mass or weight of each item. Round answers to the nearest whole number.　　**3 points**

	Baby	Child	Adult
Mass	$m = \frac{w}{g}$ $m = \frac{35 \, kg \cdot m/s^2}{9.8 \, m/s^2}$ $m = 4 \, kg$	31.7 kg	$m = \frac{w}{g}$ $m = \frac{778 \, kg \cdot m/s^2}{9.8 \, m/s^2}$ $m = 79 \, kg$
Weight	$35 \, kg \cdot m/s^2$	$31.7 \, kg = \frac{w}{9.8 \, m/s^2}$ $w = 311 \, kg \cdot m/s^2$	$778 \, kg \cdot m/s^2$
Gravity	$9.8 \, m/s^2$	$9.8 \, m/s^2$	$9.8 \, m/s^2$

② Use the formula $d = \frac{m}{v}$ to find the density of each object and identify if it will float in pure water. The density of pure water is $1000 \, kg/m^3$.　　**8 points**

Substance	Mass	Volume	Density	Float: Y/N
Cocoa beans	415.1 kg	$0.7 \, m^3$	$d = \frac{m}{v}$ $d = \frac{415.1 \, kg}{0.7 \, m^3}$ $d = 593 \, kg/m^3$	Y
Brick	1979.66 kg	$1.03 \, m^3$	$d = \frac{m}{v}$ $d = \frac{1979.66 \, kg}{1.03 \, m^3}$ $d = 1922 \, kg/m^3$	N
Furnace cinders	2008.6 kg	$2.2 \, m^3$	$d = \frac{m}{v}$ $d = \frac{2008.6 \, kg}{2.2 \, m^3}$ $d = 913 \, kg/m^3$	Y
Cobalt ore	503.6 kg	$0.08 \, m^3$	$d = \frac{m}{v}$ $d = \frac{503.6 \, kg}{0.08 \, m^3}$ $d = 6295 \, kg/m^3$	N

③ Use the formula $v = \frac{d}{t}$ to find the velocity, distance, or time.　　**3 points**

Velocity	Distance	Time
$v = \frac{605 \, miles}{11 \, hours}$ $v = 55 \, miles/hour$	605 miles	11 hours
54 miles per hour	$d = (54 \, miles/hour)(2.5 \, hours)$ $d = 135 \, miles$	2.5 hours
350 miles per hour	840 miles	$t = \frac{840 \, miles}{350 \, miles/hour}$ $t = 2.4 \, hours$

④ Identify the types of lines in the diagram below.　　**3 points**

What kind of lines are the blue lines?
Intersecting
What kind of lines are the red lines?
Parallel
What kind of lines are the green lines?
Skew

⑤ Identify each item in circle A.　　**6 points**

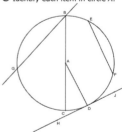

$\overline{BG}$
Secant
$\overline{BC}$
Diameter (also a chord)
$\overline{AD}$
Radius
$\overline{EF}$
Chord
$\overline{HJ}$
Tangent
$\angle CAD$
Central angle

⑥ Find the measure of each angle in the figure below.　　**19 points**

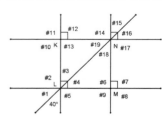

#1 = 50°	#10 = 90°
#2 = 90°	#11 = 90°
#3 = 40°	#12 = 90°
#4 = 50°	#13 = 90°
#5 = 90°	#14 = 90°
#6 = 90°	#15 = 40°
#7 = 90°	#16 = 50°
#8 = 90°	#17 = 90°
#9 = 90°	#18 = 40°
	#19 = 50°

42 points total

It's College Test Prep Time!

1. In the figure below, $AB = BC = CD = DG = GC = CF = FB = BE = EA$. Given $AC = 10$, what is the perimeter of triangle CDG?

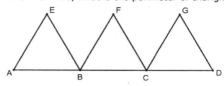

A. 5
B. 10
C. <u>15</u>
D. 30
E. 45

Since all segments are equal, each is $10 \div 2 = 5$. This makes the perimeter of each small triangle equal to $5 + 5 + 5 = 15$.

2. Find the value of x in the figure below.

A. 65°
B. <u>115°</u>
C. 130°
D. 245°
E. 295°

The total number of degrees in a quadrilateral is 360°. $360° - 65° - 65° = 230°$ left for the other two angles. $230° \div 2 = 115°$.

A Math Minute with . . .

Amie D. – Missionary Nurse

What is your occupation? I am a registered nurse and missionary wife.

Where do you work? I work in Soroti, Uganda. I am the mother of three. I am also the nurse for 30 orphans at the Soroti Orphan Assistance project (S.O.A.P) orphanage.

Did you attend college? If so, what was your major? Yes, I have a B.S. degree in nursing.

What parts of your job require the use of math? The recipes that I use have the oven temperatures in degrees Fahrenheit while the ovens I use are in Celsius. I need to convert the oven temperatures from Fahrenheit to Celsius. I also use math to calculate the medication dosages for children.

What is the biggest "problem" you have faced that required the use of math to solve? When a child needs medicine, I need to calculate the dosages of the medication for that specific child.

Are there any other interesting math uses you have experienced? I use math to determine how much flour, sugar, etc. I need to buy to make various recipes. I also need to keep within a grocery shopping budget. This is difficult because I don't know the value of the dollar until I arrive in the capital city. When I get there, I buy groceries for the next two months. I need to determine how many kilos of ground beef I will need for two months of dinners.

Teaching Tips, Cont.

➢ Have students read the Math Minute interview for lessons 111-120.

Assignments

- Complete *It's College Test Prep Time!*
- Read *A Math Minute with…* Amie D.

Lesson 111

Concepts
- Graphing inequalities
- Area of polygons
- Volume of prisms

Learning Objectives
The student will be able to:
- Solve two-variable inequalities
- Graph two-variable inequalities
- Identify whether a graph requires a solid line or a dotted line

Materials Needed
- Student Book, Lesson 111
- Graph paper
- Straightedge

Teaching Tips
➤ Review inequalities. (See Lesson 22.)

➤ Review graphing two-variable equations. (See Lesson 110.)

➤ Teach graphing linear inequalities from the teaching box. Explain that if the inequality contains the symbol < or > then the graph will have a dotted line instead of a solid line. If the graph contains the symbol ≤ or ≥ then the graph will have a solid line.

➤ Tell the students that all inequalities, regardless of the symbol used, will have one side of the graph shaded. Teach how to correctly shade the graph of an inequality.

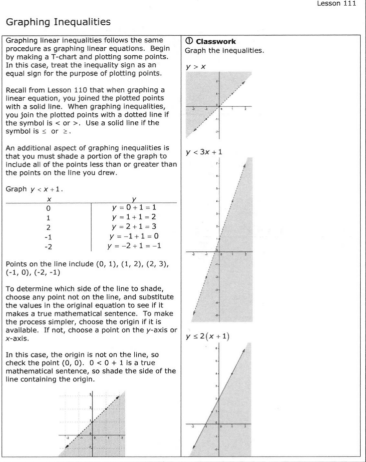

Graphing Inequalities

Graphing linear inequalities follows the same procedure as graphing linear equations. Begin by making a T-chart and plotting some points. In this case, treat the inequality sign as an equal sign for the purpose of plotting points.

Recall from Lesson 110 that when graphing a linear equation, you joined the plotted points with a solid line. When graphing inequalities, you join the plotted points with a dotted line if the symbol is < or >. Use a solid line if the symbol is ≤ or ≥.

An additional aspect of graphing inequalities is that you must shade a portion of the graph to include all of the points less than or greater than the points on the line you drew.

Graph $y < x + 1$.

x	y
0	$y = 0 + 1 = 1$
1	$y = 1 + 1 = 2$
2	$y = 2 + 1 = 3$
-1	$y = -1 + 1 = 0$
-2	$y = -2 + 1 = -1$

Points on the line include (0, 1), (1, 2), (2, 3), (-1, 0), (-2, -1)

To determine which side of the line to shade, choose any point not on the line, and substitute the values in the original equation to see if it makes a true mathematical sentence. To make the process simpler, choose the origin if it is available. If not, choose a point on the y-axis or x-axis.

In this case, the origin is not on the line, so check the point (0, 0). $0 < 0 + 1$ is a true mathematical sentence, so shade the side of the line containing the origin.

① **Classwork**
Graph the inequalities.

$y > x$

$y < 3x + 1$

$y \leq 2(x + 1)$

Activities

② Graph the following inequalities on your own graph paper.

$y < -x$ $\qquad$ $y \leq 2x - 3$ $\qquad\qquad$ $y \geq 2(x - 3)$

$y > x + 4$

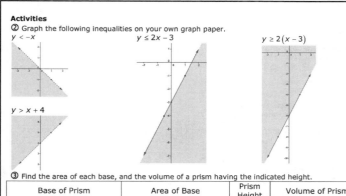

③ Find the area of each base, and the volume of a prism having the indicated height.

Base of Prism	Area of Base	Prism Height	Volume of Prism
$3\frac{1}{3}$ in. $1\frac{3}{4}$ in.	$A = bh$ $A = (3\frac{1}{3}$ in.$)(1\frac{3}{4}$ in.$)$ $A = (\frac{10}{3}$ in.$)(\frac{7}{4}$ in.$)$ $A = \frac{35}{6} = 5\frac{5}{6}$ sq. in.	$4\frac{4}{5}$ in.	$V = Bh$ $V = (5\frac{5}{6}$ sq. in.$)(4\frac{4}{5}$ in.$)$ $V = (\frac{35}{6}$ sq. in.$)(\frac{24}{5}$ in.$)$ $V = 28$ cubic in.
$\sqrt{3}$cm $\sqrt{3}$cm	$A = s^2$ $A = (\sqrt{3}$ cm$)^2$ $A = 3$ cm^2	$\sqrt{3}$ cm	$V = s^3$ $V = (\sqrt{3}$ cm$)^3$ $V = 3\sqrt{3}$ cm^3
$3\sqrt{2}$ft $2\sqrt{2}$ft. $4\sqrt{2}$ft.	$A = \frac{1}{2}bh$ $A = \frac{1}{2}(2\sqrt{2}$ ft. $+ 4\sqrt{2}$ ft.$)(3\sqrt{2}$ ft.$)$ $A = \frac{1}{2}(6\sqrt{2}$ ft.$)(3\sqrt{2}$ ft.$)$ $A = (3\sqrt{2}$ ft.$)(3\sqrt{2}$ ft.$)$ $A = 18$ sq. ft.	$4\sqrt{7}$ ft.	$V = Bh$ $V = (18$ sq. ft.$)(4\sqrt{7}$ ft.$)$ $V = 72\sqrt{7}$ cubic ft.
4.3 m 6.1 m 10.2 m	$A = bh$ $A = (10.2$ m$)(4.3$ m$)$ $A = 43.86$ m^2	5.03 m	$V = Bh$ $V = (43.86$ m$^2)(5.03$ m$)$ $V = 220.6158$ m^3
$2\sqrt{3}$yd. $2\sqrt{6}$yd. $2\sqrt{3}$yd. $2\sqrt{15}$yd. $2\sqrt{3}$yd. $6\sqrt{3}$yd.	$A = \frac{1}{2}(b_1 + b_2)h$ $A = \frac{1}{2}(2\sqrt{3}$ yd. $+ 6\sqrt{3}$ yd. $+ 2\sqrt{3}$ yd.$)(2\sqrt{3}$ yd.$)$ $A = \frac{1}{2}(10\sqrt{3}$ yd.$)(2\sqrt{3}$ yd.$)$ $A = (5\sqrt{3}$ yd.$)(2\sqrt{3}$ yd.$)$ $A = 30$ sq. yd.	$3\sqrt{2}$ yd.	$V = Bh$ $V = (30$ sq. yd.$)(3\sqrt{2}$ yd.$)$ $V = 90\sqrt{2}$ cubic yd.

Teaching Tips, Cont.

➢ The easiest way to determine which side of the graph to shade is to choose a point not on the line. Substitute the *x*- and *y*-values from the chosen point into the inequality and determine whether or not it makes a true mathematical statement. If it does, then shade that side of the line. If it does not make a true mathematical statement, shade the opposite side of the line.

➢ Complete the Classwork exercises. Have some students work the problems on the board for the class and explain their answers. All students should work the problems in their books.

Assignment

• Complete Lesson 111, Activities 2-3.

Lesson 112

Concepts

- Functions
- Graphs of functions
- Graphing two-variable equations

Learning Objectives

The student will be able to:

- Define *function*
- Define *domain*
- Define *range*
- Use the vertical line test to determine if a graph is a function
- Identify the domain and range of a function
- Draw the graph of a function

Materials Needed

- Student Book, Lesson 112
- Worksheet 56
- Graph paper
- Straightedge

Teaching Tips

➤ Have students complete Worksheet 56 in class. This may be for added practice of earlier topics or graded as a quiz, if desired.

➤ Teach the definition of *function* from the teaching box. Explain that the domain is the same as the values of the independent variable in a two-variable equation and the range is the same as the values of the dependent variable in a two-variable equation.

➤ Write these equations on the board.

$$y = x^2$$
$$x = y^2$$

Functions and Graphs

A **function** is an equation in which each value of the independent variable has exactly one corresponding value of the dependent variable.

The values assigned to the independent variable are called the **domain**.

The corresponding values of the dependent variable are called the **range**.

A function is written in the format $f(x)$ and is read, "the function f of x," or, "the f of x."

When graphing a function, the $f(x)$ side of the equation corresponds to the y portion of an equation. Plot points as usual and graph.

To look at a graph and instantly determine whether or not the graph is a function, use the **vertical line test**. If you can draw a vertical line on the graph and cross the graph in two or more points, the graph is not a function. Otherwise, the graph is a function.

Tell whether or not each graph is a function.

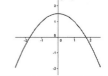

Yes. There is no way to draw a vertical line that intersects the graph in more than one point.

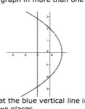

No. Notice that the blue vertical line intersects the graph in two places.

① Classwork
Tell whether or not each graph is a function.

No. A vertical line intersects the graph in two places.

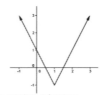

Yes. The graph is a function.

Graph the function $f(x) = 2x - 1$.

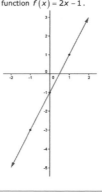

Activities
② Tell whether or not each graph is a function.

No. The graph is not a function.

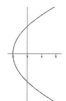

No. The graph is not a function.

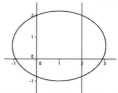

Yes. The graph is a function.

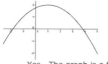

Yes. The graph is a function.

③ Graph the following functions on your own graph paper.

$f(x) = x + 1$ $f(x) = 2(x - 1)$ $f(x) = 3(x - 2)$

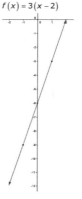

$f(x) = 2x - 3$

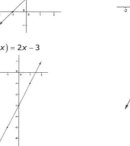

① Give the coordinates for each point and identify the quadrant.

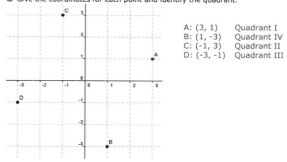

A: (3, 1)　　Quadrant I
B: (1, -3)　　Quadrant IV
C: (-1, 3)　　Quadrant II
D: (-3, -1)　　Quadrant III

② Find three possible solutions for each equation and draw the graph on your own graph paper.

$y = -x$
Possible solutions:
(-1, 1)
(0, 0)
(1, -1)

$y = 2x - 1$
Possible solutions:
(-1, -3)
(0, -1)
(1, 1)

$y = 3(x - 1)$
Possible solutions:
(-1, -6)
(0, -3)
(1, 0)

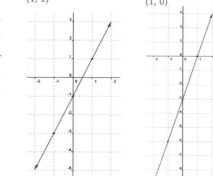

$y = x^2$

x	y
-2	4
-1	1
0	0
1	1
2	4

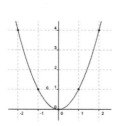

$x = y^2$

x	y
4	-2
1	-1
0	0
1	1
4	2

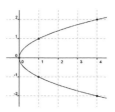

Teaching Tips, Cont.

➢ Make a T-chart for each equation and draw the graph. See the lower left of this page for details.

➢ Draw a vertical line on the second graph to show the students that it is not a function. Point out that two different values of *y* have the same value for *x*.

➢ Tell students that when graphing functions, the $f(x) =$ portion is the same as the $y =$ portion of a two-variable equation. Plot points and graph as normal.

➢ Complete the Classwork exercises. Have some students work the problems on the board for the class and explain their answers. All students should work the problems in their books.

Assignment

• Complete Lesson 112, Activities 2-3.

Lesson 113

Concepts
- Slope
- Graphing two-variable equations
- Math in the real world

Learning Objectives
The student will be able to:
- Define *slope*
- Calculate the slope between two given points
- Calculate the slope of a linear equation

Materials Needed
- Student Book, Lesson 113
- Worksheet 57
- Graph paper
- Straightedge

Teaching Tips
➤ Review how to solve two-variable equations. (See Lesson 109.)

➤ Ask the students if they have been on a mountain road and have seen a sign telling trucks to use a lower gear. Ask them why the trucks have to use a lower gear when going down a mountain road. (It is too steep of a slope.)

➤ Teach the definition of *slope* from the teaching box. Tell the students they can remember the variable *m* stands for slope if they think of slope as the steepness of a mountain.

➤ Teach the formula for finding the slope of a line joining two points on the coordinate plane.

Slope

The **slope** of a line is the ratio of its vertical change to its horizontal change. It is noted by the letter m and is described as $m = \frac{\text{rise}}{\text{run}}$.

The formula for slope is $m = \frac{y_2 - y_1}{x_2 - x_1}$, where (x_1, y_1) and (x_2, y_2) are two points on the line.

Find the slope of the line $-2x + y + 3 = 0$
Rewrite the equation to isolate y.
$y = 2x - 3$

Next, choose two values for x and solve for their corresponding values of y. Express the solution as coordinate points.

Let $x = 0$
$y = 2(0) - 3 = -3$
The first point (x_1, y_1) is (0, -3).

Let $x = 1$
$y = 2(1) - 3 = 2 - 3 = -1$
The second point (x_2, y_2) is (1, -1).

Finally, substitute the values from the coordinates into the formula for slope.
$m = \frac{y_2 - y_1}{x_2 - x_1} = \frac{-1 - (-3)}{1 - 0} = \frac{2}{1} = 2$
This means the line rises two units for every one unit that it moves forward horizontally.
You must remember:
The slope of a horizontal line is 0.
A vertical line has no slope.

① Classwork
Find the slope of the line joining the points.
(3, 7) and (8, 7)
$m = \frac{7-7}{8-3} = \frac{0}{5} = 0$
(2, 1) and (2, 4)
$m = \frac{4-1}{2-2} = \frac{3}{0} =$ no slope
Find the slope of each line.
$3x + y + 1 = 0$
$y = -3x - 1$
(0, -1) and (1, -4)
$m = \frac{y_2-y_1}{x_2-x_1} = \frac{-4-(-1)}{1-0} = \frac{-3}{1} = -3$
$x + y - 5 = 0$
$y = -x + 5$
(0, 5) and (1, 4)
$m = \frac{y_2-y_1}{x_2-x_1} = \frac{4-(5)}{1-0} = \frac{-1}{1} = -1$
$x - 2y + 3 = 0$
$2y = x + 3$
$y = \frac{x+3}{2}$
(1, 2) and (3, 3)
$m = \frac{y_2-y_1}{x_2-x_1} = \frac{3-(2)}{3-1} = \frac{1}{2}$
$3x + 2y - 4 = 0$
$2y = -3x + 4$
$y = \frac{-3x+4}{2}$
(0, 2) and (2, -1)
$m = \frac{y_2-y_1}{x_2-x_1} = \frac{-1-(2)}{2-0} = \frac{-3}{2}$

Activities
② Find the slope of the line joining the points.

(1, 4) and (2, 6)
$m = \frac{6-4}{2-1} = \frac{2}{1} = 2$
(3, 5) and (2, 3)
$m = \frac{3-5}{2-3} = \frac{-2}{-1} = 2$
(2, 3) and (8, 3)
$m = \frac{3-3}{8-2} = \frac{0}{6} = 0$
(-1, 1) and (-2, 4)
$m = \frac{4-1}{-2-(-1)} = \frac{3}{-1} = -3$
(-3, 7) and (-8, 2)
$m = \frac{2-7}{-8-(-3)} = \frac{-5}{-5} = 1$

(2, -1) and (2, 4)
$m = \frac{4-(-1)}{2-2} = \frac{5}{0} =$ no slope
(-3, -7) and (2, 1)
$m = \frac{1-(-7)}{2-(-3)} = \frac{8}{5}$
(-2, 1) and (2, -4)
$m = \frac{-4-1}{2-(-2)} = \frac{-5}{4}$
(3, 7) and (3, -3)
$m = \frac{-3-7}{3-3} = \frac{-10}{0} =$ no slope
(-2, -1) and (2, -4)
$m = \frac{-4-(-1)}{2-(-2)} = \frac{-3}{4}$

---

③ Find the slope of each line.

$x + y - 3 = 0$
$y = -x + 3$
(0, 3) and (1, 2)
$m = \frac{y_2-y_1}{x_2-x_1} = \frac{2-(3)}{1-0} = \frac{-1}{1} = -1$
$-3x + y - 2 = 0$
$y = 3x + 2$
(0, 2) and (1, 5)
$m = \frac{y_2-y_1}{x_2-x_1} = \frac{5-(2)}{1-0} = \frac{3}{1} = 3$
$2x + 2y + 1 = 0$
$2y = -2x - 1$
$\left(0, -\frac{1}{2}\right)$ and $\left(1, -\frac{3}{2}\right)$
$m = \frac{y_2-y_1}{x_2-x_1} = \frac{-\frac{3}{2}-\left(-\frac{1}{2}\right)}{1-0} = \frac{-1}{1} = -1$

$2x + y - 2 = 0$
$y = -2x + 2$
(0, 2) and (1, 0)
$m = \frac{y_2-y_1}{x_2-x_1} = \frac{0-(2)}{1-0} = \frac{-2}{1} = -2$
$-2x + y + 3 = 0$
$y = 2x - 3$
(0, -3) and (1, -1)
$m = \frac{y_2-y_1}{x_2-x_1} = \frac{-1-(-3)}{1-0} = \frac{2}{1} = 2$
$x + 2y + 4 = 0$
$2y = -x - 4$
$y = -\frac{1}{2}x - 2$
(0, -2) and (2, -3)
$m = \frac{y_2-y_1}{x_2-x_1} = \frac{-3-(-2)}{2-0} = \frac{-1}{2}$

$-x + y - 2 = 0$
$y = x + 2$
(0, 2) and (1, 3)
$m = \frac{y_2-y_1}{x_2-x_1} = \frac{3-(2)}{1-0} = \frac{1}{1} = 1$
$3x + y - 4 = 0$
$y = -3x + 4$
(0, 4) and (1, 1)
$m = \frac{y_2-y_1}{x_2-x_1} = \frac{1-(4)}{1-0} = \frac{-3}{1} = -3$
$3x + 2y + 6 = 0$
$2y = -3x - 6$
$y = -\frac{3}{2}x - 3$
(0, -3) and (2, -6)
$m = \frac{y_2-y_1}{x_2-x_1} = \frac{-6-(-3)}{2-0} = \frac{-3}{2}$

④ Graph each of the equations from Activity ③ on your own graph paper.

$x + y - 3 = 0$ $2x + y - 2 = 0$ $-x + y - 2 = 0$

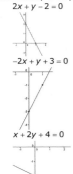

$-3x + y - 2 = 0$ $-2x + y + 3 = 0$ $3x + y - 4 = 0$

$2x + 2y + 1 = 0$ $x + 2y + 4 = 0$ $3x + 2y + 6 = 0$

⑤ Solve.
Amie and her family climbed Soroti Rock, a volcanic plug in Soroti, Uganda. Find the slope of Soroti Rock if it is 1500 feet high and 750 feet across from the base to the edge of the peak.
$m = \frac{1500}{750} = 2$

① Graph the inequalities.

$y < -x$ $y > 2x - 1$ $y \leq 3(x - 1)$

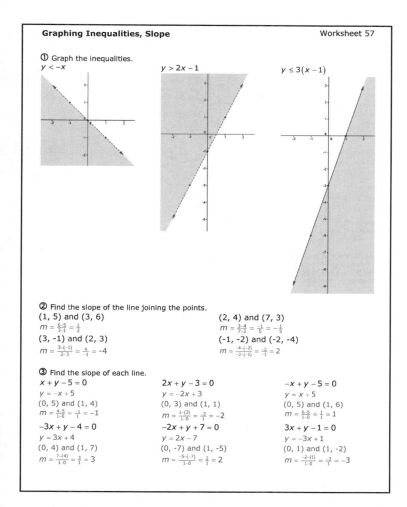

② Find the slope of the line joining the points.

(1, 5) and (3, 6)   (2, 4) and (7, 3)

$m = \frac{6-5}{3-1} = \frac{1}{2}$ $m = \frac{3-4}{7-2} = \frac{-1}{5} = -\frac{1}{5}$

(3, -1) and (2, 3)   (-1, -2) and (-2, -4)

$m = \frac{3-(-1)}{2-3} = \frac{4}{-1} = -4$ $m = \frac{-4-(-2)}{-2-(-1)} = \frac{-2}{-1} = 2$

③ Find the slope of each line.

$x + y - 5 = 0$	$2x + y - 3 = 0$	$-x + y - 5 = 0$
$y = -x + 5$	$y = -2x + 3$	$y = x + 5$
(0, 5) and (1, 4)	(0, 3) and (1, 1)	(0, 5) and (1, 6)
$m = \frac{4-5}{1-0} = \frac{-1}{1} = -1$	$m = \frac{1-(3)}{1-0} = \frac{-2}{1} = -2$	$m = \frac{6-5}{1-0} = \frac{1}{1} = 1$
$-3x + y - 4 = 0$	$-2x + y + 7 = 0$	$3x + y - 1 = 0$
$y = 3x + 4$	$y = 2x - 7$	$y = -3x + 1$
(0, 4) and (1, 7)	(0, -7) and (1, -5)	(0, 1) and (1, -2)
$m = \frac{7-(4)}{1-0} = \frac{3}{1} = 3$	$m = \frac{-5-(-7)}{1-0} = \frac{2}{1} = 2$	$m = \frac{-2-(1)}{1-0} = \frac{-3}{1} = -3$

Teaching Tips, Cont.

➢ Write the equation $-2x + y + 3 = 0$ on the board. This is the same equation from the teaching box. Ask the students how they could determine the slope of the line. (Find 2 points on the line and use the formula.)

➢ Refer to the teaching box for the solution to the above problem.

➢ Complete the Classwork exercises. Have some students work the problems on the board for the class and explain their answers. All students should work the problems in their books.

Assignments

- Complete Lesson 113, Activities 2-5.
- Worksheet 57.

Note regarding mountain roads:

Cars and trucks should adjust their speed and use a lower gear whenever the road grade is 6% or greater. Heavy trucks will often use a lower gear at lower grades when they are carrying heavy loads because gravity causes them to accelerate faster.

A 6% road grade means it has a slope of $\frac{6}{100} = \frac{3}{50}$ or greater.

Mountain roads in the western United States are generally no greater than a 6% grade. Mountain roads in the eastern United States tend to be much steeper. Grades up to 10% are common, while some locations have grades as high as 15%.

Lesson 114

Concepts
- *y*-intercept
- Slope-intercept form
- Slope
- Graphing two-variable equations
- Writing two-variable equations
- Math in the real world

Learning Objectives
The student will be able to:
- Write two-variable equations in slope-intercept form
- Identify the slope and *y*-intercept from a given equation
- Draw a graph when given the slope and *y*-intercept

Materials Needed
- Student Book, Lesson 114
- Graph paper
- Straightedge

Teaching Tips
➤ Review slope. (See Lesson 113.)

➤ Teach the *y*-intercept from the teaching box. Make sure students associate the variable *b* with the *y*-intercept.

➤ Teach how to find the *y*-intercept of an equation by substituting 0 for the value of *x*.

➤ Teach the slope-intercept form of an equation. Tell the students that by rearranging an equation to isolate the *y* on one side of the equal sign, they can quickly find the slope and the *y*-intercept.

---

y-Intercept

The **y-intercept** of a graph is the point at which the graph crosses the y-axis. The value of *x* is zero, making the coordinate appear in the format $(0, y)$. The y-intercept is represented by the letter *b*.

To find the y-intercept of a line, set $x = 0$ and solve for *y*.

Find the y-intercept of the line $-2x + y + 3 = 0$. Begin by rewriting the equation to isolate *y* on one side of the equal sign.
$y = 2x - 3$

Next, substitute 0 for *x* and solve for the corresponding value of *y*.

Let $x = 0$
$y = 2(0) - 3 = -3$
The y-intercept is -3.

Look back at the example in Lesson 113. You found the slope of this equation to be $m = 2$. Now notice how the equation looked when you isolated y on one side of the equal sign.
$y = 2x - 3$
This equation is in the **slope-intercept form** $y = mx + b$, where *m* is the slope and *b* is the y-intercept. Any time you solve an equation for y, you know both the slope and the y-intercept.

① Classwork
Rewrite each equation in slope-intercept form. Give the slope and y-intercept of each equation.

$3x + y + 1 = 0$
$y = -3x - 1$
$m = -3$
$b = -1$

$x + y - 5 = 0$
$y = -x + 5$
$m = -1$
$b = 5$

$x - 2y + 3 = 0$
$2y = x + 3$
$y = \frac{x-3}{2}$
$y = \frac{1}{2}x + \frac{3}{2}$
$m = \frac{1}{2}$
$b = \frac{3}{2}$

$3x + 2y - 4 = 0$
$2y = -3x + 4$
$y = \frac{-3x+4}{2}$
$y = -\frac{3}{2}x + 2$
$m = -\frac{3}{2}$
$b = 2$

Activities
② Rewrite each equation in slope-intercept form. Give the slope and y-intercept of each equation.

$x + y - 3 = 0$
$y = -x + 3$
$m = -1$
$b = 3$

$-3x + y - 2 = 0$
$y = 3x + 2$
$m = 3$
$b = 2$

$2x + 2y + 1 = 0$
$2y = -2x - 1$
$y = -x - \frac{1}{2}$
$m = -1$
$b = -\frac{1}{2}$

$2x + y - 2 = 0$
$y = -2x + 2$
$m = -2$
$b = 2$

$-2x + y + 3 = 0$
$y = 2x - 3$
$m = 2$
$b = -3$

$x + 2y + 4 = 0$
$2y = -x - 4$
$y = -\frac{1}{2}x - 2$
$m = -\frac{1}{2}$
$b = -2$

$-x + y - 2 = 0$
$y = x + 2$
$m = 1$
$b = 2$

$3x + y - 4 = 0$
$y = -3x + 4$
$m = -3$
$b = 4$

$3x + 2y + 6 = 0$
$2y = -3x - 6$
$y = -\frac{3}{2}x - 3$
$m = -\frac{3}{2}$
$b = -3$

---

③ Write an equation having the given slope and *y*-intercept. Graph it on your own graph paper.

$m = 3$	$m = 1$	$m = 2$
$b = -2$	$b = 3$	$b = 2$
$y = 3x - 2$	$y = x + 3$	$y = 2x + 2$

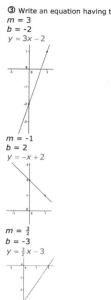

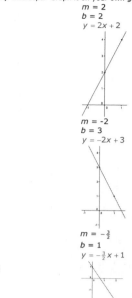

$m = -1$	$m = -3$	$m = -2$
$b = 2$	$b = -1$	$b = 3$
$y = -x + 2$	$y = -3x - 1$	$y = -2x + 3$

$m = \frac{3}{2}$		$m = -\frac{3}{2}$
$b = -3$		$b = 1$
$y = \frac{3}{2}x - 3$		$y = -\frac{3}{2}x + 1$

	$m = -\frac{1}{2}$	
	$b = 2$	
	$y = -\frac{1}{2}x + 2$	

④ Solve.

Amie has gravity-fed water towers to supply running water to her house in Uganda. The water pipe that fills the water tanks slopes down 35 feet from the water source over a ¼-mile stretch of land. Find the slope of the water pipe that fills Amie's water tanks. Leave your answer as a fraction.

¼ mile = 5280 ft. ÷ 4 = 1320 ft. This is the horizontal distance traveled.

$m = \frac{-35}{1320} = \frac{-7}{264}$ Notice that the slope is negative because it slopes down.

The water tanks are 4 feet tall. What is the maximum height the tower base can be for the tanks to be filled by gravity-fed water from the pipes if the water source is 70 feet above ground level?

The water drops 35 feet on its way to the house, leaving the fill pipes 70 − 35 = 35 feet above the ground. The tower base must not exceed 35 − 4 = 31 feet in height.

Teaching Tips, Cont.

➢ Write the equation $-2x + y + 3 = 0$ on the board. This is the same equation from the teaching box. Ask the students how they could find the slope and *y*-intercept of the line. (Rewrite the equation in slope-intercept form.)

➢ The solution to the above equation is given in the teaching box.

➢ Complete the Classwork exercises. Have some students work the problems on the board for the class and explain their answers. All students should work the problems in their books.

Assignment

• Complete Lesson 114, Activities 2-4.

Lesson 115

Concepts
- Systems of equations
- Slope-intercept form
- Coordinate points
- Math in the real world

Learning Objectives
The student will be able to:
- Describe a system of equations
- Use the substitution method to solve systems of equations
- Write a system of equations to solve a problem

Materials Needed
- Student Book, Lesson 115
- Worksheet 58

Teaching Tips
➤ Have students complete Worksheet 58 in class. This may be for added practice of earlier topics, or graded as a quiz, if desired.

➤ Review slope-intercept form. (See Lesson 114.)

➤ Ask the students how many solutions a linear equation has. (Most have an infinite number.)

➤ Ask the students what would happen if they had more than one equation to solve simultaneously. (If the equations were those of intersecting lines, there would only be one solution.) Tell the students that the solution is the point at which the two lines intersect on a graph.

Systems of Equations

A **system of linear equations** is two or more equations that all use the same set of variables. The solution of a system of equations is the point or points that are common to all lines in the system. Lines that intersect will have exactly one point as the solution. Lines that are parallel will have no points as the solution. Lines that are on top of each other will have an infinite number of points as the solution.

Find the solution of the system of equations.
$$-3x + y + 2 = 0$$
$$2x + y - 3 = 0$$
Begin by writing both equations in slope-intercept form.
$$y = 3x - 2$$
$$y = -2x + 3$$
At this point, look at the slope in both equations. Parallel lines have equal slopes. If the slopes are equal and the y-intercepts are equal, all points on the lines are the solution. If the slopes are equal and the y-intercepts are different, there are no solutions. Because the slopes are not equal, solve for the common point.

You are looking for a point whose x- and y-values are the same for both equations. Because the y-values are the same, set the right sides equal to each other.
$$3x - 2 = -2x + 3$$

Now combine terms to solve for x.
$$3x - 2 = -2x + 3$$
$$5x = 5$$
$$x = 1$$
Substitute 1 for x in either of the original equations and solve for y. Check your work by substituting in the other equation. If you are correct, you will get the same answer.
$$-3(1) + y + 2 = 0$$
$$-3 + y + 2 = 0$$
$$y = 1$$
Check:
$$2(1) + y - 3 = 0$$
$$2 + y - 3 = 0$$
$$y = 1$$

The solution is (1, 1)

① Classwork
Solve. Express the answer as a coordinate point.

$$-3x + y - 5 = 0$$
$$4x + y + 2 = 0$$
$$y = 3x + 5$$
$$y = -4x - 2$$
$$3x + 5 = -4x - 2$$
$$7x = -7$$
$$x = -1$$
$$-3(-1) + y - 5 = 0$$
$$3 + y - 5 = 0$$
$$y = 2$$
$$(-1, 2)$$

$$x - y + 2 = 0$$
$$-2x + y - 5 = 0$$
$$y = x + 2$$
$$y = 2x + 5$$
$$x + 2 = 2x + 5$$
$$-x = 3$$
$$x = -3$$
$$-3 - y + 2 = 0$$
$$y = -1$$
$$(-3, -1)$$

$$-3x - y + 5 = 0$$
$$2x - 2y - 6 = 0$$
$$y = -3x + 5$$
$$2y = 2x - 6 \quad \text{Divide each term by 2.}$$
$$y = x - 3$$
$$-3x + 5 = x - 3$$
$$-4x = -8$$
$$x = 2$$
$$-3(2) - y + 5 = 0$$
$$-6 - y + 5 = 0$$
$$y = -1$$
$$(2, -1)$$

Activities
② Solve. Express the answer as a coordinate point.

$$x + y = 0$$
$$2x + y - 1 = 0$$
$$y = -x$$
$$y = -2x + 1$$
$$-x = -2x + 1$$
$$x = 1$$
$$1 + y = 0$$
$$y = -1$$
$$(1, -1)$$

$$4x - y + 4 = 0$$
$$-2x + y - 2 = 0$$
$$y = 4x + 4$$
$$y = 2x + 2$$
$$4x + 4 = 2x + 2$$
$$2x = -2$$
$$x = -1$$
$$4(-1) - y + 4 = 0$$
$$y = -4 + 4$$
$$y = 0$$
$$(-1, 0)$$

$$-x + 2y + 1 = 0$$
$$3x - 2y - 7 = 0$$
$$2y = x - 1$$
$$2y = 3x - 7 \quad \text{Divide each term by 2.}$$
$$y = \frac{1}{2}x - \frac{1}{2}$$
$$y = \frac{3}{2}x - \frac{7}{2}$$
$$\frac{1}{2}x - \frac{1}{2} = \frac{3}{2}x - \frac{7}{2}$$
$$-\frac{2}{2}x = -\frac{6}{2}$$
$$x = 3$$
$$-3 + 2y + 1 = 0$$
$$2y = 2$$
$$y = 1$$
$$(3, 1)$$

③ Write a system of linear equations and solve.
There are 30 children in the orphanage in Soroti, Uganda. There are 10 more boys than girls. Find the number of boys and girls in the orphanage.
$$b + g = 30$$
$$b = g + 10$$
Rewrite as
$$b = 30 - g$$
$$b = g + 10$$
Solve:
$$30 - g = g + 10$$
$$-2g = -20$$
$$g = 10$$
$$b = g + 10 = 10 + 10 = 20$$
Check: 20 + 10 = 30   There are 10 girls and 20 boys.

The total number of people and dogs at Amie's house in Uganda is 8. How many dogs are there if there are a total of 22 legs in Amie's house?
Let p = the number of people
Let d = the number of dogs .
$$p + d = 8$$
$$2p + 4d = 22$$
Rewrite as
$$p + d = 8$$
$$p + 2d = 11$$
Solve for p:
$$p = 8 - d$$
$$p = 11 - 2d$$
$$8 - d = 11 - 2d$$
$$d = 3$$
There are 3 dogs at Amie's house.

④ Solve.
When the orphans went to their villages at Christmas, they each brought a gift bag containing 5 kg of dried beans, 5 kg of posho (Ugandan cornstarch), 2 kg of sugar, 500 g of salt, and 1200 g of soap. How much did each gift bag weigh? (1 kg = 2.2 pounds)
Write all measurements in kilograms:
5 kg beans
5 kg posho
2 kg sugar
0.5 kg salt
1.2 kg soap
The total is 5 + 5 + 2 + 0.5 + 1.2 = 13.7 kg
$$13.7 \text{ kg} \times \frac{2.2 \text{ lb}}{1 \text{ kg}} = 30.14 \text{ lb}$$

① Find the slope of the line joining the points.

(1, 5) and (4, 2)

$m = \frac{2-5}{4-1} = \frac{-3}{3} = -1$

(1, 5) and (7, 5)

$m = \frac{5-5}{7-1} = \frac{0}{6} = 0$

(3, -1) and (3, 5)

$m = \frac{5-(-1)}{3-3} = \frac{6}{0} = $ no slope

(3, -1) and (3, 3)

$m = \frac{3-(-1)}{3-3} = \frac{4}{0} = $ no slope

(1, 5) and (7, 2)

$m = \frac{2-5}{7-1} = \frac{-3}{6} = -\frac{1}{2}$

(1, 6) and (2, 5)

$m = \frac{5-6}{2-1} = \frac{-1}{1} = -1$

(3, -1) and (4, 1)

$m = \frac{1-(-1)}{4-3} = \frac{2}{1} = 2$

(3, -1) and (-2, -3)

$m = \frac{-3-(-1)}{-2-3} = \frac{-2}{-5} = \frac{2}{5}$

② Find the slope of each line.

$x + y - 6 = 0$
$y = -x + 6$
$m = -1$

$3x + y - 1 = 0$
$y = -3x + 1$
$m = -3$

$-x + y + 3 = 0$
$y = x - 3$
$m = 1$

$-3x + y - 7 = 0$
$y = 3x + 7$
$m = 3$

$-2x + y + 1 = 0$
$y = 2x - 1$
$m = 2$

$4x + y - 2 = 0$
$y = -4x + 2$
$m = -4$

$2x + y - 5 = 0$
$y = -2x + 5$
$m = -2$

$4x + y - 3 = 0$
$y = -4x + 3$
$m = -4$

$-3x + y - 5 = 0$
$y = 3x + 5$
$m = 3$

$-2x + y - 4 = 0$
$y = 2x + 4$
$m = 2$

$-5x + y + 7 = 0$
$y = 5x - 7$
$m = 5$

$6x + y - 5 = 0$
$y = -6x + 5$
$m = -6$

Note regarding systems of equations:

A system of linear equations may have no solutions (in the case of parallel lines), exactly one solution (in the case of intersecting lines) or an infinite number of solutions (in the case of two lines with the same slope and *y*-intercept).

In upper level mathematics, it is possible to have an exact number of solutions greater than 1. This book will deal exclusively with systems of linear equations having exactly 1 solution.

Teaching Tips, Cont.

➢ Teach systems of linear equations from the teaching box. Tell students that one method of solving systems of equations is by substitution. They should rewrite each equation in slope-intercept form. Then substitute the value of *y* in one equation for *y* in the other equation. See the teaching box for details.

➢ Emphasize the importance of students checking their work when solving systems of equations. The solution can be substituted in both original equations and will produce a correct mathematical sentence.

➢ Students may need some assistance setting up a system of equations for the word problems in this lesson. Offer assistance as needed for the first problem and encourage the students to work the second problem on their own.

➢ Complete the Classwork exercises. Have some students work the problems on the board for the class and explain their answers. All students should work the problems in their books.

Assignment

- Complete Lesson 115, Activities 2-4.

Lesson 116

Concepts
- Systems of equations
- Adding equations
- Simple interest
- Compound interest
- Math in the real world

Learning Objectives
The student will be able to:
- Use addition to solve systems of equations
- Write a system of equations to solve a problem

Materials Needed
- Student Book, Lesson 116
- Calculator

Teaching Tips
➤ Review systems of equations. (See Lesson 115.)

➤ Teach students how to solve systems of equations by addition. Emphasize the importance of lining up like terms before adding.

➤ Tell the students that they may use either method (substitution or addition) unless otherwise instructed.

➤ Show students that addition is the method of choice for solving systems of equations when the two equations have a like term that differs only in its sign. For example, one equation has $3x$ and the other equation has $-3x$.

Adding Equations

Adding equations is an alternate method of solving a system of equations. To add equations, write each equation in the form $Ax + By = C$, where A is the coefficient of x, B is the coefficient of y, and C is a constant. This is known as the **standard form** of an equation.

Solve the system of equations by adding.
$$-3x + y + 4 = 0$$
$$3x + y - 2 = 0$$

First, rewrite both equations in standard form.
$$-3x + y = -4$$
$$3x + y = 2$$

Add the terms vertically to get a new equation.
$$-3x + y = -4$$
$$\underline{3x + y = 2}$$
$$2y = -2$$

Solve for the variable that remains.
$$2y = -2$$
$$y = -1$$

Substitute -1 for y in either of the original equations and solve for x. Check your work by substituting in the other equation. If you are correct, you will get the same answer.

$$-3x + (-1) + 4 = 0$$
$$-3x + 3 = 0$$
$$-3x = -3$$
$$x = 1$$

Check:
$$3x + (-1) - 2 = 0$$
$$3x - 3 = 0$$
$$3x = 3$$
$$x = 1$$

The solution is the point (1, -1).

① Classwork
Solve by adding.
$$-3x + y - 5 = 0$$
$$4x - y + 6 = 0$$
$$-3x + y = 5$$
$$4x - y = -6$$
$$x = -1$$
$$-3(-1) + y - 5 = 0$$
$$3 + y - 5 = 0$$
$$y = 2$$
$$(-1, 2)$$

$$x - y + 2 = 0$$
$$-2x + y - 5 = 0$$
$$x - y = -2$$
$$-2x + y = 5$$
$$-x = 3$$
$$x = -3$$
$$-3 - y + 2 = 0$$
$$y = -1$$
$$(-3, -1)$$

$$-3x - y + 5 = 0$$
$$3x - 2y - 8 = 0$$
$$-3x - y = -5$$
$$3x - 2y = 8$$
$$-3y = 3$$
$$y = -1$$
$$-3x - (-1) + 5 = 0$$
$$-3x + 6 = 0$$
$$-3x = -6$$
$$x = 2$$
$$(2, -1)$$

Activities
② Solve by adding.

$$-3x + y + 7 = 0$$
$$3x - 2y - 5 = 0$$
$$-3x + y = -7$$
$$3x - 2y = 5$$
$$-y = -2$$
$$y = 2$$
$$-3x + 2 + 7 = 0$$
$$-3x = -9$$
$$x = 3$$
$$(3, 2)$$

$$4x - y + 4 = 0$$
$$-2x + y - 2 = 0$$
$$4x - y = -4$$
$$-2x + y = 2$$
$$2x = -2$$
$$x = -1$$
$$4(-1) - y + 4 = 0$$
$$-4 - y + 4 = 0$$
$$y = 0$$
$$(-1, 0)$$

$$-x + 2y + 1 = 0$$
$$3x - 2y - 7 = 0$$
$$-x + 2y = -1$$
$$3x - 2y = 7$$
$$2x = 6$$
$$x = 3$$
$$-3 + 2y + 1 = 0$$
$$2y = 2$$
$$y = 1$$
$$(3, 1)$$

---

③ Write a system of equations and solve.

On a flight across the Atlantic Ocean from New York to London, Amie's plane flew 3456 miles in 8 hours with a tail wind. On the return flight, the plane flew against the wind and took 9 hours to fly the 3456 miles. Find the average speed of the plane and the average speed of the wind. Hint: Let p represent the plane's speed and w the wind's speed. Then $p + w$ is the total speed with the wind, and $p - w$ is the net speed against the wind.

$(p+w)(8 \text{ hours}) = 3456 \text{ miles}$

$(p-w)(9 \text{ hours}) = 3456 \text{ miles}$

Divide and rewrite as

$p + w = 432 \text{ miles/hour}$

$p - w = 384 \text{ miles/hour}$

Add:

$p + w = 432 \text{ miles/hour}$

$p - w = 384 \text{ miles/hour}$

$2p = 816 \text{ miles/hour}$

$p = 408 \text{ miles/hour}$

$408 \text{ miles/hour} + w = 432 \text{ miles/hour}$

$w = 24 \text{ miles/hour}$

The plane averaged 408 miles per hour, and the wind speed averaged 24 miles per hour. Note: Airplanes travel in the 500-600 mph range at their cruising altitude. Here, you are calculating the *average* speed.

Amie's 4290-mile flight from London to Uganda lasted 10 hours with a tail wind. The return trip was flying against the wind and took 11 hours. Find the average speed of the plane and the average wind speed.

$(p+w)(10 \text{ hours}) = 4290 \text{ miles}$

$(p-w)(11 \text{ hours}) = 4290 \text{ miles}$

Divide and rewrite as

$p + w = 429 \text{ miles/hour}$

$p - w = 390 \text{ miles/hour}$

Add:

$p + w = 429 \text{ miles/hour}$

$p - w = 390 \text{ miles/hour}$

$2p = 819 \text{ miles/hour}$

$p = 409.5 \text{ miles/hour}$

$409.5 \text{ miles/hour} + w = 429 \text{ miles/hour}$

$w = 19.5 \text{ miles/hour}$

The plane averaged 409.5 miles per hour, and the wind speed averaged 19.5 miles per hour.

④ Complete the chart to show simple interest and interest compounded annually.

Principal	Interest rate	Time, in years	Total amount of simple interest	Balance, compounded annually
$14,000	6.25%	6	$i = \$14,000(0.0625)(6) = \$5250$	$A = \$14,000(1 + 0.0625)^6$ $= \$20,141.96$
$30,000	12.9%	15	$i = \$30,000(0.129)(15) = \$58,050$	$A = \$30,000(1 + 0.129)^{15}$ $= \$185,152.84$
$100,000	5.625%	30	$i = \$100,000(0.05625)(30) = \$168,750$	$A = \$100,000(1 + 0.05625)^{30}$ $= \$516,418.34$

Teaching Tips, Cont.

➢ Students may need some assistance setting up a system of equations for the word problems in this lesson. Offer assistance as needed for the first problem and encourage the students to work the second problem on their own.

➢ Complete the Classwork exercises. Have some students work the problems on the board for the class and explain their answers. All students should work the problems in their books.

Assignment

• Complete Lesson 116, Activities 2-4.

Lesson 117

Concepts
- Systems of equations
- Subtracting equations
- Divisibility tests
- Prime/composite numbers
- Angles
- Math in the real world

Learning Objectives
The student will be able to:
- Use subtraction to solve a system of equations
- Write a system of equations to solve a problem

Materials Needed
- Student Book, Lesson 117

Teaching Tips
➤ Review solving systems of equations by substitution and addition. (See Lessons 115-116.)

➤ Teach students how to solve systems of equations by subtraction. Emphasize the importance of lining up like terms before subtracting.

➤ Tell the students that they may use any method (substitution, addition, or subtraction) unless otherwise instructed.

➤ Show students that subtraction is the method of choice for solving systems of equations when the two equations have identical like terms. For example, both equations have $3x$ as a term.

Subtracting Equations

Subtracting equations is a third method of solving a system of equations.

Solve the system of equations by subtracting.
$$-3x + y + 4 = 0$$
$$3x + y - 2 = 0$$

First, rewrite both equations in standard form.
$$-3x + y = -4$$
$$3x + y = 2$$

Subtract the terms vertically to get a new equation. This is the same as changing the sign of each term in the second equation and adding.
$$-3x + y = -4$$
$$\underline{-3x - y = -2}$$
$$-6x \quad\quad = -6$$

Solve for the variable that remains.
$$-6x = -6$$
$$x = 1$$

Substitute 1 for x in either of the original equations and solve for y. Check your work by substituting in the other equation. If you are correct, you will get the same answer.

$$-3(1) + y + 4 = 0$$
$$-3 + y + 4 = 0$$
$$y = -1$$

Check:
$$3(1) + y - 2 = 0$$
$$3 + y - 2 = 0$$
$$y = -1$$

The solution is the point (1, -1).

① Classwork
Solve by subtracting.
$$-3x + y - 5 = 0$$
$$4x + y + 2 = 0$$
$$-3x + y = 5$$
$$4x + y = -2$$
$$-7x \quad\quad = 7$$
$$x \quad = -1$$
$$-3(-1) + y - 5 = 0$$
$$3 + y - 5 = 0$$
$$y = 2$$
$$(-1, 2)$$

$$x - y + 2 = 0$$
$$2x - y + 5 = 0$$
$$x - y = -2$$
$$2x - y = -5$$
$$-x \quad = 3$$
$$x \quad = -3$$
$$-3 - y + 2 = 0$$
$$y = -1$$
$$(-3, -1)$$

$$3x + y - 5 = 0$$
$$3x - 2y - 8 = 0$$
$$3x + y = 5$$
$$3x - 2y = 8$$
$$3y = -3$$
$$y = -1$$
$$3x - 1 - 5 = 0$$
$$3x - 6 = 0$$
$$3x = 6$$
$$x = 2$$
$$(2, -1)$$

Activities
② Solve by subtracting.

$$3x - y - 7 = 0$$
$$3x - 2y - 5 = 0$$
$$3x - y = 7 \quad 3x - 2 - 7 = 0$$
$$3x - 2y = 5 \quad 3x = 9$$
$$y = 2 \quad x = 3$$
$$(3, 2)$$

$$4x - y + 4 = 0$$
$$2x - y + 2 = 0$$
$$4x - y = -4 \quad 4(-1) - y + 4 = 0$$
$$2x - y = -2 \quad -4 - y + 4 = 0$$
$$2x \quad = -2 \quad y = 0$$
$$x \quad = -1 \quad (-1, 0)$$

$$x - 2y - 1 = 0$$
$$3x - 2y - 7 = 0$$
$$x - 2y = 1 \quad 3 - 2y - 1 = 0$$
$$3x - 2y = 7 \quad -2y = -2$$
$$-2x \quad = -6 \quad y = 1$$
$$x \quad = 3 \quad (3, 1)$$

③ Write a system of equations and solve.

The sum of the ages of Amie's two daughters is 10. Two years ago, the older daughter was twice as old as the younger daughter. How old are her daughters now?

Let x = the age of the older daughter now
Let y = the age of the younger daughter now

$$x + y = 10$$
$$x - 2 = 2(y - 2)$$

Rewrite as
$$x + y = 10$$
$$x - 2 = 2y - 4$$

and again as
$$x + y = 10$$
$$x - 2y = -2$$

Subtract:
$$x + y = 10$$
$$x - 2y = -2$$
$$3y = 12$$
$$y = 4$$

The younger daughter is 4 years old. This makes the older daughter $10 - 4 = 6$ years old.

Amie's middle child is twice as old as her youngest child. Next year, the sum of their ages will be 8. How old are these two children now?

Let x = the age of the middle child now
Let y = the age of the youngest child now

$$x = 2y$$
$$(x + 1) + (y + 1) = 8$$

Rewrite as
$$x = 2y$$
$$x + y + 2 = 8$$

and again as
$$x - 2y = 0$$
$$x + y = 6$$

Subtract:
$$x - 2y = 0$$
$$x + y = 6$$
$$-3y = -6$$
$$y = 2$$

The youngest child is 2 years old. This makes the middle child $2(2) = 4$ years old.

④ Use the divisibility tests to identify each number as prime or composite.

463	Prime	471	Composite (3)
465	Composite (3, 5)	475	Composite (5)
467	Prime	477	Composite (3)

⑤ Find the measure of each angle.

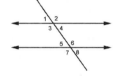

$$m\angle 2 = 180° - 42° = 138°$$
$$m\angle 3 = 180° - 42° = 138°$$
$$m\angle 4 = 42°$$
$$m\angle 5 = 42°$$
$$m\angle 6 = 180° - 42° = 138°$$
$$m\angle 7 = 180° - 42° = 138°$$
$$m\angle 8 = 42°$$

In the diagram above, there are two parallel lines cut by a transversal.
$m\angle 1 = 42°$

Teaching Tips, Cont.

➤ Students may need some assistance setting up a system of equations for the word problems in this lesson. Offer assistance as needed for the first problem and encourage the students to work the second problem on their own.

➤ Complete the Classwork exercises. Have some students work the problems on the board for the class and explain their answers. All students should work the problems in their books.

Assignment

• Complete Lesson 117, Activities 2-5.

Lesson 118

Concepts
- Fahrenheit-Celsius conversion
- Sum of interior angles of polygons
- Regular polygons
- Math in the real world

Learning Objectives
The student will be able to:
- Identify Fahrenheit as the temperature scale in the United States
- Identify Celsius as the temperature scale for the rest of the world
- Convert degrees Fahrenheit to degrees Celsius

Materials Needed
- Student Book, Lesson 118
- Worksheet 59

Teaching Tips
➢ Have students complete Worksheet 59 in class. This may be for added practice of earlier topics, or graded as a quiz, if desired.

➢ Review multiplying fractions. (See Lesson 36.)

➢ Teach the Fahrenheit and Celsius temperature scales from the teaching box.

➢ Teach the formulas for converting Fahrenheit to Celsius. Students may use either formula when calculating temperature conversions.

Fahrenheit – Celsius Conversion

Fahrenheit is the temperature scale most commonly used in the United States. Temperatures are given in degrees Fahrenheit. Water freezes at 32°F and boils at 212°F. Normal body temperature for people is 98.6°F.

Celsius is the temperature scale most commonly used everywhere except the United States. Temperatures are given in degrees Celsius. Water freezes at 0°C and boils at 100°C. Normal body temperature for people is 37°C.

To convert degrees Fahrenheit to degrees Celsius, use the formula $°C = (°F - 32°)\left(\frac{5}{9}\right)$

The Fahrenheit and Celsius scales are the same at -40°. An alternate conversion formula for finding degrees Celsius is
$°C = (°F + 40°)\left(\frac{5}{9}\right) - 40°$

Convert 41°F to degrees Celsius. Use either formula.
$°C = (41° - 32°)\left(\frac{5}{9}\right)$
$°C = (9°)\left(\frac{5}{9}\right)$
$°C = 5°$

$°C = (41° + 40°)\left(\frac{5}{9}\right) - 40°$
$°C = (81°)\left(\frac{5}{9}\right) - 40°$
$°C = 45° - 40°$
$°C = 5°$

As you can see, both formulas give the same answer. Use whichever one is the easiest.

① Classwork
Convert to degrees Celsius.

50°F
$°C = (50° - 32°)\left(\frac{5}{9}\right)$
$°C = (18°)\left(\frac{5}{9}\right)$
$°C = 10°$

32°F
$°C = (32° - 32°)\left(\frac{5}{9}\right)$
$°C = (0°)\left(\frac{5}{9}\right)$
$°C = 0°$

5°F
$°C = (5° - 32°)\left(\frac{5}{9}\right)$
$°C = (-27°)\left(\frac{5}{9}\right)$
$°C = -15°$

Activities
② Convert to degrees Celsius. Round to the nearest tenth where appropriate.

122°F
$°C = (122° - 32°)\left(\frac{5}{9}\right)$
$°C = (90°)\left(\frac{5}{9}\right)$
$°C = 50°$

86°F
$°C = (86° - 32°)\left(\frac{5}{9}\right)$
$°C = (54°)\left(\frac{5}{9}\right)$
$°C = 30°$

59°F
$°C = (59° - 32°)\left(\frac{5}{9}\right)$
$°C = (27°)\left(\frac{5}{9}\right)$
$°C = 15°$

95°F
$°C = (95° - 32°)\left(\frac{5}{9}\right)$
$°C = (63°)\left(\frac{5}{9}\right)$
$°C = 35°$

100°F
$°C = (100° - 32°)\left(\frac{5}{9}\right)$
$°C = (68°)\left(\frac{5}{9}\right)$
$°C = 37.8°$

118°F
$°C = (118° - 32°)\left(\frac{5}{9}\right)$
$°C = (86°)\left(\frac{5}{9}\right)$
$°C = 47.8°$

---

③ Complete the chart to convert oven temperatures from degrees Fahrenheit to degrees Celsius. Round your answers to the nearest 10 degrees.

°F	°C	°F	°C
200°	$°C = (200° - 32°)\left(\frac{5}{9}\right) = 90°$	375°	$°C = (375° - 32°)\left(\frac{5}{9}\right) = 190°$
225°	$°C = (225° - 32°)\left(\frac{5}{9}\right) = 110°$	400°	$°C = (400° - 32°)\left(\frac{5}{9}\right) = 200°$
250°	$°C = (250° - 32°)\left(\frac{5}{9}\right) = 120°$	425°	$°C = (425° - 32°)\left(\frac{5}{9}\right) = 220°$
275°	$°C = (275° - 32°)\left(\frac{5}{9}\right) = 140°$	450°	$°C = (450° - 32°)\left(\frac{5}{9}\right) = 230°$
300°	$°C = (300° - 32°)\left(\frac{5}{9}\right) = 150°$	475°	$°C = (475° - 32°)\left(\frac{5}{9}\right) = 250°$
325°	$°C = (325° - 32°)\left(\frac{5}{9}\right) = 160°$	500°	$°C = (500° - 32°)\left(\frac{5}{9}\right) = 260°$
350°	$°C = (350° - 32°)\left(\frac{5}{9}\right) = 180°$	525°	$°C = (525° - 32°)\left(\frac{5}{9}\right) = 270°$

④ Solve.
A recipe for pumpkin pie says to bake the pie at 425°F for 15 minutes and then reduce the temperature to 350°F and bake for an additional 45 minutes. What temperature changes does Amie need to make in the instructions to bake the pie in her Celsius oven? What changes does Amie need to make in the baking time to bake the pie in her Celsius oven?
Amie needs to bake the pie at 220°C for 15 minutes and then reduce the temperature to 180°C and bake for an additional 45 minutes. No changes to the bake time are necessary. The oven has the same amount of heat to bake the pie. Only the temperature scale has changed.

⑤ Complete the chart for regular polygons.

Number of sides	Sum of interior angles	Degrees per angle if all angles are equal
3	$sum = (3 - 2)180° = 1(180°) = 180°$	$180° \div 3 = 60°$
4	$sum = (4 - 2)180° = 2(180°) = 360°$	$360° \div 4 = 90°$
5	$sum = (5 - 2)180° = 3(180°) = 540°$	$540° \div 5 = 108°$
6	$sum = (6 - 2)180° = 4(180°) = 720°$	$720° \div 6 = 120°$
8	$sum = (8 - 2)180° = 6(180°) = 1080°$	$1080° \div 8 = 135°$
10	$sum = (10 - 2)180° = 8(180°) = 1440°$	$1440° \div 10 = 144°$
12	$sum = (12 - 2)180° = 10(180°) = 1800°$	$1800° \div 12 = 150°$

① Solve the systems of equations. Express each answer as a coordinate point.

$3x + y + 5 = 0$
$-4x + y - 2 = 0$
$3x - (-4x) + 5 - (-2) = 0$
$\qquad 7x + 7 = 0$
$\qquad\qquad 7x = -7$
$\qquad\qquad\quad x = -1$

$3(-1) + y + 5 = 0$
$-3 + y + 5 = 0$
$y = -2$
$(-1, -2)$

$-3x + 2y - 5 = 0$
$4x + 2y + 2 = 0$
$-7x - 7 = 0$
$\quad -7x = 7$
$\qquad x = -1$

$-3(-1) + 2y - 5 = 0$
$3 + 2y - 5 = 0$
$2y = 2$
$y = 1$
$(-1, 1)$

$x - 5y + 2 = 0$
$-2x + 5y - 5 = 0$
$-x - 3 = 0$
$\quad -x = 3$
$\qquad x = -3$

$-3 - 5y + 2 = 0$
$-5y = 1$
$y = -\frac{1}{5}$
$(-3, -\frac{1}{5})$

$x - 2y + 2 = 0$
$-2x + 2y - 5 = 0$
$-x - 3 = 0$
$\quad -x = 3$
$\qquad x = -3$

$-3 - 2y + 2 = 0$
$-2y = 1$
$(-3, -\frac{1}{2})$

$x - 3y + 2 = 0$
$-2x + 3y - 5 = 0$
$-x - 3 = 0$
$\quad -x = 3$
$\qquad x = -3$

$-3 - 3y + 2 = 0$
$-3y = 1$
$y = -\frac{1}{3}$
$(-3, -\frac{1}{3})$

$2x + y + 2 = 0$
$-2x + y - 2 = 0$
$y = x + 2$
$y = 2x + 5$
$2y = 0$
$\quad y = 0$

$2x + 0 + 2 = 0$
$2x = -2$
$x = -1$
$(-1, 0)$

$-3x - y + 3 = 0$
$3x - 2y - 6 = 0$
$-3y - 3 = 0$
$\quad -3y = 3$
$\qquad y = -1$

$-3x - (-1) + 3 = 0$
$-3x + 4 = 0$
$-3x = -4$
$x = \frac{4}{3}$
$(\frac{4}{3}, -1)$

$-x + y - 2 = 0$
$2x - y + 5 = 0$
$x + 3 = 0$
$\quad x = -3$

$-(-3) + y - 2 = 0$
$3 + y - 2 = 0$
$y = -1$
$(-3, -1)$

$3x - 3y + 6 = 0$
$-2x + y - 5 = 0$
$3y = 3x + 6$
$\quad y = 2x + 5$

$y = \ x + 2$
$y = 2x + 5$
$x + 2 = 2x + 5$
$\quad -x = 3$
$\qquad x = -3$
$-3 - y + 2 = 0$
$y = -1$
$(-3, -1)$

Teaching Tips, Cont.

➢ Ask the students when they might need to use temperature conversions. (Visiting a different country and performing scientific calculations.)

➢ Complete the Classwork exercises. Have some students work the problems on the board for the class and explain their answers. All students should work the problems in their books.

Assignment

- Complete Lesson 118, Activities 2-5.

Lesson 119

Concepts
- Celsius-Fahrenheit conversion
- Volume
- Surface area
- Math in the real world

Learning Objectives
The student will be able to:
- Convert degrees Celsius to degrees Fahrenheit

Materials Needed
- Student Book, Lesson 119

Teaching Tips
➢ Review converting degrees Fahrenheit to degrees Celsius. (See Lesson 118.)

➢ Review finding the volume and surface area of solid figures. (See Lessons 91-96.)

➢ Teach the two formulas for converting degrees Celsius to degrees Fahrenheit from the teaching box.

➢ Remind the students that -40° is the same on both temperature scales.

➢ Tell the students they may use either formula for calculating the temperature conversions.

➢ Note: The Celsius temperature scale was formerly called the centigrade scale. In 1948, its name was changed to Celsius to honor Anders Celsius, a scientist who developed a similar temperature scale in 1742.

Celsius – Fahrenheit Conversion

To convert degrees Celsius to degrees Fahrenheit, use the formula $°F = (°C)\left(\frac{9}{5}\right) + 32°$

The Fahrenheit and Celsius scales are the same at -40°. An alternate conversion formula for finding degrees Fahrenheit is
$°F = (°C + 40°)\left(\frac{9}{5}\right) - 40°$

Convert 5°C to degrees Fahrenheit.
Use either formula.
$°F = (5°)\left(\frac{9}{5}\right) + 32°$
$°F = 9° + 32°$
$°F = 41°$

$°F = (5° + 40°)\left(\frac{9}{5}\right) - 40°$
$°F = (45°)\left(\frac{9}{5}\right) - 40°$
$°F = 81° - 40°$
$°F = 41°$

As you can see, both formulas give the same answer. Use whichever one is the easiest.

① **Classwork.**
Convert to degrees Fahrenheit.

50°C
$°F = (50°)\left(\frac{9}{5}\right) + 32°$
$°F = 90° + 32°$
$°F = 122°$

0°C
$°F = (0°)\left(\frac{9}{5}\right) + 32°$
$°F = 0° + 32°$
$°F = 32°$

25°C
$°F = (25°)\left(\frac{9}{5}\right) + 32°$
$°F = 45° + 32°$
$°F = 77°$

Activities
② Convert to degrees Fahrenheit. Round to the nearest tenth where appropriate.

20°C
$°F = (20°)\left(\frac{9}{5}\right) + 32°$
$°F = 36° + 32°$
$°F = 68°$

30°C
$°F = (30°)\left(\frac{9}{5}\right) + 32°$
$°F = 54° + 32°$
$°F = 86°$

100°C
$°F = (100°)\left(\frac{9}{5}\right) + 32°$
$°F = 180° + 32°$
$°F = 212°$

37°C
$°F = (37°)\left(\frac{9}{5}\right) + 32°$
$°F = 66.6° + 32°$
$°F = 98.6°$

55°C
$°F = (55°)\left(\frac{9}{5}\right) + 32°$
$°F = 99° + 32°$
$°F = 131°$

80°C
$°F = (80°)\left(\frac{9}{5}\right) + 32°$
$°F = 144° + 32°$
$°F = 176°$

125°C
$°F = (125°)\left(\frac{9}{5}\right) + 32°$
$°F = 225° + 32°$
$°F = 257°$

2°C
$°F = (2°)\left(\frac{9}{5}\right) + 32°$
$°F = 3.6° + 32°$
$°F = 35.6°$

95°C
$°F = (95°)\left(\frac{9}{5}\right) + 32°$
$°F = 171° + 32°$
$°F = 203°$

45°C
$°F = (45°)\left(\frac{9}{5}\right) + 32°$
$°F = 81° + 32°$
$°F = 113°$

180°C
$°F = (180°)\left(\frac{9}{5}\right) + 32°$
$°F = 324° + 32°$
$°F = 356°$

46°C
$°F = (46°)\left(\frac{9}{5}\right) + 32°$
$°F = 82.8° + 32°$
$°F = 114.8°$

③ Solve.

The tank on Amie's water tower is a cylinder 2 feet in diameter and 4 feet high. What is the volume of the water tank? Use 3.14 for π.

$V = \pi r^2 h$

$V = \pi (1)^2 (4)$

$V = 4\pi$ cu. feet

$V = 4(3.14) = 12.56$ cu. ft.

How many gallons will the tank hold? Round your answer to the nearest gallon. (1 cubic foot = 7.48 gallons)

12.56 cu. ft. $\times \dfrac{7.48 \text{ gal.}}{1 \text{ cu. ft.}} = 94$ gallons

Amie wants to paint the outside surface of the water tank with two coats of paint to protect it from the weather. If one quart of paint will cover 75 square feet of surface area, how many whole quarts of paint will Amie need?

$SA = 2\pi rh + 2\pi r^2$

$SA = 2\pi (1)(4) + 2\pi (1)^2$

$SA = 8\pi + 2\pi$

$SA = 10\pi$

$SA = 10(3.14) = 31.4$ sq. ft.

Two coats of paint will have to cover 31.4 + 31.4 = 62.8 sq. ft. One quart of paint will be enough to put two coats of paint on the outside of the water tank.

When Amie's family moved to Uganda to begin their first term as missionaries, they had to pack everything in a shipping container. The inside dimensions of the container were as follows: 19 ft. 3 in. long, 7 ft. 7 in. wide, and 7 ft. 9 in. high. What was the volume of container in cubic feet? Round your answer to the nearest cubic foot.

Write each measurement as a mixed number and convert to an improper fraction.

Length: $19\frac{3}{12} = 19\frac{1}{4} = \frac{77}{4}$ ft.

Width: $7\frac{7}{12} = \frac{91}{12}$ ft.

Height: $7\frac{9}{12} = 7\frac{3}{4} = \frac{31}{4}$ ft.

$V = lwh$

$V = \left(\frac{77}{4}\right)\left(\frac{91}{12}\right)\left(\frac{31}{4}\right) = \frac{217,217}{192} = 1131$ cu. ft.

Amie packed a queen mattress (60 in. wide, 80 in. long, 15 in. high), two twin mattresses (39 in. wide, 75 in. long, 15 in. high each), and a crib mattress (27 in. wide, 52 in. long, 6 in. high). What percent of the packing space was used up by the mattresses? Round mattress volumes and the percent to the nearest whole.

Area of queen mattress: $V = \left(\frac{\cancel{60}^{5}}{\cancel{12}}\right)\left(\frac{\cancel{80}^{20}}{\cancel{12}_{3}}\right)\left(\frac{\cancel{15}^{5}}{\cancel{12}_{4}}\right) = \frac{125}{3} = 42$ cu. ft.

Area of twin mattresses: $V = 2\left(\frac{\cancel{39}^{13}}{\cancel{12}_{4}}\right)\left(\frac{\cancel{75}^{25}}{\cancel{12}_{4}}\right)\left(\frac{\cancel{15}^{5}}{\cancel{12}_{4}}\right) = \cancel{2}\left(\frac{1625}{\cancel{64}_{32}}\right) = 51$ cu. ft.

Area of crib mattress: $V = \left(\frac{\cancel{27}^{9}}{\cancel{12}_{4}}\right)\left(\frac{\cancel{52}^{13}}{\cancel{12}_{3}}\right)\left(\frac{6}{\cancel{12}_{2}}\right) = \frac{39}{8} = 5$ cu. ft.

Total area of mattresses: 42 + 51 + 5 = 98 cu. ft. $\frac{98}{1131} = 9\%$

Teaching Tips, Cont.

➢ Tell the students that neither the Fahrenheit scale nor the Celsius scale is the unit of temperature measurement in the SI system. The Kelvin (abbreviated K) is the SI unit of temperature. Temperature is measured in Kelvin, not degrees, and has no negative values. Absolute zero is zero Kelvin, written 0K, and is equal to -273.15°C.

➢ Complete the Classwork exercises. Have some students work the problems on the board for the class and explain their answers. All students should work the problems in their books.

Assignment

- Complete Lesson 119, Activities 2-3.

Lesson 120

Concepts
- English-metric conversions
- Ounces
- Quarts
- Gallons
- Milliliters
- Liters
- Math in the real world

Learning Objectives
The student will be able to:
- Convert ounces to milliliters
- Convert quarts and gallons to liters
- Convert milliliters to ounces
- Convert liters to quarts and gallons

Materials Needed
- Student Book, Lesson 120
- Worksheet 60

Teaching Tips
➢ Review the prefix milli- from Lesson 31.

➢ Review English-metric conversions. (See Lesson 40.)

➢ Introduce ounces, quarts, and gallons as English units of liquid measure. Explain that the abbreviation for ounces is *oz.* because the Italian word for ounce is *oncia*, which was spelled *onza* when the abbreviation was instituted.

➢ Introduce liters as the unit of liquid measure in the SI system. Larger and smaller units are formed by adding prefixes.

English – Metric Conversions: Liquids

In the English system of measurement, the standard units of liquid measure are ounces, quarts, and gallons. Use the following conversion factors to convert English units to SI units.

1 ounce (oz.) = 30 mL
1 quart (qt.) = 0.95 L
1 gallon (gal.) = 3.8 L

In the SI system, the standard unit of liquid measure is the liter. Recall that 1 liter is equal to 1000 milliliters. Use the following conversion factors to convert SI units to English units.

1 mL = 0.034 oz.
1 L = 1.06 qt.
1 L = 0.26 gal.

Convert 8 ounces to milliliters.

$$8 \text{ oz.} \times \frac{30 \text{ mL}}{1 \text{ oz.}} = 240 \text{ mL}$$

Convert 75 milliliters to ounces.

$$75 \text{ mL} \times \frac{0.034 \text{ oz.}}{1 \text{ mL}} = 2.55 \text{ oz.}$$

① Classwork

Convert 2.5 quarts to liters.

$$2.5 \text{ qt.} \times \frac{0.95 \text{ L}}{1 \text{ qt.}} = 2.375 \text{ L}$$

Convert 5 gallons to liters.

$$5 \text{ gal.} \times \frac{3.8 \text{ L}}{1 \text{ gal.}} = 19 \text{ L}$$

Convert 2 liters to quarts.

$$2 \text{ L} \times \frac{1.06 \text{ qt.}}{1 \text{ L}} = 2.12 \text{ qt.}$$

Convert 10 liters to gallons.

$$10 \text{ L} \times \frac{0.26 \text{ gal.}}{1 \text{ L}} = 2.6 \text{ gal.}$$

Activities

② Solve.

Convert 12 ounces to milliliters.

$$12 \text{ oz.} \times \frac{30 \text{ mL}}{1 \text{ oz.}} = 360 \text{ mL}$$

Convert 4 quarts to liters.

$$4 \text{ qt.} \times \frac{0.95 \text{ L}}{1 \text{ qt.}} = 3.8 \text{ L}$$

Convert 15 gallons to liters.

$$15 \text{ gal.} \times \frac{3.8 \text{ L}}{1 \text{ gal.}} = 57 \text{ L}$$

Convert 100 milliliters to ounces.

$$100 \text{ mL} \times \frac{0.034 \text{ oz.}}{1 \text{ mL}} = 3.4 \text{ oz.}$$

Convert 6 liters to quarts.

$$6 \text{ L} \times \frac{1.06 \text{ qt.}}{1 \text{ L}} = 6.36 \text{ qt.}$$

Convert 12 liters to gallons.

$$12 \text{ L} \times \frac{0.26 \text{ gal.}}{1 \text{ L}} = 3.12 \text{ gal.}$$

Convert 2500 milliliters to quarts.

$$2500 \text{ mL} \times \frac{1 \text{ L}}{1000 \text{ mL}} \times \frac{1.06 \text{ qt.}}{1 \text{ L}} = 2.65 \text{ qt.}$$

Convert 100 ounces to liters.

$$100 \text{ oz.} \times \frac{30 \text{ mL}}{1 \text{ oz.}} \times \frac{1 \text{ L}}{1000 \text{ mL}} = 3 \text{ L}$$

Convert 1500 milliliters to gallons.

$$1500 \text{ mL} \times \frac{1 \text{ L}}{1000 \text{ mL}} \times \frac{0.26 \text{ gal.}}{1 \text{ L}} = 0.39 \text{ gal.}$$

③ Complete the charts.

Amie must calculate medicine doses for the children at the orphanage and patients at the clinic. The maximum daily dose of acetaminophen is 75 mg per kg, divided into five equal doses. (1 pound = 0.45 kg)

Pounds	Kilograms	Maximum Daily Dose	Single dose
20	20 × 0.45 = 9 kg	9 × 75 = 675 mg	675 ÷ 5 = 135 mg
30	30 × 0.45 = 13.5 kg	13.5 × 75 = 1012.5 mg	1012.5 ÷ 5 = 202.5 mg
40	40 × 0.45 = 18 kg	18 × 75 = 1350 mg	1350 ÷ 5 = 270 mg
50	50 × 0.45 = 22.5 kg	22.5 × 75 = 1687.5 mg	1687.5 ÷ 5 = 337.5 mg
60	60 × 0.45 = 27 kg	27 × 75 = 2025 mg	2025 ÷ 5 = 405 mg

Acetaminophen is packaged as a liquid suspension of 160 mg per 5 mL. For each weight in the chart above, calculate the number of milliliters Amie should give in one dose. Round all answers down to a whole milliliter.

Pounds	Milligrams in single dose	Milliliters of suspension
20	135 mg	$135 \text{ mg} \times \frac{5 \text{ mL}}{160 \text{ mg}} = 4 \text{ mL}$
30	202.5 mg	$202.5 \text{ mg} \times \frac{5 \text{ mL}}{160 \text{ mg}} = 6 \text{ mL}$
40	270 mg	$270 \text{ mg} \times \frac{5 \text{ mL}}{160 \text{ mg}} = 8 \text{ mL}$
50	337.5 mg	$337.5 \text{ mg} \times \frac{5 \text{ mL}}{160 \text{ mg}} = 10 \text{ mL}$
60	405 mg	$405 \text{ mg} \times \frac{5 \text{ mL}}{160 \text{ mg}} = 12 \text{ mL}$

④ Solve.

How many doses of acetaminophen can Amie get from a 4-oz. bottle for a 50-pound child?

$$4 \text{ oz.} \times \frac{30 \text{ mL}}{1 \text{ oz.}} = 120 \text{ mL}$$

120 mL ÷ 10 mL = 12 doses

Amie's car holds 16 gallons of fuel. It costs 2550 Ugandan shillings per liter of fuel. If the current exchange rate is 2050 Ugandan shillings per US dollar, what is the cost per gallon of fuel?

1 gallon = 3.8 liters

$$3.8 \text{ L} \times \frac{2550 \text{ shillings}}{1 \text{ L}} \times \frac{\$1}{2050 \text{ shillings}} = \$4.73 \text{ per gallon of fuel}$$

If Amie's fuel tank is ¼ full, how much will it cost in US dollars to fill the tank?

¾ × 16 = 12 gallons to fill the tank.

12($4.73) = $56.76

Horizons Pre-Algebra, Teacher's Guide

① Convert to degrees Celsius. Round answers to the nearest tenth.

125°F
$°C = (125° - 32°)(\frac{5}{9})$
$°C = (93°)(\frac{5}{9})$
$°C = 51.7°$

80°F
$°C = (80° - 32°)(\frac{5}{9})$
$°C = (48°)(\frac{5}{9})$
$°C = 26.7°$

55°F
$°C = (55° - 32°)(\frac{5}{9})$
$°C = (23°)(\frac{5}{9})$
$°C = 12.8°$

90°F
$°C = (90° - 32°)(\frac{5}{9})$
$°C = (58°)(\frac{5}{9})$
$°C = 32.2°$

120°F
$°C = (120° - 32°)(\frac{5}{9})$
$°C = (88°)(\frac{5}{9})$
$°C = 48.9°$

115°F
$°C = (115° - 32°)(\frac{5}{9})$
$°C = (83°)(\frac{5}{9})$
$°C = 46.1°$

② Convert to degrees Fahrenheit.

125°C
$°F = (125°)(\frac{9}{5}) + 32°$
$°F = 225° + 32°$
$°F = 257°$

80°C
$°F = (80°)(\frac{9}{5}) + 32°$
$°F = 144° + 32°$
$°F = 176°$

55°C
$°F = (55°)(\frac{9}{5}) + 32°$
$°F = 99° + 32°$
$°F = 131°$

90°C
$°F = (90°)(\frac{9}{5}) + 32°$
$°F = 162° + 32°$
$°F = 194°$

120°C
$°F = (120°)(\frac{9}{5}) + 32°$
$°F = 216° + 32°$
$°F = 248°$

115°C
$°F = (115°)(\frac{9}{5}) + 32°$
$°F = 207° + 32°$
$°F = 239°$

③ Solve.

Convert 16 ounces to milliliters.
$16 \text{ oz.} \times \frac{30 \text{ mL}}{1 \text{ oz.}} = 480 \text{ mL}$

Convert 6 quarts to liters.
$6 \text{ qt.} \times \frac{0.95 \text{ L}}{1 \text{ qt.}} = 5.7 \text{ L}$

Convert 18 gallons to liters.
$18 \text{ gal.} \times \frac{3.8 \text{ L}}{1 \text{ gal.}} = 68.4 \text{ L}$

Convert 150 milliliters to ounces.
$150 \text{ mL} \times \frac{0.034 \text{ oz.}}{1 \text{ mL}} = 5.1 \text{ oz.}$

Convert 7 liters to quarts.
$7 \text{ L} \times \frac{1.06 \text{ qt.}}{1 \text{ L}} = 7.42 \text{ qt.}$

Convert 19 liters to gallons.
$19 \text{ L} \times \frac{0.26 \text{ gal.}}{1 \text{ L}} = 4.94 \text{ gal.}$

Convert 2900 milliliters to quarts.
$2900 \text{ mL} \times \frac{1 \text{ L}}{1000 \text{ mL}} \times \frac{1.06 \text{ qt.}}{1 \text{ L}}$
$= 3.074 \text{ qt.}$

Convert 125 ounces to liters.
$125 \text{ oz.} \times \frac{30 \text{ mL}}{1 \text{ oz.}} \times \frac{1 \text{ L}}{1000 \text{ mL}}$
$= 3.75 \text{ L}$

Convert 1700 milliliters to gallons.
$1700 \text{ mL} \times \frac{1 \text{ L}}{1000 \text{ mL}} \times \frac{0.26 \text{ gal.}}{1 \text{ L}}$
$= 0.442 \text{ gal.}$

Teaching Tips, Cont.

➢ Teach how to convert English liquid measures to SI units. Students are not expected to memorize the conversion factors, but must know how to use them.

➢ Teach how to convert SI units of liquid measure to English units. Again, students are not expected to memorize the conversion factors, but must be able to use them.

➢ Complete the Classwork exercises. Have some students work the problems on the board for the class and explain their answers. All students should work the problems in their books.

Assignments

• Complete Lesson 120, Activities 2-4.
• Worksheet 60.
• Study for Test 12. (Lessons 108-117)
• Study for Exam 3 (Lessons 81-117)

Test 12

Testing Objectives

The student will:

- Graph points on a coordinate plane
- Identify the origin and quadrants of a coordinate plane
- Solve two-variable equations when the value of one variable is given
- Graph two-variable equations
- Graph two-variable inequalities
- Identify functions
- Identify parts of a circle
- Calculate the measure of complementary angles
- Calculate the measure of angles formed by two parallel lines and a transversal

Materials Needed

- Test 12
- *It's College Test Prep Time!* from the Student Book
- *A Math Minute with…* Lee T. from the Student Book

Teaching Tips

➤ Administer Test 12, allowing the students 30-40 minutes to complete the test.

➤ When all students are finished taking the test, introduce *It's College Test Prep Time* from the student book. This page may be completed in class or assigned as homework.

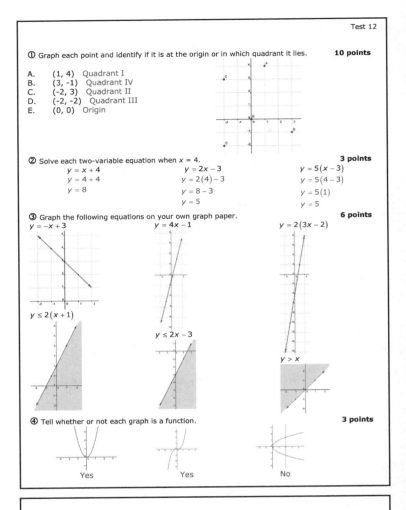

① Graph each point and identify if it is at the origin or in which quadrant it lies.   **10 points**

A.	(1, 4)	Quadrant I
B.	(3, -1)	Quadrant IV
C.	(-2, 3)	Quadrant II
D.	(-2, -2)	Quadrant III
E.	(0, 0)	Origin

② Solve each two-variable equation when $x = 4$.   **3 points**

$y = x + 4$
$y = 4 + 4$
$y = 8$

$y = 2x - 3$
$y = 2(4) - 3$
$y = 8 - 3$
$y = 5$

$y = 5(x - 3)$
$y = 5(4 - 3)$
$y = 5(1)$
$y = 5$

③ Graph the following equations on your own graph paper.   **6 points**

$y = -x + 3$

$y = 4x - 1$

$y = 2(3x - 2)$

$y \le 2(x + 1)$

$y \le 2x - 3$

$y > x$

④ Tell whether or not each graph is a function.   **3 points**

Yes   Yes   No

⑤ Write each equation in slope-intercept form and identify the slope and y-intercept.   **27 points**

$2x + y - 5 = 0$
$y = -2x + 5$
$m = -2$
$b = 5$

$3x + y - 4 = 0$
$y = -3x + 4$
$m = -3$
$b = 4$

$-7x + y - 3 = 0$
$y = 7x + 3$
$m = 7$
$b = 3$

$-3x + y - 4 = 0$
$y = 3x + 4$
$m = 3$
$b = 4$

$-4x + y + 6 = 0$
$y = 4x - 6$
$m = 4$
$b = -6$

$8x + y - 9 = 0$
$y = -8x + 9$
$m = -8$
$b = 9$

$2x + 2y + 5 = 0$
$2y = -2x - 5$
$y = -x - \frac{5}{2}$
$m = -1$
$b = -\frac{5}{2}$

$x + 2y + 6 = 0$
$2y = -x - 6$
$y = -\frac{1}{2}x - 3$
$m = -\frac{1}{2}$
$b = -3$

$5x + 2y - 8 = 0$
$2y = -5x + 8$
$y = -\frac{5}{2}x + 4$
$m = -\frac{5}{2}$
$b = 4$

⑥ Solve. Express the answer as a coordinate point.   **6 points**

$x + y + 1 = 0$
$2x + y - 1 = 0$
$-x + 2 = 0$
$x = 2$
$2 + y + 1 = 0$
$y = -3$
$(2, -3)$

$4x - y + 4 = 0$
$-3x + y - 3 = 0$
$x + 1 = 0$
$x = -1$
$4(-1) - y + 4 = 0$
$-4 - y + 4 = 0$
$y = 0$
$(-1, 0)$

$3x + y + 5 = 0$
$2x + y - 1 = 0$
$x + 6 = 0$
$x = -6$
$3(-6) + y + 5 = 0$
$-18 + y + 5 = 0$
$y = 13$
$(-6, 13)$

$x + 2y - 7 = 0$
$2x + 2y + 3 = 0$
$-x - 10 = 0$
$x = -10$
$-10 + 2y - 7 = 0$
$2y = 17$
$y = \frac{17}{2}$
$(-10, \frac{17}{2})$

$3x + 2y + 4 = 0$
$2x + 2y - 1 = 0$
$x + 5 = 0$
$x = -5$
$3(-5) + 2y + 4 = 0$
$-15 + 2y + 4 = 0$
$2y = 11$
$y = \frac{11}{2}$
$(-5, \frac{11}{2})$

$2x + 3y + 3 = 0$
$2x + y - 1 = 0$
$2y + 4 = 0$
$2y = -4$
$y = -2$
$2x + 3(-2) + 3 = 0$
$2x - 6 + 3 = 0$
$2x = 3$
$x = \frac{3}{2}$
$(\frac{3}{2}, -2)$

55 points total

It's College Test Prep Time!

1. Given *a* and *d*, defined by the equations below, find the value of *d* if *b* = 5 and *c* = 2.

$a = 2bc$

$d = (b - 2)a$

A. 0
B. 6
C. 20
D. <u>60</u>
E. 98

Start by finding the value of *a*: $a = 2(5)(2) = 20$.
Substitute the values of *b* and *a* in the second equation: $d = (5 - 2)(20) = 3(20) = 60$.

2. Find the slope of the line joining points (1, 3) and (2, 5) in a coordinate plane.

A. $\frac{3}{8}$
B. $\frac{1}{2}$
C. 1
D. <u>2</u>
E. $\frac{8}{3}$

$m = \frac{5-3}{2-1} = \frac{2}{1} = 2$

3. In the diagram below, $\overline{AB} \parallel \overline{CD}$. What is the value of *x*?

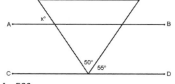

A. 50°
B. 55°
C. <u>75°</u>
D. 105°
E. 180°

X is a corresponding angle to the angle that makes a straight angle with the two labeled angles.
$180° - 50° - 55° = 75°$

Teaching Tips, Cont.

➤ Have students read the Math Minute interview for lessons 111-120.

Assignments

• Complete *It's College Test Prep Time!*
• Read *A Math Minute with...* Lee T.

A Math Minute with . . .

Lee T. – Firefighter/Paramedic

What is your occupation? I am a firefighter and paramedic.

Where do you work? I work at the county fire department as well as the local emergency medical service ambulance company.

Did you attend college? If so, what was your major? No.

What parts of your job require the use of math? When operating the fire pump at a fire, you use math formulas to determine how many pounds of water to pump and at what pressure. On medical calls, many medications are given in a weight-based dose, but in kilograms. You must convert the patient's pounds to kilograms and then determine the correct dose to give.

What is the biggest "problem" you have faced that required the use of math to solve? At a large warehouse fire, I had to calculate the water needed based on the square footage of the building, the pressure coming from the hydrant, and the fire load the building contained.

Are there any other interesting math uses you have experienced? At 3:00 in the morning, I needed to calculate a dopamine drip rate. I used the formula of 2-10 micrograms per kilogram of patient's weight per minute when the drug was supplied at 5 grams per 1 cubic centimeter of fluid. What made the task more difficult was the patient's weight needed to be guessed because he/she was unresponsive.

Horizons Pre-Algebra, Teacher's Guide

Exam 3

Testing Objectives

The student will:

- Calculate probabilities
- Calculate the lateral area of solid figures
- Calculate the surface area of solid figures
- Calculate the volume of solid figures
- Calculate the mass of an object
- Calculate the weight of an object
- Calculate the density of an object
- Calculate velocity
- Calculate distance
- Calculate time
- Identify parts of a circle
- Graph two-variable equations
- Graph two-variable inequalities
- Solve systems of equations
- Write equations in slope-intercept form
- Find the slope of a line
- Identify the *y*-intercept of a line
- Calculate the measures of angles

Materials Needed

- Exam 3
- Formula strip, Exam 3

Teaching Tips

- ➤ Give the students the formula strip for Exam 3 from the *Tests and Resources* book.
- ➤ Administer Exam 3, allowing the students 45-50 minutes to complete the test.

---

① Find the probabilities. **3 points**

When a standard six-sided game die is rolled one time, what is the probability that it will be a 1 or a 6?

$$P(1 \cup 6) = \frac{1}{6} + \frac{1}{6} = \frac{2}{6} = \frac{1}{3}$$

When a standard six-sided game die is rolled twice, what is the probability that the first roll will be a 1 and the second roll will be a 6?

$$P(1)P(6) = \frac{1}{6}\left(\frac{1}{6}\right) = \frac{1}{36}$$

When a standard six-sided game die is rolled twice, what is the probability that a 1 and a 6 will be rolled in either order?

$$P(1 \cup 6)P(\text{other number}) = \frac{1}{3}\left(\frac{1}{6}\right) = \frac{1}{18}$$

② Find the lateral area, surface area, and volume of each solid figure. **14 points**

A prism with a height of 8 feet and a rectangular base that is 7 feet long and 4 feet wide.

$LA = PL$	$SA = PL + 2B$	$V = Bh$
$LA = 22(8) = 176$ sq. ft.	$SA = 176 + 2(28)$	$V = (28)(8)$
	$SA = 176 + 56 = 232$ sq. ft.	$V = 224$ cu. ft.

A pyramid with a height of 12 meters, a slant height of 13 meters, and a square base that is 10 meters on each side.

$LA = \frac{1}{2}PL$	$SA = \frac{1}{2}PL + B$	$V = \frac{1}{3}Bh$
$LA = \frac{1}{2}(4 \times 10)(13)$	$SA = 260 + 100$	$V = \frac{1}{3}(100)(12)$
$LA = (20)(13) = 260$ m²	$SA = 360$ m²	$V = 400$ m³

A cylinder with a height of 7 inches and a base that has a diameter of 4 inches.

$LA = 2\pi rL$	$SA = 2\pi rL + 2\pi r^2$	$V = \pi r^2 h$
$LA = 2\pi(2)(7)$	$SA = 28\pi + 2\pi(2)^2$	$V = \pi(2)^2(7)$
$LA = 28\pi$ sq. in.	$SA = 28\pi + 2\pi(4)$	$V = 28\pi$ cu. in.
	$SA = 36\pi$ sq. in.	

A cone with a height of 8 yards, a slant height of 10 yards, and a base that has a diameter of 12 yards.

$LA = \pi rL$	$SA = \pi rL + \pi r^2$	$V = \frac{1}{3}\pi r^2 h$
$LA = \pi(6)(10)$	$SA = 60\pi + \pi(6)^2$	$V = \frac{1}{3}\pi(6)^2(8)$
$LA = 60\pi$ sq. yd.	$SA = 60\pi + 36\pi = 96\pi$ sq. yd.	$V = \pi(12)(8)$
		$V = 96\pi$ cu. yd.

A sphere with a diameter of 18 cm.

A sphere has no lateral area.	$SA = 4\pi(9)^2$	$V = \frac{4}{3}\pi r^3$
	$SA = 4\pi(81)$	$V = \frac{4}{3}\pi(9)^3$
	$SA = 324\pi$ cm²	$V = \frac{4}{3}\pi(729)$
		$V = 972\pi$ cm³

---

③ Use the formula $m = \frac{w}{g}$ to find the mass or weight of each item. Round answers to the nearest whole number. **3 points**

	Baby	Child	Adult
Mass	$m = \frac{w}{g}$ $m = \frac{40 \text{ kg} \cdot m/s^2}{9.8 \text{ m/s}^2}$ $m = 4$ kg	32.1 kg	$m = \frac{w}{g}$ $m = \frac{800 \text{ kg} \cdot m/s^2}{9.8 \text{ m/s}^2}$ $m = 82$ kg
Weight	40 kg • m/s²	$m = \frac{w}{g}$ 32.1 kg $= \frac{w}{9.8 \text{ m/s}^2}$ $w = 315$ kg • m/s²	800 kg • m/s²
Gravity	9.8 m/s²	9.8 m/s²	9.8 m/s²

④ Use the formula $d = \frac{m}{v}$ to find the density of each object and identify if it will float in pure water. The density of pure water is 1000 kg/m³. **6 points**

Substance	Mass	Volume	Density	Float: Y/N
Cocoa beans	237.2 kg	0.4 m³	$d = \frac{m}{v}$ $d = \frac{237.2 \text{ kg}}{0.4 \text{ m}^3}$ $d = 593$ kg/m³	Y
Brick	2325.62 kg	1.21 m³	$d = \frac{m}{v}$ $d = \frac{2325.62 \text{ kg}}{1.21 \text{ m}^3}$ $d = 1922$ kg/m³	N
Furnace cinders	2282.5 kg	2.5 m³	$d = \frac{m}{v}$ $d = \frac{2282.5 \text{ kg}}{2.5 \text{ m}^3}$ $d = 913$ kg/m³	Y

⑤ Use the formula $v = \frac{d}{t}$ to find the velocity, distance, or time. **3 points**

Velocity	Distance	Time
$v = \frac{585 \text{ miles}}{9 \text{ hours}}$ $v = 65$ miles/hour	585 miles	9 hours
48 miles per hour	$d = (48 \text{ miles/hour})(1.5 \text{ hours})$ $d = 72$ miles	1.5 hours
340 miles per hour	884 miles	$t = \frac{884 \text{ miles}}{340 \text{ miles/hour}}$ $t = 2.6$ hours

⑥ Identify one of each item in circle *A*. Write the appropriate symbol for each figure. **6 points**

Secant	Chord
$\overline{BG}$	$\overline{EF}$, $\overline{BG}$, or $\overline{BC}$
Diameter	Tangent
$\overline{BC}$	$\overline{HJ}$
Radius	Central angle
$\overline{AB}$, $\overline{AC}$, or $\overline{AD}$	$\angle CAD$ or $\angle BAD$

---

⑦ Graph the following equations on your own graph paper.   **3 points**

$y = x - 3$ $y = -4x + 1$ $y \geq 2(x + 1)$

⑧ Write each equation in slope-intercept form and identify the slope and y-intercept.   **18 points**

$-4x + y - 5 = 0$ $-3x + y + 7 = 0$ $10x + y - 13 = 0$
$y = 4x + 5$ $y = 3x - 7$ $y = -10x + 13$
$m = 4$ $m = 3$ $m = -10$
$b = 5$ $b = -7$ $b = 13$

$4x + 2y + 7 = 0$ $6x + 2y + 9 = 0$ $7x + 2y - 5 = 0$
$2y = -4x - 7$ $2y = -6x - 9$ $2y = -7x + 5$
$y = -2x - \frac{7}{2}$ $y = -3x - \frac{9}{2}$ $y = -\frac{7}{2}x + \frac{5}{2}$
$m = -2$ $m = -3$ $m = -\frac{7}{2}$
$b = -\frac{7}{2}$ $b = -\frac{9}{2}$ $b = \frac{5}{2}$

⑨ Solve. Express the answer as a coordinate point.   **6 points**

$2x + 2y + 1 = 0$ $4x - 2y + 4 = 0$ $3x + y + 5 = 0$
$2x + y - 1 = 0$ $-4x + 3y - 3 = 0$ $-2x - y + 1 = 0$
$y + 2 = 0$ $y + 1 = 0$ $x + 6 = 0$
$y = -2$ $y = -1$ $x = -6$
$2x - 2 - 1 = 0$ $4x + 2 + 4 = 0$ $3(-6) + y + 5 = 0$
$2x = 3$ $4x + 6 = 0$ $-18 + y + 5 = 0$
$x = \frac{3}{2}$ $x = -\frac{6}{4} = -\frac{3}{2}$ $y = 13$
$\left(\frac{3}{2}, -2\right)$ $\left(-\frac{3}{2}, -1\right)$ $(-6, 13)$

⑩ Find the measure of each angle in the figure below.   **13 points**

$\overline{AB} \parallel \overline{CD}$

$\overline{EF} \perp \overline{GH}$

75 points total

Lesson 121

Concepts
- English-metric conversions
- Weight
- Mass
- Temperature
- Math in the real world

Learning Objectives
The student will be able to:
- Convert ounces to grams
- Convert pounds and short tons to kilograms
- Convert grams to ounces
- Convert kilograms to pounds
- Convert metric tons to short tons

Materials Needed
- Student Book, Lesson 121

Teaching Tips
- Review English-metric conversions. (See Lessons 40 and 120.)

- Review mass and weight. (See Lesson 98.)

- Introduce ounces, pounds, and short tons as units of weight in the English system. Explain that the abbreviation for pound is *lb*. from the Latin expression *libra pondo*, which means *pound of weight*. The abbreviation comes from the first word of the expression and the unit from the second word of the expression.

- Explain that the abbreviation is always written as *lb*, never *lbs*. While *lbs* is accurate as a shorthand writing of "pounds weight," it is not an abbreviation of the word *pounds*.

English – Metric Conversions: Weight and Mass

In the English system of measurement, the standard units of weight are ounces, pounds, and tons. There are different definitions of ton in the measurement system. This book will use the short ton, which is equal to 2000 pounds.

Use the following conversion factors to convert English units to SI units.

1 ounce (oz.) = 28.35 g
1 pound (lb.) = 0.454 kg
1 short ton (S. ton) = 907 kg

In the SI system, the standard unit of mass is the gram. Recall that 1 gram is equal to 1000 milligrams. One metric ton is equal to 1000 kg.

Use the following conversion factors to convert SI units to English units.

1 g = 0.035 oz.
1 kg = 2.2 lb.
1 metric ton (M. ton) = 1.1 S. ton

Convert 8 ounces to grams.

$8 \text{ oz.} \times \dfrac{28.35 \text{ g}}{1 \text{ oz.}} = 226.8 \text{ g}$

Convert 75 kg to pounds.

$75 \text{ kg} \times \dfrac{2.2 \text{ lb.}}{1 \text{ kg}} = 165 \text{ lb.}$

① Classwork
Convert the measurements.

Convert 95 pounds to kilograms.

$95 \text{ lb.} \times \dfrac{0.454 \text{ kg}}{1 \text{ lb.}} = 43.13 \text{ kg}$

Convert 3 M. tons to S. tons.

$3 \text{ M-ton} \times \dfrac{1.1 \text{ S.ton}}{1 \text{ M-ton}} = 3.3 \text{ S. ton}$

Activities
② Complete the chart to show conversion between the metric and English systems.

14 oz.	$14 \text{ oz.} \left(\frac{28.35 \text{ g}}{1 \text{ oz.}}\right) = 396.9$ g
42 lb.	$42 \text{ lb.} \left(\frac{0.454 \text{ kg}}{1 \text{ lb.}}\right) = 19.068$ kg
24 S. ton	$24 \text{ S. ton} \left(\frac{907 \text{ kg}}{1 \text{ S. ton}}\right) = 21,768$ kg
16 g	$16 \text{ g} \left(\frac{0.035 \text{ oz.}}{1 \text{ g}}\right) = 0.56$ oz.
60 kg	$60 \text{ kg} \left(\frac{2.2 \text{ lb.}}{1 \text{ kg}}\right) = 132$ lb.
8 M. ton	$8 \text{ M. ton} \left(\frac{1.1 \text{ S. ton}}{1 \text{ M. ton}}\right) = 8.8$ S. ton

---

③ Solve.

The primary water tank on a fire truck holds 1000 gallons of water. How many liters of water can the primary water tank hold?

$1000 \text{ gal.} \times \dfrac{3.8 \text{ L}}{1 \text{ gal.}} = 3800 \text{ L}$

The crosslay hoses on a fire truck are 200 feet long and $1\frac{1}{2}$ inches in diameter. What is the volume of a crosslay hose in cubic feet? Use 3.14 for the value of π. Round your answer to the nearest hundredth.

The radius is $1\frac{1}{2}\left(\frac{1}{2}\right) = \frac{3}{2}\left(\frac{1}{2}\right) = \frac{3}{4}$ inches. Convert to feet: $\frac{3}{4}\left(\frac{1}{12}\right) = \frac{1}{16}$ ft.

$V = \pi r^2 h$

$V = \pi \left(\frac{1}{16}\right)^2 (200)$

$V = \pi \left(\frac{1}{256}\right)\left(200\right) = \frac{25}{32}\pi = 2.45$ cu. ft.

One cubic foot equals 7.48 gallons. How many gallons of water will one crosslay hose hold?

$2.45 \text{ cu. ft.} \times \dfrac{7.48 \text{ gal.}}{1 \text{ cu. ft.}} = 18.326 \text{ gal.}$

A crosslay hose sprays 95 gallons of water per minute. How long will the water in the primary water tank last with two crosslay hoses spraying water from the tank? Express your answer in terms of minutes and seconds. Round to the nearest tenth of a second.

One hose uses 95 gallons per minute, so two hoses use 95(2) = 190 gallons per minute.

$1000 \text{ gal.} \times \dfrac{1 \text{ min.}}{190 \text{ gal.}} = 5.26 \text{ min.}$

$0.26 \text{ min.} \times \dfrac{60 \text{ sec.}}{1 \text{ min.}} = 15.6 \text{ sec.}$

The water in the tank will last 5 minutes 15.6 seconds.

The deluge gun on a fire truck can spray 1000 gallons per minute. How many crosslay hoses would it take to have the same water output?

$1000 \div 95 = 10.5$ It will take 11 crosslay hoses to have the output of 1 deluge gun.

④ Solve. Round answers to the nearest tenth where appropriate.

°F	°C	°C	°F
0°	$°C = (0° - 32°)\left(\frac{5}{9}\right) = -17.8°$	0°	$°F = (0°)\left(\frac{9}{5}\right) + 32° = 0° + 32° = 32°$
30°	$°C = (30° - 32°)\left(\frac{5}{9}\right) = -1.1°$	30°	$°F = (30°)\left(\frac{9}{5}\right) + 32° = 54° + 32° = 86°$
50°	$°C = (50° - 32°)\left(\frac{5}{9}\right) = 10°$	50°	$°F = (50°)\left(\frac{9}{5}\right) + 32° = 90° + 32° = 122°$
75°	$°C = (75° - 32°)\left(\frac{5}{9}\right) = 23.9°$	75°	$°F = (75°)\left(\frac{9}{5}\right) + 32° = 135° + 32° = 167°$
100°	$°C = (100° - 32°)\left(\frac{5}{9}\right) = 37.8°$	100°	$°F = (100°)\left(\frac{9}{5}\right) + 32° = 180° + 32° = 212°$
125°	$°C = (125° - 32°)\left(\frac{5}{9}\right) = 51.7°$	125°	$°F = (125°)\left(\frac{9}{5}\right) + 32° = 225° + 32° = 257°$
150°	$°C (150° - 32°)\left(\frac{5}{9}\right) = 65.6°$	150°	$°F = (150°)\left(\frac{9}{5}\right) + 32° = 270° + 32° = 302°$

Teaching Tips, Cont.

➢ Teach how to convert English weight measures to SI units of mass. Students are not expected to memorize the conversion factors, but must know how to use them.

➢ Teach how to convert SI units of mass measure to English units of weight. Again, students are not expected to memorize the conversion factors, but must be able to use them.

➢ Complete the Classwork exercises. Have some students work the problems on the board for the class and explain their answers. All students should work the problems in their books.

Assignment

• Complete Lesson 121, Activities 2-4.

Lesson 122

Concepts
- Pythagorean formula
- Hypotenuse
- Right triangles
- Math in the real world

Learning Objectives
The student will be able to:
- Explain the Pythagorean formula
- Define *hypotenuse*
- Calculate the length of a missing side of a right triangle
- Use the Pythagorean formula to find Pythagorean triples

Materials Needed
- Student Book, Lesson 122
- Worksheet 61
- Formula strip, Lesson 122

Teaching Tips
➤ Give the students the formula strip for Lesson 122 from the *Tests and Resources* book.

➤ Have students complete Worksheet 61 in class. This may be for added practice of earlier topics, or graded as a quiz, if desired.

➤ Review square roots. (See Lesson 18.)

➤ Teach the Pythagorean formula from the teaching box. Make sure students understand that c is always the hypotenuse, no matter which sides are given.

➤ Explain that in a right triangle, the side opposite the right angle is called the hypotenuse and the other two sides are the legs. The hypotenuse is always the longest side in a right triangle.

Pythagorean Formula

The **Pythagorean formula** is used to find the lengths of the sides of right triangles.

In a right triangle, the legs are the sides that make the right angle, and the **hypotenuse** is the side opposite the right angle.

In any right triangle, the sum of the squares of the lengths of the legs is equal to the square of the length of the hypotenuse.

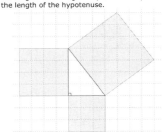

Written as a formula, $a^2 + b^2 = c^2$, where a and b are the lengths of the legs, and c is the length of the hypotenuse.

Find the length of the hypotenuse in the figure above.

$a^2 + b^2 = c^2$
$3^2 + 4^2 = c^2$
$9 + 16 = c^2$
$25 = c^2$
$\sqrt{25} = \sqrt{c^2}$
$5 = c$

① Classwork
Find the length of the missing sides.

$a^2 + b^2 = c^2$
$6^2 + 8^2 = c^2$
$36 + 64 = c^2$
$100 = c^2$
$\sqrt{100} = \sqrt{c^2}$
$10 = c$

$a^2 + b^2 = c^2$
$5^2 + 12^2 = c^2$
$25 + 144 = c^2$
$169 = c^2$
$\sqrt{169} = \sqrt{c^2}$
$13 = c$

Activities

② Find the length of the missing sides.

$a^2 + b^2 = c^2$
$a^2 + 3^2 = 5^2$
$a^2 + 9 = 25$
$a^2 = 16$
$\sqrt{a^2} = \sqrt{16}$
$a = 4$

$a^2 + b^2 = c^2$
$8^2 + 15^2 = c^2$
$64 + 225 = c^2$
$289 = c^2$
$\sqrt{289} = \sqrt{c^2}$
$17 = c$

③ A Pythagorean triple is a set of three positive integers that satisfy the formula $a^2 + b^2 = c^2$. Complete the chart to find the Pythagorean triples.

a	b	c
3	4	$c = \sqrt{3^2 + 4^2} \rightarrow c = 5$
$a = \sqrt{13^2 - 12^2} \rightarrow a = 5$	12	13
8	$b = \sqrt{17^2 - 8^2} \rightarrow b = 15$	17
7	24	$c = \sqrt{7^2 + 24^2} \rightarrow c = 25$
6	$b = \sqrt{10^2 - 6^2} \rightarrow b = 8$	10
$a = \sqrt{41^2 - 40^2} \rightarrow a = 9$	40	41

④ Solve.
An aerial ladder fire truck has a 100-ft. ladder attached to the top of the truck. If the base of the truck-mounted ladder is 10 feet above the ground, how far from a building can the truck park and still reach a window that is 90 feet above the ground?
Because the base of the ladder is already 10 feet above the ground, it only needs to reach an additional 90 − 10 = 80 feet.
Use the Pythagorean formula, with the ladder as the hypotenuse.
$a^2 + (80)^2 = 100^2$
$a^2 + 6400 = 10,000$
$a^2 = 3600$
$a = \sqrt{3600} = 60$
The truck must be no more than 60 feet from the building.

English—SI Conversions

Worksheet 61

① Complete the chart to convert from degrees Fahrenheit to degrees Celsius. Round answers to the nearest tenth where necessary.

°F	°C
20°	$°C = (20° - 32°)\left(\frac{5}{9}\right) = 6.7°$
25°	$°C = (25° - 32°)\left(\frac{5}{9}\right) = -3.9°$
30°	$°C = (30° - 32°)\left(\frac{5}{9}\right) = -1.1°$
35°	$°C = (35° - 32°)\left(\frac{5}{9}\right) = 1.7°$
40°	$°C = (40° - 32°)\left(\frac{5}{9}\right) = 4.4°$
45°	$°C = (45° - 32°)\left(\frac{5}{9}\right) = 7.2°$
50°	$°C = (50° - 32°)\left(\frac{5}{9}\right) = 10°$

② Complete the chart to convert from degrees Celsius to degrees Fahrenheit.

°C	°F
20°	$°F = (20°)\left(\frac{9}{5}\right) + 32° = 36° + 32° = 68°$
25°	$°F = (25°)\left(\frac{9}{5}\right) + 32° = 45° + 32° = 77°$
30°	$°F = (30°)\left(\frac{9}{5}\right) + 32° = 54° + 32° = 86°$
35°	$°F = (35°)\left(\frac{9}{5}\right) + 32° = 63° + 32° = 95°$
40°	$°F = (40°)\left(\frac{9}{5}\right) + 32° = 72° + 32° = 104°$
45°	$°F = (45°)\left(\frac{9}{5}\right) + 32° = 81° + 32° = 113°$
50°	$°F = (50°)\left(\frac{9}{5}\right) + 32° = 90° + 32° = 122°$

③ Solve.

Convert 16 ounces to milliliters.
$16 \text{ oz.} \times \frac{30 \text{ mL}}{1 \text{ oz.}} = 480 \text{ mL}$

Convert 2 quarts to liters.
$2 \text{ qt.} \times \frac{0.95 \text{ L}}{1 \text{ qt.}} = 1.9 \text{ L}$

Convert 20 gallons to liters.
$20 \text{ gal.} \times \frac{3.8 \text{ L}}{1 \text{ gal.}} = 76 \text{ L}$

Convert 150 milliliters to ounces.
$150 \text{ mL} \times \frac{0.034 \text{ oz.}}{1 \text{ mL}} = 5.1 \text{ oz.}$

Convert 2 liters to quarts.
$2 \text{ L} \times \frac{1.06 \text{ qt.}}{1 \text{ L}} = 2.12 \text{ qt.}$

Convert 15 liters to gallons.
$15 \text{ L} \times \frac{0.26 \text{ gal.}}{1 \text{ L}} = 3.9 \text{ gal.}$

Convert 2000 milliliters to quarts.
$2000 \text{ mL} \times \frac{1 \text{ L}}{1000 \text{ mL}} \times \frac{1.06 \text{ qt.}}{1 \text{ L}} = 2.12 \text{ qt.}$

Convert 150 ounces to liters.
$150 \text{ oz.} \times \frac{30 \text{ mL}}{1 \text{ oz.}} \times \frac{1 \text{ L}}{1000 \text{ mL}} = 4.5 \text{ L}$

Convert 2500 milliliters to gallons.
$2500 \text{ mL} \times \frac{1 \text{ L}}{1000 \text{ mL}} \times \frac{0.26 \text{ gal.}}{1 \text{ L}} = 0.65 \text{ gal.}$

Teaching Tips, Cont.

➢ Teach the students how to use the Pythagorean formula to find the length of a missing side in a right triangle. Emphasize that this formula will work only for right triangles. Students must memorize this formula.

➢ Complete the Classwork exercises. Have some students work the problems on the board for the class and explain their answers. All students should work the problems in their books.

Assignment

• Complete Lesson 122, Activities 2-4.

Horizons Pre-Algebra, Teacher's Guide

Lesson 123

Concepts
- 30-60-90 triangles
- Pythagorean formula
- Math in the real world

Learning Objectives
The student will be able to:
- Find the lengths of the missing sides when given the length of one side of a 30-60-90 triangle
- Identify ratios in 30-60-90 triangles

Materials Needed
- Student Book, Lesson 123
- Worksheet 62
- Formula strip, Lesson 123

Teaching Tips
- ➤ Review ratios. (See Lesson 43.)

- ➤ Review the Pythagorean formula. (See Lesson 122.)

- ➤ Teach 30-60-90 triangles from the teaching box. Explain that the sides have a ratio that is constant for all 30-60-90 triangles. The short leg (x) is always opposite the 30° angle. The long leg ($x\sqrt{3}$) is always opposite the 60° angle. The hypotenuse ($2x$) is always opposite the right angle.

- ➤ Show the students that the ratio of the sides follows the Pythagorean formula.

$$\left(x\right)^2 + \left(x\sqrt{3}\right)^2 = \left(2x\right)^2$$
$$x^2 + 3x^2 = 4x^2$$
$$4x^2 = 4x^2$$

30° – 60° – 90° Triangles

Any right triangle whose other two angles measure exactly 30° and 60° is called a **30-60-90 triangle**. The sides of a 30-60-90 triangle have a known ratio that makes it easy to calculate the lengths of unknown sides. Notice the diagram below.

When the short leg (the side opposite the 30° angle) is x units long, the hypotenuse is $2x$ units long, and the long leg (the side opposite the 60° angle) is $x\sqrt{3}$ units long.

In a 30-60-90 triangle, find the lengths of the legs if the hypotenuse is 10 cm.

Draw a diagram and label what you know.

Solve for x: $2x = 10$; $x = 5$ cm.
The short leg is 5 cm.
The long leg is $5\sqrt{3}$ cm.

① Classwork
Solve for x.

$2x = 20$
$x = 10$

$x\sqrt{3} = 4\sqrt{3}$
$x = 4$

Activities
② Find the lengths of the missing sides.

---

③ Solve.
When setting up ground ladders at a fire, Lee must position the base of the ladder away from the building a distance equal to ¼ the length of the ladder. For each ladder, calculate the distance from the building the base must be positioned, and the height on the building the ladder will reach. Round answers to the nearest tenth where necessary.

Ladder length	Base distance from building	Height on building
24 feet	24 feet ÷ 4 = 6 feet	$a^2 = 24^2 - 6^2$; $a = 23.2$ ft.
16 feet	16 feet ÷ 4 = 4 feet	$a^2 = 16^2 - 4^2$; $a = 15.5$ ft.
12 feet	12 feet ÷ 4 = 3 feet	$a^2 = 12^2 - 3^2$; $a = 11.6$ ft.
10 feet	10 feet ÷ 4 = 2.5 feet	$a^2 = 10^2 - \left(2\frac{1}{2}\right)^2$; $a = 9.7$ ft.

④ Solve.
Lee responded to a 911 call to aid a 150-pound adult. How many kilograms does the adult weigh?

$150 \text{ lb.} \left(\frac{0.454 \text{ kg}}{1 \text{ lb.}}\right) = 68.1$ lb.

Lee must start an IV to give the patient 5 micrograms of medication per kilogram of weight each minute. How many micrograms of medication should Lee give the patient each minute?

$68.1 \text{ lb.} \left(\frac{5 \text{ micrograms}}{1 \text{ lb.}}\right) = 340.5$ micrograms

How many milligrams of medication should Lee give the patient each minute?
1 milligram = 1000 micrograms

$340.5 \text{ micrograms} \left(\frac{1 \text{ mg}}{1000 \text{ micrograms}}\right) = 0.3405$ mg

How many grams of medication should Lee give the patient each minute?

$0.3405 \text{ mg} \left(\frac{1 \text{ g}}{1000 \text{ mg}}\right) = 0.0003405$ g

The liquid medication is packaged so that 1 cubic centimeter of fluid contains 5 grams of the medication. How many cubic centimeters of medication should Lee give the patient each minute?

$0.0003405 \text{ g} \left(\frac{1 \text{ cc}}{5 \text{ g}}\right) = 0.0000681$ cubic centimeters

The ambulance arrived at the hospital 7 minutes after the IV was started. How many grams of the medication did the patient receive before arriving at the hospital?

$\frac{0.0003405 \text{ g}}{1 \text{ minute}} (7 \text{ minutes}) = 0.0023835$ grams

How many milligrams of medication did the patient receive before arriving at the hospital?

$0.0023835 \text{ g} \left(\frac{1000 \text{ mg}}{1 \text{ g}}\right) = 2.3835$ mg

How many micrograms of medication did the patient receive before arriving at the hospital?

$2.3835 \text{ mg} \left(\frac{1000 \text{ micrograms}}{1 \text{ mg}}\right) = 2383.5$ mg

① Label the missing sides in each of the triangles below.

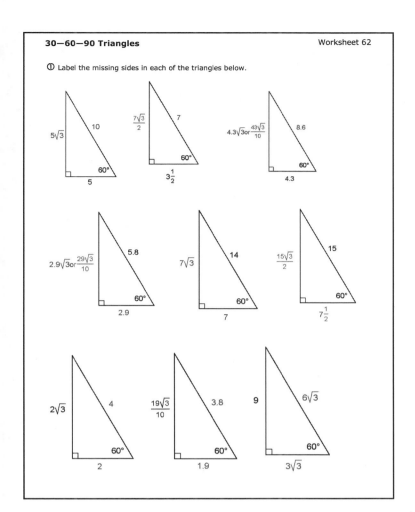

Teaching Tips, Cont.

➢ Teach the students to solve for the lengths of the sides of a 30-60-90 triangle by setting up a ratio and solving for *x*. This value can then be substituted in the ratio of the unknown sides to calculate the lengths of those sides.

➢ Complete the Classwork exercises. Have some students work the problems on the board for the class and explain their answers. All students should work the problems in their books.

➢ Give the students the formula strip for Lesson 123 from the *Tests and Resources* book.

Assignments
- Complete Lesson 123, Activities 2-4.
- Worksheet 62.

Lesson 124

Concepts
- 45-45-90 triangles
- Pythagorean formula
- Math in the real world

Learning Objectives
The student will be able to:
- Find the lengths of the missing sides when given the length of one side of a 45-45-90 triangle
- Identify ratios in 45-45-90 triangles

Materials Needed
- Student Book, Lesson 124

Teaching Tips
- ➢ Review the Pythagorean formula. (See Lesson 122.)

- ➢ Review 30-60-90 triangles. (See Lesson 123.)

- ➢ Teach 45-45-90 triangles from the teaching box. Explain that the sides have a ratio that is constant for all 45-45-90 triangles. The legs (x) are always opposite the 45° angles and are always equal. The hypotenuse ($x\sqrt{2}$) is always opposite the right angle.

- ➢ Show the students that the ratio of the sides follows the Pythagorean formula.

$$(x)^2 + (x)^2 = \left(x\sqrt{2}\right)^2$$
$$x^2 + x^2 = 2x^2$$
$$2x^2 = 2x^2$$

45° – 45° – 90° Triangles

Any right triangle whose other two angles both measure exactly 45° is called a **45-45-90 triangle**. The sides of a 45-45-90 triangle have a known ratio that makes it easy to calculate the lengths of unknown sides. Notice the diagram below.

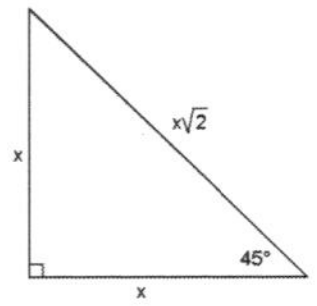

When a leg (the side opposite a 45° angle) is x units long, the hypotenuse is $x\sqrt{2}$ units long. Notice that both legs are the same length.

In a 45-45-90 triangle, find the lengths of the hypotenuse and second leg if one leg is 10 cm.

Draw a diagram and label what you know.

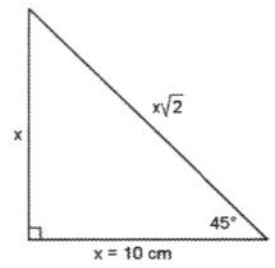

If one leg is 10 cm, then the other leg is also 10 cm and the hypotenuse is $10\sqrt{2}$ cm.

① Classwork
Solve for x.

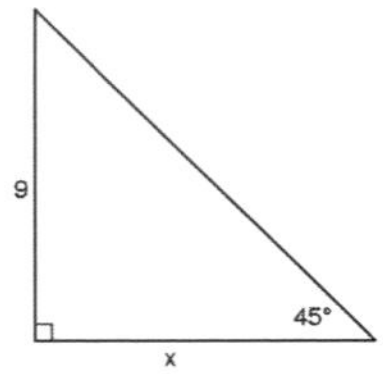

$x = 9$

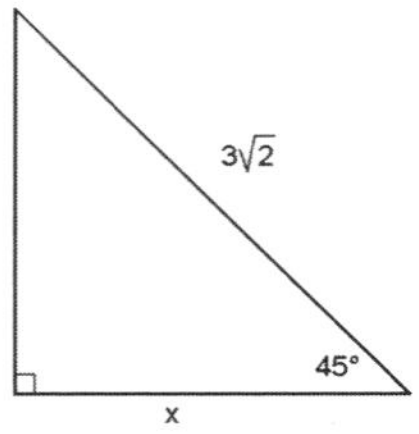

$x\sqrt{2} = 3\sqrt{2}$
$x = 3$

Activities
② Find the lengths of the missing sides.

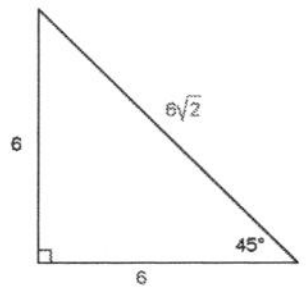

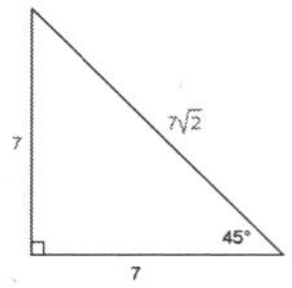

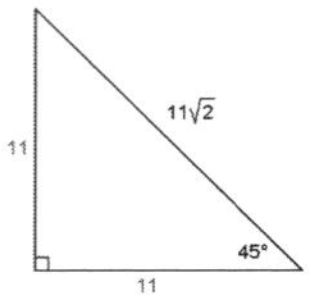

③ Write a system of equations and solve.
When a rescue truck is dispatched, there are 2 emergency responders on board. When a fire truck is dispatched, there are 4 emergency responders on board. In one 24-hour shift, trucks were dispatched a total of 26 times and required a total of 68 emergency responders. How many rescue trucks were dispatched? How many fire trucks were dispatched?
Let r = the number of rescue trucks.
Let f = the number of fire trucks.

$r + f = 26$	$r = 26 - f$	$52 - 2f + 4f = 68$	$2f = 16$
$2r + 4f = 68$	$2(26 - f) + 4f = 68$	$52 + 2f = 68$	$f = 8$

There were 8 fire trucks and $26 - 8 = 18$ rescue trucks dispatched.

Each section of supply hose that connects to fire hydrants is 100 feet long, and each section of crosslay hose is 200 feet long. If a fire truck carries a total of 1600 feet of hose in 13 sections, how many supply hoses does it have? How many crosslay hoses?
Let s = the number of supply hoses.
Let c = the number of crosslay hoses.

$s + c = 13$	$1300 - 100c + 200c = 1600$
$100s + 200c = 1600$	$1300 + 100c = 1600$
$s = 13 - c$	$100c = 300$
$100(13 - c) + 200c = 1600$	$c = 3$

There are 3 crosslay hoses and $13 - 3 = 10$ supply hoses.

④ Solve.
A fire at an industrial plant requires 15,000 gallons of water per minute to get the fire under control. If the plant has a deluge sprinkler system that delivers 100 gallons of water per minute from each of its 15 sprinkler heads, how many gallons of water per minute must the fire department provide?
$100(15) = 1500$ gallons of water per minute from the sprinkler system.
$15,000 - 1500 = 13,500$ gallons of water per minute from the fire department
A fire truck's medium hoses can each provide 750 gallons of water per minute. The large hoses can each provide 1250 gallons of water per minute. If 12 hoses are used, how many of each size are needed to provide the remaining required amount of water?
Let m = medium hoses.
Let L = large hoses.

$m + L = 12$	$9000 - 750L + 1250L = 13,500$
$750m + 1250L = 13,500$	$9000 + 500L = 13,500$
$m = 12 - L$	$500L = 4500$
$750(12 - L) + 1250L = 13,500$	$L = 9$

9 large hoses and $12 - 9 = 3$ medium hoses are needed to control the fire.

Teaching Tips, Cont.

➤ Teach the students to solve for the lengths of the sides of a 45-45-90 triangle by setting up a ratio and solving for x. This value can then be substituted in the ratio of the unknown sides to calculate the lengths of those sides. The process is simplified because the two legs are always equal.

➤ Complete the Classwork exercises. Have some students work the problems on the board for the class and explain their answers. All students should work the problems in their books.

Assignments

- Complete Lesson 124, Activities 2-4.
- Bring scissors for Lesson 129.

Lesson 125

Concepts
- Sine
- Right triangles
- Divisibility tests
- Prime/composite numbers
- Greatest common factor
- Least common multiple
- Math in the real world

Learning Objectives
The student will be able to:
- Define *sine*
- Write a ratio to express the sine of an angle
- Calculate the sine of the acute angles in a right triangle

Materials Needed
- Student Book, Lesson 125
- Worksheet 63

Teaching Tips
➢ Have students complete Worksheet 63 in class. This may be for added practice of earlier topics, or graded as a quiz, if desired.

➢ Ask the students what right triangle ratios they have learned so far. (30-60-90 triangles and 45-45-90 triangles.)

➢ Review 30-60-90 and 45-45-90 triangles. (See Lessons 123-124.)

➢ Review angles. (See Lesson 104.)

➢ Tell the students there are a special set of ratios that apply to all right triangles. Introduce *sine* as the first of the ratios they will learn.

Sine

The **sine** (abbreviated **sin**) of an angle in a right triangle is the ratio of the length of the opposite side to the length of the hypotenuse.

$$sine = \frac{opposite\ side}{hypotenuse}$$

Find sin 45°.
Recall this diagram from Lesson 123.

The side opposite the 45° angle is x. The hypotenuse is $x\sqrt{2}$.

$$\sin 45° = \frac{x}{x\sqrt{2}}$$
$$\sin 45° = \frac{1}{\sqrt{2}} \cdot \frac{\sqrt{2}}{\sqrt{2}}$$
$$\sin 45° = \frac{\sqrt{2}}{2}$$

It is improper to leave radicals in the denominator. Rationalize the denominator by multiplying both the numerator and the denominator by the root in the denominator.

① Classwork
Solve.

Find sin 60°. (Refer to this diagram from Lesson 123.)

The side opposite the 60° angle is $x\sqrt{3}$. The hypotenuse is $2x$.

$$\sin 60° = \frac{x\sqrt{3}}{2x}$$
$$\sin 60° = \frac{\sqrt{3}}{2}$$

Activities

② Find the length of the hypotenuse and calculate sin x and sin y.

$\sin x = \frac{4}{5}$	$\sin x = \frac{12}{13}$	$\sin x = \frac{3}{\sqrt{13}} \cdot \frac{\sqrt{13}}{\sqrt{13}} = \frac{3\sqrt{13}}{13}$
$\sin y = \frac{3}{5}$	$\sin y = \frac{5}{13}$	$\sin y = \frac{2}{\sqrt{13}} \cdot \frac{\sqrt{13}}{\sqrt{13}} = \frac{2\sqrt{13}}{13}$

---

③ Solve.
Lee must position his ladder at a 75° angle with the ground to ensure stability at a fire. If he positions the base of the ladder away from the building a distance equal to ¼ the length of the ladder, will he have the ladder at the proper angle? Use your calculator to find sin 75°. Round calculations to the nearest hundredth where necessary.

Ladder length	Base distance from building	Height on building	sin 75°	Ratio of building height to ladder length
24 feet	24 feet ÷ 4 = 6 feet	$a^2 = 24^2 - 6^2$; $a = 23.24$ ft.	0.97	$\frac{23.24}{24} = 0.97$
16 feet	16 feet ÷ 4 = 4 feet	$a^2 = 16^2 - 4^2$; $a = 15.49$ ft.	0.97	$\frac{15.49}{16} = 0.97$
12 feet	12 feet ÷ 4 = 3 feet	$a^2 = 12^2 - 3^2$; $a = 11.62$ ft.	0.97	$\frac{11.62}{12} = 0.97$
10 feet	10 feet ÷ 4 = 2.5 feet	$a^2 = 10^2 - \left(2\frac{1}{2}\right)^2$; $a = 9.68$ ft.	0.97	$\frac{9.68}{10} = 0.97$

Yes. All the ladders will be at the proper angle with the ground.

④ Use the divisibility tests to identify each number as prime or composite.
479 Prime   487 Prime
483 Composite (3)   489 Composite (3)
485 Composite (5)   491 Prime

⑤ Find the greatest common factor of each set of numbers.

16, 28, and 40   18, 24, and 36   24, 32, and 36
16 = 2×2×2×2   18 = 2×3×3   24 = 2×2×2×3
28 = 2×2×7   24 = 2×2×2×3   32 = 2×2×2×2×2
40 = 2×2×2×5   36 = 2×2×3×3   36 = 2×2×3×3
GCF: 2 × 2 = 4   GCF: 2 × 3 = 6   GCF: 2 × 2 = 4

⑥ Find the least common multiple of each set of numbers.

5, 7, and 10   6, 9, and 15   12, 15, and 18
$5 = 1 \times \boxed{5}$ $6 = \boxed{2} \times 3$ $12 = 2 \times 2 \times 3 = \boxed{2^2} \times 3$
$7 = 1 \times \boxed{7}$ $9 = 3 \times 3 = \boxed{3^2}$ $15 = 3 \times \boxed{5}$
$10 = \boxed{2} \times 5$ $15 = 3 \times \boxed{5}$ $18 = 2 \times 3 \times 3 = 2 \times \boxed{3^2}$
LCM: $2 \times 5 \times 7 = 70$ LCM: $2 \times 3^2 \times 5 = 90$ LCM: $2^2 \times 3^2 \times 5 = 180$

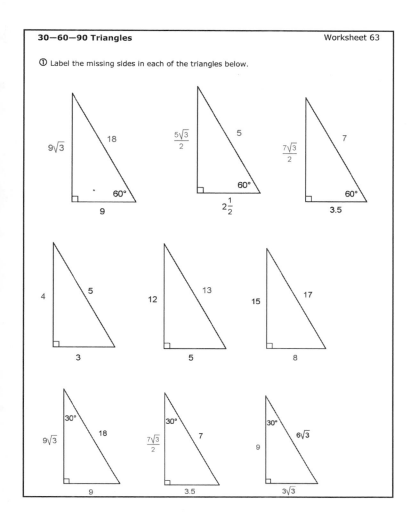

30—60—90 Triangles   Worksheet 63

① Label the missing sides in each of the triangles below.

Teaching Tips, Cont.

➤ Teach sine from the teaching box. Explain that although the abbreviation spells a word (sin), it is still read *sine*.

➤ Tell the students that this ratio will work for any acute angle of a right triangle.

➤ Ask the students what sin 90° would be. (1) Generally, the trigonometric ratios apply to the acute angles of a right triangle. In this case, because the side opposite the right angle is the hypotenuse, the ratio works to give the correct answer.

➤ Tell the students that the sine of an acute angle will always be greater than 0 but less than 1.

➤ Complete the Classwork exercises. Have some students work the problems on the board for the class and explain their answers. All students should work the problems in their books.

Assignments

• Complete Lesson 125, Activities 2-6.
• Bring scissors for Lesson 129.

Lesson 126

Concepts
- Cosine
- Right triangles
- Sine
- Math in the real world

Learning Objectives
The student will be able to:
- Define *cosine*
- Write a ratio to express the cosine of an angle
- Calculate the cosine of the acute angles in a right triangle

Materials Needed
- Student Book, Lesson 126

Teaching Tips
➢ Ask the students what right triangle ratios they have learned so far. (30-60-90 triangles, 45-45-90 triangles, and sine.)

➢ Review 30-60-90 and 45-45-90 triangles. (See Lessons 123-124.)

➢ Review sine. (See Lesson 125.)

➢ Introduce cosine as the second special ratio for right triangles.

➢ Teach cosine from the teaching box. Explain that although the abbreviation looks like a word (cos), it is still read *cosine*.

➢ Tell the students that this ratio will work for any acute angle of a right triangle.

Cosine

The **cosine** (abbreviated **cos**) of an angle in a right triangle is the ratio of the length of the adjacent side to the length of the hypotenuse.

$$cosine = \frac{adjacent\ side}{hypotenuse}$$

Find cos 45°.
Recall this diagram from Lesson 123.

The side adjacent to the 45° angle is x. The hypotenuse is $x\sqrt{2}$.

$$\cos 45° = \frac{x}{x\sqrt{2}}$$
$$\cos 45° = \frac{1}{\sqrt{2}} \cdot \frac{\sqrt{2}}{\sqrt{2}}$$
$$\cos 45° = \frac{\sqrt{2}}{2}$$

① **Classwork**
Solve.

Find cos 60°. (Refer to this diagram from Lesson 123.)

The side adjacent the 60° angle is x. The hypotenuse is $2x$.

$$\cos 60° = \frac{x}{2x}$$
$$\cos 60° = \frac{1}{2}$$

Activities
② Find the length of the hypotenuse and calculate cos x and cos y.

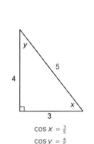

$$\cos x = \frac{3}{5}$$
$$\cos y = \frac{4}{5}$$

$$\cos x = \frac{5}{13}$$
$$\cos y = \frac{12}{13}$$

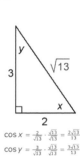

$$\cos x = \frac{2}{\sqrt{13}} \cdot \frac{\sqrt{13}}{\sqrt{13}} = \frac{2\sqrt{13}}{13}$$
$$\cos y = \frac{3}{\sqrt{13}} \cdot \frac{\sqrt{13}}{\sqrt{13}} = \frac{3\sqrt{13}}{13}$$

③ Solve.

Complete the chart to show the height on a building a ladder will reach when placed at a 75° angle with the ground. The first one has been done for you. Round answers to the nearest hundredth where appropriate.

	10-ft. ladder	12-ft. ladder	16-ft. ladder	24-ft. ladder
sin 75°	0.97	0.97	0.97	0.97
Equation using sin 75°	$\sin 75° = \frac{h}{10 \text{ ft.}}$ $0.97 = \frac{h}{10 \text{ ft.}}$	$\sin 75° = \frac{h}{12 \text{ ft.}}$ $0.97 = \frac{h}{12 \text{ ft.}}$	$\sin 75° = \frac{h}{16 \text{ ft.}}$ $0.97 = \frac{h}{16 \text{ ft.}}$	$\sin 75° = \frac{h}{24 \text{ ft.}}$ $0.97 = \frac{h}{24 \text{ ft.}}$
Height on building	$h = 9.7$ ft.	$h = 11.64$ ft.	$h = 15.52$ ft.	$h = 23.28$ ft.

Look at the chart from Lesson 125. Is the height on the building you calculated for each ladder in Lesson 125 equal to the height on the building for the same ladders in this exercise? Explain.
No. The calculations are based on rounded numbers. (The square roots were rounded in Lesson 125 and sin 75° was rounded in this exercise.) When rounded numbers are used in calculations, it affects the accuracy of the answer.

④ Solve.
When a ladder is placed at a 75° angle with the ground, what angle does it form with the building? (Assume the building is perpendicular to the ground.)
There are 180° in a triangle. Perpendicular lines form right angles. The angle between the ladder and the building is 180° − 90° − 75° = 15°.

What is the cosine of this angle? Round your answer to the nearest hundredth.
cos 15° = 0.97

What is the sine of this angle? Round your answer to the nearest hundredth.
sin 15° = 0.26

What is the measure of its complementary angle?
90° − 15° = 75°

What are the sine and cosine of the complementary angle?
sin 75° = 0.97
cos 75° = 0.26

What do you notice about the sine and cosine of complementary angles?
The sine of an angle is equal to the cosine of its complementary angle.
The cosine of an angle is equal to the sine of its complementary angle.

Teaching Tips, Cont.

➤ Ask the students if this ratio will work to find cos 90°. (No.) Why not? (It is a right angle.) Point out that there are two legs adjacent to the right angle, so the formula does not work. For reference, cos 90° = 0.

➤ Refer the students to the teaching box of lesson 125. Have them compare the sample problem there to the sample problem in this lesson. Ask the students what they notice about sin 45° and cos 45°. (They are equal.)

➤ Tell the students that the cosine of an acute angle will always be greater than 0 but less than 1.

➤ Complete the Classwork exercises. Have some students work the problems on the board for the class and explain their answers. All students should work the problems in their books.

Assignments
- Complete Lesson 126, Activities 2-4.
- Bring scissors for Lesson 129.

Horizons Pre-Algebra, Teacher's Guide

Lesson 127

Concepts
- Tangent
- 30-60-90 triangles
- 45-45-90 triangles
- Area of triangles
- Pythagorean formula

Learning Objectives
The student will be able to:
- Define *tangent*
- Write a ratio to express the tangent of an angle
- Calculate the tangent of the acute angles in a right triangle

Materials Needed
- Student Book, Lesson 127
- Scientific calculator

Teaching Tips
➤ Ask the students what right triangle ratios they have learned so far. (30-60-90 triangles, 45-45-90 triangles, sine, and cosine.)

➤ Review 30-60-90 and 45-45-90 triangles. (See Lessons 123-124.)

➤ Review sine and cosine. (See Lessons 125-126.)

➤ Introduce tangent as the third special ratio for right triangles.

➤ Teach tangent from the teaching box. Explain that although the abbreviation spells a word (tan), it is still read *tangent*.

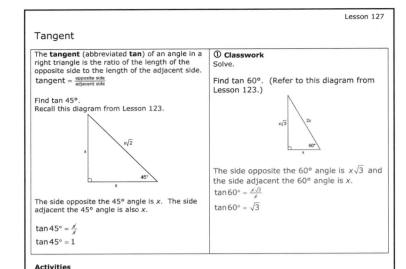

Tangent

The **tangent** (abbreviated **tan**) of an angle in a right triangle is the ratio of the length of the opposite side to the length of the adjacent side.

$$tangent = \frac{opposite\ side}{adjacent\ side}$$

Find tan 45°.
Recall this diagram from Lesson 123.

The side opposite the 45° angle is x. The side adjacent the 45° angle is also x.

$$tan\,45° = \frac{x}{x}$$
$$tan\,45° = 1$$

① **Classwork**
Solve.

Find tan 60°. (Refer to this diagram from Lesson 123.)

The side opposite the 60° angle is $x\sqrt{3}$ and the side adjacent the 60° angle is x.

$$tan\,60° = \frac{x\sqrt{3}}{x}$$
$$tan\,60° = \sqrt{3}$$

Activities
② Find the length of the hypotenuse and calculate tan x and tan y.

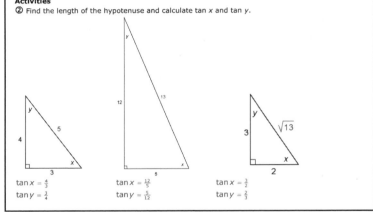

$tan\,x = \frac{4}{3}$
$tan\,y = \frac{3}{4}$

$tan\,x = \frac{12}{5}$
$tan\,y = \frac{5}{12}$

$tan\,x = \frac{3}{2}$
$tan\,y = \frac{2}{3}$

③ Solve.

In the 30-60-90 triangle below, label the sides in terms of x and the acute angles in degrees.

Find the area of a 30-60-90 triangle in terms of x.

$A = \frac{1}{2}bh$

$A = \frac{1}{2}(x)(x\sqrt{3})$

$A = \frac{x^2\sqrt{3}}{2}$

What is the area of a 30-60-90 triangle if the hypotenuse is 6 cm?

$2x = 6$ cm

$x = 3$ cm

$A = \frac{x^2\sqrt{3}}{2}$

$A = \frac{3^2\sqrt{3}}{2}$

$A = \frac{9\sqrt{3}}{2}$ cm^2

In the 45-45-90 triangle below, label the sides in terms of x and the acute angles in degrees.

Find the area of a 45-45-90 triangle in terms of x.

$A = \frac{1}{2}bh$

$A = \frac{1}{2}(x)(x)$

$A = \frac{x^2}{2}$

Teaching Tips, Cont.

➤ Tell the students that this ratio will work for any acute angle of a right triangle.

➤ Ask the students if this ratio will work to find tan 90°. (No.) Why not? (It is not a right angle.) Point out that there are two legs adjacent to the right angle and no leg opposite, so the formula does not work. Have the students find tan 90° on their calculators. What happens? (It is an error.)

➤ Tell the students that the tangent of an acute angle will always be greater than 0. Unlike sine and cosine, it has no upper limit.

➤ Complete the Classwork exercises. Have some students work the problems on the board for the class and explain their answers. All students should work the problems in their books.

Assignments

- Complete Lesson 127, Activities 2-3.
- Bring scissors for Lesson 129.

Horizons Pre-Algebra, Teacher's Guide

Lesson 128

Concepts
- Trigonometric ratios
- Sine
- Cosine
- Tangent
- Pythagorean formula
- 30-60-90 triangles
- 45-45-90 triangles

Learning Objectives
The student will be able to:
- State the three trigonometric ratios
- Calculate the sine, cosine, and tangent of each acute angle in a right triangle when given two of the three sides

Materials Needed
- Student Book, Lesson 128
- Worksheet 64

Teaching Tips
➢ Have students complete Worksheet 64 in class. This may be for added practice of earlier topics, or graded as a quiz, if desired.

➢ Review sine, cosine, and tangent. (See Lessons 125-127.)

➢ Teach the mnemonic device for memorizing the three ratios. Sohcahtoa sounds like "soak a toe." Point out to the students that it gives all three trigonometric ratios in the pattern Sine Opposite Hypotenuse Cosine Adjacent Hypotenuse Tangent Opposite Adjacent.

Trigonometric Ratios

Recall the three trigonometric ratios you learned in Lessons 125-127.

$\text{sine} = \frac{\text{opposite side}}{\text{hypotenuse}}$

$\text{cosine} = \frac{\text{adjacent side}}{\text{hypotenuse}}$

$\text{tangent} = \frac{\text{opposite side}}{\text{adjacent side}}$

You can remember them by turning the initial letters of each word into a phrase.

$\text{sine} = \frac{\text{opposite side}}{\text{hypotenuse}}$

$\text{cosine} = \frac{\text{adjacent side}}{\text{hypotenuse}}$

$\text{tangent} = \frac{\text{opposite side}}{\text{adjacent side}}$

Sohcahtoa sounds like "soak a toe."

Find sin x, cos x, and tan x.

$\sin x = \frac{\text{opposite side}}{\text{hypotenuse}} = \frac{4}{5}$

$\cos x = \frac{\text{adjacent side}}{\text{hypotenuse}} = \frac{3}{5}$

$\tan x = \frac{\text{opposite side}}{\text{adjacent side}} = \frac{4}{3}$

① **Classwork**
Find sin x, cos x, and tan x.

$\sin x = \frac{\text{opposite side}}{\text{hypotenuse}} = \frac{12}{13}$

$\cos x = \frac{\text{adjacent side}}{\text{hypotenuse}} = \frac{5}{13}$

$\tan x = \frac{\text{opposite side}}{\text{adjacent side}} = \frac{12}{5}$

Activities
② Find the length of the hypotenuse and the sine, cosine, and tangent of the marked angles.

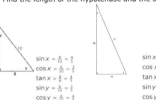

$\sin x = \frac{8}{10} = \frac{4}{5}$
$\cos x = \frac{6}{10} = \frac{3}{5}$
$\tan x = \frac{8}{6} = \frac{4}{3}$
$\sin y = \frac{6}{10} = \frac{3}{5}$
$\cos y = \frac{8}{10} = \frac{4}{5}$
$\tan y = \frac{6}{8} = \frac{3}{4}$

$\sin x = \frac{24}{26} = \frac{12}{13}$
$\cos x = \frac{10}{26} = \frac{5}{13}$
$\tan x = \frac{24}{10} = \frac{12}{5}$
$\sin y = \frac{10}{26} = \frac{5}{13}$
$\cos y = \frac{24}{26} = \frac{12}{13}$
$\tan y = \frac{10}{24} = \frac{5}{12}$

$\sin x = \frac{6}{2\sqrt{13}} \cdot \frac{\sqrt{13}}{\sqrt{13}} = \frac{6\sqrt{13}}{26} = \frac{3\sqrt{13}}{13}$
$\cos x = \frac{4}{2\sqrt{13}} \cdot \frac{\sqrt{13}}{\sqrt{13}} = \frac{4\sqrt{13}}{26} = \frac{2\sqrt{13}}{13}$
$\tan x = \frac{6}{4} = \frac{3}{2}$
$\sin y = \frac{4}{2\sqrt{13}} \cdot \frac{\sqrt{13}}{\sqrt{13}} = \frac{4\sqrt{13}}{26} = \frac{2\sqrt{13}}{13}$
$\cos y = \frac{6}{2\sqrt{13}} \cdot \frac{\sqrt{13}}{\sqrt{13}} = \frac{6\sqrt{13}}{26} = \frac{3\sqrt{13}}{13}$
$\tan y = \frac{4}{6} = \frac{2}{3}$

---

③ Solve.
In the 30-60-90 triangle below, label the sides in terms of x and the acute angles in degrees.

Find the sine, cosine, and tangent of each acute angle.

$\sin 30° = \frac{x}{2x} = \frac{1}{2}$

$\cos 30° = \frac{x\sqrt{3}}{2x} = \frac{\sqrt{3}}{2}$

$\tan 30° = \frac{x}{x\sqrt{3}} \cdot \frac{\sqrt{3}}{\sqrt{3}} = \frac{\sqrt{3}}{3}$

$\sin 60° = \frac{x\sqrt{3}}{2x} = \frac{\sqrt{3}}{2}$

$\cos 60° = \frac{x}{2x} = \frac{1}{2}$

$\tan 60° = \frac{x\sqrt{3}}{x} = \sqrt{3}$

In the 45-45-90 triangle below, label the sides in terms of x and the acute angles in degrees.

Find the sine, cosine, and tangent of each acute angle.

$\sin 45° = \frac{x}{x\sqrt{2}} \cdot \frac{\sqrt{2}}{\sqrt{2}} = \frac{\sqrt{2}}{2}$

$\cos 45° = \frac{x}{x\sqrt{2}} \cdot \frac{\sqrt{2}}{\sqrt{2}} = \frac{\sqrt{2}}{2}$

$\tan 45° = \frac{x}{x} = 1$

What is sin 30° ÷ cos 30°?
$\frac{1}{2} \div \frac{\sqrt{3}}{2} = \frac{1}{2} \cdot \frac{2}{\sqrt{3}} = \frac{1}{\sqrt{3}} \left(\frac{\sqrt{3}}{\sqrt{3}} \right) = \frac{\sqrt{3}}{3}$

What is sin 60° ÷ cos 60°?
$\frac{\sqrt{3}}{2} \div \frac{1}{2} = \frac{\sqrt{3}}{2} \cdot \frac{2}{1} = \sqrt{3}$

What is sin 45° ÷ cos 45°?
$\frac{\sqrt{2}}{2} \div \frac{\sqrt{2}}{2} = \frac{\sqrt{2}}{2} \cdot \frac{2}{\sqrt{2}} = 1$

Compare your answers with the tangent of the respective angles. What do you notice?
For any given angle, sine ÷ cosine = tangent
As a formula, $\frac{\sin x}{\cos x} = \tan x$ for any given angle x.

45—45—90 Triangles, Sine, Cosine

Worksheet 64

① Label the missing sides in each of the triangles below.

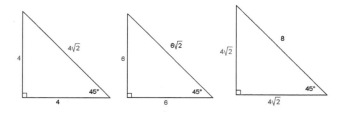

② Label the missing sides and find the sine and cosine of each acute angle.

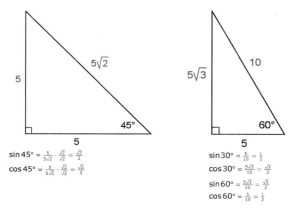

$\sin 45° = \frac{5}{5\sqrt{2}} \cdot \frac{\sqrt{2}}{\sqrt{2}} = \frac{\sqrt{2}}{2}$

$\cos 45° = \frac{5}{5\sqrt{2}} \cdot \frac{\sqrt{2}}{\sqrt{2}} = \frac{\sqrt{2}}{2}$

$\sin 30° = \frac{5}{10} = \frac{1}{2}$

$\cos 30° = \frac{5\sqrt{3}}{10} = \frac{\sqrt{3}}{2}$

$\sin 60° = \frac{5\sqrt{3}}{10} = \frac{\sqrt{3}}{2}$

$\cos 60° = \frac{5}{10} = \frac{1}{2}$

Teaching Tips, Cont.

➤ Tell the students that they now have the mathematical tools to solve right triangles.

➤ Complete the Classwork exercises. Have some students work the problems on the board for the class and explain their answers. All students should work the problems in their books.

Assignments

- Complete Lesson 128, Activities 2-3.
- Bring scissors for the next lesson.

Lesson 129

Concepts
- Algebra tiles
- Multiplying binomials by monomials
- Math in the real world

Learning Objectives
The student will be able to:
- Use algebra tiles to represent algebraic expressions
- Show the solution of an algebraic problem using algebra tiles

Materials Needed
- Student Book, Lesson 129
- Algebra tiles from the *Tests and Resources* book
- Scissors
- Zip-top sandwich bags
- Tape

Teaching Tips
- Review signed numbers. (See Lesson 3)

- Have the students cut out the algebra tiles from the Tests and Resources book if they have not already done so. Tiles should be stored in a zip-top bag taped inside the cover of the book for use in future lessons.

- Introduce algebra tiles as a method of representing expressions with variables. Tell the students that their set has four colors: yellow, blue, green, and red. The yellow tiles represent x^2 terms; the blue tiles represent x terms; the green tiles represent constant terms; the corresponding red tiles represent negative terms.

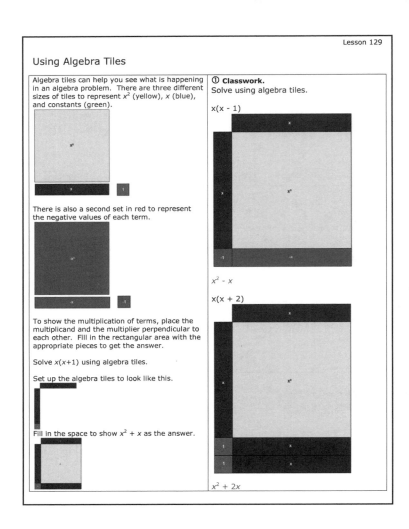

Activities

② Solve using algebra tiles.

$2x(x+1)$ $\qquad$ $x(2x-1)$ $\qquad$ $x(2x+2)$ $\qquad$ $2x(x-2)$

$2x^2+2x$ $\qquad$ $2x^2-x$ $\qquad$ $2x^2+2x$ $\qquad$ $2x^2-4x$

③ Solve.

An ambulance driver averages about 10 miles per hour over the posted speed limit. Calculate the travel time to the nearest minute for an ambulance traveling 30 miles at each of the following posted speed limits.

Posted speed limit	Travel time	Ambulance speed	Travel time
40 mph	30^{15} miles $\left(\frac{1\ hr.}{40\ miles}\right)\left(\frac{60^{3}\ min.}{1\ hr.}\right) = 45$ min.	50 mph	30^{6} miles $\left(\frac{1\ hr.}{50\ miles}\right)\left(\frac{60^{6}\ min.}{1\ hr.}\right) = 36$ min.
50 mph	30^{6} miles $\left(\frac{1\ hr.}{50\ miles}\right)\left(\frac{60\ min.}{1\ hr.}\right) = 36$ min.	60 mph	30 miles $\left(\frac{1\ hr.}{60\ miles}\right)\left(\frac{60\ min.}{1\ hr.}\right) = 30$ min.
60 mph	30 miles $\left(\frac{1\ hr.}{60\ miles}\right)\left(\frac{60\ min.}{1\ hr.}\right) = 30$ min.	70 mph	30 miles $\left(\frac{1\ hr.}{70\ miles}\right)\left(\frac{60\ min.}{1\ hr.}\right) = 26$ min.
70 mph	30 miles $\left(\frac{1\ hr.}{70\ miles}\right)\left(\frac{60^{6}\ min.}{1\ hr.}\right) = 26$ min.	80 mph	30^{15} miles $\left(\frac{1\ hr.}{80\ miles}\right)\left(\frac{60\ min.}{1\ hr.}\right) = 23$ min.

In which area does an ambulance benefit the most from traveling at a higher speed – areas with low posted speed limits or areas with high posted speed limits? Low

④ Solve.

Lee's ambulance company has 18 paramedics to work on its 9 ambulances each shift. How many different ways can the 18 paramedics be paired up?

$C(18,2) = \frac{18!}{(18-2)!(2!)} = \frac{18\cdot 17\cdot 16!}{16!(2!)} = 153$ different ways the paramedics can be paired up.

On each ambulance, one paramedic drives while the other one tends to the patient. Calculate the number of permutations of 18 paramedics on 9 ambulances to find the total number of different ways the paramedics can be assigned an ambulance and responsibility.

$P(18,2) = \frac{18!}{(18-2)!} = \frac{18\cdot 17\cdot 16!}{16!} = 306$ different ways the paramedics can be assigned an ambulance and responsibility.

How many different ways can the 9 ambulances be assigned to the 9 groups of paramedics?

There are 9 different ambulances available for the first group; 8 ambulances available for the second group; 7 ambulances available for the third group, etc.

Therefore, there are $9! = 362,880$ different ways the ambulances can be assigned.

Teaching Tips, Cont.

➢ Show students how to place the tiles representing the multiplicand and the multiplier perpendicular to each other to represent a multiplication problem. Fill in the space in the middle to get the answer.

➢ Remind the students that red tiles represent negative terms, and the rules of signed number apply. A red (negative) multiplied by any other color (positive) is red (negative). A red (negative) multiplied by a red (negative) is the regular color (positive).

➢ Complete the Classwork exercises. Have some students work the problems on the board for the class and explain their answers. All students should work the problems in their books.

Assignment

• Complete Lesson 129, Activities 2-4.

Lesson 130

Concepts
- Polynomial expressions
- Constants
- Coefficients
- Monomials
- Binomials
- Trinomials
- Simple interest
- Compound interest
- Math in the real world

Learning Objectives
The student will be able to:
- Identify algebraic expressions as monomials, binomials, trinomials, and polynomials
- Define *constant*
- Define *coefficient*

Materials Needed
- Student Book, Lesson 130
- Calculator
- Formula strip, Lesson 130

Teaching Tips
- ➢ Teach polynomials from the teaching box. Emphasize that plus and minus signs are the only symbols that separate terms. Items that are multiplied or divided are considered one term.

- ➢ Define *constant* and *coefficient* from the teaching box. Explain that although they are both numbers, a constant is never attached to a variable, and a coefficient is always attached to a variable.

- ➢ Teach how to identify monomials, binomials, and trinomials based on the number of terms.

Polynomial Expressions

A **polynomial** is an algebraic expression. If that expression contains two or more terms, the terms must be separated by a plus or minus sign. All variables must have a positive integer as an exponent, and no variable may appear in a denominator.

A **constant** is a term that has a number but no variable.

A **coefficient** is a number that is multiplied by a variable.

A **monomial** is an expression containing one term, such as x^2, $3x$, or 5. A constant is a monomial.

A **binomial** is a polynomial containing two terms, such as $3x + 5$ or $x^2 - 4x$.

A **trinomial** is a polynomial containing three terms, such as $x^2 - 4x + 3$.

Identify whether or not each expression is a polynomial. For each polynomial, identify it as a constant, monomial, binomial, or trinomial.

$x^2 + 2x - 1$
This is a polynomial and a trinomial.

$4x^{-2} - 3x + 7$
This is not a polynomial because there is a -2 as an exponent.

① Classwork
Identify whether or not each expression is a polynomial. For each polynomial, identify it as a constant, monomial, binomial, or trinomial.

$4x - 7$
This is a polynomial and a binomial.

12
This is a polynomial, a monomial, and a constant.

$5x^2 + \frac{3}{x} - 4$
This is not a polynomial because the x is in the denominator.

$x^{-2} - 1$
This is not a polynomial because there is a negative exponent.

$x^2 - 2x + 1$
This is a polynomial and a trinomial.

Activities
② Identify whether or not each expression is a polynomial. For each polynomial, identify it as a constant, monomial, binomial, or trinomial.

$7x - 2$	This is a polynomial and a binomial.
$4x^2 + \frac{6}{x} - 5$	This is not a polynomial because the x is in the denominator.
$3x^{-2} + 2$	This is not a polynomial because there is a negative exponent.
26	This is a polynomial, a monomial, and a constant.
$4x^2 - 3x + 5$	This is a polynomial and a trinomial.
$-7x$	This is a polynomial and a monomial.

③ Complete the chart to show simple interest and interest compounded annually.

Principal	Interest rate	Time, in years	Total amount of simple interest	Balance, compounded annually
$10,000	8.5%	5	$i = \$10,000(0.085)(5) = \$4250$	$A = \$10,000(1 + 0.085)^5$ $= \$15,036.57$
$17,000	11%	10	$i = \$17,000(0.11)(10) = \$18,700$	$A = \$17,000(1 + 0.11)^{10}$ $= \$48,270.16$
$95,000	5.25%	30	$i = \$95,000(0.0525)(30) = \$149,625$	$A = \$95,000(1 + 0.0525)^{30}$ $= \$440,947.35$

④ Solve.

The portable oxygen tanks on an ambulance hold 300 liters of oxygen. If oxygen is delivered to a patient at a rate of 15 liters per minute, how long will one tank of oxygen last?

300^{20} liters $\left(\frac{1\ minute}{15\ liters}\right)$ = 20 minutes

The ambulance is 15 miles from the nearest hospital. If the ambulance averages 40 miles per hour, will the patient arrive at the hospital before the oxygen in the tank runs out?

15 miles $\left(\frac{1\ hr.}{40\ miles}\right)\left(\frac{60\ min.}{1\ hr.}\right)$ = 22.5 min.

No. The patient will require a second tank of oxygen.

The cylindrical portion of an oxygen tank is 4.4 inches in diameter and 18.6 inches tall. What is the volume of the oxygen tank in cubic inches? Use 3.14 as the value of pi, and round to the nearest cubic inch.

$V = \pi r^2 h$

$V = \pi \left(\frac{4.4}{2}\right)^2 (18.6)$

$V = \pi (2.2)^2 (18.6)$

$V = (3.14)(4.84)(18.6) = 283$ cubic inches

The oxygen tank holds 679 liters of compressed oxygen. How many liters of compressed oxygen fit in one cubic inch? Round your answer to the nearest tenth.

$679 \div 283 = 2.4$ liters per cubic inch

At a rate of 15 liters per minute, how long will the tank of oxygen last? Round your answer to the nearest minute.

679 liters $\left(\frac{1\ minute}{15\ liters}\right)$ = 45 minutes

Teaching Tips, Cont.

➤ Emphasize that all variables must have positive exponents, and no variable may appear in the denominator of a polynomial. If either of these situations occurs, the expression is not a polynomial.

➤ Complete the Classwork exercises. Have some students work the problems on the board for the class and explain their answers. All students should work the problems in their books.

➤ Give the students the formula strip for Lesson 130 from the *Tests and Resources* book.

Assignments

• Complete Lesson 130, Activities 2-4.
• Study for Test 13. (Lessons 118-127)

Test 13

Testing Objectives

The student will:

- Convert degrees Fahrenheit to Celsius
- Convert degrees Celsius to Fahrenheit
- Convert English liquid measures to the SI system
- Convert SI liquid measures to the English system
- Convert weight to mass
- Convert mass to weight
- Solve 30-60-90 triangles
- Solve 45-45-90 triangles
- Use the Pythagorean formula to solve right triangles
- Find the sine, cosine, and tangent of angles

Materials Needed

- Test 13
- *It's College Test Prep Time!* from Student Book
- *A Math Minute with…* Duncan M. from Student Book
- Formula strip, Test 13

Teaching Tips

➢ Give the students the formula strip for Test 13 from the *Tests and Resources* book.

➢ Administer Test 13, allowing the students 30-40 minutes to complete the test.

➢ When all students are finished taking the test, introduce *It's College Test Prep Time* from the student book. This page may be completed in class or assigned as homework.

① Complete the chart to show temperature conversions. Round answers to the nearest whole.
14 points

°F	°C
25°	°C = $(25° - 32°)(\frac{5}{9}) = -4°$
35°	°C = $(35° - 32°)(\frac{5}{9}) = 2°$
45°	°C = $(45° - 32°)(\frac{5}{9}) = 7°$
55°	°C = $(55° - 32°)(\frac{5}{9}) = 13°$
65°	°C = $(65° - 32°)(\frac{5}{9}) = 18°$
75°	°C = $(75° - 32°)(\frac{5}{9}) = 24°$
85°	°C = $(85° - 32°)(\frac{5}{9}) = 29°$

°C	°F
25°	°F = $(25°)(\frac{9}{5}) + 32° = 77°$
35°	°F = $(35°)(\frac{9}{5}) + 32° = 95°$
45°	°F = $(45°)(\frac{9}{5}) + 32° = 113°$
55°	°F = $(55°)(\frac{9}{5}) + 32° = 131°$
65°	°F = $(65°)(\frac{9}{5}) + 32° = 149°$
75°	°F = $(75°)(\frac{9}{5}) + 32° = 167°$
85°	°F = $(85°)(\frac{9}{5}) + 32° = 185°$

② Solve. **15 points**

Convert 18 ounces to milliliters.
$18 \text{ oz.} \times \frac{30 \text{ mL}}{1 \text{ oz.}} = 540 \text{ mL}$

Convert 6 quarts to liters.
$6 \text{ qt.} \times \frac{0.95 \text{ L}}{1 \text{ qt.}} = 5.7 \text{ L}$

Convert 25 gallons to liters.
$25 \text{ gal.} \times \frac{3.8 \text{ L}}{1 \text{ gal.}} = 95 \text{ L}$

Convert 250 milliliters to ounces.
$250 \text{ mL} \times \frac{0.034 \text{ oz.}}{1 \text{ mL}} = 8.5 \text{ oz.}$

Convert 8 liters to quarts.
$8 \text{ L} \times \frac{1.06 \text{ qt.}}{1 \text{ L}} = 8.48 \text{ qt.}$

Convert 60 liters to gallons.
$60 \text{ L} \times \frac{0.26 \text{ gal.}}{1 \text{ L}} = 15.6 \text{ gal.}$

Convert 1500 milliliters to quarts.
$1500 \text{ mL} \times \frac{1 \text{ L}}{1000 \text{ mL}} \times \frac{1.06 \text{ qt.}}{1 \text{ L}}$
$= 1.59 \text{ qt.}$

Convert 125 ounces to liters.
$125 \text{ oz.} \times \frac{30 \text{ mL}}{1 \text{ oz.}} \times \frac{1 \text{ L}}{1000 \text{ mL}}$
$= 3.75 \text{ L}$

Convert 2500 milliliters to gallons.
$2500 \text{ mL} \times \frac{1 \text{ L}}{1000 \text{ mL}} \times \frac{0.26 \text{ gal.}}{1 \text{ L}}$
$= 0.65 \text{ gal.}$

Convert 18 ounces to grams.
$18 \text{ oz.} \left(\frac{28.35 \text{ g}}{1 \text{ oz.}}\right) = 510.3 \text{ g}$

Convert 48 pounds to kilograms.
$48 \text{ lb.} \left(\frac{0.454 \text{ kg}}{1 \text{ lb.}}\right) = 21.792 \text{ kg}$

Convert 60 S. ton to kilograms.
$60 \text{ S. ton} \left(\frac{907 \text{ kg}}{1 \text{ S. ton}}\right) = 54,420 \text{ kg}$

Convert 250 grams to ounces.
$250 \text{ g} \left(\frac{0.035 \text{ oz.}}{1 \text{ g}}\right) = 8.75 \text{ oz.}$

Convert 125 kilograms to pounds.
$125 \text{ kg} \left(\frac{2.2 \text{ lb.}}{1 \text{ kg}}\right) = 275 \text{ lb.}$

Convert 2500 M. ton to S. ton.
$2500 \text{ M. ton} \left(\frac{1.1 \text{ S. ton}}{1 \text{ M. ton}}\right)$
$= 2,750 \text{ S. ton}$

③ Find the lengths of the missing sides. Then find the sine, cosine, and tangent of each acute angle. **27 points**

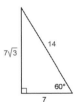

$\sin 30° = \frac{7}{14} = \frac{1}{2}$
$\cos 30° = \frac{7\sqrt{3}}{14} = \frac{\sqrt{3}}{2}$
$\tan 30° = \frac{7}{7\sqrt{3}} \cdot \frac{\sqrt{3}}{\sqrt{3}} = \frac{\sqrt{3}}{3}$

$\sin 60° = \frac{7\sqrt{3}}{14} = \frac{\sqrt{3}}{2}$
$\cos 60° = \frac{7}{14} = \frac{1}{2}$
$\tan 60° = \frac{7\sqrt{3}}{7} = \sqrt{3}$

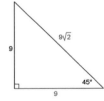

$\sin 45° = \frac{9}{9\sqrt{2}} \cdot \frac{\sqrt{2}}{\sqrt{2}} = \frac{\sqrt{2}}{2}$
$\cos 45° = \frac{9}{9\sqrt{2}} \cdot \frac{\sqrt{2}}{\sqrt{2}} = \frac{\sqrt{2}}{2}$
$\tan 45° = \frac{9}{9} = 1$

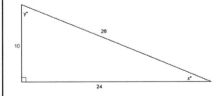

$\sin x = \frac{10}{26} = \frac{5}{13}$
$\cos x = \frac{24}{26} = \frac{12}{13}$
$\tan x = \frac{10}{24} = \frac{5}{12}$
$\sin y = \frac{24}{26} = \frac{12}{13}$
$\cos y = \frac{10}{26} = \frac{5}{13}$
$\tan y = \frac{24}{10} = \frac{12}{5}$

$\sin x = \frac{12}{15} = \frac{4}{5}$
$\cos x = \frac{9}{15} = \frac{3}{5}$
$\tan x = \frac{12}{9} = \frac{4}{3}$
$\sin y = \frac{9}{15} = \frac{3}{5}$
$\cos y = \frac{12}{15} = \frac{4}{5}$
$\tan y = \frac{9}{12} = \frac{3}{4}$

56 points total

It's College Test Prep Time!

1. In triangle *ABC* below, find the length of *BC*.

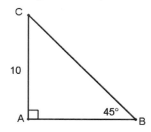

A. 5
B. $5\sqrt{2}$
C. $5\sqrt{3}$
D. $\underline{10\sqrt{2}}$ This is a 45-45-90 triangle. The hypotenuse is $\sqrt{2}$ times
E. $10\sqrt{3}$ the length of a leg.

2. In the figure below, square *TUVW* is inscribed in square *PQRS* to form four congruent triangles. What is the area of square *TUVW* if *PT* = 3?

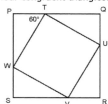

A. 9
B. 12
C. 18
D. 27
E. $\underline{36}$ The congruent triangles are 30-60-90 triangles. The given side is *x* and the hypotenuse is 2*x*, or 6. $6^2 = 36$.

A Math Minute with . . .

Duncan M. – Construction

What is your occupation? Carpenter and builder

Where do you work? I work at various construction sites near my home and in the surrounding counties.

Did you attend college? If so, what was your major? No.

What parts of your job require the use of math? Construction projects require a good understanding of geometry. I use geometry when building roofs, stairs, and making sure all of the walls are square. I also use math when centering windows on wall and determining the height of walls. Math is an essential part of my job.

What is the biggest "problem" you have faced that required the use of math to solve? Properly installing circular stairs requires the careful use of math. I must determine the vertical distance between each step so that it is consistent throughout the entire staircase. I make sure there is enough clearance on the curves. It's also important that the staircase lines up on both levels of the building. An additional challenge is that the steps on a curved staircase are not rectangular like a regular staircase. All of the angles must be precise to the make the curved effect.

Are there any other interesting math uses you have experienced? Some include figuring out how to create compound angles, rounded corners, and sculpted trays. I also have to use formulas for both true and segmented arches in walls and doorways.

Teaching Tips, Cont.
➢ Have students read the Math Minute interview for lessons 131-140.

Assignments
• Complete *It's College Test Prep Time!*
• Read *A Math Minute with…* Duncan M.

Lesson 131

Concepts
- Adding polynomials
- Algebra tiles
- Pythagorean formula
- Math in the real world

Learning Objectives
The student will be able to:
- Add polynomials
- Align like terms when writing polynomial addition problems vertically
- Use algebra tiles to check polynomial addition problems

Materials Needed
- Student Book, Lesson 131
- Algebra tiles
- Worksheet 65

Teaching Tips
➢ Review combining like terms. (See Lesson 20.)

➢ Teach adding polynomials from the teaching box.

➢ Explain that adding polynomials is simply the process of combining like terms from two or more polynomials.

➢ Show the students how to write polynomial addition problems vertically. It is essential to line up the like terms. If one polynomial does not have a like term for a term in the other polynomial, write that term with a 0 as a coefficient and add. See the example at the right.

Adding Polynomials

Adding polynomials is simply the process of combining like terms. Look at this equation.

$$(x^2 + 2x + 3) + (2x^2 - x + 1) =$$

Clear the parentheses to get

$$x^2 + 2x + 3 + 2x^2 - x + 1 =$$

and then combine like terms.

$$x^2 + 2x + 3 + 2x^2 - x + 1 = 3x^2 + x + 4$$

Polynomials may also be added vertically. Recall that when adding integers and decimals vertically, digits in the same place value must be lined up. In the case of polynomials, terms with the same variable and degree (exponent) must be lined up in the same column. Add the columns to get the answer.

$$\begin{array}{r} (x^2 + 2x + 3) \\ +(2x^2 - x + 1) \\ \hline 3x^2 + x + 4 \end{array}$$

You may use algebra tiles to check your answer.

When adding with algebra tiles, a red piece paired with a different color of the same size will always result in both pieces being removed because the red is the negative of the other color and $1 - 1 = 0$. Therefore, the sum looks like the diagram below.

① Classwork
Write the problem vertically and add.

$$(2x^2 + x + 1) + (x^2 + x + 2) =$$

$$\begin{array}{r} 2x^2 + x + 1 \\ +\ x^2 + x + 2 \\ \hline 3x^2 + 2x + 3 \end{array}$$

$$(x^2 + 3x + 4) + (x^2 - x + 1) =$$

$$\begin{array}{r} x^2 + 3x + 4 \\ +x^2 - x + 1 \\ \hline 2x^2 + 2x + 5 \end{array}$$

$$(2x^2 + x + 2) + (3x^2 - 2x - 1) =$$

$$\begin{array}{r} 2x^2 + x + 2 \\ +3x^2 - 2x - 1 \\ \hline 5x^2 - x + 1 \end{array}$$

Activities
② Add.

$$\begin{array}{r} 2x^2 + 3x + 2 \\ +\ 3x^2 + 2x + 1 \\ \hline 5x^2 + 5x + 3 \end{array} \qquad \begin{array}{r} 4x^2 + 2x + 4 \\ +x^2 - 4x - 1 \\ \hline 5x^2 - 2x + 3 \end{array} \qquad \begin{array}{r} 2x^2 - 3x + 2 \\ +5x^2 + 2x - 3 \\ \hline 7x^2 - x - 1 \end{array}$$

③ Write the problem vertically and add.

$$(2x^2 + 3x + 1) + (x^2 + 2x + 3) =$$

$$\begin{array}{r} 2x^2 + 3x + 1 \\ +\ x^2 + 2x + 3 \\ \hline 3x^2 + 5x + 4 \end{array}$$

$$(3x^2 + 4x + 2) + (4x^2 - 2x + 3) =$$

$$\begin{array}{r} 3x^2 + 4x + 2 \\ +4x^2 - 2x + 3 \\ \hline 7x^2 + 2x + 5 \end{array}$$

$$(2x^2 - 3x + 2) + (-x^2 + 2x - 3) =$$

$$\begin{array}{r} 2x^2 - 3x + 2 \\ -x^2 + 2x - 3 \\ \hline x^2 - x - 1 \end{array}$$

$$(2x^2 + 4x + 3) + (6x^2 + 3x + 1) =$$

$$\begin{array}{r} 2x^2 + 4x + 3 \\ +6x^2 + 3x + 1 \\ \hline 8x^2 + 7x + 4 \end{array}$$

$$(4x^2 + 3x - 1) + (2x^2 - 4x + 2) =$$

$$\begin{array}{r} 4x^2 + 3x - 1 \\ +2x^2 - 4x + 2 \\ \hline 6x^2 - x + 1 \end{array}$$

$$(5x^2 + 2x + 3) + (-2x^2 - 5x - 6) =$$

$$\begin{array}{r} 5x^2 + 2x + 3 \\ -2x^2 - 5x - 6 \\ \hline 3x^2 - 3x - 3 \end{array}$$

④ Solve. Round calculations to the nearest hundredth as necessary.
When Duncan builds a house, he uses the Pythagorean formula to check each corner to make sure it is a right angle. If a bedroom is 12 feet wide and 16 feet long, what must the diagonal distance be for the corner to be a right angle?

$$a^2 + b^2 = c^2$$
$$12^2 + 16^2 = c^2$$
$$144 + 256 = c^2$$
$$\sqrt{400} = \sqrt{c^2}$$
$$20 = c$$

The diagonal must be 20 feet.

A bedroom is exactly 11 feet wide and 12 feet long. If the diagonal is exactly 16 feet 3¼ inches, is the corner a right angle?

$$a^2 + b^2 = c^2$$
$$11^2 + 12^2 = c^2$$
$$121 + 144 = c^2$$
$$\sqrt{265} = \sqrt{c^2}$$
$$16.279 = c$$

The diagonal should be 16.279 feet.
3¼ inches = 0.271 feet, so the diagonal measures 16.271 feet. (If the diagonal measures 16 feet $3\frac{11}{32}$ inches, the corner will be a right angle.)

① Add.

$$3x^2 + 4x + 1$$
$$\underline{+\ 2x^2 + 4x + 3}$$
$$5x^2 + 8x + 4$$

$$9x^2 + 5x + 3$$
$$\underline{+x^2 - 3x - 2}$$
$$10x^2 + 2x + 1$$

$$4x^2 - 5x + 6$$
$$\underline{+3x^2 + 2x - 4}$$
$$7x^2 - 3x + 2$$

$$7x^2 + 4x + 3$$
$$\underline{+\ 5x^2 + 3x + 6}$$
$$12x^2 + 7x + 9$$

$$3x^2 + 5x + 5$$
$$\underline{+4x^2 - 9x - 7}$$
$$7x^2 - 4x - 2$$

$$3x^2 - 5x + 8$$
$$\underline{+11x^2 + 2x - 4}$$
$$14x^2 - 3x + 4$$

$$3x^2 + 5x + 7$$
$$\underline{+\ 2x^2 + 6x + 4}$$
$$5x^2 + 11x + 11$$

$$3x^2 + 4x + 8$$
$$\underline{+x^2 - 7x - 9}$$
$$4x^2 - 3x - 1$$

$$3x^2 - 5x + 4$$
$$\underline{+4x^2 + 9x - 7}$$
$$7x^2 + 4x - 3$$

② Write the problem vertically and add.

$$(3x^2 + 4x + 2) + (x^2 + 5x + 4) =$$
$$3x^2 + 4x + 2$$
$$\underline{+\ x^2 + 5x + 4}$$
$$4x^2 + 9x + 6$$

$$(2x^2 + 7x + 4) + (5x^2 - 9x + 2) =$$
$$2x^2 + 7x + 4$$
$$\underline{+5x^2 - 9x + 2}$$
$$7x^2 - 2x + 6$$

$$(7x^2 - 5x + 4) + (-x^2 + 6x - 2) =$$
$$7x^2 - 5x + 4$$
$$\underline{-x^2 + 6x - 2}$$
$$6x^2 +\ x + 2$$

$$(3x^2 + 2x + 7) + (x^2 + 9x + 8) =$$
$$3x^2 + 2x + 7$$
$$\underline{+\ x^2 + 9x + 8}$$
$$4x^2 + 11x + 15$$

$$(6x^2 + 7x + 3) + (5x^2 - 4x + 8) =$$
$$6x^2 + 7x + 3$$
$$\underline{+5x^2 - 4x + 8}$$
$$11x^2 + 3x + 11$$

$$(6x^2 + 5x + 7) + (3x^2 + 4x + 8) =$$
$$6x^2 + 5x + 7$$
$$\underline{+3x^2 + 4x + 8}$$
$$9x^2 + 9x + 15$$

$$(2x^2 + 7x - 6) + (5x^2 - 3x + 7) =$$
$$2x^2 + 7x - 6$$
$$\underline{+5x^2 - 3x + 7}$$
$$7x^2 + 4x + 1$$

$$(9x^2 + 2x + 9) + (-8x^2 - 4x - 5) =$$
$$9x^2 + 2x + 9$$
$$\underline{-8x^2 - 4x - 5}$$
$$x^2 - 2x + 4$$

$$(9x^2 + 7x + 9) + (2x^2 + 9x + 8) =$$
$$9x^2 + 7x + 9$$
$$\underline{+2x^2 + 9x + 8}$$
$$11x^2 + 16x + 17$$

$$(7x^2 + 3x - 5) + (4x^2 - 9x + 3) =$$
$$7x^2 + 3x - 5$$
$$\underline{+4x^2 - 9x + 3}$$
$$11x^2 - 6x + 2$$

Teaching Tips, Cont.

➢ Tell the students they may use their algebra tiles to check their work in this lesson. Encourage them to work the problems first and only use the algebra tiles to check their answers.

➢ Complete the Classwork exercises. Have some students work the problems on the board for the class and explain their answers. All students should work the problems in their books.

Assignments

- Complete Lesson 131, Activities 2-4.
- Worksheet 65.

Adding polynomials with missing terms

$$(2x^3 + 5x + 4) + (3x^2 + 2x + 8) =$$

Rewrite vertically. Insert the missing terms with a 0 coefficient and add like terms.

$$2x^3 + 0x^2 + 5x + 4$$
$$\underline{+\ 0x^3 + 3x^2 + 2x + 8}$$
$$2x^3 + 3x^2 + 7x + 12$$

Lesson 132

Concepts
- Subtracting polynomials
- Algebra tiles
- 30-60-90 triangles
- Area of rectangles
- Percent
- Math in the real world

Learning Objectives
The student will be able to:
- Subtract polynomials
- Align like terms when writing polynomial subtraction problems vertically
- Use algebra tiles to check polynomial subtraction problems

Materials Needed
- Student Book, Lesson 132
- Worksheet 66
- Algebra tiles

Teaching Tips
➢ Have students complete Worksheet 66 in class. This may be for added practice of earlier topics or graded as a quiz, if desired.

➢ Review adding polynomials. (See Lesson 131.)

➢ Review the distributive property. (See Lesson 13.)

➢ Teach subtracting polynomials from the teaching box. Tell the students to use the distributive property to distribute the negative of the minus sign to each term in the second set of parentheses and add the resulting like terms.

Subtracting Polynomials

Recall the rules for working with signed numbers. When you are subtracting a number, change the sign and add. This rule also applies to subtracting polynomials. Look at this problem.

$(2x^2 + 2x + 3) - (x^2 - x + 1) =$

The negative applies to everything in the second set of parentheses. Change each sign in the second parentheses and add.

$(2x^2 + 2x + 3) + (-x^2 + x - 1) =$

$2x^2 + 2x + 3 - x^2 + x - 1 =$

$x^2 + 3x + 2$

Polynomials may also be subtracted by writing the problem vertically. Like addition problems, like terms must appear in the same column.

$$\begin{array}{c}(2x^2 + 2x + 3)\\-(x^2 - x + 1)\end{array} \text{ becomes } \begin{array}{c}(2x^2 + 2x + 3)\\+(-x^2 + x - 1)\\\hline x^2 + 3x + 2\end{array}$$

You may use algebra tiles to check your answer.

+

When adding with algebra tiles, a red piece paired with a different color of the same size will always result in both pieces being removed because the red is the negative of the other color and $1 - 1 = 0$. Therefore, the sum looks like the diagram below.

① Classwork
Write the problem vertically and subtract.

$(3x^2 + 2x + 3) - (x^2 + x + 2) =$

$$\begin{array}{c}(3x^2 + 2x + 3)\\-(x^2 + x + 2)\end{array} \text{ becomes } \begin{array}{c}3x^2 + 2x + 3\\-x^2 - x - 2\\\hline 2x^2 + x + 1\end{array}$$

$(2x^2 + 2x + 5) - (x^2 - x + 1) =$

$$\begin{array}{c}(2x^2 + 2x + 5)\\-(x^2 - x + 1)\end{array} \text{ becomes } \begin{array}{c}2x^2 + 2x + 5\\-x^2 + x - 1\\\hline x^2 + 3x + 4\end{array}$$

$(5x^2 - x + 1) - (3x^2 - 2x - 1) =$

$$\begin{array}{c}(5x^2 - x + 1)\\-(3x^2 - 2x - 1)\end{array} \text{ becomes } \begin{array}{c}5x^2 - x + 1\\-3x^2 + 2x + 1\\\hline 2x^2 + x + 2\end{array}$$

Activities
② Subtract.

$$\begin{array}{c}(5x^2 + 5x + 3)\\-(3x^2 + 2x + 1)\\\hline 2x^2 + 3x + 2\end{array} \qquad \begin{array}{c}(5x^2 - 2x + 3)\\-(x^2 - 4x - 1)\\\hline 4x^2 + 2x + 4\end{array} \qquad \begin{array}{c}(7x^2 - x - 1)\\-(5x^2 + 2x - 3)\\\hline 2x^2 - 3x + 2\end{array}$$

---

③ Write the problem vertically and subtract.

$(3x^2 + 5x + 4) - (x^2 + 2x + 3) =$

$$\begin{array}{c}(3x^2 + 5x + 4)\\-(x^2 + 2x + 3)\end{array} \text{ becomes } \begin{array}{c}3x^2 + 5x + 4\\-x^2 - 2x - 3\\\hline 2x^2 + 3x + 1\end{array}$$

$(8x^2 + 7x + 4) - (6x^2 + 3x + 1) =$

$$\begin{array}{c}(8x^2 + 7x + 4)\\-(6x^2 + 3x + 1)\end{array} \text{ becomes } \begin{array}{c}8x^2 + 7x + 4\\-6x^2 - 3x - 1\\\hline 2x^2 + 4x + 3\end{array}$$

$(7x^2 + 2x + 5) - (4x^2 - 2x + 3) =$

$$\begin{array}{c}(7x^2 + 2x + 5)\\-(4x^2 - 2x + 3)\end{array} \text{ becomes } \begin{array}{c}7x^2 + 2x + 5\\-4x^2 + 2x - 3\\\hline 3x^2 + 4x + 2\end{array}$$

$(6x^2 - x + 1) - (2x^2 - 4x + 2) =$

$$\begin{array}{c}(6x^2 - x + 1)\\-(2x^2 - 4x + 2)\end{array} \text{ becomes } \begin{array}{c}6x^2 - x + 1\\-2x^2 + 4x - 2\\\hline 4x^2 + 3x - 1\end{array}$$

$(x^2 - x - 1) - (-x^2 + 2x - 3) =$

$$\begin{array}{c}(x^2 - x - 1)\\-(-x^2 + 2x - 3)\end{array} \text{ becomes } \begin{array}{c}x^2 - x - 1\\+x^2 - 2x + 3\\\hline 2x^2 - 3x + 2\end{array}$$

$(3x^2 - 3x - 3) - (-2x^2 - 5x - 6) =$

$$\begin{array}{c}(3x^2 - 3x - 3)\\-(-2x^2 - 5x - 6)\end{array} \text{ becomes } \begin{array}{c}3x^2 - 3x - 3\\+2x^2 + 5x + 6\\\hline 5x^2 + 2x + 3\end{array}$$

④ Solve.
Duncan is building a rectangular house that is 60 feet long and 30 feet wide. If the base of the roof makes a 30° angle with the house on each of the long sides and forms a peak in the middle, how many feet high is the roof above the walls of the house? Round your answer to the nearest hundredth of a foot.

$15 \text{ ft.} = x\sqrt{3}$

$x = \frac{15}{\sqrt{3}} \cdot \frac{\sqrt{3}}{\sqrt{3}} = \frac{15\sqrt{3}}{3} = 5\sqrt{3} = 8.66 \text{ ft.}$

The length of each roof section is 60 feet, the same as the house. What is the width of each roof section? Hint: find the length of the hypotenuse in the figure above. Round your answer to the nearest hundredth of a foot.
The hypotenuse is double the height, or 2(8.66 ft.) = 17.32 ft.

What is the area of each rectangular roof section? Round your answer to the nearest square foot.
(60 ft.)(17.32 ft.) = 1039 sq. ft.

How many square feet are in the entire roof?
(1039 sq. ft.)(2) = 2078 sq. ft.

Duncan must purchase 10% more shingles than the measurements indicate to allow for waste. If one square of roofing shingles covers 100 square feet, how many squares should Duncan buy to ensure he has enough for the job?
110% of 2078 = (1.1)(2078) = 2285.8
Each roofing square covers 100 square feet, so Duncan needs 2285.8 ÷ 100 = 22.858 or 23 roofing squares.

Teaching Tips, Cont.

➤ Tell the students they may use their algebra tiles to check their work in this lesson. Encourage them to work the problems first and only use the algebra tiles to check their answers.

➤ Complete the Classwork exercises. Have some students work the problems on the board for the class and explain their answers. All students should work the problems in their books.

Assignment

- Complete Lesson 132, Activities 2-4.

Lesson 133

Concepts
- Multiplying monomials
- Exponents
- Adding polynomials
- Subtracting polynomials
- Math in the real world

Learning Objectives
The student will be able to:
- Multiply monomials
- Add exponents when multiplying like variables
- Write the product of monomials in proper form

Materials Needed
- Student Book, Lesson 133
- Worksheet 67

Teaching Tips
➤ Review the rules of working with exponents. (See Lesson 14.)

➤ Teach multiplying monomials from the teaching box.

➤ Explain that the rules of multiplying with exponents apply to monomials having the same variable as the base.

➤ Emphasize that exponents are added only when the bases are identical.

➤ Tell the students that the coefficients are multiplied regardless of the variables involved.

Multiplying Monomials

When multiplying monomials, multiply the coefficients to get the new coefficient, and multiply the variables to get the new variable. The following rules apply to all instances of multiplying with variables.
- When multiplying like variables, add the exponents to get the new exponent.
- When multiplying different variables, write all variables as a single product.
- List like variables in order from highest degree to lowest degree.
- List unlike variables in alphabetical order.

$x^2(2x) = (1 \cdot 2)x^{2+1} = 2x^3$

Notice that the coefficients were multiplied and the exponents were added.

$(3x)(2y) = (3 \cdot 2)(xy) = 6xy$

Notice that the coefficients were multiplied. The variables are different, so they were written in alphabetical order as a product.

① **Classwork**
Multiply.

$2x(3x^2)$
$(2 \cdot 3)x^{1 \cdot 2} = 6x^3$

$2x(3y^2)$
$(2 \cdot 3)(xy^2) = 6xy^2$

$2x(3xy^2)$
$(2 \cdot 3)(x^{1 \cdot 1})(y^2) = 6x^2y^2$

Activities
② Multiply.

$3x(4x^2)$
$(3 \cdot 4)x^{1 \cdot 2} = 12x^3$

$3x(4y^2)$
$(3 \cdot 4)(xy^2) = 12xy^2$

$3x(4xy^2)$
$(3 \cdot 4)(x^{1 \cdot 1})(y^2) = 12x^2y^2$

$3x^2(2x^2)$
$(3 \cdot 2)x^{2 \cdot 2} = 6x^4$

$3x^2(2y^2)$
$(3 \cdot 2)(x^2y^2) = 6x^2y^2$

$3x^2(2xy^2)$
$(3 \cdot 2)(x^{2 \cdot 1})(y^2) = 6x^3y^2$

$x^3(2x^2)$
$(1 \cdot 2)x^{3 \cdot 2} = 2x^5$

$x^3(2y^2)$
$(1 \cdot 2)(x^3y^2) = 2x^3y^2$

$x^3(2xy^2)$
$(1 \cdot 2)(x^{3 \cdot 1})(y^2) = 2x^4y^2$

$y(4y^2)$
$(1 \cdot 4)y^{1 \cdot 2} = 4y^3$

$x(4y^2)$
$(1 \cdot 4)(xy^2) = 4xy^2$

$x(4x^2y^2)$
$(1 \cdot 4)(x^{2 \cdot 1})(y^2) = 4x^3y^2$

$3y^2(5y^2)$
$(3 \cdot 5)y^{2 \cdot 2} = 15y^4$

$3x^2(5y^2)$
$(3 \cdot 5)(x^2y^2) = 15x^2y^2$

$3x^2(5x^2y^2)$
$(3 \cdot 5)(x^{2 \cdot 2})(y^2) = 15x^4y^2$

$2y^3(5y^2)$
$(2 \cdot 5)y^{3 \cdot 2} = 10y^5$

$2x^3(5y^2)$
$(2 \cdot 5)(x^3y^2) = 10x^3y^2$

$2x^3(5x^2y^2)$
$(2 \cdot 5)(x^{3 \cdot 2})(y^2) = 10x^5y^2$

$3y^3(4y^4)$
$(3 \cdot 4)y^{3 \cdot 4} = 12y^7$

$3x^3(4y^4)$
$(3 \cdot 4)(x^3y^4) = 12x^3y^4$

$3x^3(4x^2y^4)$
$(3 \cdot 4)(x^{3 \cdot 2})(y^4) = 12x^5y^4$

---

③ Add.

$$\begin{array}{r} 3x^2 + 2x - 4 \\ + \ 4x^2 + 3x + 1 \\ \hline 7x^2 + 5x - 3 \end{array} \qquad \begin{array}{r} 3x^2 + 4x + 2 \\ +2x^2 - 2x - 5 \\ \hline 5x^2 + 2x - 3 \end{array} \qquad \begin{array}{r} 2x^2 - 5x - 2 \\ +3x^2 + 2x - 3 \\ \hline 5x^2 - 3x - 5 \end{array}$$

$$\begin{array}{r} 2x^2 + 3x + 2 \\ + \ 4x^2 + 5x - 3 \\ \hline 6x^2 + 8x - 1 \end{array} \qquad \begin{array}{r} 4x^2 + 3x + 2 \\ +3x^2 - 7x - 5 \\ \hline 7x^2 - 4x - 3 \end{array} \qquad \begin{array}{r} 2x^2 - 3x + 2 \\ +5x^2 - 2x - 3 \\ \hline 7x^2 - 5x - 1 \end{array}$$

④ Subtract.

$$\begin{array}{r} (5x^2 + 4x + 3) \\ -(2x^2 + 2x - 1) \\ \hline 3x^2 + 2x + 4 \end{array} \qquad \begin{array}{r} (4x^2 - 5x + 2) \\ -(x^2 - 2x - 1) \\ \hline 3x^2 - 3x + 3 \end{array} \qquad \begin{array}{r} (6x^2 - 5x - 2) \\ -(3x^2 + 3x - 3) \\ \hline 3x^2 - 8x + 1 \end{array}$$

$$\begin{array}{r} (5x^2 + 3x + 2) \\ -(3x^2 - 2x + 1) \\ \hline 2x^2 + 5x + 1 \end{array} \qquad \begin{array}{r} (6x^2 + 3x - 5) \\ -(2x^2 - 7x - 2) \\ \hline 4x^2 + 10x - 3 \end{array} \qquad \begin{array}{r} (7x^2 - 3x - 3) \\ -(2x^2 - 5x - 5) \\ \hline 5x^2 + 2x + 2 \end{array}$$

⑤ Solve.
Duncan is building a rectangular house that is 60 feet long and 30 feet wide. If the base of the roof makes a 45° angle with the house on each of the long sides and forms a peak in the middle, how many feet high is the roof above the walls of the house?

The height is equal to the base in a 45-45-90 triangle. 15 ft. = x

The length of each roof section is 60 feet, the same as the house. What is the width of each roof section? Hint: find the length of the hypotenuse in the figure above. Round your answer to the nearest hundredth of a foot.
The hypotenuse is $x\sqrt{2}$, or $15\sqrt{2} = 21.21$ ft.

What is the area of each rectangular roof section? Round your answer to the nearest square foot.
(60 ft.)(21.21 ft.) = 1273 sq. ft.

How many square feet are in the entire roof?
(1273 sq. ft.)(2) = 2546 sq. ft.

Duncan must purchase 10% more shingles than the measurements indicate to allow for waste. If one square of roofing shingles covers 100 square feet, how many squares should Duncan buy to ensure he has enough for the job?
110% of 2546 = (1.1)(2546) = 2800.6
Each roofing square covers 100 square feet, so Duncan needs 2800.6 ÷ 100 = 28.006 or 29 roofing squares. (Technically he could get away with 28 squares.)

Subtracting Polynomials

① Subtract.

$$
\begin{array}{r}
(3x^2 + 4x + 1) \\
- (2x^2 + 2x + 3) \\
\hline
x^2 + 2x - 2
\end{array}
\qquad
\begin{array}{r}
(9x^2 + 5x + 3) \\
-(x^2 - 3x - 2) \\
\hline
8x^2 + 8x + 5
\end{array}
\qquad
\begin{array}{r}
(4x^2 - 5x + 6) \\
-(3x^2 + 2x - 4) \\
\hline
x^2 - 7x + 10
\end{array}
$$

$$
\begin{array}{r}
(7x^2 + 4x + 3) \\
-(5x^2 + 3x + 6) \\
\hline
2x^2 + \ x - 3
\end{array}
\qquad
\begin{array}{r}
(3x^2 + 5x + 5) \\
-(4x^2 - 9x - 7) \\
\hline
-x^2 + 14x + 12
\end{array}
\qquad
\begin{array}{r}
(3x^2 - 5x + 8) \\
-(11x^2 + 2x - 4) \\
\hline
-8x^2 - 7x + 12
\end{array}
$$

$$
\begin{array}{r}
(3x^2 + 5x + 7) \\
-(2x^2 + 6x + 4) \\
\hline
x^2 - \ x + 3
\end{array}
\qquad
\begin{array}{r}
(3x^2 + 4x + 8) \\
- (x^2 - 7x - 9) \\
\hline
2x^2 + 11x + 17
\end{array}
\qquad
\begin{array}{r}
(3x^2 - 5x + 4) \\
-(4x^2 + 9x - 7) \\
\hline
-x^2 - 14x + 11
\end{array}
$$

② Write the problem vertically and subtract.

$(3x^2 + 4x + 2) - (x^2 + 5x + 4) =$
$$
\begin{array}{r}
(3x^2 + 4x + 2) \\
- (x^2 + 5x + 4) \\
\hline
2x^2 - \ x - 2
\end{array}
$$

$(6x^2 + 5x + 7) - (3x^2 + 4x + 8) =$
$$
\begin{array}{r}
(6x^2 + 5x + 7) \\
-(3x^2 + 4x + 8) \\
\hline
3x^2 + \ x - 1
\end{array}
$$

$(2x^2 + 7x + 4) - (5x^2 - 9x + 2) =$
$$
\begin{array}{r}
(2x^2 + 7x + 4) \\
-(5x^2 - 9x + 2) \\
\hline
-3x^2 + 16x + 2
\end{array}
$$

$(2x^2 + 7x - 6) - (5x^2 - 3x + 7) =$
$$
\begin{array}{r}
(2x^2 + 7x - 6) \\
-(5x^2 - 3x + 7) \\
\hline
-3x^2 + 10x - 13
\end{array}
$$

$(7x^2 - 5x + 4) - (-x^2 + 6x - 2) =$
$$
\begin{array}{r}
(7x^2 - 5x + 4) \\
-(-x^2 + 6x - 2) \\
\hline
8x^2 - 11x + 6
\end{array}
$$

$(9x^2 + 2x + 9) - (-8x^2 - 4x - 5) =$
$$
\begin{array}{r}
(9x^2 + 2x + 9) \\
-(-8x^2 - 4x - 5) \\
\hline
17x^2 + 6x + 14
\end{array}
$$

$(3x^2 + 2x + 7) - (x^2 + 9x + 8) =$
$$
\begin{array}{r}
(3x^2 + 2x + 7) \\
- (x^2 + 9x + 8) \\
\hline
2x^2 - 7x - 1
\end{array}
$$

$(9x^2 + 7x + 9) - (2x^2 + 9x + 8) =$
$$
\begin{array}{r}
(9x^2 + 7x + 9) \\
-(2x^2 + 9x + 8) \\
\hline
7x^2 - 2x + 1
\end{array}
$$

Teaching Tips, Cont.

➢ Explain that the product contains all the variables from the original terms listed in alphabetical order.

➢ Point out the third rule in the list. (List like variables in order from highest degree to lowest degree.) This rule will not affect multiplying two monomials, but is important if one of the factors has more than one term.

➢ Complete the Classwork exercises. Have some students work the problems on the board for the class and explain their answers. All students should work the problems in their books.

Assignments

- Complete Lesson 133, Activities 2-5.
- Worksheet 67.

Lesson 134

Concepts

- Dividing monomials
- Simple interest
- Compound interest
- Math in the real world

Learning Objectives

The student will be able to:

- Divide monomials
- Subtract exponents when dividing like variables
- Write the quotient of monomials in proper form

Materials Needed

- Student Book, Lesson 134
- Calculator
- Formula strip, Lesson 134

Teaching Tips

➤ Review the rules of working with exponents. (See Lesson 14.)

➤ Teach dividing monomials from the teaching box.

➤ Explain that the rules of dividing with exponents apply to monomials having the same variable as the base.

➤ Emphasize that exponents are subtracted only when the bases are identical.

➤ Tell the students that the coefficients are divided regardless of the variables involved.

Dividing Monomials

When dividing monomials, divide the coefficients to get the new coefficient, and divide the variables to get the new variable. The following rules apply to all instances of dividing with variables.

- When dividing like variables, subtract the exponents to get the new exponent.
- When dividing different variables, write the divisor in the denominator.
- List like variables in order from highest degree to lowest degree.
- List unlike variables in alphabetical order.

$2x^2 \div x = (2 \div 1)x^{2-1} = x$

This may also be solved this way.

$2x^2 \div x = \frac{2x\cancel{x}}{\cancel{x}} = 2x$

Notice that the coefficients were divided and the exponents were subtracted.

$(3x) \div (2y) = (3 \div 2)(x \div y) = \frac{3}{2}\left(\frac{x}{y}\right) = \frac{3x}{2y}$

This may also be solved in one step by writing the divisor in the denominator.

$(3x) \div (2y) = \frac{3x}{2y}$

① Classwork

Divide.

$6x^3 \div 3x^2$
$(6 \div 3)x^{3-2} = 2x$

$6xy^2 \div 3y^2$
$(6 \div 3)(xy^{2-2}) = 2x$

$6x^2y^2 \div 3xy$
$(6 \div 3)(x^{2-1})(y^{2-2}) = 2x$

Activities

② Divide.

$2x^5 \div x^3$
$\frac{2x^5}{x^3} = 2x^{5-3} = 2x^2$

$4x^3 \div x$
$\frac{4x^3}{x} = 4x^{3-1} = 4x^2$

$15y^4 \div 3y^2$
$\frac{15y^4}{3y^2} = 5y^{4-2} = 5y^2$

$10y^5 \div 2y^2$
$\frac{10y^5}{2y^2} = 5y^{5-2} = 5y^3$

$12y^7 \div 3y^3$
$\frac{12y^7}{3y^3} = 4y^{7-3} = 4y^4$

$2x^3y^2 \div x^3$
$\frac{2x^3y^2}{x^3} = 2x^{3-3}y^2 = 2y^2$

$4xy^2 \div 2x$
$\frac{4xy^2}{2x} = 2x^{1-1}y^2 = 2y^2$

$15x^2y^3 \div 5y^2$
$\frac{15x^2y^3}{5y^2} = 3x^2y^{3-2} = 3x^2y$

$10x^3y^2 \div 5y$
$\frac{10x^3y^2}{5y} = 2x^3y^{2-1} = 2x^3y$

$12x^3y^4 \div 4xy$
$\frac{12x^3y^4}{4xy} = 3x^{3-1}y^{4-1} = 3x^2y^3$

$2x^4y^3 \div 2xy^2$
$\frac{2x^4y^3}{2xy^2} = x^{4-1}y^{3-2} = x^3y$

$8x^3y^3 \div 4x^2y^2$
$\frac{8x^3y^3}{4x^2y^2} = 2x^{3-2}y^{3-2} = 2xy$

$15x^4y^2 \div 5x^2y^2$
$\frac{15x^4y^2}{5x^2y^2} = 3x^{4-2}y^{2-2} = 3x^2$

$10x^5y^4 \div 5x^2y^2$
$\frac{10x^5y^4}{5x^2y^2} = 2x^{5-2}y^{4-2} = 2x^3y^2$

$12x^5y^4 \div 4x^2y^3$
$\frac{12x^5y^4}{4x^2y^3} = 3x^{5-2}y^{4-3} = 3x^3y$

---

③ Solve.

Duncan is designing a spiral staircase for a house. The distance between the first floor and the second floor is 9 feet. If Duncan wants 12 steps in the spiral staircase, what must be the distance between steps to ensure that all steps are evenly spaced?

9 feet = 9(12) = 108 inches

108 ÷ 12 = 9 inches between each step

Duncan wants the entire staircase to turn exactly 360°. How many degrees should each step turn?

360° ÷ 12 = 30°

What is the circumference of the staircase if the radius (the length of each step) is 36 inches? Use 3.14 for the value of π.

$C = 2\pi r$

$C = 2\pi(36 \text{ in.})$

$C = 72\pi$ in.

$C = 226.08$ in.

If the circumference is divided evenly among the 12 steps, how wide is each step?

226.08 in. ÷ 12 = 18.84 in.

What is the area of each step in square feet? Round your answer to the nearest hundredth.

radius: 36 inches = 3 feet

area of entire circle:

$A = \pi r^2$

$A = \pi(3)^2$

$A = 9\pi$ sq. ft.

$A = 28.26$ sq. ft.

area of each step: 28.26 ÷ 12 = 2.36 sq. ft.

④ Complete the chart to show simple interest and interest compounded annually.

Principal	Interest rate	Time, in years	Total amount of simple interest	Balance, compounded annually
$10,000	7.25%	5	$i = \$10,000(0.0725)(5) = \$3625$	$A = \$10,000(1 + 0.0725)^5$ $= \$14,190.13$
$18,000	10.125%	10	$i = \$18,000(0.10125)(10) = \$18,225$	$A = \$18,000(1 + 0.10125)^{10}$ $= \$47,220.62$
$100,000	4.875%	30	$i = \$100,000(0.04875)(30) = \$146,250$	$A = \$100,000(1 + 0.04875)^{30}$ $= \$417,022.24$

Teaching Tips, Cont.

➢ Explain that the quotient contains all the variables from the original terms listed in alphabetical order.

➢ Point out the third rule in the list. (List like variables in order from highest degree to lowest degree.) This rule will not affect dividing two monomials, but it is important if the dividend has more than one term.

➢ Complete the Classwork exercises. Have some students work the problems on the board for the class and explain their answers. All students should work the problems in their books.

➢ Give the students the formula strip for Lesson 134 from the *Tests and Resources* book.

Assignment

- Complete Lesson 134, Activities 2-4.

Lesson 135

Concepts
- Multiplying a polynomial by a monomial
- Algebra tiles
- Greatest common factor
- Divisibility tests
- Prime/composite numbers
- Least common multiple
- Temperature conversion
- Math in the real world

Learning Objectives
The student will be able to:
- Multiply a polynomial by a monomial
- Use algebra tiles to represent the product of a polynomial and a monomial
- Write the product of a polynomial and a monomial in proper form

Materials Needed
- Student Book, Lesson 135
- Worksheet 68
- Algebra tiles

Teaching Tips
➤ Have students complete Worksheet 68 in class. This may be for added practice of earlier topics or graded as a quiz, if desired.

➤ Review the rules for multiplying monomials. (See Lesson 133.) Explain that the third rule will be used in this lesson. (List like variables in order from highest degree to lowest degree.)

➤ Review the distributive property. (See Lesson 13.)

Multiplying a Polynomial by a Monomial

To multiply a polynomial by a monomial, use the distributive property and follow the rules of multiplying monomials for each term. (See Lesson 133.)

Distribute the monomial across the polynomial by multiplying each term of the polynomial by the monomial and adding.
$$3x(2x-1) = 3x(2x) + 3x(-1)$$

Solve each monomial product.
$$3x(2x) + 3x(-1) = 6x^2 - 3x$$

This can also be represented using algebra tiles. Place the monomial pieces vertically and the polynomial pieces horizontally to form the edges of a rectangle. Fill in the space in the middle of the rectangle to see the answer.

① Classwork
Multiply.

$5(3x-2)$
$5(3x) + 5(-2) = 15x - 10$

$2x(3x+4)$
$2x(3x) + 2x(4) = 6x^2 + 8x$

$2x(x^2 + 2x - 3)$
$2x(x^2) + 2x(2x) + 2x(-3) =$
$2x^3 + 4x^2 - 6x$

Activities
② Multiply.

$2(4x+1)$
$2(4x) + 2(1) = 8x + 2$

$3(2x-2)$
$3(2x) + 3(-2) = 6x - 6$

$5(2x-1)$
$5(2x) + 5(-1) = 10x - 5$

$2(4x+3)$
$2(4x) + 2(3) = 8x + 6$

$3(5x-3)$
$3(5x) + 3(-3) = 15x - 9$

$3x(4x+1)$
$3x(4x) + 3x(1) = 12x^2 + 3x$

$2x(2x-3)$
$2x(2x) + 2x(-3) = 4x^2 - 6x$

$3x(2x-4)$
$3x(2x) + 3x(-4) = 6x^2 - 12x$

$4x(4x-1)$
$4x(4x) + 4x(-1) = 16x^2 - 4x$

$3x(5x-2)$
$3x(5x) + 3x(-2) = 15x^2 - 6x$

$3x(4x^2 + 2x - 3)$
$3x(4x^2) + 3x(2x) + 3x(-3) =$
$12x^3 + 6x^2 - 9x$

$3x(2x^2 + x - 1)$
$3x(2x^2) + 3x(x) + 3x(-1) =$
$6x^3 + 3x^2 - 3x$

$2x(2x^2 - 3x + 4)$
$2x(2x^2) + 2x(-3x) + 2x(4) =$
$4x^3 - 6x^2 + 8x$

$3x(4x^2 - 2x + 1)$
$3x(4x^2) + 3x(-2x) + 3x(1) =$
$12x^3 - 6x^2 + 3x$

$3x(5x^2 + 3x - 2)$
$3x(5x^2) + 3x(3x) + 3x(-2) =$
$15x^3 + 9x^2 - 6x$

③ Find the greatest common factor of each set of numbers.

20, 32, and 40
$20 = ②×②×5$
$32 = ②×②×2×2×2$
$40 = ②×②×2×5$
GCF: $2 × 2 = 4$

18, 27, and 36
$18 = 2×③×③$
$27 = ③×③×3$
$36 = 2×2×③×③$
GCF: $3 × 3 = 9$

24, 30, and 36
$24 = ②×2×2×③$
$30 = ②×③×5$
$36 = ②×2×③×3$
GCF: $2 × 3 = 6$

④ Use the divisibility tests to identify each number as prime or composite.

495   Composite (3, 5)
499   Prime
501   Composite (3)
503   Prime
505   Composite (5)
507   Composite (3)

⑤ Find the least common multiple of each set of numbers.

3, 7, and 9
$3 = 1 × 3$
$7 = 1 × \boxed{7}$
$9 = 3 × 3 = \boxed{3^2}$
LCM: $7 × 3^2 = 63$

6, 9, and 12
$6 = 2 × 3$
$9 = 3 × 3 = \boxed{3^2}$
$12 = 2 × 2 × 3 = \boxed{2^2} × 3$
LCM: $2^2 × 3^2 = 36$

12, 18, and 20
$12 = 2 × 2 × 3 = \boxed{2^2} × 3$
$18 = 2 × 3 × 3 = 2 × \boxed{3^2}$
$20 = 2 × 2 × 5 = 2^2 × \boxed{5}$
LCM: $2^2 × 3^2 × 5 = 180$

⑥ Solve. Round answers to the nearest tenth where appropriate.

°F	°C
10°	$°C = (10° - 32°)(\frac{5}{9}) = -12.2°$
25°	$°C = (25° - 32°)(\frac{5}{9}) = -3.9°$
40°	$°C = (40° - 32°)(\frac{5}{9}) = 4.4°$
60°	$°C = (60° - 32°)(\frac{5}{9}) = 15.6°$
80°	$°C = (80° - 32°)(\frac{5}{9}) = 26.7°$
120°	$°C = (120° - 32°)(\frac{5}{9}) = 48.9°$
135°	$°C(135° - 32°)(\frac{5}{9}) = 57.2°$

°C	°F
10°	$°F = (10°)(\frac{9}{5}) + 32° = 18° + 32° = 50°$
25°	$°F = (25°)(\frac{9}{5}) + 32° = 45° + 32° = 77°$
40°	$°F = (40°)(\frac{9}{5}) + 32° = 72° + 32° = 104°$
60°	$°F = (60°)(\frac{9}{5}) + 32° = 108° + 32° = 140°$
80°	$°F = (80°)(\frac{9}{5}) + 32° = 144° + 32° = 176°$
120°	$°F = (120°)(\frac{9}{5}) + 32° = 216° + 32° = 248°$
135°	$°F = (135°)(\frac{9}{5}) + 32° = 243° + 32° = 275°$

⑦ Solve.
Duncan is building a landing that is 8 feet 6 inches above the floor below. How many steps must he install to have the steps exactly 8.5 inches apart? (Include the step at the landing.)
8 feet = 8(12) = 96 inches
96 + 6 = 102 inches between the floor and the landing
102 ÷ 8.5 = 12
Duncan must install 12 steps between the floor and the landing.

Addition and Subtraction of Polynomials Worksheet 68

① Add.

$$8x^2 + 4x + 6$$
$$+\ 2x^2 + 6x + 5$$
$$\overline{10x^2 + 10x + 11}$$

$$3x^2 + 2x + 7$$
$$+x^2 - 3x - 5$$
$$\overline{4x^2 -\ x + 2}$$

$$2x^2 - 4x + 7$$
$$+6x^2 + 5x - 1$$
$$\overline{8x^2 +\ x + 6}$$

$$6x^2 + 4x + 2$$
$$+\ 7x^2 + 2x + 5$$
$$\overline{13x^2 + 6x + 7}$$

$$5x^2 + 4x + 7$$
$$+6x^2 - 5x - 8$$
$$\overline{11x^2 -\ x - 1}$$

$$9x^2 - 4x + 3$$
$$+5x^2 + 6x - 1$$
$$\overline{14x^2 + 2x + 2}$$

$$3x^2 + 4x + 8$$
$$+\ 6x^2 + 2x + 7$$
$$\overline{9x^2 + 6x + 15}$$

$$7x^2 + 5x + 3$$
$$+x^2 - 4x - 6$$
$$\overline{8x^2 +\ x - 3}$$

$$7x^2 - 5x + 8$$
$$+3x^2 + 4x - 6$$
$$\overline{10x^2 -\ x + 2}$$

$$2x^2 + 9x + 2$$
$$+\ 3x^2 + 4x + 8$$
$$\overline{5x^2 + 13x + 10}$$

$$2x^2 + 5x + 8$$
$$+x^2 - 4x - 7$$
$$\overline{3x^2 +\ x + 1}$$

$$7x^2 - 5x + 6$$
$$+8x^2 + 2x - 8$$
$$\overline{15x^2 - 3x - 2}$$

② Subtract.

$$(9x^2 + 7x + 8)$$
$$-\ (6x^2 + 5x + 4)$$
$$\overline{3x^2 + 2x + 4}$$

$$(7x^2 + 5x + 6)$$
$$-(x^2 - 5x - 4)$$
$$\overline{6x^2 + 10x + 10}$$

$$(6x^2 - 4x + 5)$$
$$-(2x^2 + 7x - 6)$$
$$\overline{4x^2 - 11x + 11}$$

$$(5x^2 + 7x + 8)$$
$$-(3x^2 + 5x + 4)$$
$$\overline{2x^2 + 2x + 4}$$

$$(2x^2 + 4x + 7)$$
$$-(4x^2 - 5x - 9)$$
$$\overline{-2x^2 + 9x + 16}$$

$$(5x^2 - 7x + 3)$$
$$-(7x^2 + 6x - 4)$$
$$\overline{-2x^2 - 13x + 7}$$

$$(2x^2 + 4x + 5)$$
$$-(3x^2 + 8x + 7)$$
$$\overline{-x^2 - 4x - 2}$$

$$(7x^2 + 2x + 4)$$
$$-\ (x^2 - 5x - 8)$$
$$\overline{6x^2 + 7x + 12}$$

$$(7x^2 - 2x + 4)$$
$$-(5x^2 + 7x - 8)$$
$$\overline{2x^2 - 9x + 12}$$

$$(2x^2 + 7x + 5)$$
$$-(6x^2 + 5x + 8)$$
$$\overline{-4x^2 + 2x - 3}$$

$$(5x^2 + 6x + 8)$$
$$-\ (x^2 - 5x - 1)$$
$$\overline{4x^2 + 11x + 9}$$

$$(2x^2 - 6x + 7)$$
$$-(5x^2 + 2x - 3)$$
$$\overline{-3x^2 - 8x + 10}$$

Teaching Tips, Cont.

➤ Teach multiplying a polynomial by a monomial from the teaching box. The students should understand they are applying the distributive property and then following the rules for multiplying monomials to get the individual terms of the product.

➤ Explain that the product contains all the variables from the original terms listed in alphabetical order.

➤ Tell the students they may use their algebra tiles to check their work in this lesson. Encourage them to work the problems first and only use the algebra tiles to check their answers.

➤ Complete the Classwork exercises. Have some students work the problems on the board for the class and explain their answers. All students should work the problems in their books.

Assignment

• Complete Lesson 135, Activities 2-7.

Lesson 136

Concepts

- Dividing a polynomial by a monomial
- Algebra tiles
- Math in the real world

Learning Objectives

The student will be able to:

- Divide a polynomial by a monomial
- Use long division to find quotients
- Write quotients in proper form

Materials Needed

- Student Book, Lesson 136
- Algebra tiles

Teaching Tips

➢ Review the rules for dividing monomials. (See Lesson 134.) Explain that the third rule will be used in this lesson. (List like variables in order from highest degree to lowest degree.)

➢ Teach dividing a polynomial by a monomial from the teaching box. Explain that each term in the polynomial is divided by the monomial.

➢ Remind the students that the quotient contains all the variables from the original terms listed in alphabetical order.

➢ Show the students how to set up a long division problem. Each term of the quotient should be written above its dividend.

Dividing a Polynomial by a Monomial

To divide a polynomial by a monomial, divide each term of the polynomial by the monomial. Follow the rules for dividing monomials. (See Lesson 134.)

$$(6x^2 - 3x) \div 3x = (6x^2) \div (3x) + (-3x) \div (3x)$$

Solve each monomial quotient.

$$(6x^2) \div (3x) + (-3x) \div (3x) =$$
$$(6 \div 3)(x^{2-1}) + (-3 \div 3)(x^{1-1}) =$$
$$2x + (-1)x^0$$

Remember that anything raised to the 0 power is equal to 1.
$$2x + (-1)x^0 = 2x - 1$$

Alternately, polynomials may be written using long division. This method can make it easier to avoid mistakes, especially in long polynomials.

$$
\begin{array}{r}
2x - 1 \\
3x \overline{) 6x^2 - 3x} \\
\underline{6x^2} \\
-3x \\
\underline{-3x}
\end{array}
$$

This can also be represented using algebra tiles. Place the divisor vertically, and fill in the dividend next to the divisor so that all divided pieces are divided equally among the divisor pieces. The quotient will then go across the top, as in a long division problem.

① Classwork

Divide.

$$(15x - 10) \div 5$$

$$
\begin{array}{r}
3x - 2 \\
5 \overline{) 15x - 10} \\
\underline{15x} \\
-10 \\
\underline{-10}
\end{array}
$$

$$(6x^2 + 8x) \div 2x$$

$$
\begin{array}{r}
3x + 4 \\
2x \overline{) 6x^2 + 8x} \\
\underline{6x^2} \\
8x \\
\underline{8x}
\end{array}
$$

$$(2x^3 + 4x^2 - 6x) \div 2x$$

$$
\begin{array}{r}
x^2 + 2x - 3 \\
2x \overline{) 2x^3 + 4x^2 - 6x} \\
\underline{2x^3} \\
4x^2 \\
\underline{4x^2} \\
-6x \\
\underline{-6x}
\end{array}
$$

---

② Divide.

$(8x + 2) \div 2$

$$2\overline{)\,8x + 2} \quad \frac{4x + 1}{}$$
$$\underline{8x}$$
$$2$$
$$\underline{2}$$

$(6x - 6) \div 3$

$$3\overline{)\,6x - 6} \quad \frac{2x - 2}{}$$
$$\underline{6x}$$
$$-6$$
$$\underline{-6}$$

$(10x - 5) \div 5$

$$5\overline{)\,10x - 5} \quad \frac{2x - 1}{}$$
$$\underline{10x}$$
$$-5$$
$$\underline{-5}$$

$(8x + 6) \div 2$

$$2\overline{)\,8x + 6} \quad \frac{4x + 3}{}$$
$$\underline{8x}$$
$$6$$
$$\underline{6}$$

$(15x - 9) \div 3$

$$3\overline{)\,15x - 9} \quad \frac{5x - 3}{}$$
$$\underline{15x}$$
$$-9$$
$$\underline{-9}$$

$(12x^2 + 3x) \div 3x$

$$3x\overline{)\,12x^2 + 3x} \quad \frac{4x + 1}{}$$
$$\underline{12x^2}$$
$$3x$$
$$\underline{3x}$$

$(4x^2 - 6x) \div 2x$

$$2x\overline{)\,4x^2 - 6x} \quad \frac{2x - 3}{}$$
$$\underline{4x^2}$$
$$-6x$$
$$\underline{-6x}$$

$(6x^2 - 12x) \div 3x$

$$3x\overline{)\,6x^2 - 12x} \quad \frac{2x - 4}{}$$
$$\underline{6x^2}$$
$$-12x$$
$$\underline{-12x}$$

$(16x^2 - 4x) \div 4x$

$$4x\overline{)\,16x^2 - 4x} \quad \frac{4x - 1}{}$$
$$\underline{16x^2}$$
$$-4x$$
$$\underline{-4x}$$

$(15x^2 - 6x) \div 3x$

$$3x\overline{)\,15x^2 - 6x} \quad \frac{5x - 2}{}$$
$$\underline{15x^2}$$
$$-6x$$
$$\underline{-6x}$$

$(12x^3 + 6x^2 - 9x) \div 3x$

$$3x\overline{)\,12x^3 + 6x^2 - 9x} \quad \frac{4x^2 + 2x - 3}{}$$
$$\underline{12x^3}$$
$$6x^2$$
$$\underline{6x^2}$$
$$-9x$$
$$\underline{-9x}$$

$(6x^3 + 3x^2 - 3x) \div 3x$

$$3x\overline{)\,6x^3 + 3x^2 - 3x} \quad \frac{2x^2 + x - 1}{}$$
$$\underline{6x^3}$$
$$3x^2$$
$$\underline{3x^2}$$
$$-3x$$
$$\underline{-3x}$$

$(4x^3 - 6x^2 + 8x) \div 2x$

$$2x\overline{)\,4x^3 - 6x^2 + 8x} \quad \frac{2x^2 - 3x + 4}{}$$
$$\underline{4x^3}$$
$$-6x^2$$
$$\underline{-6x^2}$$
$$8x$$
$$\underline{8x}$$

$(12x^3 - 6x^2 + 3x) \div 3x$

$$3x\overline{)\,12x^3 - 6x^2 + 3x} \quad \frac{4x^2 - 2x + 1}{}$$
$$\underline{12x^3}$$
$$-6x^2$$
$$\underline{-6x^2}$$
$$3x$$
$$\underline{3x}$$

$(15x^3 + 9x^2 - 6x) \div 3x$

$$3x\overline{)\,15x^3 + 9x^2 - 6x} \quad \frac{5x^2 + 3x - 2}{}$$
$$\underline{15x^3}$$
$$9x^2$$
$$\underline{9x^2}$$
$$-6x$$
$$\underline{-6x}$$

③ Solve.
Duncan is installing drywall on a wall measuring 16 feet by 10 feet. If the drywall comes in sheets that are 8 feet long and 4 feet wide, how many sheets of drywall will Duncan need to cover the wall?
The wall is 16 × 10 = 160 square feet.
The drywall is 8 × 4 = 32 square feet.
Duncan will need 160 ÷ 32 = 5 sheets of drywall to cover the wall.

Teaching Tips, Cont.

➢ Tell the students they may use their algebra tiles to check their work in this lesson. Encourage them to work the problems first and only use the algebra tiles to check their answers.

➢ Complete the Classwork exercises. Have some students work the problems on the board for the class and explain their answers. All students should work the problems in their books.

Assignment

- Complete Lesson 136, Activities 2-3.

Lesson 137

Concepts
- Multiplying polynomials
- Algebra tiles
- Math in the real world

Learning Objectives
The student will be able to:
- Multiply two binomials
- Represent the product of two binomials using algebra tiles
- Write the product of two binomials in proper form

Materials Needed
- Student Book, Lesson 137
- Algebra tiles
- Formula strip, Lesson 137

Teaching Tips
➤ Review the rules for multiplying monomials. (See Lesson 133.)

➤ Review multiplying a polynomial by a monomial. (See Lesson 135.)

➤ Teach multiplying polynomials from the teaching box. Explain that this is like applying the distributive property multiple times – once for each term in the multiplicand.

➤ Tell the students that often there will be like terms that must be combined once the multiplication is completed.

➤ Show the students how to set up the problem with algebra tiles. The multiplicand and multiplier should be placed at right angles and the center space filled in with the answer.

Multiplying Polynomials

To multiply two polynomials, multiply each term in the first polynomial by each term in the second polynomial and add the resulting products.
$$(x+2)(2x+3) = x(2x) + x(3) + 2(2x) + 2(3)$$

Follow the rules for multiplying monomials to simplify the answer.
$$x(2x) + x(3) + 2(2x) + 2(3) = 2x^2 + 3x + 4x + 6$$

Combine like terms. Remember to arrange the terms in order from the highest degree to the lowest degree, placing variables of equal degree in alphabetical order.
$$2x^2 + 7x + 6$$

This can also be represented using algebra tiles. Place one polynomial vertically and the other one horizontally. Fill in the center of the rectangle to get the answer.

① Classwork
Multiply.

$(x+1)(x+2)$
$x(x) + x(2) + 1(x) + 1(2) =$
$x^2 + 2x + x + 2 = x^2 + 3x + 2$

$(x+1)(x-2)$
$x(x) + x(-2) + 1(x) + 1(-2) =$
$x^2 - 2x + x - 2 = x^2 - x - 2$

$(2x+1)(x-3)$
$2x(x) + 2x(-3) + 1(x) + 1(-3) =$
$2x^2 - 6x + x - 3 = 2x^2 - 5x - 3$

Activities
② Multiply.

$(x+3)(x+2)$
$x(x) + x(2) + 3(x) + 3(2) =$
$x^2 + 2x + 3x + 6 = x^2 + 5x + 6$

$(x-1)(x-2)$
$x(x) + x(-2) - 1(x) - 1(-2) =$
$x^2 - 2x - x + 2 = x^2 - 3x + 2$

$(x+4)(x-3)$
$x(x) + x(-3) + 4(x) + 4(-3) =$
$x^2 - 3x + 4x - 12 = x^2 + x - 12$

$(x+2)(x-2)$
$x(x) + x(-2) + 2(x) + 2(-2) =$
$x^2 - 2x + 2x - 4 = x^2 - 4$

$(2x-1)(x+2)$
$2x(x) + 2x(2) - 1(x) - 1(2) =$
$2x^2 + 4x - x - 2 = 2x^2 + 3x - 2$

$(2x+3)(x-1)$
$2x(x) + 2x(-1) + 3(x) + 3(-1) =$
$2x^2 - 2x + 3x - 3 = 2x^2 + x - 3$

---

③ Solve.

A segmented arch has a radius equal to the width of the opening of the arch. If Duncan is cutting a segmented arch in a 20-ft. long wall so that the arch is centered along the wall, leaving 8 feet on either side of the arch, what will be the radius of the arch?

$20 - 8 - 8 = 4$
The radius will be 4 feet since the radius equal the width of the opening of the arch.

If a complete circle were drawn with this radius, what would be the circumference of the circle? Use $\frac{22}{7}$ for the value of π.

$C = 2\pi r$

$C = 2\pi(4)$

$C = 8\left(\frac{22}{7}\right) = \frac{176}{7} = 25\frac{1}{7}$ ft.

What is the measure of the angle formed when the two radii are drawn to the edges of the arc? (Draw and label a picture.)

Students should recognize this as an equilateral triangle. This makes all angles equal to 60°. Alternately, students may notice the 30-60-90 triangle pattern and conclude that the angle must be 60°.

What fraction of a circle does the arch make?

$\frac{60°}{360°} = \frac{1}{6}$

What is the length of the arch?

$\frac{1}{\cancel{6}}\left(\frac{\cancel{176}^{88}}{7}\right) = \frac{88}{21} = 4\frac{4}{21}$ ft.

Duncan installed a total of 21 doors and windows in a house. Doors cost $20 each and windows cost $175 each. If the total cost of the doors and windows was $2125, how many windows and how many doors did Duncan install in the house?

Let d = the number of doors.
Let w = the number of windows.

$d + w = 21$
$20d + 175w = 2125$

$d = 21 - w$
$20(21 - w) + 175w = 2125$
$420 - 20w + 175w = 2125$
$420 + 155w = 2125$
$155w = 1705$
$w = 11$

There are 11 windows and $21 - 11 = 10$ doors in the house.

Teaching Tips, Cont.

➤ Remind the students to list the product terms in order from the highest degree to the lowest degree. If there are different variables, they should be listed in alphabetical order.

➤ Complete the Classwork exercises. Have some students work the problems on the board for the class and explain their answers. All students should work the problems in their books.

➤ Give the students the formula strip for Lesson 137 from the *Tests and Resources* book.

Assignment

• Complete Lesson 137, Activities 2-3.

Lesson 138

Concepts
- The FOIL method
- Multiplying polynomials
- Adding polynomials
- Subtracting polynomials
- Multiplying a polynomial by a monomial
- Dividing a polynomial by a monomial

Learning Objectives
The student will be able to:
- Multiply binomials
- Explain the FOIL method of multiplying binomials
- Write the product of two binomials in proper form

Materials Needed
- Student Book, Lesson 138
- Worksheet 69

Teaching Tips
> Have students complete Worksheet 69 in class. This may be for added practice of earlier topics, or graded as a quiz, if desired.

> Review multiplying polynomials. (See Lesson 137.)

> Tell the students that there is an easy way to remember the process when the multiplicand and multiplier are both binomials.

> Teach the FOIL method from the teaching box.

The FOIL Method

The **FOIL method** is a mnemonic device to help you remember how to multiply two binomials.

Look at this example from Lesson 137:
$(x+2)(2x+3) = x(2x) + x(3) + 2(2x) + 2(3)$
$= 2x^2 + 3x + 4x + 6$
$= 2x^2 + 7x + 6$

F: Multiply the **first** term of each binomial.
  In this case, $x(2x)$
O: Multiply the two **outer** terms.
  In this case, $x(3)$
I: Multiply the two **inner** terms.
  In this case, $2(2x)$
L: Multiply the **last** term of each binomial.
  In this case, $2(3)$

Add the result of each, and combine like terms to simplify.
$2x^2 + 3x + 4x + 6 = 2x^2 + 7x + 6$

This can also be represented using algebra tiles. See Lesson 137 for details.

① **Classwork**
Multiply, using the FOIL method.

$(x+2)(x+2)$
$x(x) + x(2) + 2(x) + 2(2) =$
$x^2 + 2x + 2x + 4 = x^2 + 4x + 4$

$(x-1)(x-1)$
$x(x) + x(-1) - 1(x) - 1(-1) =$
$x^2 - x - x + 1 = x^2 - 2x + 1$

$(2x+1)(x-2)$
$2x(x) + 2x(-2) + 1(x) + 1(-2) =$
$2x^2 - 4x + x - 2 = 2x^2 - 3x - 2$

Activities

② Multiply, using the FOIL method.

$(x+1)(x+4)$
$x(x) + x(4) + 1(x) + 1(4) =$
$x^2 + 4x + x + 4 = x^2 + 5x + 4$

$(x+2)(x-3)$
$x(x) + x(-3) + 2(x) + 2(-3) =$
$x^2 - 3x + 2x - 6 = x^2 - x - 6$

$(x+3)(x-2)$
$x(x) + x(-2) + 3(x) + 3(-2) =$
$x^2 - 2x + 3x - 6 = x^2 + x - 6$

$(2x+3)(x-2)$
$2x(x) + 2x(-2) + 3(x) + 3(-2) =$
$2x^2 - 4x + 3x - 6 = 2x^2 - x - 6$

$(2x-1)(x-2)$
$2x(x) + 2x(-2) - 1(x) - 1(-2) =$
$2x^2 - 4x - x + 2 = 2x^2 - 5x + 2$

$(2x+1)(3x-2)$
$2x(3x) + 2x(-2) + 1(3x) + 1(-2) =$
$6x^2 - 4x + 3x - 2 = 6x^2 - x - 2$

$(3x+2)(x-2)$
$3x(x) + 3x(-2) + 2(x) + 2(-2) =$
$3x^2 - 6x + 2x - 4 = 3x^2 - 4x - 4$

$(2x-3)(4x+1)$
$2x(4x) + 2x(1) - 3(4x) - 3(1) =$
$8x^2 + 2x - 12x - 3 = 8x^2 - 10x - 3$

③ Add.

$$\begin{array}{r} 4x^2 + 3x - 5 \\ + \ 7x^2 + \ x + 3 \\ \hline 11x^2 + 4x - 2 \end{array}$$

$$\begin{array}{r} 6x^2 + 2x + 3 \\ +3x^2 - 5x - 8 \\ \hline 9x^2 - 3x - 5 \end{array}$$

$$\begin{array}{r} 6x^2 - 7x - 4 \\ +5x^2 + 2x - 3 \\ \hline 11x^2 - 5x - 7 \end{array}$$

$$\begin{array}{r} 3x^2 + 2x + 1 \\ + \ 4x^2 + 7x - 4 \\ \hline 7x^2 + 9x - 3 \end{array}$$

$$\begin{array}{r} 2x^2 + 4x + 2 \\ +8x^2 - 7x - 6 \\ \hline 10x^2 - 3x - 4 \end{array}$$

$$\begin{array}{r} 8x^2 - 7x + 5 \\ +5x^2 - 6x - 8 \\ \hline 13x^2 - 13x - 3 \end{array}$$

④ Subtract.

$$\begin{array}{r} (7x^2 + 4x + 5) \\ -(4x^2 + 3x - 3) \\ \hline 3x^2 + \ x + 8 \end{array}$$

$$\begin{array}{r} (6x^2 - 2x + 3) \\ -(3x^2 - 5x - 8) \\ \hline 3x^2 + 3x + 11 \end{array}$$

$$\begin{array}{r} (6x^2 - 7x - 4) \\ -(5x^2 + 2x - 3) \\ \hline x^2 - 9x - 1 \end{array}$$

$$\begin{array}{r} (3x^2 + 2x + 1) \\ -(4x^2 - 7x + 4) \\ \hline -x^2 + 9x - 3 \end{array}$$

$$\begin{array}{r} (2x^2 + 4x - 2) \\ -(8x^2 - 7x - 6) \\ \hline -6x^2 + 11x + 4 \end{array}$$

$$\begin{array}{r} (8x^2 - 7x - 5) \\ -(5x^2 - 6x - 8) \\ \hline 3x^2 - \ x + 3 \end{array}$$

⑤ Multiply.

$4x(3x^2 + 2x - 5)$
$4x(3x^2) + 4x(2x) + 4x(-5) =$
$12x^3 + 8x^2 - 20x$

$2x(5x^2 - 3x + 3)$
$2x(5x^2) + 2x(-3x) + 2x(3) =$
$10x^3 - 6x^2 + 6x$

$2x^2(3x^2 - 2x + 5)$
$2x^2(3x^2) + 2x^2(-2x) + 2x^2(5) =$
$6x^4 - 4x^3 + 10x^2$

$3x^2(7x^2 + 4x - 6)$
$3x^2(7x^2) + 3x^2(4x) + 3x^2(-6) =$
$21x^4 + 12x^3 - 18x^2$

⑥ Divide.

$(9x + 6) \div 3$

$$\begin{array}{r} 3x + 2 \\ 3)\overline{9x + 6} \\ \underline{9x} \\ 6 \\ \underline{6} \end{array}$$

$(10x - 5) \div 5$

$$\begin{array}{r} 2x - 1 \\ 5)\overline{10x - 5} \\ \underline{10x} \\ -5 \\ \underline{-5} \end{array}$$

$(15x - 9) \div 3$

$$\begin{array}{r} 5 - 3 \\ 3)\overline{15x - 9} \\ \underline{15x} \\ -9 \\ \underline{-9} \end{array}$$

$(6x^2 - 6x + 9) \div 3$

$$\begin{array}{r} 2x^2 - 2x + 3 \\ 3)\overline{6x^2 - 6x + 9} \\ \underline{6x^2} \\ -6x \\ \underline{-6x} \\ 9 \\ \underline{9} \end{array}$$

$(8x^2 + 6x - 4) \div 2$

$$\begin{array}{r} 4x^2 + 3x - 2 \\ 2)\overline{8x^2 + 6x - 4} \\ \underline{8x^2} \\ 6x \\ \underline{6x} \\ -4 \\ \underline{-4} \end{array}$$

$(12x^3 + 3x^2 - 9x) \div 3x$

$$\begin{array}{r} 4x^2 + \ x - 3 \\ 3x)\overline{12x^3 + 3x^2 - 9x} \\ \underline{12x^3} \\ 3x^2 \\ \underline{3x^2} \\ -9x \\ \underline{-9x} \end{array}$$

① Multiply.

$4x\left(7xy^2\right)$

$(4\cdot 7)\left(x^{1\cdot 1}\right)\left(y^2\right)=28x^2y^2$

$5x^2\left(3xy^2\right)$

$(5\cdot 3)\left(x^{2\cdot 1}\right)\left(y^2\right)=15x^3y^2$

$x^3\left(5xy^2\right)$

$(1\cdot 5)\left(x^{3\cdot 1}\right)\left(y^2\right)=5x^4y^2$

$x^3\left(11xy^2\right)$

$(1\cdot 11)\left(x^{3\cdot 1}\right)\left(y^2\right)=11x^4y^2$

$5x^2\left(7x^2y^2\right)$

$(5\cdot 7)\left(x^{2\cdot 2}\right)\left(y^2\right)=35x^4y^2$

$3x^3\left(6x^2y^2\right)$

$(3\cdot 6)\left(x^{3\cdot 2}\right)\left(y^2\right)=18x^5y^2$

$2x^3\left(9x^2y^4\right)$

$(2\cdot 9)\left(x^{3\cdot 2}\right)\left(y^4\right)=18x^5y^4$

$10x^3\left(4x^2y^4\right)$

$(10\cdot 4)\left(x^{3\cdot 2}\right)\left(y^4\right)=40x^5y^4$

$9x\left(6x^2+x-3\right)$

$9x\left(6x^2\right)+9x\left(x\right)+9x\left(-3\right)=$
$54x^3+9x^2-27x$

$3x\left(4x^2-2x+3\right)$

$3x\left(4x^2\right)+3x\left(-2x\right)+3x\left(3\right)=$
$12x^3-6x^2+9x$

$4x\left(2x^2-3x+7\right)$

$4x\left(2x^2\right)+4x\left(-3x\right)+4x\left(7\right)=$
$8x^3-12x^2+28x$

$6x\left(3x^2-5x+4\right)$

$6x\left(3x^2\right)+6x\left(-5x\right)+6x\left(4\right)=$
$18x^3-30x^2+24x$

② Divide.

$5x^5\div x^3$

$\frac{5x^5}{x^3}=5x^{5-3}=5x^2$

$7x^3\div x$

$\frac{7x^3}{x}=7x^{3-1}=7x^2$

$16y^4\div 8y^2$

$\frac{16y^4}{8y^2}=2y^{4-2}=2y^2$

$12y^5\div 3y^2$

$\frac{12y^5}{3y^2}=4y^{5-2}=4y^3$

$15y^7\div 5y^3$

$\frac{15y^7}{5y^3}=3y^{7-3}=3y^4$

$12x^3y^2\div x^3$

$\frac{12x^3y^2}{x^3}=12x^{3-3}y^2=12y^2$

$6xy^2\div 2x$

$\frac{6xy^2}{2x}=3x^{1-1}y^2=3y^2$

$18x^2y^3\div 6y^2$

$\frac{18x^2y^3}{6y^2}=3x^2y^{3-2}=3x^2y$

$21x^3y^2\div 3y$

$\frac{21x^3y^2}{3y}=7x^3y^{2-1}=7x^3y$

$24x^3y^4\div 4xy$

$\frac{24x^3y^4}{4xy}=6x^{3-1}y^{4-1}=6x^2y^3$

$9x^4y^3\div 9xy^2$

$\frac{9x^4y^3}{9xy^2}=x^{4-1}y^{3-2}=x^3y$

$22x^3y^3\div 2x^2y^2$

$\frac{22x^3y^3}{2x^2y^2}=11x^{3-2}y^{3-2}=11xy$

$24x^4y^2\div 8x^2y^2$

$\frac{24x^4y^2}{8x^2y^2}=3x^{4-2}y^{2-2}=3x^2$

$16x^5y^4\div 4x^2y^2$

$\frac{16x^5y^4}{4x^2y^2}=4x^{5-2}y^{4-2}=4x^3y^2$

$36x^5y^4\div 4x^2y^3$

$\frac{36x^5y^4}{4x^2y^3}=9x^{5-2}y^{4-3}=9x^3y$

Teaching Tips, Cont.

➢ Remind the students to combine like terms and simplify when they have completed the multiplication.

➢ Complete the Classwork exercises. Have some students work the problems on the board for the class and explain their answers. All students should work the problems in their books.

Assignment

- Complete Lesson 138, Activities 2-6.

Lesson 139

Concepts
- Dividing polynomials
- Area of plane figures
- Percent
- Math in the real world

Learning Objectives
The student will be able to:
- Divide a polynomial by a polynomial
- Write polynomial division problems as long division
- Express the quotient in proper form

Materials Needed
- Student Book, Lesson 139
- Formula strip, Lesson 139

Teaching Tips
➢ Review dividing a polynomial by a monomial. (See Lesson 136.)

➢ Teach dividing polynomials from the teaching box. Explain that these problems must be set up as a long division problem.

➢ Tell the students to just look at the first term of the divisor when finding the quotient. They should divide the first term of the divisor into the first term of the dividend to get the first term of the quotient.

➢ Multiply the term in the quotient by each term of the divisor before subtracting. Bring down one term at a time and repeat the process like normal long division.

Dividing Polynomials

When dividing two polynomials, set up the problem as a long division problem.

$(2x^2 + 7x + 6) \div (x + 2)$ must be rewritten.

$$x + 2 \overline{)2x^2 + 7x + 6}$$

Treat this just like a long division problem, dividing the first term of the dividend by the first term of the divisor. In this case, think: $2x^2 \div x$. The answer to this is $2x$. Write this in the quotient area above the x-term of the dividend. Make sure you keep like terms lined up.

$$x + 2 \overline{)2x^2 + 7x + 6}$$ quotient: $2x$

Multiply the term in the quotient by the entire divisor. Write the product terms in their corresponding columns and subtract.

$$\begin{array}{r} 2x \\ x + 2 \overline{)2x^2 + 7x + 6} \\ \underline{2x^2 + 4x} \\ 3x \end{array}$$

Bring down the next term in the dividend and repeat the above steps with the remaining polynomial.

$$\begin{array}{r} 2x + 3 \\ x + 2 \overline{)2x^2 + 7x + 6} \\ \underline{2x^2 + 4x} \\ 3x + 6 \\ 3x + 6 \end{array}$$

The answer is $2x + 3$.

① Classwork.
Divide.

$(x^2 + 4x + 4) \div (x + 2)$

$$\begin{array}{r} x + 2 \\ x + 2 \overline{)x^2 + 4x + 4} \\ \underline{x^2 + 2x} \\ 2x + 4 \\ \underline{2x + 4} \end{array}$$

$(x^2 - 2x + 1) \div (x - 1)$

$$\begin{array}{r} x - 1 \\ x - 1 \overline{)x^2 - 2x + 1} \\ \underline{x^2 - x} \\ -x + 1 \\ \underline{-x + 1} \end{array}$$

$(2x^2 - 3x - 2) \div (2x + 1)$

$$\begin{array}{r} x - 2 \\ 2x + 1 \overline{)2x^2 - 3x - 2} \\ \underline{2x^2 + x} \\ -4x - 2 \\ \underline{-4x - 2} \end{array}$$

Activities
② Divide.

$$\begin{array}{r} x + 2 \\ x + 1 \overline{)x^2 + 3x + 2} \\ \underline{x^2 + x} \\ 2x + 2 \\ \underline{2x + 2} \end{array}$$

$$\begin{array}{r} x + 1 \\ x - 2 \overline{)x^2 - x - 2} \\ \underline{x^2 - 2x} \\ x - 2 \\ \underline{x - 2} \end{array}$$

$$\begin{array}{r} 2x + 1 \\ x - 3 \overline{)2x^2 - 5x - 3} \\ \underline{2x^2 - 6x} \\ x - 3 \\ \underline{x - 3} \end{array}$$

---

③ Divide.

$(x^2 + 5x + 6) \div (x + 2)$

$$x + 2 \overline{)\begin{array}{l} x + 3 \\ x^2 + 5x + 6 \end{array}}$$
$$\underline{x^2 + 2x}$$
$$3x + 6$$
$$\underline{3x + 6}$$

$(2x^2 - 5x + 2) \div (x - 2)$

$$x - 2 \overline{)\begin{array}{l} 2x - 1 \\ 2x^2 - 5x + 2 \end{array}}$$
$$\underline{2x^2 - 4x}$$
$$-x + 2$$
$$\underline{-x + 2}$$

$(6x^2 - x - 2) \div (3x - 2)$

$$3x - 2 \overline{)\begin{array}{l} 2x + 1 \\ 6x^2 - x - 2 \end{array}}$$
$$\underline{6x^2 - 4x}$$
$$3x - 2$$
$$\underline{3x - 2}$$

$(x^2 - x - 6) \div (x + 2)$

$$x + 2 \overline{)\begin{array}{l} x - 3 \\ x^2 - x - 6 \end{array}}$$
$$\underline{x^2 + 2x}$$
$$-3x + 6$$
$$\underline{-3x + 6}$$

$(3x^2 - 4x - 4) \div (x - 2)$

$$x - 2 \overline{)\begin{array}{l} 3x + 2 \\ 3x^2 - 4x - 4 \end{array}}$$
$$\underline{3x^2 - 6x}$$
$$2x - 4$$
$$\underline{2x - 4}$$

$(8x^2 - 10x - 3) \div (2x - 3)$

$$2x - 3 \overline{)\begin{array}{l} 4x + 1 \\ 8x^2 - 10x - 3 \end{array}}$$
$$\underline{8x^2 - 12x}$$
$$2x - 3$$
$$\underline{2x - 3}$$

④ Solve.

Duncan is building a door with a circular window centered at the top of the door, creating an arch. If the door is 3 feet wide, and the window has a 6-inch frame around it, what size window should Duncan order for the door? Express the measurement as the diameter in inches.

The door is 3 feet, or 36 inches wide. The frame around the window uses 6 inches on each side, so there are $36 - 6 - 6 = 24$ inches left for the diameter of the window.

What is the area of the door in square feet if it is 80 inches tall?

$$\cancel{80}^{20} \text{ in.} \cdot \left(\frac{1 \text{ ft.}}{\cancel{3} \, \cancel{12} \text{ in.}}\right) = \frac{20}{3} \text{ ft.} = 6\tfrac{2}{3} \text{ ft. tall}$$

$A = bh$
$A = 3 \text{ ft.} \cdot (\tfrac{20}{3} \text{ ft.}) = 20 \text{ sq. ft.}$

What is the area of the window without the frame in square feet? Use 3.14 for the value of π.

The radius is $24 \div 2 = 12$ inches, or 1 foot.

$A = \pi r^2$
$A = (3.14)(1)^2$
$A = 3.14$ sq. ft.

What is the area of the framed window in square feet? Use 3.14 for the value of π. Round your answer to the nearest square foot.

The radius is $(24 + 6 + 6) \div 2 = 36 \div 2 = 18$ inches or 1.5 feet.

$A = \pi r^2$
$A = (3.14)(1.5)^2$
$A = 7.065 = 7$ sq. ft.

Duncan must remove an area of the door equal to half the framed window to complete the construction. What percent of the area of the door must Duncan remove?

Half of the framed window is 3.5 square feet.

Duncan must remove $3\tfrac{1}{2} \div 20 = 17.5\%$ of the area of the door.

Teaching Tips, Cont.

➤ Tell the students they can check their work by multiplying the quotient by the divisor. If they get the dividend as their answer, their work is correct.

➤ Complete the Classwork exercises. Have some students work the problems on the board for the class and explain their answers. All students should work the problems in their books.

➤ Give the students the formula strip for Lesson 139 from the *Tests and Resources* book.

Assignment

- Complete Lesson 139, Activities 2-4.

Lesson 140

Concepts
- Flips
- Graphing points
- Scale drawings
- Math in the real world

Learning Objectives
The student will be able to:
- Define *flip*
- Graph a flip over the *x*-axis
- Graph a flip over the *y*-axis

Materials Needed
- Student Book, Lesson 140
- Worksheet 70
- Graph paper

Teaching Tips
➢ Review the coordinate plane. (See Lesson 108.)

➢ Ask the students what it means to transform something. (To change it.) Tell them that they will be learning several different ways to transform, or change, a graph.

➢ Introduce flips as the first transformation. Explain that while a graph may be flipped over any line, this book will focus only on flips over the two axes.

➢ Teach flips from the teaching box. Students should memorize the changes to the coordinates for each transformation.

Flips

A **flip** is a transformation in which an image is reflected over a line. The simplest flips are those reflected over the *x*-axis or the *y*-axis.

To find the coordinate points for an image flipped over the *x*-axis, multiply each *y*-coordinate by -1. The *x*-coordinates stay the same.

To find the coordinate points for an image flipped over the *y*-axis, multiply each *x*-coordinate by -1. The *y*-coordinates stay the same.

Graph the line segment that joins points (1, 3) and (2, 5) in blue. Calculate the coordinates of the flip over the *y*-axis and draw its graph in red on the same Cartesian plane.

The new coordinates are (-1, 3) and (-2, 5).

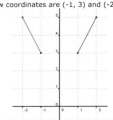

① **Classwork**
Graph.

Graph the line segment that joins points (2, 3) and (1, 5) in blue. Calculate the coordinates of the flip over the *x*-axis and draw its graph in green on the same Cartesian plane. Calculate the coordinates of the flip of the original segment over the *y*-axis and draw its graph in red on the same Cartesian plane.

The coordinates of the flip over the *x*-axis are (-2, 3) and (-1, 5).
The new coordinates of the flip over the *x*-axis are (2, -3) and (1, -5).

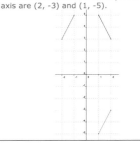

Activities
② Graph on your own graph paper on a single Cartesian plane.
Plot the points (4, 0), (4, 3), and (2, 4), and plot the flip of the points over the *x*-axis. Plot the flip of the original points over the *y*-axis. Plot the flip of the last set of points over the *x*-axis. (You should have points in all four quadrants.) Draw line segments to connect the plotted points, beginning on the positive *x*-axis and moving through all four quadrants in order, returning to the positive *x*-axis. Plot the point (2, 2) and plot the flip of the point over the *y*-axis. Plot the points (2, -1) and (1, -2) and plot the flip over

the *y*-axis. Draw line segments to join the four points in order from the lowest *x*-coordinate to the highest *x*-coordinate.

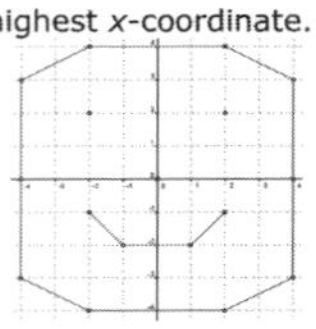

Plot the point (0, 0).

③ Solve.
Blueprints are drawn to a ¼-inch scale. This means that every ¼ inch on the blueprint represents 1 foot in real life. If the blueprint shows a window starting ¾ inch away from a corner, how much space must Duncan allow between the window and the corner?

$\frac{¼ \text{ in.}}{1 \text{ ft.}} = \frac{¾ \text{ in.}}{x \text{ ft.}}$

$¼ x = ¾$

$4(¼ x) = 4(¾)$

$x = 3$ ft.

If a bedroom on the blueprint is $2\frac{3}{4}$ in. × $3\frac{1}{2}$ in., what are the actual dimensions of the bedroom?

$\frac{¼ \text{ in.}}{1 \text{ ft.}} = \frac{2¾ \text{ in.}}{x \text{ ft.}}$ $\frac{¼ \text{ in.}}{1 \text{ ft.}} = \frac{3½ \text{ in.}}{x \text{ ft.}}$

$¼ x = 2¾$ $¼ x = 3½$

$¼ x = 11/4$ $¼ x = 7/2$

$4(¼ x) = 4(11/4)$ $4(¼ x) = 4(7/2)$

$x = 11$ ft. $x = 14$ ft.

The room is 11 feet × 14 feet.
If a living room is 16 feet × 22 feet, what should the measurements be on the blueprint?

$\frac{¼ \text{ in.}}{1 \text{ ft.}} = \frac{x \text{ in.}}{16 \text{ ft.}}$ $\frac{¼ \text{ in.}}{1 \text{ ft.}} = \frac{x \text{ in.}}{22 \text{ ft.}}$

$¼(16) = x$ $¼(22) = x$

$x = 4$ in. $x = \frac{22}{4} = 5\frac{2}{4} = 5\frac{1}{2}$ in.

The blueprint should be 4 in. $× 5\frac{1}{2}$ in.
Choose a room in your house or school. Draw a blueprint of that room. Mark the location of walls, doors, windows, and fireplaces. Label each scale measurement on the drawing with the actual measurement in the format $3\frac{1}{2}$ in. = 14 ft.

Answers will vary. Teachers should check to ensure drawings are reasonable.

Division of Polynomials, FOIL   Worksheet 70

① Multiply, using the FOIL method.

$(x+2)(x+3)$
$x(x)+x(3)+2(x)+2(3)=$
$x^2+3x+2x+6=x^2+5x+6$

$(x+4)(x-3)$
$x(x)+x(-3)+4(x)+4(-3)=$
$x^2-3x+4x-12=x^2+x-12$

$(x+4)(x-1)$
$x(x)+x(-1)+4(x)+4(-1)=$
$x^2-x+4x-4=x^2+3x-4$

$(2x+5)(x-4)$
$2x(x)+2x(-4)+5(x)+5(-4)=$
$2x^2-8x+5x-20=2x^2-3x-20$

$(2x-3)(x-1)$
$2x(x)+2x(-1)-3(x)-3(-1)=$
$2x^2-2x-3x+3=2x^2-5x+3$

$(2x+7)(3x-4)$
$2x(3x)+2x(-4)+7(3x)+7(-4)=$
$6x^2-8x+21x-28=6x^2+13x-28$

$(3x+1)(x-4)$
$3x(x)+3x(-4)+1(x)+1(-4)=$
$3x^2-12x+x-4=3x^2-11x-4$

$(2x-6)(4x+3)$
$2x(4x)+2x(3)-6(4x)-6(3)=$
$8x^2+6x-24x-18=8x^2-18x-18$

② Divide.

$(x^2-5x+6)\div(x-2)$

$$\begin{array}{r} x-3 \\ x-2\overline{)x^2-5x+6} \\ \underline{x^2-2x} \\ -3x+6 \\ \underline{-3x+6} \end{array}$$

$(2x^2+5x+2)\div(x+2)$

$$\begin{array}{r} 2x+1 \\ x+2\overline{)2x^2+5x+2} \\ \underline{2x^2+4x} \\ +x+2 \\ \underline{x+2} \end{array}$$

$(6x^2-7x+2)\div(3x-2)$

$$\begin{array}{r} 2x-1 \\ 3x-2\overline{)6x^2-7x+2} \\ \underline{6x^2-4x} \\ -3x+2 \\ \underline{-3x+2} \end{array}$$

$(x^2+x-6)\div(x-2)$

$$\begin{array}{r} x+3 \\ x-2\overline{)x^2+x-6} \\ \underline{x^2-2x} \\ 3x-6 \\ \underline{3x-6} \end{array}$$

$(3x^2+4x-4)\div(x+2)$

$$\begin{array}{r} 3x-2 \\ x+2\overline{)3x^2+4x-4} \\ \underline{3x^2+6x} \\ -2x-4 \\ \underline{-2x-4} \end{array}$$

$(8x^2+10x-3)\div(2x+3)$

$$\begin{array}{r} 4x-1 \\ 2x+3\overline{)8x^2+10x-3} \\ \underline{8x^2+12x} \\ -2x-3 \\ \underline{-2x-3} \end{array}$$

Teaching Tips, Cont.

➢ Show the students how to change the coordinates to flip over the *x*-axis and the *y*-axis.

➢ Complete the Classwork exercises. Have some students work the problems on the board for the class and explain their answers. All students should work the problems in their books.

Assignments

- Complete Lesson 140, Activities 2-3.
- Worksheet 70.
- Study for Test 14. (Lessons 128-137)

Test 14

Testing Objectives

The student will:
- Add polynomials
- Subtract polynomials
- Identify polynomials, constants, monomials, binomials, and trinomials
- Multiply monomials
- Multiply monomials by trinomials
- Multiply binomials
- Divide monomials
- Divide binomials by monomials

Materials Needed
- Test 14
- *It's College Test Prep Time!* from Student Book
- *A Math Minute with…* David G. from Student Book

Teaching Tips
➢ Administer Test 14, allowing the students 30-40 minutes to complete the test.

➢ When all students are finished taking the test, introduce *It's College Test Prep Time* from the student book. This page may be completed in class or assigned as homework.

Test 14

① Add. **9 points**

$$6x^2 + 7x + 5$$
$$+\ 2x^2 + 3x + 1$$
$$8x^2 + 10x + 6$$

$$6x^2 + 4x + 3$$
$$+x^2 - 5x - 2$$
$$7x^2 - \ x + 1$$

$$4x^2 - 2x + 6$$
$$+5x^2 + 1x - 2$$
$$9x^2 - \ x + 4$$

$$3x^2 + 4x + 6$$
$$+\ 2x^2 + 7x + 4$$
$$5x^2 + 11x + 10$$

$$3x^2 + 4x + 8$$
$$+x^2 - 6x - 3$$
$$4x^2 - 2x + 5$$

$$6x^2 - 7x + 3$$
$$+2x^2 + 4x - 7$$
$$8x^2 - 3x - 4$$

$$4x^2 + 5x + 2$$
$$+\ 7x^2 + 3x + 8$$
$$11x^2 + 8x + 10$$

$$2x^2 + 5x + 3$$
$$+x^2 - 7x - 9$$
$$3x^2 - 2x - 6$$

$$4x^2 - 5x + 3$$
$$+6x^2 + 7x - 8$$
$$10x^2 + 2x - 5$$

② Subtract. **9 points**

$$(7x^2 + 3x + 5)$$
$$-(3x^2 + 2x + 1)$$
$$4x^2 + \ x + 4$$

$$(4x^2 - 6x + 5)$$
$$-(x^2 - 4x - 1)$$
$$3x^2 - 2x + 6$$

$$(3x^2 - 4x - 2)$$
$$-(5x^2 + 2x - 3)$$
$$-2x^2 - 6x + 1$$

$$(2x^2 + 4x + 5)$$
$$-(3x^2 + 2x + 1)$$
$$-x^2 + 2x + 4$$

$$(2x^2 - 7x + 6)$$
$$-(x^2 - 4x - 1)$$
$$x^2 - 3x + 7$$

$$(5x^2 - 1x - 3)$$
$$-(3x^2 + 2x - 3)$$
$$-2x^2 - 3x + 0$$

$$(x^2 + 2x + 7)$$
$$-(4x^2 + 7x + 3)$$
$$-3x^2 - 5x + 4$$

$$(4x^2 - 7x + 2)$$
$$-(x^2 - 4x - 1)$$
$$3x^2 - 3x + 3$$

$$(2x^2 - 5x - 3)$$
$$-(5x^2 + 2x - 8)$$
$$-3x^2 - 7x + 5$$

③ Identify whether or not each expression is a polynomial. For each polynomial, identify it as a constant, monomial, binomial, or trinomial. **13 points**

$9x - 5$ This is a polynomial and a binomial.

$3x^2 + \frac{Z}{x} - 4$ This is not a polynomial because the x is in the denominator.

$4x^{-2} + 3$ This is not a polynomial because there is a negative exponent.

71 This is a polynomial, a monomial, and a constant.

$9x^2 - 5x + 7$ This is a polynomial and a trinomial.

$-2x$ This is a polynomial and a monomial.

Test 14

④ Multiply. **15 points**

$5x(7xy^2)$
$(5 \cdot 7)(x^{1+1})(y^2) = 35x^2y^2$

$8x^2(3xy^2)$
$(8 \cdot 3)(x^{2+1})(y^2) = 24x^3y^2$

$x^3(6xy^2)$
$(1 \cdot 6)(x^{3+1})(y^2) = 6x^4y^2$

$3x(11x^2y^2)$
$(3 \cdot 11)(x^{2+1})(y^2) = 33x^3y^2$

$9x^2(6x^2y^2)$
$(9 \cdot 6)(x^{2+2})(y^2) = 54x^4y^2$

$8x^3(5x^2y^2)$
$(8 \cdot 5)(x^{3+2})(y^2) = 40x^5y^2$

$9x^3(2x^2y^4)$
$(9 \cdot 2)(x^{3+2})(y^4) = 18x^5y^4$

$4x(2x^2 + 6x - 9)$
$4x(2x^2) + 4x(6x) + 4x(-9) =$
$8x^1 + 24x^2 - 36x$

$6x(3x^2 - 7x + 8)$
$6x(3x^2) + 6x(-7x) + 6x(8) =$
$18x^3 - 42x^2 + 48x$

$7x(3x^2 - 4x + 9)$
$7x(3x^2) + 7x(-4x) + 7x(9) =$
$21x^3 - 28x^2 + 63x$

$4x(2x^2 + 7x - 3)$
$4x(2x^2) + 4x(7x) + 4x(-3) =$
$8x^3 + 28x^2 - 12x$

$(x + 5)(x - 4)$
$x(x) + x(-4) + 5(x) + 5(-4) =$
$x^2 - 4x + 5x - 20 = x^2 + x - 20$

$(2x + 1)(x - 4)$
$2x(x) + 2x(-4) + 1(x) + 1(-4) =$
$2x^2 - 8x + x - 4 = 2x^2 - 7x - 4$

$(2x + 3)(3x - 5)$
$2x(3x) + 2x(-5) + 3(3x) + 3(-5) =$
$6x^2 - 10x + 9x - 15 = 6x^2 - x - 15$

$(5x - 6)(3x + 4)$
$5x(3x) + 5x(4) - 6(3x) - 6(4) =$
$15x^2 + 20x - 18x - 24 = 15x^2 + 2x - 24$

⑤ Divide. **11 points**

$9x^4y^3 \div 3xy^2$

$\frac{9x^4y^3}{3xy^2} = 3x^{4-1}y^{3-2} = 3x^3y$

$18x^3y^3 \div 2x^2y^2$

$\frac{18x^3y^3}{2x^2y^2} = 9x^{3-2}y^{3-2} = 9xy$

$30x^4y^2 \div 5x^2y^2$

$\frac{30x^4y^2}{5x^2y^2} = 6x^{4-2}y^{2-2} = 6x^2$

$24x^5y^4 \div 3x^2y^2$

$\frac{24x^5y^4}{3x^2y^2} = 8x^{5-2}y^{4-2} = 8x^3y^2$

$32x^5y^4 \div 8x^2y^3$

$\frac{32x^5y^4}{8x^2y^3} = 4x^{5-2}y^{4-3} = 4x^3y$

$(9x + 3) \div 3$

$$\begin{array}{r} 3x + 1 \\ 3\overline{)9x + 3} \\ \underline{9x} \\ 3 \\ \underline{3} \end{array}$$

$(12x - 8) \div 4$

$$\begin{array}{r} 3x - 2 \\ 4\overline{)12x - 8} \\ \underline{12x} \\ -8 \\ \underline{-8} \end{array}$$

$(15x - 5) \div 5$

$$\begin{array}{r} 3x - 1 \\ 5\overline{)15x - 5} \\ \underline{15x} \\ -5 \\ \underline{-5} \end{array}$$

$(10x + 8) \div 2$

$$\begin{array}{r} 5x + 4 \\ 2\overline{)10x + 8} \\ \underline{10x} \\ 8 \\ \underline{8} \end{array}$$

$(18x - 12) \div 6$

$$\begin{array}{r} 3x - 2 \\ 6\overline{)18x - 12} \\ \underline{18x} \\ -12 \\ \underline{-12} \end{array}$$

$(24x - 9) \div 3$

$$\begin{array}{r} 8x - 3 \\ 3\overline{)24x - 9} \\ \underline{24x} \\ -9 \\ \underline{-9} \end{array}$$

57 points total

It's College Test Prep Time!

1. Given $f(x) = 2x^2 + x - 1$, what is the value of $f(5)$?

   A. 14
   B. <u>54</u> $2(5)^2 + 5 - 1 = 2(25) + 5 - 1 = 50 + 5 - 1 = 54$
   C. 58
   D. 104
   E. 108

2. Which of the following (x, y) coordinates is a solution of the equation $2x + 5y = -4$?

   A. (-3, -2)
   B. (-2, 3)
   C. (2, -3)
   D. <u>(3, -2)</u> $2(3) + 5(-2) = 6 - 10 = -4$
   E. (3, 2)

3. Given $(x - 2)^2 = 16$, find the value of $(x + 2)(x - 3)$.

   A. -4
   B. 6 $\sqrt{(x-2)^2} = \sqrt{16}$
   C. <u>24</u> $x - 2 = 4$
   D. 176 $x = 6$
   E. 300 $(6 + 2)(6 - 3) = 8(3) = 24$

Assignments

- Complete *It's College Test Prep Time!*
- Read *A Math Minute with...* David G.

A Math Minute with . . .

David G. – HVAC

What is your occupation? Heating, Ventilation, and Air Conditioning

Where do you work? I work at a prison and I am also self-employed.

Did you attend college? If so, what was your major? Yes. Heating and Air Conditioning at a technical college

What parts of your job require the use of math? The HVAC business involves the use of many formulas. For example, I need to calculate the RPM's, airflow and horsepower for motors. I also need to size the duct work when installing a unit so there is the right amount of area for the air to flow for the amount of space that is heated or cooled. Math is also involved in figuring out the cost of parts and labor to determine what to charge a customer.

What is the biggest "problem" you have faced that required the use of math to solve? Designing systems for newly constructed buildings is very challenging. I need to take into consideration the square footage of the building, the distance the air must travel through the duct work, and the proper size of ductwork for each section of the building.

Are there any other interesting math uses you have experienced? Calculating the pressure for a water system is interesting as well as challenging. Changing the height of a water tank affects the force of the water in the system. Raising a water tank increases the force of the water while lowering the tank decreases the force.

Lesson 141

Concepts
- Turns
- Divisibility tests
- Prime/composite numbers
- Volume of prisms
- Math in the real world

Learning Objectives
The student will be able to:
- Define *turn*
- Calculate the coordinates of turns 90° clockwise and counterclockwise on a coordinate plane
- Calculate the coordinates of turns 180° on a coordinate plane
- Draw the graphs of images turned on the coordinate plane

Materials Needed
- Student Book, Lesson 141
- Blue, red, green, and orange colored pencils
- Graph paper

Teaching Tips
➤ Review flips. (See Lesson 140.)

➤ Introduce turns as the second transformation. Explain that a graph can be turned any amount in any direction about any point, but this book will focus only on turns about the origin 180° or 90° clockwise and counterclockwise.

➤ Teach turns from the teaching box. Students should memorize the changes to the coordinates for each transformation.

Turns

A **turn** is a transformation in which an image pivots about a single point. The easiest turns to calculate are those that turn 90° or 180° about the origin.

To find the coordinate points for an image turned 90° counterclockwise about the origin, use the formula $(x,y) \rightarrow (-y,x)$

To find the coordinate points for an image turned 90° clockwise about the origin, use the formula $(x,y) \rightarrow (y,-x)$

To find the coordinate points for an image turned 180° about the origin, use the formula $(x,y) \rightarrow (-x,-y)$

Graph the figure formed by joining points (1, 3), (2, 2), and (2, 5) in blue. Calculate the coordinates of the figure turned 90° counterclockwise about the origin and draw its graph in red on the same Cartesian plane.

The new coordinates are (-3, 1) and (-2, 2), and (-5, 2).

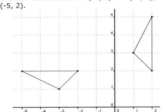

① Classwork
Graph the figure formed by joining points (1, 1), (2, 1), and (1, 4) in blue. Calculate the coordinates of the figure turned 90° clockwise about the origin and draw its graph in red on the same Cartesian plane.

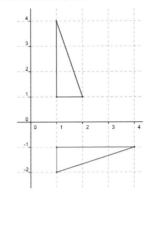

Activities
② Graph the following figures on a single Cartesian plane. Graph the points (2, 1), (3, 1), (3, 3), and (1, 2) in blue. Join them to form a quadrilateral. Graph the image turned 90° clockwise about the origin in red. Graph the image turned 90° counterclockwise about the origin in green. Graph the image turned 180° about the origin in orange.

③ Use the divisibility tests to identify each number as prime or composite.

509	Prime	519	Composite (3)
513	Composite (3, 9)	521	Prime
515	Composite (5)	523	Prime

④ Solve.

David is installing an attic ventilation fan for a customer. If the attic is a right triangular prism as shown below, what is the volume of air in the attic?

Area of one triangular side:

$A = \frac{1}{2}bh$

$A = \frac{1}{2}(25 \text{ ft.})(10 \text{ ft.})$

$A = 125$ sq. ft.

Volume of attic:

$V = Bh$

$V = (125 \text{ sq. ft.})(60 \text{ ft.})$

$V = 7500$ cu. ft.

The attic fan moves 1200 cubic feet of air per minute. At this rate, how long will it take the fan to circulate all the air in the attic? Give your answer to the nearest second.

$7500 \div 1200 = 6.25$

Convert 0.25 minutes to seconds.

0.25(60 seconds) = 15 seconds

It will take 6.25 minutes, or 6 minutes 15 seconds to circulate all the air in the attic.

An attic fan cools the attic during the summer and can lower energy bills by 20%. If the customer's energy bills for the summer months without the attic fan were $150, $144, and $162, what should the total energy bill be for the summer months with the attic fan?

Total energy bill without the attic fan: $150 + $144 + $162 = $456

The total energy bill with the attic fan is 100% - 20% = 80% of $456.

$456(0.80) = $364.80

How much money will David's customer save after 3 years of using the attic fan?

The savings in one year is $456 - $364.80 = $91.20

The savings after three years is 3($91.20) = $273.60

If David charges his customer $179 for parts and labor to install an attic fan, what is the total percent savings over a three-year period? Round your answer to the nearest percent.

Net saved over three years: $273.60 - $179 = $94.60

Original energy bill for three years: 3($456) = $1368

Percent saved for three years: $94.60 ÷ $1368 = 7%

What is the total percent savings over a five-year period?

Net saved over five years: $456 - $179 = $277

Original energy bill for five years: 5($456) = $2280

Percent saved for five years: $277 ÷ $2280 = 12%

Teaching Tips, Cont.

➢ Show the students how to change the coordinates to turn the graph about the origin 90° clockwise, 90° counterclockwise, and 180°. Note that turning the graph 180° clockwise is the same result as turning the graph 180° counterclockwise.

➢ Complete the Classwork exercise. Have one student work the problem on the board for the class and explain the answer. All students should work the problem in their books.

Assignment

• Complete Lesson 141, Activities 2-4.

Lesson 142

Concepts
- Slides
- Greatest common factor
- Least common multiple
- Simple interest
- Compound interest
- Temperature conversions

Learning Objectives
The student will be able to:
- Define *slide*
- Calculate the coordinates of slides right, left, up, and down
- Draw the graphs of images that have been slid on the coordinate plane

Materials Needed
- Student Book, Lesson 142
- Worksheet 71
- Blue, red, and green colored pencils
- Calculator
- Graph paper

Teaching Tips
➤ Have students complete Worksheet 71 in class. This may be for added practice of earlier topics or graded as a quiz, if desired.

➤ Review flips and turns. (See Lessons 140-141.)

➤ Introduce slides as the third transformation. Explain that a graph can be slid any amount in any direction, but this book will focus only on horizontal and vertical slides.

Slides

A **slide** is a transformation in which an image moves in a straight line. The easiest slides are those that move horizontally or vertically.

To slide an image to the right u units, use the formula $(x, y) \rightarrow (x + u, y)$

To slide an image to the left u units, use the formula $(x, y) \rightarrow (x - u, y)$

To slide an image up u units, use the formula $(x, y) \rightarrow (x, y + u)$

To slide an image down u units, use the formula $(x, y) \rightarrow (x, y - u)$

Graph the figure formed by joining points (1, 3), (2, 2), and (2, 5) in blue. Calculate the coordinates of the figure when you slide it 2 units to the right and draw its graph in red on the same Cartesian plane.

The new coordinates are (3, 3) and (4, 2), and (4, 5).

① Classwork
Graph the figure formed by joining points (1, 1), (2, 1), and (1, 4) in blue. Calculate the coordinates of the figure when you slide it 4 units to the left and draw its graph in red on the same Cartesian plane.

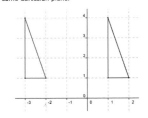

Activities
② Graph the following figures on a single Cartesian plane. Graph the points (2, 1), (3, 1), (3, 3), and (1, 2) in blue. Join them to form a quadrilateral. Graph the image when you slide it 3 units to the left in red. Graph the image when you slide it 4 units down in green.

---

③ Find the greatest common factor of each set of numbers.

28, 32, and 36	18, 36, and 45	18, 30, and 36
$28 = ②\times②\times 7$	$18 = 2 \times ③\times ③$	$18 = ②\times ③\times 3$
$32 = ②\times②\times 2 \times 2 \times 2$	$36 = 2 \times 2 \times ③\times ③$	$30 = ②\times ③\times 5$
$36 = ②\times②\times 3 \times 3$	$45 = ③\times ③\times 5$	$36 = ②\times 2 \times ③\times 3$
GCF: $2 \times 2 = 4$	GCF: $3 \times 3 = 9$	GCF: $2 \times 3 = 6$

④ Find the least common multiple of each set of numbers.

4, 8, and 9	9, 10, and 12	18, 20, and 24
$4 = 2 \times 2$	$9 = 3 \times 3 = \boxed{3^2}$	$18 = 2 \times 3 \times 3 = 2 \times \boxed{3^2}$
$8 = 2 \times 2 \times 2 = \boxed{2^3}$	$10 = 2 \times \boxed{5}$	$20 = 2 \times 2 \times 5 = 2^2 \times \boxed{5}$
$9 = 3 \times 3 = \boxed{3^2}$	$12 = 2 \times 2 \times 3 = \boxed{2^2} \times 3$	$24 = 2 \times 2 \times 2 \times 3 = \boxed{2^3} \times 3$
LCM: $2^3 \times 3^2 = 72$	LCM: $2^2 \times 3^2 \times 5 = 180$	LCM: $2^3 \times 3^2 \times 5 = 360$

⑤ Complete the chart to show simple interest and interest compounded annually.

Principal	Interest rate	Time, in years	Total amount of simple interest	Balance, compounded annually
$10,500	7.5%	5	$i = \$10,500(0.075)(5) = \$3937.50$	$A = \$10,500(1 + 0.075)^5$ $= \$15,074.11$
$18,250	10.25%	10	$i = \$18,250(0.1025)(10) = \$18,706.25$	$A = \$18,250(1 + 0.1025)^{10}$ $= \$48,422.68$
$99,900	4.625%	30	$i = \$99,900(0.04625)(30) = \$138,611.25$	$A = \$99,900(1 + 0.04625)^{30}$ $= \$387,819.48$

⑥ Solve. Round answers to the nearest tenth where appropriate.

°F	°C
15°	$°C = (15° - 32°)\left(\frac{5}{9}\right) = -9.4°$
35°	$°C = (35° - 32°)\left(\frac{5}{9}\right) = 1.7°$
45°	$°C = (45° - 32°)\left(\frac{5}{9}\right) = 7.2°$
65°	$°C = (65° - 32°)\left(\frac{5}{9}\right) = 18.3°$
85°	$°C = (85° - 32°)\left(\frac{5}{9}\right) = 29.4°$
125°	$°C = (125° - 32°)\left(\frac{5}{9}\right) = 51.7°$
140°	$°C(140° - 32°)\left(\frac{5}{9}\right) = 60°$

°C	°F
15°	$°F = (15°)\left(\frac{9}{5}\right) + 32° = 18° + 32° = 59°$
35°	$°F = (35°)\left(\frac{9}{5}\right) + 32° = 45° + 32° = 95°$
45°	$°F = (45°)\left(\frac{9}{5}\right) + 32° = 72° + 32° = 113°$
65°	$°F = (65°)\left(\frac{9}{5}\right) + 32° = 108° + 32° = 149°$
85°	$°F = (85°)\left(\frac{9}{5}\right) + 32° = 144° + 32° = 185°$
125°	$°F = (125°)\left(\frac{9}{5}\right) + 32° = 216° + 32° = 257°$
140°	$°F = (140°)\left(\frac{9}{5}\right) + 32° = 243° + 32° = 284°$

① Divide.

$$\begin{array}{r} x+4 \\ x+2\overline{\smash{\big)}\,x^2+6x+8} \\ \underline{x^2+2x} \\ 4x+8 \\ \underline{4x+8} \end{array}$$

$$\begin{array}{r} x+5 \\ x-3\overline{\smash{\big)}\,x^2+2x-15} \\ \underline{x^2-3x} \\ 5x-15 \\ \underline{5x-15} \end{array}$$

$$\begin{array}{r} 3x+2 \\ x-7\overline{\smash{\big)}\,3x^2-19x-14} \\ \underline{3x^2-21x} \\ 2x-14 \\ \underline{2x-14} \end{array}$$

$(x^2+15x+54)\div(x+6)$ $(x^2-3x-4)\div(x+1)$ $(6x^2+x-12)\div(3x-4)$

$$\begin{array}{r} x+9 \\ x+6\overline{\smash{\big)}\,x^2+15x+54} \\ \underline{x^2+6x} \\ 9x+54 \\ \underline{9x+54} \end{array}$$

$$\begin{array}{r} x-4 \\ x+1\overline{\smash{\big)}\,x^2-3x-4} \\ \underline{x^2+\ x} \\ -4x+4 \\ \underline{-4x+4} \end{array}$$

$$\begin{array}{r} 2x+3 \\ 3x-4\overline{\smash{\big)}\,6x^2+\ x-12} \\ \underline{6x^2-8x} \\ 9x-12 \\ \underline{9x-12} \end{array}$$

$(3x^2-14x-24)\div(x-6)$ $(2x^2-11x+15)\div(x-3)$ $(10x^2-39x-27)\div(2x-9)$

$$\begin{array}{r} 3x+4 \\ x-6\overline{\smash{\big)}\,3x^2-14x-24} \\ \underline{3x^2-18x} \\ 4x-24 \\ \underline{4x-24} \end{array}$$

$$\begin{array}{r} 2x-5 \\ x-3\overline{\smash{\big)}\,2x^2-11x+15} \\ \underline{2x^2-6x} \\ -5x+15 \\ \underline{-5x+15} \end{array}$$

$$\begin{array}{r} 5x+3 \\ 2x-9\overline{\smash{\big)}\,10x^2-39x-27} \\ \underline{10x^2-45x} \\ 6x-27 \\ \underline{6x-27} \end{array}$$

② Multiply.

$(x+6)(x-7)$
$x(x)+x(-7)+6(x)+6(-7)=$
$x^2-7x+6x-42=x^2-x-42$

$(2x+5)(3x-8)$
$2x(3x)+2x(-8)+5(3x)+5(-8)=$
$6x^2-16x+15x-40=6x^2-x-40$

$(2x+1)(x-6)$
$2x(x)+2x(-6)+1(x)+1(-6)=$
$2x^2-12x+x-6=2x^2-11x-6$

$(2x-5)(4x+3)$
$2x(4x)+2x(3)-5(4x)-5(3)=$
$8x^2+6x-20x-15=8x^2-14x-15$

Teaching Tips, Cont.

➤ Teach slides from the teaching box. Students should memorize the changes to the coordinates for each transformation.

➤ Show the students how to change the coordinates to slide the graph up, down, left, and right.

➤ Complete the Classwork exercise. Have one student work the problem on the board for the class and explain the answer. All students should work the problem in their books.

Assignment

- Complete Lesson 142, Activities 2-6.

Lesson 143

Concepts
- Scaling
- Enlargements
- Reductions
- Math in the real world

Learning Objectives
The student will be able to:
- Define *scaling*
- Calculate the coordinates enlargements and reductions
- Draw the graphs of images that have been enlarged or reduced on the coordinate plane

Materials Needed
- Student Book, Lesson 143
- Worksheet 72
- Blue, red, and green colored pencils
- Graph paper

Teaching Tips
➤ Review flips, turns, and slides. (See Lessons 140-142.)

➤ Introduce scaling as the fourth transformation. Explain that a scale drawing can be made of any graph by enlarging or reducing it.

➤ Teach scaling from the teaching box. Students should memorize the changes to the coordinates for each transformation.

➤ Show the students how to change the coordinates to enlarge a graph.

Scaling

Scaling is a transformation in which a figure is enlarged or reduced.

To enlarge an image, multiply both the *x*- and *y*-coordinates by a number greater than 1.

To reduce an image, multiply both the *x*- and *y*-coordinates by a positive number less than one. (This is the same thing as dividing by a number greater than 1.)

Graph the figure formed by joining points (1, 3), (2, 2), and (2, 5) in blue. Calculate the coordinates of the figure when you scale it by a factor of 2 and draw its graph in red on the same Cartesian plane.

The new coordinates are (2, 6) and (4, 4), and (4, 10).

① **Classwork**
Graph the figure formed by joining points (2, 2), (4, 2), and (2, 8) in blue. Calculate the coordinates of the figure when you scale it by a factor of ½ and draw its graph in red on the same Cartesian plane.

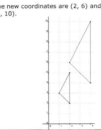

Activities
② Graph the following figures on a single Cartesian plane. Graph the figure formed by joining points (2, 2), (4, 0), and (6, 4) in blue. Calculate the coordinates of the figure when you scale it by a factor of ½ and draw its graph in red. Calculate the coordinates of the figure when you scale it by a factor of 2 and draw its graph in green.

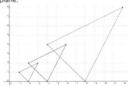

---

③ Solve.
David is installing an air conditioner and filter system for a customer. The customer wants a system with two 25-inch square return air vents. What is the area of one air vent? Give your answer in square inches and in square feet. Round answers to the nearest hundredth where necessary.
(25 inches)(25 inches) = 625 square inches
There are (12 inches)(12 inches) = 144 square inches in a square foot.
625 ÷ 144 = 4.34 square feet in one air vent
How many square feet are in two air vents?
(4.34 square feet)(2) = 8.68 square feet
A return air vent can expect to have 75% of its area available for free air movement. What is the area of free air movement for two air vents?
(0.75)(8.68 square feet) = 6.51 square feet
An air conditioner filter reduces the effective area of free air movement by 25%. What is the effective area of free air movement for this system at the filter? Round your answer to the nearest hundredth.
(1 – 0.25)(6.51 square feet) = (0.75)(6.51 square feet) = 4.88 square feet
If the air conditioner blows 1600 cubic feet per minute, how many feet of air are moving across the filters each minute?
1600 cubic feet ÷ 4.88 square feet = 327.87 feet
An air conditioner system should have less than 300 feet of air moving across a filter each minute. Will a system that blows 1600 cubic feet of air per minute work with these two return air vents? Why or why not?
No. The return air vents do not allow enough area for free air movement. The customer should either install more return air vents or larger return air vents to increase the area of free air movement, or install a smaller air conditioner that does not blow as many cubic feet of air per minute.
What is the minimum number of square feet of free air movement this system requires?
$\frac{1600 \text{ cubic feet}}{x \text{ square feet}} < 300$ feet

1600 cubic feet < 300 feet(x square feet)

$\frac{1600 \text{ cubic feet}}{300 \text{ feet}} < x$

$\frac{15}{3}$ square feet or $5\frac{1}{3}$ square feet < x
What is the minimum number of square inches of free air movement this system requires?
$\frac{15}{3}$ square feet(144 square inches/square foot) = 768 square inches

Remember that the number of square inches of free air movement is reduced by 25% when it crosses the filter. Calculate the minimum number of square inches of free air movement the return air vents must have in this system.
768 square inches < 0.75x

x > 1024 square inches
Keeping in mind that the number of square inches of free air movement represents 75% of the surface area of the return air vent, how many square inches of return air vents must be installed for this air conditioning system?
1024 square inches < 0.75x

x > $1365\frac{1}{3}$ square inches

① Plot the given points in blue and join them to form a polygon. Graph the flip over the *x*-axis in green and the flip over the *y*-axis in red.

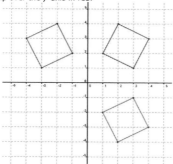

(1, 2), (3, 1), (4, 3), and (2, 4)

② Plot the given points in blue and join them to form a polygon. Graph the turn 90° counterclockwise in green and the turn 90° clockwise in red.

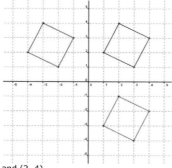

(1, 2), (3, 1), (4, 3), and (2, 4)

Teaching Tips, Cont.

➤ Show the students how to change the coordinates to reduce a graph.

➤ Complete the Classwork exercise. Have one student work the problem on the board for the class and explain the answer. All students should work the problem in their books.

Assignments

- Complete Lesson 143, Activities 2-3.
- Worksheet 72.

Lesson 144

Concepts
- Reflections
- Flips
- Adding polynomials
- Subtracting polynomials
- Multiplying polynomials by monomials
- Dividing polynomials by monomials

Learning Objectives
The student will be able to:
- Define *reflection*
- Calculate the coordinates of an image reflected over the *x*-axis and the *y*-axis
- Draw the graph of a reflection over the *x*-axis and the *y*-axis on the coordinate plane

Materials Needed
- Student Book, Lesson 144
- Blue, red, and green colored pencils
- Graph paper

Teaching Tips
➢ Ask the students to name and describe the four transformations they have learned so far. (Flips – transformations in which an image is reflected over a line; turns – transformations in which an image pivots about a single point; slides – transformations in which an image moves in a straight line; and scaling – transformations in which a figure is enlarged or reduced.)

➢ Explain that each of the transformations has a "mathematical" name.

➢ Introduce *reflections* as the mathematical name for *flips*.

Reflections

A **reflection** is another term for a flip. All of the rules for flips apply to reflections.

To find the coordinate points for an image reflected about the *x*-axis, multiply each *x*-coordinate by -1. The *y*-coordinates stay the same.

To find the coordinate points for an image reflected about the *y*-axis, multiply each *y*-coordinate by -1. The *x*-coordinates stay the same.

Graph the line segment that joins points (1, 3) and (2, 5) in blue. Draw the reflection about the *x*-axis and draw its graph in red on the same Cartesian plane.

The new coordinates are (-1, 3) and (-2, 5).

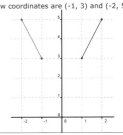

① Classwork
Solve.

Graph the line segment that joins points (2, 3) and (1, 5) in blue. Draw the reflection about the *x*-axis in green on the same Cartesian plane. Draw the reflection of the original segment about the *y*-axis in red on the same Cartesian plane.

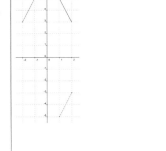

Activities
② Graph the following figures on a single Cartesian plane. Graph the points (2, 1), (3, 1), (3, 3), and (1, 2) in blue. Join them to form a quadrilateral. Graph the reflection about the *y*-axis in red. Graph the reflection about the *x*-axis in green.

③ Add.

$$6x^2 + 2x - 7$$
$$\underline{+\ 5x^2 + 5x + 3}$$
$$11x^2 + 7x - 4$$

$$8x^2 + 3x + 4$$
$$\underline{+7x^2 - 8x - 9}$$
$$15x^2 - 5x - 5$$

$$7x^2 - 3x - 5$$
$$\underline{+9x^2 + 8x - 9}$$
$$16x^2 + 5x - 14$$

$$4x^2 + 6x + 8$$
$$\underline{+\ 5x^2 + 7x - 9}$$
$$9x^2 + 13x - 1$$

$$3x^2 + 2x + 6$$
$$\underline{+9x^2 - 7x - 8}$$
$$12x^2 - 5x - 2$$

$$9x^2 - 2x + 4$$
$$\underline{+9x^2 - 7x - 8}$$
$$18x^2 - 9x - 4$$

④ Subtract.

$$(6x^2 + 3x + 9)$$
$$\underline{-(3x^2 + 5x - 7)}$$
$$3x^2 - 2x + 16$$

$$(5x^2 - 7x + 6)$$
$$\underline{-(2x^2 - 4x - 5)}$$
$$3x^2 - 3x + 11$$

$$(7x^2 - 9x - 9)$$
$$\underline{-(4x^2 + 5x - 2)}$$
$$3x^2 - 14x - 7$$

$$(3x^2 + 6x + 5)$$
$$\underline{-(7x^2 - 8x + 3)}$$
$$-4x^2 + 14x + 2$$

$$(4x^2 + 2x - 5)$$
$$\underline{-(9x^2 - 5x - 6)}$$
$$-5x^2 + 7x + 1$$

$$(2x^2 - 4x - 3)$$
$$\underline{-(8x^2 - 9x - 7)}$$
$$-6x^2 + 5x + 4$$

⑤ Multiply.

$$3x(5x^2 + 3x - 4)$$
$$3x(5x^2) + 3x(3x) + 3x(-4) =$$
$$15x^3 + 9x^2 - 12x$$

$$6x(7x^2 - 4x + 8)$$
$$6x(7x^2) + 6x(-4x) + 6x(8) =$$
$$42x^3 - 24x^2 + 48x$$

$$5x^2(2x^2 - 6x + 4)$$
$$5x^2(2x^2) + 5x^2(-6x) + 5x^2(4) =$$
$$10x^4 - 30x^3 + 20x^2$$

$$7x^2(7x^2 + 5x - 9)$$
$$7x^2(7x^2) + 7x^2(5x) + 7x^2(-9) =$$
$$49x^4 + 35x^3 - 63x^2$$

⑥ Divide.

$$(10x + 15) \div 5$$

$$5\overline{)10x + 15} \quad \to \quad 2x + 3$$
$$10x$$
$$15$$
$$15$$

$$(18x - 27) \div 9$$

$$9\overline{)18x - 27} \quad \to \quad 2x - 3$$
$$18x$$
$$-27$$
$$-27$$

$$(16x - 32) \div 4$$

$$4\overline{)16x - 32} \quad \to \quad 4x - 8$$
$$16x$$
$$-32$$
$$-32$$

$$(14x^2 - 7x + 21) \div 7$$

$$7\overline{)14x^2 - 7x + 21} \quad \to \quad 2x^2 - x + 3$$
$$14x^2$$
$$-7x$$
$$-7x$$
$$21$$
$$21$$

$$(10x^4 + 6x^3 - 8x^2) \div 2x^2$$

$$2x^2\overline{)10x^4 + 6x^3 - 8x^2} \quad \to \quad 5x^2 + 3x - 4$$
$$10x^4$$
$$6x^3$$
$$6x^3$$
$$-8x^2$$
$$-8x^2$$

$$(12x^5 + 8x^4 - 20x^3) \div 4x$$

$$4x\overline{)12x^5 + 8x^4 - 20x^3} \quad \to \quad 3x^4 + 2x^3 - 5x^2$$
$$12x^5$$
$$8x^4$$
$$8x^4$$
$$-20x^3$$
$$-20x^3$$

Teaching Tips, Cont.

➤ Teach reflections from the teaching box.

➤ Explain that problems involving reflections are worked in exactly the same way as problems involving flips. All of the formulas remain the same.

➤ Show the students how to graph the reflection of an image.

➤ Complete the Classwork exercises. Have some students work the problems on the board for the class and explain their answers. All students should work the problems in their books.

Assignment

• Complete Lesson 144, Activities 2-6.

Lesson 145

Concepts
- Rotations
- Turns
- Math in the real world

Learning Objectives
The student will be able to:
- Define rotation
- Calculate the coordinates of an image rotated about the origin 90° or 180°
- Draw the graph of the rotation of an image on the coordinate plane

Materials Needed
- Student Book, Lesson 145
- Worksheet 73
- Blue, red, green, and orange colored pencils
- Graph paper

Teaching Tips
➤ Have students complete Worksheet 73 in class. This may be for added practice of earlier topics or graded as a quiz, if desired.

➤ Ask the students to name and describe the four transformations they have learned so far. (Flips or reflections – transformations in which an image is reflected over a line; turns – transformations in which an image pivots about a single point; slides – transformations in which an image moves in a straight line; and scaling – transformations in which a figure is enlarged or reduced.)

➤ Introduce *rotations* as the mathematical name for *turns*.

Rotations

A **rotation** is another name for a turn. All the rules of turns apply to rotations.

To find the coordinate points for an image rotated 90° counterclockwise about the origin, use the formula $(x, y) \rightarrow (-y, x)$

To find the coordinate points for an image rotated 90° clockwise about the origin, use the formula $(x, y) \rightarrow (y, -x)$

To find the coordinate points for an image rotated 180° about the origin, use the formula $(x, y) \rightarrow (-x, -y)$

Graph the figure formed by joining points (1, 3), (2, 2), and (2, 5) in blue. Calculate the coordinates of the figure rotated 90° counterclockwise about the origin and draw its graph in red on the same Cartesian plane.

The new coordinates are (-3, 1) and (-2, 2), and (-5, 2).

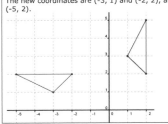

① Classwork
Solve.

Graph the figure formed by joining points (1, 1), (2, 1), and (1, 4) in blue. Calculate the coordinates of the figure rotated 90° clockwise about the origin and draw its graph in red on the same Cartesian plane.

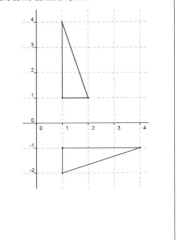

Activities
② Graph the following figures on a single Cartesian plane. Graph the points (2, 1), (3, 1), (3, 3), and (1, 2) in blue. Join them to form a quadrilateral. Graph the image rotated 90° clockwise about the origin in red. Graph the image rotated 90° counterclockwise about the origin in green. Graph the image rotated 180° about the origin in orange.

---

③ Solve.
David is installing an air conditioner system that uses flexible duct with a 12-inch diameter. What is the area of the opening of the flexible duct? Use 3.14 for the value of π. Give your answer to the nearest hundredth.
The radius of the opening is 12 ÷ 2 = 6 inches
$A = \pi r^2$
$A = (3.14)(6 \text{ inches})^2$
$A = (3.14)(36 \text{ square inches})$
$A = 113.04$ square inches

Because of the design of the building, David must install rectangular rigid duct instead of the round flexible duct. If the ratio of the sides of the rectangular duct is 1:2, find, to the nearest inch, the length of the sides of rectangular duct that will allow at least the same area for air flow. (Use a calculator to solve this problem.)
Let x and $2x$ represent the sides of the rectangle.
The area of the rectangle is then $A = x(2x) = 2x^2$.
Set the area of the rectangular duct greater than or equal to the area of the round duct and solve for x.
$2x^2 \geq 113.04$ square inches
$x^2 \geq 56.52$ square inches
$\sqrt{x^2} \geq \sqrt{56.52}$ square inches
$x \geq 7.52$ inches
The short side must be 8 inches, and the long side must be 2(8) = 16 inches.
What is the area of the opening of the rectangular duct?
$A = 8 \text{ inches}(16 \text{ inches})$
$A = 128$ square inches

An air return vent has 75% of its area available for free air movement. What is the minimum area of a return air vent to maximize air flow in the rectangular duct?
Let x = the area of the return air vent.
$0.75x = 128$ square inches
$x = 170\frac{2}{3}$ square inches

David wants to install a return air vent in the same ratio as the duct. What are the minimum dimensions of the return air vent, in whole inches?
Let x and $2x$ represent the sides of the rectangle.
The area of the rectangle is then $A = x(2x) = 2x^2$.
Set the area of the rectangular duct greater than or equal to the area of the round duct and solve for x.
$2x^2 \geq 170\frac{2}{3}$ square inches
$x^2 \geq 85\frac{1}{3}$ square inches
$\sqrt{x^2} \geq \sqrt{85\frac{1}{3}}$ square inches
$x \geq 9.24$ inches
The short side must be 10 inches, and the long side must be 2(10) = 20 inches.

Flips, Turns, Slides   Worksheet 73

① Plot the given points in blue and join them to form a polygon. Graph the flip over the *x*-axis in green and the flip over the *y*-axis in red.

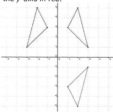

(3, 1), (1, 3), and (2, 5)

② Plot the given points in blue and join them to form a polygon. Graph the turn 90° clockwise in green and the turn 90° counterclockwise in red.

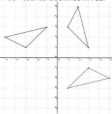

(3, 1), (1, 3), and (2, 5)

③ Plot the given points in blue and join them to form a polygon. Graph the slide down 4 units in green and the slide left 2 units in red.

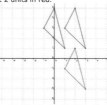

(3, 1), (1, 3), and (2, 5)

Teaching Tips, Cont.

➢ Teach rotations from the teaching box.

➢ Explain that problems involving rotations are worked in exactly the same way as problems involving turns. All of the formulas remain the same.

➢ Show the students how to graph the rotation of an image.

➢ Complete the Classwork exercise. Have one student work the problem on the board for the class and explain the answer. All students should work the problem in their books.

Assignment
• Complete Lesson 145, Activities 2-3.

Lesson 146

Concepts
- Translations
- Slides
- Slope
- y-intercept
- Graphing linear equations
- Systems of equations

Learning Objectives
The student will be able to:
- Define *translation*
- Calculate the coordinates of an image translated up, down, left, or right
- Draw the graph of the translation of an image on the coordinate plane

Materials Needed
- Student Book, Lesson 146
- Blue, red, and green colored pencils
- Graph paper
- Straightedge

Teaching Tips
➢ Ask the students to name and describe the four transformations they have learned so far. (Flips or reflections – transformations in which an image is reflected over a line; turns or rotations – transformations in which an image pivots about a single point; slides – transformations in which an image moves in a straight line; and scaling – transformations in which a figure is enlarged or reduced.)

➢ Introduce *translations* as the mathematical name for *slides*.

Translations

A **translation** is another name for a slide. All the rules of slides apply to translations.

To translate an image right u units, use the formula $(x, y) \rightarrow (x + u, y)$

To translate an image left u units, use the formula $(x, y) \rightarrow (x - u, y)$

To translate an image up u units, use the formula $(x, y) \rightarrow (x, y + u)$

To translate an image down u units, use the formula $(x, y) \rightarrow (x, y - u)$

Graph the figure formed by joining points (1, 3), (2, 2), and (2, 5) in blue. Calculate the coordinates of the figure translated right 2 units and draw its graph in red on the same Cartesian plane.

The new coordinates are (3, 3) and (4, 2), and (4, 5).

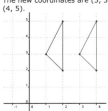

① Classwork
Solve.

Graph the figure formed by joining points (1, 1), (2, 1), and (1, 4) in blue. Calculate the coordinates of the figure translated 4 units to the left and draw its graph in red on the same Cartesian plane.

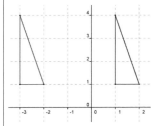

Activities
② Graph the following figures on a single Cartesian plane. Graph the points (2, 1), (3, 1), (3, 3), and (1, 2) in blue. Join them to form a quadrilateral. Graph the image when you translate it 3 units to the left in red. Graph the image when you translate it 4 units down in green.

③ For each equation, identify the slope and y-intercept. Solve each system of equations. Write the solution as a coordinate point.

$y = 3x - 3$
$y = -4x + 11$
slope = 3; y-intercept = −3
slope = −4; y-intercept = 11
$3x - 3 = -4x + 11$
$7x = 14$
$x = 2$
$y = 3(2) - 3$
$y = 6 - 3 = 3$
$(2,3)$

$-3x + y - 7 = 0$
$4x + y + 7 = 0$
$y = 3x + 7$ slope = 3; y-intercept = 7
$y = -4x - 7$ slope = −4; y-intercept = −7
$3x + 7 = -4x - 7$
$7x = -14;\ x = -2$
$-3(-2) + y - 7 = 0$
$6 + y - 7 = 0$
$y = 1$
$(-2,1)$

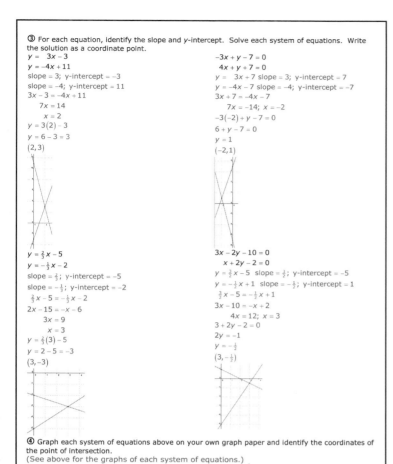

$y = \frac{2}{3}x - 5$
$y = -\frac{1}{3}x - 2$
slope = $\frac{2}{3}$; y-intercept = −5
slope = $-\frac{1}{3}$; y-intercept = −2
$\frac{2}{3}x - 5 = -\frac{1}{3}x - 2$
$2x - 15 = -x - 6$
$3x = 9$
$x = 3$
$y = \frac{2}{3}(3) - 5$
$y = 2 - 5 = -3$
$(3,-3)$

$3x - 2y - 10 = 0$
$x + 2y - 2 = 0$
$y = \frac{3}{2}x - 5$ slope = $\frac{3}{2}$; y-intercept = −5
$y = -\frac{1}{2}x + 1$ slope = $-\frac{1}{2}$; y-intercept = 1
$\frac{3}{2}x - 5 = -\frac{1}{2}x + 1$
$3x - 10 = -x + 2$
$4x = 12;\ x = 3$
$3 + 2y - 2 = 0$
$2y = -1$
$y = -\frac{1}{2}$
$(3,-\frac{1}{2})$

④ Graph each system of equations above on your own graph paper and identify the coordinates of the point of intersection.
(See above for the graphs of each system of equations.)

Teaching Tips, Cont.

➢ Teach translations from the teaching box.

➢ Explain that problems involving translations are worked in exactly the same way as problems involving slides. All of the formulas remain the same.

➢ Show the students how to graph the translation of an image.

➢ Complete the Classwork exercises. Have some students work the problems on the board for the class and explain their answers. All students should work the problems in their books.

Assignment

• Complete Lesson 146, Activities 2-4.

Lesson 147

Concepts
- Dilations
- Compressions
- Scaling
- Graphing inequalities
- Math in the real world

Learning Objectives
The student will be able to:
- Define *dilation*
- Define *compression*
- Calculate the coordinates of a dilated image
- Calculate the coordinates of a compressed image
- Draw the graph of the dilation of an image on the coordinate plane
- Draw the graph of the compression of an image on the coordinate plane

Materials Needed
- Student Book, Lesson 147
- Blue, red, and green colored pencils
- Graph paper
- Straightedge

Teaching Tips
➢ Ask the students to name and describe the four transformations they have learned so far. (Flips or reflections – transformations in which an image is reflected over a line; turns or rotations – transformations in which an image pivots about a single point; slides or translations – transformations in which an image moves in a straight line; and scaling – transformations in which a figure is enlarged or reduced.)

Dilations and Compressions

Dilation is another name for enlarging an image.

Compression is another name for reducing an image.

The rules of scaling apply to dilations and compressions.

To dilate an image, multiply both the *x*- and *y*-coordinates by a number greater than 1.

To compress an image, multiply both the *x*- and *y*-coordinates by a positive number less than one. (This is the same thing as dividing by a number greater than 1.)

Graph the figure formed by joining points (1, 3), (2, 2), and (2, 5) in blue. Calculate the coordinates of the figure when you dilate it by a factor of 2 and draw its graph in red on the same Cartesian plane.

The new coordinates are (2, 6) and (4, 4), and (4, 10).

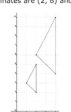

① **Classwork**
Solve.

Graph the figure formed by joining points (2, 2), (4, 2), and (2, 8) in blue. Calculate the coordinates of the figure when you compress it by a factor of ½ and draw its graph in red on the same Cartesian plane.

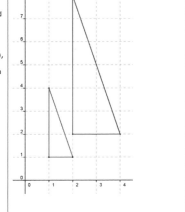

Activities
② Graph the following figures on a single Cartesian plane. Graph the figure formed by joining points (2, 2), (4, 0), and (6, 4) in blue. Calculate the coordinates of the figure when you scale it by a factor of ½ and draw its graph in red. Calculate the coordinates of the figure when you scale it by a factor of 2 and draw its graph in green.

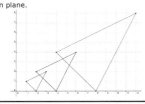

---

③ Graph the inequalities on your own graph paper.

$y < -2x$ $y \le 2x - 5$ $y \ge 2(x - 1)$

  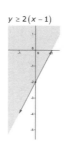

$y > x + 3$

④ Solve.

David is installing round air conditioning ducts with a 12-inch diameter. What is the volume of a section of duct that is 40 feet long? Use 3.14 for the value of π.
The radius of the duct is 6 inches or 0.5 foot.

$V = \pi r^2 h$ $V = \pi r^2 h$

$V = 3.14(0.5 \text{ foot})^2 (40 \text{ feet})$ or $V = 3.14(6 \text{ inches})^2 (480 \text{ inches})$

$V = 31.4$ cubic feet $V = 54{,}259.2$ cubic inches

David is connecting three 40-ft. sections of duct to an air conditioner that blows 1600 cubic feet of air per minute. How many seconds will it take the air conditioner to blow air to the end of all three sections of duct? Round your answer to the nearest tenth of a second.
The total volume of all three sections of duct is 3(31.4 cubic feet) = 94.2 cubic feet.

$\left(94.2 \text{ cubic feet}\right)\left(\dfrac{1 \text{ minute}}{1600 \text{ cubic feet}}\right)\left(\dfrac{60 \text{ seconds}}{1 \text{ minute}}\right) = 3.5325$ seconds

It will take the system 3.5 seconds to blow air to the end of all three sections of duct.
If David's customer opts for a less expensive air conditioner that only blows 1200 cubic feet of air per minute, how many seconds will it take the air conditioner to blow air to the end of all three sections of duct? Round your answer to the nearest tenth of a second.

$\left(94.2 \text{ cubic feet}\right)\left(\dfrac{1 \text{ minute}}{1200 \text{ cubic feet}}\right)\left(\dfrac{60 \text{ seconds}}{1 \text{ minute}}\right) = 4.71$ seconds

It will take the system 4.7 seconds to blow air to the end of all three sections of duct.
What is the percent decrease in air flow from the first system to the second system?

$\dfrac{1600 - 1200}{1600} = \dfrac{400}{1600} = 0.25 = 25\%$

What is the percent increase in time from the first system to the second system for air to move to the end of the ducts? Round your answer to the nearest percent.

$\dfrac{4.7 - 3.5}{3.5} = \dfrac{1.2}{3.5} = 0.34 = 34\%$

Teaching Tips, Cont.

➤ Introduce *dilations* and *compressions* as the mathematical names for *enlargements* and *reductions.*

➤ Teach dilations and compressions from the teaching box.

➤ Explain that problems involving dilations and compressions are worked in exactly the same way as problems involving scaling. All of the formulas remain the same.

➤ Show the students how to graph the dilation of an image.

➤ Show the students how to graph the compression of an image.

➤ Complete the Classwork exercise. Have one student work the problem on the board for the class and explain the answer. All students should work the problem in their books.

Assignment

• Complete Lesson 147, Activities 2-4.

Lesson 148

Concepts
- Area of regular polygons
- Apothem
- Perimeter
- Math in the real world

Learning Objectives
The student will be able to:
- Calculate the area of regular polygons
- Define *regular polygon*
- Define *apothem*
- Use the apothem and perimeter to find the area of a regular polygon
- Determine the area of irregular shapes

Materials Needed
- Student Book, Lesson 148
- Worksheet 74

Teaching Tips
➢ Have students complete Worksheet 74 in class. This may be for added practice of earlier topics or graded as a quiz, if desired.

➢ Review 30-60-90 triangles. (See Lesson 123.)

➢ Teach regular polygons from the teaching box. Explain that it does not matter how many sides a polygon has, as long as all sides are congruent and all angles are congruent.

➢ Ask the students what *congruent* means. (Having the same size and shape.)

Area of Regular Polygons

A **regular polygon** is a polygon with all sides congruent and all angles equal. There is an alternate formula for finding the area of a regular polygon if you know the length of the **apothem** – the perpendicular distance from the center of the polygon to a side.
Use the formula $A = \frac{aP}{2}$, where a is the apothem and P is the perimeter.

To find the area of irregular polygons, you may divide the polygon into known shapes and add the individual areas, find the area of the entire region and subtract the missing areas, or use a combination of the two methods.

Find the area of the figure below.

Without the triangle removed, the figure would be a regular hexagon with $P = 6(2) = 12$.
The area of the entire hexagon is
$A = \frac{\sqrt{3}(12)}{2} = 6\sqrt{3}$
The area of the missing triangle is
$A = \frac{1}{2}(2)\left(\sqrt{3}\right) = \sqrt{3}$
Subtract this from the original hexagon to get the area of the given figure.
$A = 6\sqrt{3} - \sqrt{3} = 5\sqrt{3}$ sq. units

① **Classwork**
Find the area of the figure below.

A regular octagon has a piece removed as shown.

Area without the piece removed:
$A = \frac{(2.4 \text{ cm})(16 \text{ cm})}{2} = 19.2 \text{ cm}^2$

The area of the missing triangle:
$A = \frac{1}{2}(2 \text{ cm})(2.4 \text{ cm}) = 2.4 \text{ cm}^2$
Subtract this from the area of the entire octagon to get the area of the given figure.
$19.2 \text{ cm}^2 - 2.4 \text{ cm}^2 = 16.8 \text{ cm}^2$

Activities
② Find the area of the figure below.

A regular pentagon has a piece removed as shown.

Area without the piece removed:
$A = \frac{(1.4 \text{ cm})(10 \text{ cm})}{2} = 7 \text{ cm}^2$
The area of the missing triangle:
$A = \frac{1}{2}(2 \text{ cm})(1.4 \text{ cm}) = 1.4 \text{ cm}^2$
Subtract this from the area of the entire pentagon to get the area of the given figure.
$7 \text{ cm}^2 - 1.4 \text{ cm}^2 = 5.6 \text{ cm}^2$

---

③ Find the area of each shaded region.

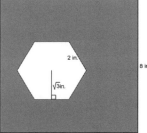

A square with a regular hexagon removed
Area of square: $(8 \text{ in.})^2 = 64$ sq. in.
Perimeter of hexagon: $6(2 \text{ in.}) = 12$ in.
Area of hexagon:
$A = \frac{aP}{2}$
$A = \frac{\sqrt{3} \text{ in.}(12 \text{ in.})}{2}$
$A = 6\sqrt{3}$ sq. in.
Area of blue region: $64 - 6\sqrt{3}$ sq. in.

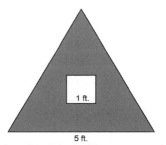

An equilateral triangle with a square removed
An equilateral triangle can be divided into two 30-60-90 triangles. The height of this triangle is $\frac{5\sqrt{3}}{2}$ feet. The area of the triangle is
$A = \frac{1}{2}bh$
$A = \frac{1}{2}(5 \text{ ft.})\left(\frac{5\sqrt{3}}{2} \text{ ft.}\right) = \frac{25\sqrt{3}}{4}$ sq. ft.
Area of square: 1 sq. ft.
Area of green region:
$\frac{25\sqrt{3}}{4} - 1$ sq. ft. $= \frac{25\sqrt{3}}{4} - \frac{4}{4}$ sq. ft. $= \frac{25\sqrt{3}-4}{4}$ sq. ft.

④ Solve.
The air flow velocity in an air conditioner duct is calculated using the formula $v_i = \frac{576q_i}{\pi(d_i)^2}$, where v_i is the air velocity in feet per minute, q_i is the air flow in cubic feet per minute, and d_i is the diameter of the duct in inches. Calculate the air flow velocity for a system blowing 1600 cubic feet per minute through a duct with a 12-inch diameter. Use 3.14 for the value of π. Round your answer to the nearest tenth.
$v_i = \frac{576q_i}{\pi(d_i)^2}$
$v_i = \frac{576(1600)}{\pi(12)^2} = 2038.2$ feet per minute
What is the velocity in feet per second? Round your answer to the nearest tenth.
$\frac{2038.2 \text{ feet}}{1 \text{ min.}}\left(\frac{1 \text{ min.}}{60 \text{ sec.}}\right) = 34.0$ ft. per sec.

① Plot the given points in blue and join them to form a polygon. Graph the reflection over the *x*-axis in green and the reflection over the *y*-axis in red.

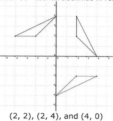

(2, 2), (2, 4), and (4, 0)

② Plot the given points in blue and join them to form a polygon. Graph the rotation 90° clockwise in green and the rotation 90° counterclockwise in red.

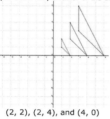

(2, 2), (2, 4), and (4, 0)

③ Plot the given points in blue and join them to form a polygon. Calculate the coordinates of the figure when you scale it by a factor of 0.5 and draw its graph in green. Calculate the coordinates of the figure when you scale it by a factor of 1.5 and draw its graph in red.

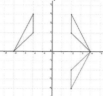

(2, 2), (2, 4), and (4, 0)

Teaching Tips, Cont.

➢ Teach the definition of *apothem* from the teaching box. This word is pronounced with the emphasis on the first syllable, like *apple*. Many students try to pronounce it so it sounds like "a possum," but this is incorrect. Stress the correct pronunciation from the beginning.

➢ Teach the formula for finding the area of a regular polygon using the apothem and perimeter. Students are not expected to memorize this formula, but they must know what each variable represents.

➢ Ask the students how they would find the area of a figure that looked like part of it was missing. (Find the area of the entire piece and the area of the missing section. Subtract the area of the missing section from the area of the whole thing.)

➢ Complete the Classwork exercise. Have one student work the problem on the board for the class and explain the answer. All students should work the problem in their books.

Assignment

- Complete Lesson 148, Activities 2-4.

Lesson 149

Concepts
- Terms and definitions
- Number terminology
- Order of operations
- Divisibility tests
- Prime/composite numbers
- Absolute value
- Exponents

Learning Objectives
The student will be able to:
- Match key terms and definitions
- Identify numbers as natural, whole, integer, rational, irrational, and real
- Simplify expressions

Materials Needed
- Student Book, Lesson 149

Teaching Tips
➤ This lesson begins a 12-lesson review of the concepts taught this year. The final test of the year (Exam 4) allows the teacher two options. You may administer the entire test as a final comprehensive exam or you may administer the first two pages as a fourth quarter exam.

➤ Review Lessons 1-15.

➤ Quiz the students on the terms and definitions from the first 15 lessons.

➤ Ask the students what the proper order of operations is for simplifying mathematical expressions. (Parentheses, exponents, multiplication and division, addition and subtraction.)

Review

Activities

① Matching.
Write the letter of the correct term to the left of each definition.

I. Counting numbers

N. Counting numbers and zero

F. Positive and negative whole numbers

L. Numbers that can be written as a fraction

G. Numbers that CANNOT be written as a fraction

M. A method of approximating a given number

C. A method of quickly arriving at an approximate answer

A. A number's distance from zero on a number line

E. A natural number that divides into another number with no remainder

H. The result of skip counting

K. Natural number whose only factors are 1 and itself

B. All numbers greater than 1 that are not prime

J. Prime numbers that divide into a number with no remainder

D. Tells how many times a number is multiplied by itself

A. Absolute value

B. Composite numbers

C. Estimation

D. Exponent

E. Factor

F. Integers

G. Irrational numbers

H. Multiple

I. Natural numbers

J. Prime factors

K. Prime number

L. Rational numbers

M. Rounding

N. Whole numbers

② Identify each number as *natural*, *whole*, *integer*, *rational*, *irrational*, or *real*. Some numbers may have more than one answer.

	31	$-\sqrt{11}$	$4\frac{5}{9}$	-17	0	53.28	π	$\frac{1}{12}$	-0.06
Natural	x								
Whole	x				x				
Integer	x			x	x				
Rational	x		x	x	x	x		x	x
Irrational		x					x		
Real	x	x	x	x	x	x	x	x	x

③ Simplify each expression, following the proper order of operations.

$\left(7(4+3)^0 + 12 - 3\right) \div 4 =$

$\left(7(7)^0 + 12 - 3\right) \div 4 = \left(7(1) + 12 - 3\right) \div 4 = (7 + 12 - 3) \div 4 = (19 - 3) \div 4 = 16 \div 4 = 4$

$\left(3 \times 5 \div (7 - 2)\right)^3 = (3 \times 5 \div 5)^3 = (15 \div 5)^3 = 3^3 = 27$

$\left(11^0 + 2^2 + 2^3 \left(3^2 - 1 \times 8\right) - 3\right) \div 2 = \left(11^0 + 2^2 + 2^3(9 - 1 \times 8) - 3\right) \div 2 =$

$\left(11^0 + 2^2 + 2^3(9 - 8) - 3\right) \div 2 = \left(11^0 + 2^2 + 2^3(1) - 3\right) \div 2 = (1 + 4 + 8 - 3) \div 2 =$

$(5 + 8 - 3) \div 2 = (13 - 3) \div 2 = 10 \div 2 = 5$

$\left(3\left(6^2 - 5^2 - 3 \times 2\right) + 35 \div 7 + 14^0\right) \div 7^1 = \left(3(36 - 25 - 3 \times 2) + 35 \div 7 + 14^0\right) \div 7^1 =$

$\left(3(36 - 25 - 6) + 35 \div 7 + 14^0\right) \div 7^1 = \left(3(11 - 6) + 35 \div 7 + 14^0\right) \div 7^1 = \left(3(5) + 35 \div 7 + 14^0\right) \div 7^1 =$

$(15 + 35 \div 7 + 1) \div 7^1 = (15 + 5 + 1) \div 7 = (20 + 1) \div 7 = 21 \div 7 = 3$

④ Use the divisibility tests to identify each number as prime or composite.

525	Composite (3, 5)	537	Composite (3)
531	Composite (3, 9)	541	Prime
535	Composite (3, 5)	543	Composite (3)

⑤ Solve, using the rules of absolute values.

$-|51| - |-38| =$

$-51 - 38 = -89$

$|76| - |55| =$

$76 - 55 = 21$

$-|-35| - |-42| =$

$-35 - 42 = -77$

$|19 + 28| + |33 - 27| =$

$47 + 6 = 53$

$-|54 - 26| + |45 - 17| =$

$-28 + 28 = 0$

$-|26 + 14| - |42 - 28| =$

$-40 - 14 = -54$

⑥ Simplify the expressions. You do not have to solve exponents greater than 3.

$23^0 = 1$

$7^5 \div 7^3 = 7^2 = 49$

$(2 \times 5)^2 = 2^2 \times 5^2 = 4 \times 25 = 100$

$3^{-3} = \left(\frac{1}{3}\right)^3 = \frac{1^3}{3^3} = \frac{1}{27}$

$\left(\frac{1}{6}\right)^2 = \frac{1^2}{6^2} = \frac{1}{36}$

$\left(\frac{7}{8}\right)^{-2} = \left(\frac{8}{7}\right)^2 = \frac{8^2}{7^2} = \frac{64}{49}$

$37^1 = 37$

$6^3 \times 6^2 = 6^5$

$13^8 \div 13^6 = 13^2 = 169$

$11^{-2} = \left(\frac{1}{11}\right)^2 = \frac{1^2}{11^2} = \frac{1}{121}$

$\left(\frac{1}{3}\right)^3 = \frac{1^3}{3^3} = \frac{1}{27}$

$\left(\frac{5}{3}\right)^{-3} = \left(\frac{3}{5}\right)^3 = \frac{3^3}{5^3} = \frac{27}{125}$

Teaching Tips, Cont.

➢ Review absolute value. (See Lesson 5.)

➢ Review the rules for working with exponents. (See Lessons 10 and 14.)

➢ Allow students to begin working on the review exercises in class as time permits. Assist individual students as needed.

Assignment

• Complete Lesson 149, Activities 1-6.

Lesson 150

Concepts
- Divisibility tests
- Factors
- Greatest common factor
- Least common multiple
- Roots
- Inequalities
- Powers of 10
- Metric conversions

Learning Objectives
The student will be able to:
- Use divisibility tests to find factors of large numbers
- Find the greatest common factor of a set of three numbers
- Find the least common multiple of a set of three numbers
- Solve problems containing roots
- Solve inequalities
- Convert measurements within the SI system

Materials Needed
- Student Book, Lesson 150
- Worksheet 75

Teaching Tips
➢ Review Lessons 16-31.

➢ Review how to find the greatest common factor. (See Lesson 16.)

➢ Review how to find the least common multiple. (See Lesson 17.)

➢ Review the rules for working with roots. (See Lesson 18.)

Review

Activities

① Use the divisibility tests to determine which numbers are factors of the given numbers.

	189	201	372	450	555	690	948
2			x	x		x	x
3	x	x	x	x	x	x	x
4			x				x
5				x	x	x	
6			x	x		x	x
9	x			x			
10				x		x	

② Find the greatest common factor of each set of numbers.

125, 150, and 185
$125 = 5 \times 5 \times ⑤$
$150 = 2 \times 3 \times 5 \times ⑤$
$185 = ⑤ \times 37$
GCF is 5

69, 96, and 135
$69 = ③ \times 23$
$96 = 2 \times 2 \times 2 \times 2 \times 2 \times ③$
$135 = ③ \times 3 \times 3 \times 5$
GCF is 3

100, 180, and 300
$100 = ② \times ② \times ⑤ \times 5$
$180 = ② \times ② \times 3 \times 3 \times ⑤$
$300 = ② \times ② \times 3 \times ⑤ \times 5$
GCF is $2 \times 2 \times 5 = 20$

56, 84, and 168
$56 = ② \times ② \times 2 \times ⑦$
$84 = ② \times ② \times 3 \times ⑦$
$168 = ② \times ② \times 2 \times 3 \times ⑦$
GCF: $2^2 \times 7 = 28$

84, 126, and 189
$84 = 2 \times 2 \times ③ \times ⑦$
$126 = 2 \times ③ \times 3 \times ⑦$
$189 = ③ \times 3 \times 3 \times ⑦$
GCF: $3 \times 7 = 21$

90, 108, and 126
$90 = ② \times ③ \times ③ \times 5$
$108 = ② \times 2 \times ③ \times ③ \times 3$
$126 = ② \times ③ \times ③ \times 7$
GCF: $2 \times 3^2 = 18$

③ Find the least common multiple of each set of numbers.

6, 8, and 9
$6 = 2 \times 3$
$8 = 2 \times 2 \times 2 = \boxed{2^3}$
$9 = 3 \times 3 = \boxed{3^2}$
LCM: $2^3 \times 3^2 = 72$

9, 12, and 15
$9 = 3 \times 3 = \boxed{3^2}$
$12 = 2 \times 2 \times 3 = \boxed{2^2} \times 3$
$15 = 3 \times \boxed{5}$
LCM: $2^2 \times 3^2 \times 5 = 180$

12, 15, and 18
$12 = 2 \times 2 \times 3 = \boxed{2^2} \times 3$
$15 = 3 \times \boxed{5}$
$18 = 2 \times 3 \times 3 = 2 \times \boxed{3^2}$
LCM: $2^2 \times 3^2 \times 5 = 180$

18, 27, and 36
$18 = 2 \times 3 \times 3 = 2 \times 3^2$
$27 = 3 \times 3 \times 3 = \boxed{3^3}$
$36 = 2 \times 2 \times 3 \times 3 = \boxed{2^2} \times 3^2$
LCM: $2^2 \times 3^3 = 108$

36, 45, and 63
$36 = 2 \times 2 \times 3 \times 3 = \boxed{2^2} \times \boxed{3^2}$
$45 = 3 \times 3 \times 5 = 3^2 \times \boxed{5}$
$63 = 3 \times 3 \times 7 = 3^2 \times \boxed{7}$
LCM: $2^2 \times 3^2 \times 5 \times 7 = 1260$

90, 120, and 150
$90 = 2 \times 3 \times 3 \times 5 = 2 \times \boxed{3^2} \times 5$
$120 = 2 \times 2 \times 2 \times 3 \times 5 = \boxed{2^3} \times 3 \times 5$
$150 = 2 \times 3 \times 5 \times 5 = 2 \times 3 \times \boxed{5^2}$
LCM: $2^3 \times 3^2 \times 5^2 = 1800$

---

④ Solve the following roots.

$$\frac{\sqrt[3]{16}}{2} + \frac{5\sqrt[3]{54}}{3} = \frac{\sqrt[3]{2 \times 2 \times 2 \times 2}}{2} + \frac{5\sqrt[3]{2 \times 3 \times 3 \times 3}}{3} = \frac{2\sqrt[3]{2}}{2} + \frac{5(3)\sqrt[3]{2}}{3} = \sqrt[3]{2} + 5\sqrt[3]{2} = 6\sqrt[3]{2}$$

$$\frac{5\sqrt{45}}{2} - \frac{\sqrt{125}}{2} = \frac{5\sqrt{3 \times 3 \times 5}}{2} - \frac{\sqrt{5 \times 5 \times 5}}{2} = \frac{5(3)\sqrt{5}}{2} - \frac{5\sqrt{5}}{2} = \frac{15\sqrt{5}}{2} - \frac{5\sqrt{5}}{2} = \frac{10\sqrt{5}}{2} = 5\sqrt{5}$$

$$\frac{3\sqrt[3]{48}}{2}\left(\frac{5\sqrt[3]{96}}{4}\right) = \frac{3\sqrt[3]{2 \times 2 \times 2 \times 2 \times 3}}{2}\left(\frac{5\sqrt[3]{2 \times 2 \times 2 \times 2 \times 2 \times 3}}{4}\right) = \frac{3(2)\sqrt[3]{3}}{2}\left(\frac{5(2)\sqrt[3]{6}}{4}\right) = 3\sqrt[3]{3}\left(\frac{5\sqrt[3]{6}}{2}\right) = \frac{15\sqrt[3]{18}}{2}$$

$$\frac{8\sqrt[3]{270}}{3} \div \frac{4\sqrt[3]{135}}{3} = \frac{8\sqrt[3]{2 \times 3 \times 3 \times 3 \times 5}}{3} \div \frac{4\sqrt[3]{3 \times 3 \times 3 \times 5}}{3} = \frac{8(3)\sqrt[3]{2} \times 5}{3} \div \frac{4(3)\sqrt[3]{5}}{3} = 8\sqrt[3]{10} \div 4\sqrt[3]{5} = \frac{2\,8\sqrt[3]{10}^2}{1\,4\sqrt[3]{5}_1} = 2\sqrt[3]{2}$$

⑤ Solve the inequalities.

$\frac{3x}{5} + 1 < -8$
$\frac{3x}{5} < -9$
$5\left(\frac{3x}{5}\right) < 5(-9)$
$3x < -45$
$x < -15$

$\frac{4x}{9} + 1 < -3$
$\frac{4x}{9} < -4$
$9\left(\frac{4x}{9}\right) < 9(-4)$
$4x < -36$
$x < -9$

$\frac{5x - 4}{2} - 7 > 4x - 3$
$\frac{5x - 4}{2} > 4x + 4$
$2\left(\frac{5x - 4}{2}\right) > 2(4x + 4)$
$5x - 4 > 8x + 8$
$-3x > 12$
$-x > 4$
$x < -4$

$\frac{x}{5} + 6 < 3x - 8$
$\frac{x}{5} < 3x - 14$
$5\left(\frac{x}{5}\right) < 5(3x - 14)$
$x < 15x - 70$
$-14x < -70$
$-x < -\frac{70}{14}$
$x > 5$

$\frac{3x}{4} + 2 < 4x + 3$
$\frac{3x}{4} < 4x + 1$
$4\left(\frac{3x}{4}\right) < 4(4x + 1)$
$3x < 16x + 4$
$-13x < 4$
$-x < \frac{4}{13}$
$x > -\frac{4}{13}$

$\frac{6x - 5}{3} - 7 > 7x - 2$
$\frac{6x - 5}{3} > 7x + 5$
$3\left(\frac{6x - 5}{3}\right) > 3(7x + 5)$
$6x - 5 > 21x + 15$
$-15x > 20$
$-x > \frac{20}{15}$
$x < -\frac{4}{3}$

⑥ Multiply or divide the appropriate powers of 10 to complete the metric conversions.

23.4 mm = ___0.0234___ m

0.07 mL = ___0.00007___ L

0.5 cg = ___0.005___ g

86.03 mW = ___0.08603___ W

40,000 m = ___40___ km

2035 L = ___2,035,000___ mL

901 W = ___90,100___ cW

4.01 g = ___4010___ mg

① Matching.
Write the letter of the correct term on the blank of each definition.

C.	Fractions that have different numerators and denominators but are equal in value	A. Commission
D.	A fraction whose numerator is greater than its denominator	B. Compound interest
H.	The result of adding a whole number and a fraction	C. Equivalent fractions
M.	An expression that compares two quantities	D. Improper fraction
L.	A mathematical sentence showing two ratios are equal	E. Interest
O.	A proportionally accurate representation of a real thing	F. Interest rate
P.	A method of writing very large and very small numbers	G. Mark-up
I.	Hundredth	H. Mixed number
G.	The amount the price of an item is increased	I. Percent
E.	The fee paid for the use of money	J. Principal
J.	The amount of money borrowed or invested	K. Profit
F.	The percent of the principal that is paid each term	L. Proportion
Q.	Interest charged on the original amount of the principal	M. Ratio
A.	The amount a sales person earns based on a percent of the price of the item sold	N. Royalties
K.	The difference between an item's selling price and the costs incurred to sell the item	O. Scale drawing
N.	Payment for the use of property	P. Scientific notation
B.	Interest paid on the principle *and* the previously earned interest	Q. Simple interest

Teaching Tips, Cont.

➤ Review inequalities. Pay special attention to the rules of signed numbers when solving inequalities. (See Lesson 22.)

➤ Review multiplying and dividing by powers of 10 as it relates to conversions within the SI system. (See Lessons 27-31.)

➤ Allow students to begin working on the review exercises in class as time permits. Assist individual students as needed.

Assignments

- Complete Lesson 150, Activities 1-6.
- Worksheet 75.
- Study for Test 15. (Lessons 138-147.)

Test 15

Testing Objectives

The student will:

- Multiply two binomials
- Divide trinomials by binomials
- Graph reflections over the x-axis
- Graph reflections over the y-axis
- Graph translations
- Graph rotations clockwise
- Graph rotations counterclockwise
- Graph dilations
- Graph compressions

Materials Needed

- Test 15
- *It's College Test Prep Time!* from Student Book
- *A Math Minute with…* You! from Student Book
- Blue, red, and green colored pencils

Teaching Tips

➢ Administer Test 15, allowing the students 30-40 minutes to complete the test.

➢ When all students are finished taking the test, introduce *It's College Test Prep Time* from the student book. This page may be completed in class or assigned as homework.

Test 15

① Multiply, using the FOIL method.　　　　　　　　**8 points**

$(x+3)(x+5)$
$x(x)+x(5)+3(x)+3(5)=$
$x^2+5x+3x+15 = x^2+8x+15$

$(x+8)(x-3)$
$x(x)+x(-3)+8(x)+8(-3)=$
$x^2-3x+8x-24 = x^2+5x-24$

$(x+4)(x-6)$
$x(x)+x(-6)+4(x)+4(-6)=$
$x^2-6x+4x-24 = x^2-2x-24$

$(2x+5)(x-4)$
$2x(x)+2x(-4)+5(x)+5(-4)=$
$2x^2-8x+5x-20 = 2x^2-3x-20$

$(2x-7)(x-4)$
$2x(x)+2x(-4)-7(x)-7(-4)=$
$2x^2-8x-7x+28 = 2x^2-15x+28$

$(2x+3)(3x-4)$
$2x(3x)+2x(-4)+3(3x)+3(-4)=$
$6x^2-8x+9x-12 = 6x^2+x-12$

$(4x+3)(x-6)$
$4x(x)+4x(-6)+3(x)+3(-6)=$
$4x^2-24x+3x-18 = 4x^2-21x-18$

$(2x-5)(4x+3)$
$2x(4x)+2x(3)-5(4x)-5(3)=$
$8x^2+6x-20x-15 = 8x^2-14x-15$

② Divide.　　　　　　　　**9 points**

$x+3\overline{)x^2+7x+12}$ 　quotient $x+4$
$\underline{x^2+3x}$
$4x+12$
$\underline{4x+12}$

$x-2\overline{)x^2+\ x-6}$ 　quotient $x+3$
$\underline{x^2-2x}$
$+3x-6$
$\underline{3x-6}$

$x-4\overline{)2x^2-3x-20}$ 　quotient $2x+5$
$\underline{2x^2-8x}$
$5x-20$
$\underline{5x-20}$

$(x^2+6x+8)\div(x+2)$
$x+2\overline{)x^2+6x+8}$ 　quotient $x+4$
$\underline{x^2+2x}$
$4x+8$
$\underline{4x+8}$

$(2x^2-7x+6)\div(x-2)$
$x-2\overline{)2x^2-7x+6}$ 　quotient $2x-3$
$\underline{2x^2-4x}$
$-3x+6$
$\underline{-3x+6}$

$(6x^2-5x-4)\div(3x-4)$
$3x-4\overline{)6x^2-5x-4}$ 　quotient $2x+1$
$\underline{6x^2-8x}$
$3x-4$
$\underline{3x-4}$

$(x^2-x-12)\div(x+3)$
$x+3\overline{)x^2-\ x-12}$ 　quotient $x-4$
$\underline{x^2+3x}$
$-4x-12$
$\underline{-4x-12}$

$(3x^2-14x-5)\div(x-5)$
$x-5\overline{)3x^2-14x-5}$ 　quotient $3x+1$
$\underline{3x^2-15x}$
$x-5$
$\underline{x-5}$

$(6x^2-17x-14)\div(2x-7)$
$2x-7\overline{)6x^2-17x-14}$ 　quotient $3x+2$
$\underline{6x^2-21x}$
$4x-14$
$\underline{4x-14}$

Test 15

③ Graph.　　　　　　　　**48 points**

Plot the given points in blue and join them to form a polygon. Graph the reflection over the x-axis in green and the reflection over the y-axis in red.

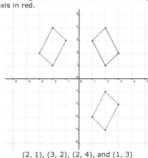

(2, 1), (3, 2), (2, 4), and (1, 3)

Plot the given points in blue and join them to form a polygon. Graph the translation down 4 units in green and the translation left 3 units in red.

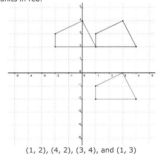

(1, 2), (4, 2), (3, 4), and (1, 3)

Plot the given points in blue and join them to form a polygon. Graph the rotation 90° clockwise in green and the rotation 90° counterclockwise in red.

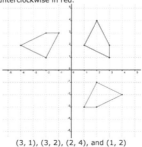

(3, 1), (3, 2), (2, 4), and (1, 2)

Plot the given points in blue and join them to form a polygon. Calculate the coordinates of the figure when you scale it by a factor of 0.5 and draw its graph in red. Calculate the coordinates of the figure when you scale it by a factor of 1.5 and draw its graph in green.

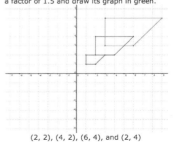

(2, 2), (4, 2), (6, 4), and (2, 4)

65 points total

Assignments

- Complete *It's College Test Prep Time!*
- Complete *A Math Minute with...* You! Set the due date at least one week away.

It's College Test Prep Time!

1. Given the sequence 8, 12, 20, 36, 68, ..., where 8 is the first number in the sequence, what is a rule for finding each successive number in the sequence?

   A. Add 4 to the preceding number.
   B. Divide the preceding number by 2 and add 8 to the result.
   C. Double the preceding number and subtract 4 from the result.
   D. Divide the preceding number by 4 and add 10 to the result.
   E. Triple the preceding number and divide the result by 2.

2. Given x is an integer and $\frac{x}{15} < \frac{7}{15} < \frac{x+2}{15}$, what is the value of x?

   A. 5   The denominators are equal, so set up inequalities
   B. 6   with the numerators and solve.
   C. 7 $x < 7$ and $7 < x + 2$
   D. 8 $x < 7$ and $5 < x$
   E. 9   The only integer less than 7 and greater than 5 is 6.

3. There are 24 different 4-digit numbers that can be formed by arranging the numbers 1, 2, 3, and 4. How many <u>more</u> 5-digit numbers can be formed by arranging the numbers 1, 2, 3, 4, and 5?

   A. 15   There are 5(4)(3)(3)(1) = 120 different 5-digit
   B. 29   numbers possible. The difference is
   C. 96   120 – 24 = 96.
   D. 120
   E. 124

A Math Minute with . . .

You!

This year, you have read interviews with people in fifteen different occupations. Think of a career that interests you and interview someone who either currently works in that field or has worked in that field in the past. If you want to be a stay-at-home parent, interview a stay-at-home parent. Ask the following questions and record the answers on your own paper.

What is your occupation?

Where do you work?

Did you attend college? If so, what was your major?

What parts of your job require the use of math?

What is the biggest "problem" you have faced that required the use of math to solve?

Are there any other interesting math uses you have experienced?

Lesson 151

Concepts
- Adding mixed numbers
- Subtracting mixed numbers
- Multiplying mixed numbers
- Dividing mixed numbers
- English-metric conversions
- English length conversions
- Math in the real world

Learning Objectives
The student will be able to:
- Add, subtract, multiply, and divide mixed numbers
- Convert between English and metric units of length
- Calculate equivalent English lengths
- Apply the multiplication principle of counting to real world math

Materials Needed
- Student Book, Lesson 151
- Formula strip, Lesson 151

Teaching Tips
➢ Review Lessons 32-43.

➢ Review adding fractions and mixed numbers. (See Lessons 34 and 39.)

➢ Review subtracting fractions and mixed numbers. (See Lessons 35 and 39.)

➢ Review multiplying fractions and mixed numbers. (See Lessons 36 and 41.)

➢ Review dividing fractions and mixed numbers. (See Lessons 37 and 42.)

Review

Activities

① Add.

$$2\frac{2}{7} + 5\frac{4}{7} = (2+5) + \frac{2}{7} + \frac{4}{7} = 7 + \frac{2+4}{7} = 7\frac{6}{7}$$

$$2\frac{3}{8} + 3\frac{1}{4} = (2+3) + \frac{3}{8} + \frac{1}{4} = 5 + \frac{3}{8} + \frac{2}{8} = 5 + \frac{3+2}{8} = 5\frac{5}{8}$$

$$1\frac{3}{5} + 6\frac{3}{10} = (1+6) + \frac{3}{5} + \frac{3}{10} = 7 + \frac{6}{10} + \frac{3}{10} = 7 + \frac{6+3}{10} = 7\frac{9}{10}$$

$$3\frac{3}{5} + 2\frac{1}{8} = (3+2) + \frac{3 \times 8}{5 \times 8} + \frac{1 \times 5}{8 \times 5} = 5 + \frac{24}{40} + \frac{5}{40} = 5 + \frac{24+5}{40} = 5\frac{29}{40}$$

② Subtract.

$$7\frac{5}{8} - 4\frac{1}{8} = \frac{7 \times 8 + 5}{8} - \frac{4 \times 8 + 1}{8} = \frac{61-33}{8} = \frac{28}{8} = \frac{7}{2} = 3\frac{1}{2}$$

$$4\frac{3}{4} - 2\frac{1}{2} = \frac{4 \times 4 + 3}{4} - \frac{2 \times 2 + 1}{2} = \frac{19}{4} - \frac{5}{2} = \frac{19}{4} - \frac{10}{4} = \frac{9}{4} = 2\frac{1}{4}$$

$$3\frac{2}{3} - 1\frac{1}{6} = \frac{3 \times 3 + 2}{3} - \frac{1 \times 6 + 1}{6} = \frac{11}{3} - \frac{7}{6} = \frac{22}{6} - \frac{7}{6} = \frac{22-7}{6} = \frac{15}{6} = \frac{5}{2} = 2\frac{1}{2}$$

$$8\frac{3}{10} - 5\frac{1}{5} = \frac{8 \times 10 + 3}{10} - \frac{5 \times 5 + 1}{5} = \frac{83}{10} - \frac{26}{5} = \frac{83}{10} - \frac{52}{10} = \frac{31}{10} = 3\frac{1}{10}$$

③ Multiply.

$$2\frac{5}{8} \times 3\frac{2}{3} = \frac{\overset{7}{\cancel{21}}}{8} \times \frac{11}{\cancel{3}_1} = \frac{7 \times 11}{8 \times 1} = \frac{77}{8} = 9\frac{5}{8}$$

$$2\frac{2}{5} \times 3\frac{3}{4} = \frac{\overset{3}{\cancel{12}}}{\cancel{5}_1} \times \frac{\overset{3}{\cancel{15}}}{\cancel{4}_1} = \frac{3 \times 3}{1 \times 1} = \frac{9}{1} = 9$$

$$2\frac{9}{13} \times 2\frac{1}{5} = \frac{\overset{7}{\cancel{35}}}{13} \times \frac{11}{\cancel{5}_1} = \frac{7 \times 11}{13 \times 1} = \frac{77}{13} = 5\frac{12}{13}$$

$$1\frac{2}{9} \times 6\frac{3}{4} = \frac{11}{\cancel{9}_1} \times \frac{\overset{3}{\cancel{27}}}{4} = \frac{11 \times 3}{1 \times 4} = \frac{33}{4} = 8\frac{1}{4}$$

④ Divide.

$$5\frac{1}{3} \div 6\frac{2}{5} = \frac{16}{3} \div \frac{32}{5} = \frac{\overset{1}{\cancel{16}}}{3} \times \frac{5}{\cancel{32}_2} = \frac{5}{6}$$

$$1\frac{3}{12} \div 2\frac{1}{7} = \frac{15}{12} \div \frac{15}{7} = \frac{\overset{1}{\cancel{15}}}{12} \times \frac{7}{\cancel{15}_1} = \frac{7}{12}$$

$$3\frac{3}{4} \div 1\frac{2}{3} = \frac{15}{4} \div \frac{5}{3} = \frac{\overset{3}{\cancel{15}}}{4} \times \frac{3}{\cancel{5}_1} = \frac{9}{4} = 2\frac{1}{4}$$

$$5\frac{1}{3} \div 4\frac{4}{5} = \frac{16}{3} \div \frac{24}{5} = \frac{\overset{2}{\cancel{16}}}{3} \times \frac{5}{\cancel{24}_3} = \frac{10}{9} = 1\frac{1}{9}$$

⑤ Complete the chart to show correct English-Metric conversions.

16 inches	$16 \text{ inches} \left(\frac{2.54 \text{ cm}}{1 \text{ inch}} \right) = 40.64$	cm
11 inches	$11 \text{ inches} \left(\frac{25.4 \text{ mm}}{1 \text{ inch}} \right) = 279.4$	mm
9 yards	$9 \text{ yards} \left(\frac{0.91 \text{ meter}}{1 \text{ yard}} \right) = 8.19$	meters
14 miles	$14 \text{ miles} \left(\frac{1.61 \text{ km}}{1 \text{ mile}} \right) = 22.54$	km
25 cm	$25 \text{ cm} \left(\frac{0.39 \text{ in.}}{1 \text{ cm}} \right) = 9.75$	inches
7 meters	$7 \text{ meters} \left(\frac{1.09 \text{ yd.}}{1 \text{ meter}} \right) = 7.63$	yards
12 km	$12 \text{ km} \left(\frac{0.62 \text{ mi.}}{1 \text{ km}} \right) = 7.44$	miles

⑥ Complete the chart to show correct English length equivalents.

9 miles	$9 \text{ miles} \left(\frac{1760 \text{ yards}}{1 \text{ mile}} \right) = 15,840$	yards
7 miles	$7 \text{ miles} \left(\frac{5280 \text{ feet}}{1 \text{ mile}} \right) = 36,960$	feet
10 yards	$10 \text{ yards} \left(\frac{36 \text{ inches}}{1 \text{ yards}} \right) = 360$	inches
69 feet	$_{23}69 \text{ feet} \left(\frac{1 \text{ yard}}{3 \text{ feet}} \right) = 23$	yards
11 yards	$11 \text{ yards} \left(\frac{3 \text{ feet}}{1 \text{ yard}} \right) = 33$	feet
21,120 feet	$_{4}21,120 \text{ feet} \left(\frac{1 \text{ mile}}{5280 \text{ feet}} \right) = 4$	miles
15,840 yards	$_{9}15,840 \text{ yards} \left(\frac{1 \text{ mile}}{1760 \text{ yards}} \right) = 9$	miles
13 feet	$13 \text{ feet} \left(\frac{12 \text{ inches}}{1 \text{ foot}} \right) = 156$	inches
108 inches	$_{9}108 \text{ inches} \left(\frac{1 \text{ foot}}{12 \text{ inches}} \right) = 9$	feet
396 inches	$_{11}396 \text{ inches} \left(\frac{1 \text{ yard}}{36 \text{ inches}} \right) = 11$	yards

⑦ Solve.
A restaurant has 16 different hamburger entrées, 15 different chicken entrées, and 1 fish entrée. It also has 6 different salads and 6 different non-salads for side items. The restaurant offers 18 different beverage choices.

What is the ratio of entrees to side items? $(16 + 15 + 1) : (6 + 6) = 32 : 12 = 8 : 3$

What is the ratio of chicken entrées to beverages? $15 : 18 = 5 : 6$

What is the ratio of hamburger entrées to beverages? $16 : 18 = 8 : 9$

How many different meals are possible with one entrée, one side item, and one beverage?

$(16 + 15 + 1)(6 + 6)(18) = (32)(12)(18) = 6912$ different meal combinations

Teaching Tips, Cont.

➢ Review English and metric system length conversions. (See Lesson 40.)

➢ Review ratios. (See Lesson 43.)

➢ Allow students to begin working on the review exercises in class as time permits. Assist individual students as needed.

➢ Give the students the formula strip for Lesson 151 from the *Tests and Resources* book.

Assignment
• Complete Lesson 151, Activities 1-7.

Lesson 152

Concepts
- Proportions
- Percents
- Fraction-percent equivalents
- Simple interest
- Compound interest
- Math in the real world

Learning Objectives
The student will be able to:
- Solve proportions
- Solve problems involving percents
- Convert between fractions and percents
- Calculate simple interest
- Calculate interest compounded annually
- Calculate interest compounded quarterly

Materials Needed
- Student book, Lesson 152
- Worksheet 76
- Calculator

Teaching Tips
- Review Lessons 44-59.

- Review proportions. (See Lesson 44.)

- Review percent. (See Lessons 47-48, 50-53, 55-57, 59.)

- Have students complete Worksheet 76 in class as a review exercise. Provide assistance as needed.

Review

Activities

① Solve the proportions. Leave answers as improper fractions where appropriate.

$\dfrac{x}{6} = \dfrac{26}{4}$
$4x = 6(26)$
$4x = 156$
$x = 39$

$\dfrac{6}{39} = \dfrac{x}{156}$
$6(156) = 39x$
$936 = 39x$
$24 = x$

$\dfrac{12}{x} = \dfrac{8}{12}$
$12(12) = 8x$
$144 = 8x$
$18 = x$

$\dfrac{4}{7} = \dfrac{28}{x}$
$4x = 7(28)$
$4x = 196$
$x = 49$

$\dfrac{x}{2} = \dfrac{9}{7}$
$7x = 2(9)$
$7x = 18$
$x = \dfrac{18}{7}$

$\dfrac{4}{34} = \dfrac{x}{8}$
$4(8) = 34x$
$32 = 34x$
$\dfrac{32}{34} = x$
$x = \dfrac{16}{17}$

$\dfrac{21}{x} = \dfrac{14}{9}$
$21(9) = 14x$
$189 = 14x$
$\dfrac{189}{14} = x$
$x = \dfrac{27}{2}$

$\dfrac{5}{6} = \dfrac{2}{x}$
$5x = 6(2)$
$5x = 12$
$x = \dfrac{12}{5}$

② Solve.

What is 30% of 90?
$x = 0.3(90)$
$x = 27$

What is 25% of 92?
$x = 0.25(92)$
$x = 23$

What is 18% of 40?
$x = 0.18(40)$
$x = 7.2$

What is 7% of 50?
$x = 0.07(50)$
$x = 3.5$

What is 1.5% of 60?
$x = 0.015(60)$
$x = 0.9$

What is 220% of 80?
$x = 2.2(80)$
$x = 176$

25 is 40% of what number?
$25 = 0.4x$
$25 \div 0.4 = x$
$x = 62.5$

66 is 55% of what number?
$66 = 0.55x$
$66 \div 0.55 = x$
$x = 120$

30 is 120% of what number?
$30 = 1.2x$
$30 \div 1.2 = x$
$x = 25$

30 is what percent of 150?
$30 = 150x$
$30 \div 150 = x$
$0.2 = x$
$x = 20\%$

75 is what percent of 30?
$75 = 30x$
$75 \div 30 = x$
$2.5 = x$
$x = 250\%$

9 is what percent of 180?
$9 = 180x$
$9 \div 180 = x$
$0.05 = x$
$x = 5\%$

③ Complete the fraction-percent conversions.

Fraction	Percent
$\dfrac{1}{4}$	25%
$\dfrac{1}{3}$	33.$\overline{3}$%
$\dfrac{1}{5}$	20%
$\dfrac{1}{10}$	10%
$\dfrac{3}{5}$	60%
$\dfrac{5}{6}$	83.$\overline{3}$%
$\dfrac{5}{8}$	62.5%
$\dfrac{9}{10}$	90%
$\dfrac{7}{8}$	87.5%

Percent	Fraction
66.$\overline{6}$%	$\dfrac{2}{3}$
40%	$\dfrac{2}{5}$
16.$\overline{6}$%	$\dfrac{1}{6}$
12.5%	$\dfrac{1}{8}$
75%	$\dfrac{3}{4}$
30%	$\dfrac{3}{10}$
80%	$\dfrac{4}{5}$
70%	$\dfrac{7}{10}$
37.5%	$\dfrac{3}{8}$

④ Complete the chart to reflect simple interest.

Principal	Interest rate	Time, in years	Amount of interest	Total amount paid
$5000	8.2%	5	$i = \$5000(0.082)(5) = \$2050$	$5000 + $2050 = $7050
$10,000	6.125%	10	$i = \$10,000(0.06125)(10) = \$6125$	$10,000 + $6125 = $16,125
$12,500	7%	9	$i = \$12,500(0.07)(9) = \$7875$	$12,500 + $7875 = $20,375
$15,000	10%	6	$i = \$15,000(0.1)(6) = \$9000$	$15,000 + $9000 = $24,000

⑤ Complete the table to show compound interest.

Initial principal	Interest rate	Time, in years	Total compounded annually	Total compounded quarterly
$1000	3%	3	$A = \$1000(1+.03)^3$ $= \$1092.73$	$A = \$1000(1+0.03 \div 4)^{3 \times 4}$ $= \$1093.81$
$5000	7%	3	$A = \$5000(1.07)^3$ $= \$6125.22$	$A = \$5000(1+0.07 \div 4)^{3 \cdot 4}$ $= \$6157.20$
$7500	10%	5	$A = \$7500(1.1)^5$ $= \$12,078.83$	$A = \$7500(1+0.1 \div 4)^{5 \cdot 4}$ $= \$12,289.62$
$12,000	15%	10	$A = \$12,000(1.15)^{10}$ $= \$48,546.69$	$A = \$12,000(1+0.15 \div 4)^{10 \cdot 4}$ $= \$52,324.55$

Percent Problems   Worksheet 76

① Complete the chart for each scenario.

Waiters and waitresses generally earn 15% to 20% in tips based on the price of the food they serve. Calculate the amount each customer should leave as a tip. Round each answer to the nearest cent.

Amount of bill	15% tip	20% tip
$5.00	($5.00)(0.15) = $0.75	($5.00)(0.20) = $1.00
$7.50	($7.50)(0.15) = $1.13	($7.50)(0.20) = $1.50
$10.25	($10.25)(0.15) = $1.54	($10.25)(0.20) = $2.05
$20.75	($20.75)(0.15) = $3.11	($20.75)(0.20) = $4.15
$35.00	($35.00)(0.15) = $5.25	($35.00)(0.20) = $7.00

You own a retail store and mark up the selling price to reflect a 30% increase over the wholesale price. Calculate the selling price based on the given wholesale price, and then calculate the sale price if all items are marked 20% off. Round each answer to the nearest cent.

Wholesale price	Selling price	Sale price
$2.27	($2.27)(1.30) = $2.95	($2.95)(0.80) = $2.36
$5.50	($5.50)(1.30) = $7.15	($7.15)(0.80) = $5.72
$6.73	($6.73)(1.30) = $8.75	($8.75)(0.80) = $7.00
$8.50	($8.50)(1.30) = $11.05	($11.05)(0.80) = $8.84
$10.00	($10.00)(1.30) = $13.00	($13.00)(0.80) = $10.40

If you had up to $8375 of taxable income as an individual in 2010, you owed 10% in income tax, 12.4% for Social Security, and 2.9% for Medicare. Calculate the amount of each tax. Round your answers to the nearest dollar.

Taxable income	Income tax	Social Security	Medicare
$1500	($1500)(0.10) = $150	($1500)(0.124) = $186	($1500)(0.029) = $44
$2775	($2775)(0.10) = $278	($2775)(0.124) = $344	($2775)(0.029) = $80
$5800	($5800)(0.10) = $580	($5800)(0.124) = $719	($5800)(0.029) = $168
$7900	($7900)(0.10) = $790	($7900)(0.124) = $980	($7900)(0.029) = $229
$8375	($8375)(0.10) = $838	($8375)(0.124) = $1039	($8375)(0.029) = $243

Teaching Tips, Cont.

➢ Drill the students on fraction-percent equivalents. (See Lesson 49.)

➢ Review simple interest. (See Lesson 54.)

➢ Review compound interest. (See Lesson 58.)

➢ Allow students to begin working on the review exercises in class as time permits. Assist individual students as needed.

Assignment

• Complete Lesson 152, Activities 1-5.

Lesson 153

Concepts
- Pictograph
- Circle graph
- Bar graph
- Probability
- Stem-and-leaf plot
- Mean, median, mode, and range
- Box-and-whisker plot
- Histogram
- Math in the real world
- Permutations
- Combinations

Learning Objectives
The student will be able to:
- Draw graphs to represent a set of data
- Calculate probabilities
- Calculate the mean, median, mode, and range of a set of numerical data
- Draw a box-and-whisker plot to represent a 5-number summary
- Calculate permutations and combinations

Materials Needed
- Student book, Lesson 153
- Worksheet 77

Teaching Tips
➢ Review Lessons 60-80.

➢ Review pictographs. (See Lesson 60.)

➢ Review circle graphs. (See Lesson 61.)

➢ Review bar graphs. (See Lesson 71.)

Review

Activities

① Draw the graphs on your own paper.
A restaurant has 32 different entrées, 12 different side items, and 18 different beverages. Draw a pictograph showing the number of each type of menu item at the restaurant.

Items on the Restaurant Menu	
Entrées	🍽🍽🍽🍽🍽🍽🍽🍽🍽🍽🍽🍽🍽🍽🍽🍽
Side items	🍽🍽🍽🍽🍽🍽
Beverages	🍽🍽🍽🍽🍽🍽🍽🍽🍽

🍽 = 2 items

Draw a circle graph showing the percent each category represents of the entire menu.

Items on the Restaurant Menu

- ■ Entrées
- ■ Side items
- ■ Beverages

Draw a bar graph showing the number of each type of menu item.

Items on the Restaurant Menu

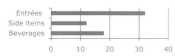

② Calculate the probability of each scenario.
A restaurant has 16 different hamburger entrées, 15 different chicken entrées, and 1 fish entrée. It also has 6 different salads and 6 different non-salads for side items. The restaurant offers 18 different beverage choices.
What is the probability a customer will select a hamburger as his entrée?
$P(\text{hamburger}) = \frac{16}{16+15+1} = \frac{16}{32} = \frac{1}{2}$
What is the probability a customer will select a salad as his side item?
$P(\text{salad}) = \frac{6}{6+6} = \frac{16}{32} = \frac{1}{2}$
What is the probability a customer will select chicken or fish as his entrée?
$P(\text{chicken or fish}) = \frac{15+1}{16+15+1} = \frac{16}{32} = \frac{1}{2}$
What is the probability a customer will select a hamburger entrée and a non-salad side item? $P(\text{hamburger})P(\text{non-salad}) = \left(\frac{16}{16+15+1}\right)\left(\frac{6}{6+6}\right) = \left(\frac{16}{32}\right)\left(\frac{6}{12}\right) = \left(\frac{1}{2}\right)\left(\frac{1}{2}\right) = \frac{1}{4}$

---

③ Solve.
The number of entrées available at various fast food restaurants are as follows: 16, 15, 12, 16, 14, 6, 7, 9, 9, 19, 17, 8, 5, 10, 3, 2, 4, 9, 3, and 31.

Make a stem-and-leaf plot and find the mean, median, mode, and range.

Stems	Leaves
0	2, 3, 3, 4, 5, 6, 7, 8, 9, 9, 9
1	0, 2, 4, 5, 6, 6, 7, 9
2	
3	1

Mean: 215 ÷ 20 = 10.75
Median: (9 + 10) ÷ 2 = 19 ÷ 2 = 9.5
Mode: 9
Range: 31 – 2 = 29
Give the 5-number summary and draw a box-and whisker plot.
The 5-number summary is the minimum (2), first quartile [(5 + 6) ÷ 2 = 11 ÷ 2 = 5.5], median (9.5), third quartile [(15 + 16) ÷ 2 = 31 ÷ 2 = 15.5], and the maximum (31).

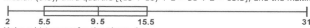

| 2 | 5.5 | 9.5 | 15.5 | | 31 |

Make a histogram for the above data.

Number of Entrees at Restaurants

| 0 - 9 | 10 - 19 | 20 - 29 | 30 - 39 | 40 - 49 |

④ Solve.
You get a job working after school at a day care center. There are 25 3-year-olds at the day care center. How many ways can you form a group of three children?

$C(25,3) = \frac{25!}{3!(25-3)!} = \frac{25 \times 24^4 \times 23 \times 22^{11}}{(3 \times 2 \times 1)22!} = 2300$

A parent arrives to pick up three children in a carpool. What is the probability that three children selected at random will be the correct children?

$\frac{3}{25}\left(\frac{2}{24_4}\right)\left(\frac{1}{23}\right) = \frac{1}{2300}$

Notice that this is not the same as selecting a group as a whole. There are 3 chances the first child selected will be in the correct group. There are 2 chances the second child selected will be in the correct group. There is 1 chance the third child will be in the correct group.

Permutations, Combinations

① Calculate the permutations and combinations.

$p(7,2) = \dfrac{7!}{(7-2)!} = \dfrac{7 \times 6 \times \cancel{5!}}{\cancel{5!}} = 42$

$p(5,3) = \dfrac{5!}{(5-3)!} = \dfrac{5 \times 4 \times 3 \times \cancel{2!}}{\cancel{2!}} = 60$

$p(9,4) = \dfrac{9!}{(9-4)!} = \dfrac{9 \times 8 \times 7 \times 6 \times \cancel{5!}}{\cancel{5!}} = 3024$

$p(6,2) = \dfrac{6!}{(6-2)!} = \dfrac{6 \times 5 \times \cancel{4!}}{\cancel{4!}} = 30$

$p(8,3) = \dfrac{8!}{(8-3)!} = \dfrac{8 \times 7 \times 6 \times \cancel{5!}}{\cancel{5!}} = 336$

$p(6,4) = \dfrac{6!}{(6-4)!} = \dfrac{6 \times 5 \times 4 \times 3 \times \cancel{2!}}{\cancel{2!}} = 360$

$p(7,5) = \dfrac{7!}{(7-5)!} = \dfrac{7 \times 6 \times 5 \times 4 \times 3 \times \cancel{2!}}{\cancel{2!}} = 2520$

$C(7,2) = \dfrac{7!}{2!(7-2)!} = \dfrac{7 \times 6 \times \cancel{5!}}{2!(\cancel{5!})} = \dfrac{7 \times \cancel{6}^3 \times \cancel{5!}}{\cancel{2} \times 1 (\cancel{5!})} = 21$

$C(5,3) = \dfrac{5!}{3!(5-3)!} = \dfrac{5 \times 4 \times 3 \times \cancel{2!}}{3!(\cancel{2!})} = \dfrac{5 \times \cancel{4}^2 \times \cancel{3} \times \cancel{2!}}{\cancel{3} \times \cancel{2} \times 1 (\cancel{2!})} = 10$

$C(9,4) = \dfrac{9!}{4!(9-4)!} = \dfrac{9 \times \cancel{8}^2 \times 7 \times \cancel{6} \times \cancel{5!}}{\cancel{4} \times \cancel{3} \times \cancel{2} \times 1 (\cancel{5!})} = 126$

$C(6,2) = \dfrac{6!}{2!(6-2)!} = \dfrac{6 \times 5 \times \cancel{4!}}{2!(\cancel{4!})} = \dfrac{\cancel{6}^3 \times 5 \times \cancel{4!}}{\cancel{2} \times 1 (\cancel{4!})} = 15$

$C(8,3) = \dfrac{8!}{3!(8-3)!} = \dfrac{8 \times 7 \times 6 \times \cancel{5!}}{3!(\cancel{5!})} = \dfrac{8 \times 7 \times \cancel{6} \times \cancel{5!}}{\cancel{3} \times \cancel{2} \times 1 (\cancel{5!})} = 56$

$C(6,4) = \dfrac{6!}{4!(6-4)!} = \dfrac{6 \times 5 \times 4 \times 3 \times \cancel{2!}}{4!(\cancel{2!})} = \dfrac{\cancel{6} \times 5 \times \cancel{4} \times \cancel{3} \times \cancel{2!}}{\cancel{4} \times \cancel{3} \times \cancel{2} \times 1 (\cancel{2!})} = 15$

$C(7,5) = \dfrac{7!}{5!(7-5)!} = \dfrac{7 \times 6 \times \cancel{5!}}{\cancel{5!}(2!)} = \dfrac{7 \times \cancel{6}^3}{\cancel{2} \times 1} = 21$

Teaching Tips, Cont.

> - Review line graphs. (See Lesson 72.)

> - Review statistics. (See Lessons 62-69.)

> - Review probability and odds. (See Lessons 70 and 73-75.)

> - Review permutations and combinations. (See Lessons 76-79.)

> - Allow students to begin working on the review exercises in class as time permits. Assist individual students as needed.

Assignments
- Complete Lesson 153, Activities 1-4.
- Worksheet 77.

Lesson 154

Concepts
- Probability and odds
- Permutations
- Combinations
- Angles
- Lines
- Points
- Rays
- Segments

Learning Objectives
The student will be able to:
- Calculate the probability and odds of given scenarios
- Calculate permutations
- Calculate combinations
- Identify geometric figures by their symbol

Materials Needed
- Student book, Lesson 154

Teaching Tips
➢ Review Lessons 62-81.

➢ This lesson allows for a second day of review in the area of probability and statistics. Review the concepts from Lesson 153 as needed.

➢ Review plane geometry terms. (See Lesson 81.)

Review

Activiti

① Find the probability and odds.

Suppose you roll a standard six-sided game die 6 times. What is the probability that you will roll a 4 on all six rolls of the die?

$P(4) = \frac{1}{6}$

$P(4)P(4)P(4)P(4)P(4)P(4) = \frac{1}{6}\left(\frac{1}{6}\right)\left(\frac{1}{6}\right)\left(\frac{1}{6}\right)\left(\frac{1}{6}\right)\left(\frac{1}{6}\right) = \left(\frac{1}{46,656}\right)$

What are the odds that you will roll a 6 on all six rolls of the die?

Out of a possible 46,656 outcomes, there is only 1 desirable outcome and 46,655 other outcomes. Therefore the odds are: $\left(\frac{1}{46,655}\right)$

What is the probability that a different number will appear on each of the six rolls?

The first roll can have any of the six numbers appear, or $\frac{6}{6}$.

The second roll can have 5 of the six numbers, or $\frac{5}{6}$.

The third roll can have 4 of the six numbers, or $\frac{4}{6}$.

Continue this pattern and multiply the fractions.

$\frac{6}{6}\left(\frac{5}{6}\right)\left(\frac{4^2}{6_3}\right)\left(\frac{3^1}{6_2}\right)\left(\frac{2^1}{6_3}\right)\left(\frac{1}{6}\right) = \frac{5}{324}$

What are the odds that a different number will appear on each of the six rolls?

$\frac{5}{324-5} = \frac{5}{319}$

What is the probability that the first roll will be a 1 or a 2?

$P(1 \cup 2) = P(1) + P(2)$

$P(1) = \frac{1}{6} \qquad P(2) = \frac{1}{6}$

$P(1 \cup 2) = \frac{1}{6} + \frac{1}{6} = \frac{2}{6} = \frac{1}{3}$

What is the probability that the second roll will be even or a 3?

$P(\text{even} \cup 3) = P(\text{even}) + P(3)$

$P(\text{even}) = \frac{3}{6} = \frac{1}{2} \qquad P(3) = \frac{1}{6}$

$P(\text{even} \cup 3) = \frac{3}{6} + \frac{1}{6} = \frac{4}{6} = \frac{2}{3}$

What is the probability that the first three rolls will be the three different even numbers and the last three rolls will be the three different odd numbers?

$\frac{3}{6}\left(\frac{2}{6}\right)\left(\frac{1}{6}\right)\left(\frac{3}{6}\right)\left(\frac{2}{6}\right)\left(\frac{1}{6}\right) = \frac{1}{2}\left(\frac{1}{3}\right)\left(\frac{1}{6}\right)\left(\frac{1}{2}\right)\left(\frac{1}{3}\right)\left(\frac{1}{6}\right) = \frac{1}{1296}$

② Calculate the permutations and combinations.

$p(8,3) = \dfrac{8!}{(8-3)!} = \dfrac{8 \times 7 \times 6 \times 5!}{5!} = 336$

$C(8,3) = \dfrac{8!}{3!(8-3)!} = \dfrac{8 \times 7 \times 6 \times 5!}{3!(5!)} = \dfrac{8 \times 7 \times 6}{3 \times 2 \times 1} = 56$

$p(5,3) = \dfrac{5!}{(5-3)!} = \dfrac{5 \times 4 \times 3 \times 2!}{2!} = 60$

$C(5,3) = \dfrac{5!}{3!(5-3)!} = \dfrac{5 \times 4 \times 3 \times 2!}{3!(2!)} = \dfrac{5 \times 4 \times 3 \times 2!}{3 \times 2 \times 1(2!)} = 10$

$p(7,4) = \dfrac{7!}{(7-4)!} = \dfrac{7 \times 6 \times 5 \times 4 \times 3!}{3!} = 840$

$C(7,4) = \dfrac{7!}{4!(7-4)!} = \dfrac{7 \times 6 \times 5 \times 4!}{4!(3!)} = \dfrac{7 \times 6 \times 5}{3 \times 2 \times 1} = 35$

$p(6,2) = \dfrac{6!}{(6-2)!} = \dfrac{6 \times 5 \times 4!}{4!} = 30$

$C(6,2) = \dfrac{6!}{2!(6-2)!} = \dfrac{6 \times 5 \times 4!}{2!(4!)} = \dfrac{^3 6 \times 5 \times 4!}{2 \times 1(4!)} = 15$

$p(6,3) = \dfrac{6!}{(6-3)!} = \dfrac{6 \times 5 \times 4 \times 3!}{3!} = 120$

$C(6,3) = \dfrac{6!}{3!(6-3)!} = \dfrac{6 \times 5 \times 4 \times 3!}{3!(3!)} = \dfrac{6 \times 5 \times 4 \times 3!}{3 \times 2 \times 1(3!)} = 20$

$p(8,4) = \dfrac{8!}{(8-4)!} = \dfrac{8 \times 7 \times 6 \times 5 \times 4!}{4!} = 1680$

$C(8,4) = \dfrac{8!}{4!(8-4)!} = \dfrac{8 \times 7 \times 6 \times 5 \times 4!}{4!(4!)} = \dfrac{^2 8 \times 7 \times 6 \times 5}{4 \times 3 \times 2 \times 1} = 70$

③ Write the letter of the correct notation beside each description.

B. Angle D

C. Line EF

G. MN is congruent to PQ

F. MN is parallel to PQ

H. MN is perpendicular to PQ

A. Point D

E. Ray EF

D. Segment EF

A. D

B. $\angle D$

C. $\overleftrightarrow{EF}$

D. $\overline{EF}$

E. $\overrightarrow{EF}$

F. $\overline{MN} \parallel \overline{PQ}$

G. $\overline{MN} \cong \overline{PQ}$

H. $\overline{MN} \perp \overline{PQ}$

Teaching Tips, Cont.

➢ Allow students to begin working on the review exercises in class as time permits. Assist individual students as needed.

Assignment

- Complete Lesson 154, Activities 1-3.

Lesson 155

Concepts
- Terms and definitions
- Volume of cylinders
- Surface area of cylinders
- Surface area of pyramids
- Volume of spheres
- Surface area of spheres
- Velocity
- Distance
- Time

Learning Objectives
The student will be able to:
- Match terms with their definitions
- Calculate the volume and surface area of cylinders
- Calculate the lateral area and total surface area of pyramids having different bases
- Calculate the volume and surface area of spheres
- Calculate velocity, distance, or time when two of the three are known

Materials Needed
- Student book, Lesson 155
- Worksheet 78
- Formula strip, Lesson 155

Teaching Tips
➤ The terms and definitions reviewed in this lesson are taken from material that has already been reviewed.

➤ Review Lessons 82-100.

➤ Review finding the area of plane figures. (See Lessons 82-86.)

Review

Activities

① Matching.
Write the letter of the correct term to the left of each definition.

C. The largest factor that is common to all the given numbers

G. The smallest number that is a multiple of all the given numbers

N. A letter used to represent an unknown numerical value

H. Identical variables with identical exponents

B. Numbers with no variables

E. Show the relationship between two things that are not equal

F. One thousand

A. One hundredth

I. One thousandth

L. The result of swapping the numerator and denominator of a fraction

D. A fraction whose numerator is greater than its denominator

J. The result of adding a whole number and a fraction

K. A mathematical sentence showing two ratios are equal

M. A proportionally accurate representation of a real thing

A. Centi-

B. Constants

C. Greatest common factor

D. Improper fraction

E. Inequalities

F. Kilo-

G. Least common multiple

H. Like terms

I. Milli-

J. Mixed number

K. Proportion

L. Reciprocal

M. Scale drawing

N. Variable

② Complete the chart for cylinders.

Radius	Height	Slant Height	Volume	Lateral Area	Surface Area
5.2 in.	1.8 in.	1.8 in.	$V = \pi(5.2)^2(1.8)$ $V = \pi(27.04)(1.8)$ $V = 48.672\pi$ cu. in.	$LA = 2\pi(5.2)(1.8)$ $LA = 2\pi(9.36)$ $LA = 18.72\pi$ sq. ft.	$SA = 18.72\pi + 2\pi(5.2)^2$ $SA = 18.72\pi + 2\pi(27.04)$ $SA = 18.72\pi + 54.08\pi = 72.8\pi$ sq. in
$2\sqrt{3}$ ft.	$5\sqrt{3}$ ft.	$5\sqrt{3}$ ft.	$V = \pi(2\sqrt{3})^2(5\sqrt{3})$ $V = \pi(12)(5\sqrt{3})$ $V = 60\pi\sqrt{3}$ cu. ft.	$LA = 2\pi(2\sqrt{3})(5\sqrt{3})$ $LA = 2\pi(30)$ $LA = 60\pi$ sq. ft.	$SA = 60\pi + 2\pi(2\sqrt{3})^2$ $SA = 60\pi + 2\pi(12)$ $SA = 60\pi + 24\pi = 84\pi$ sq. ft.

③ Find the lateral area and total surface area of each pyramid.

Base of Pyramid	Slant Height	Lateral Area	Surface area
$3\frac{1}{3}$ in. $1\frac{3}{4}$ in.	$3\frac{3}{5}$ in.	$LA = \frac{1}{2}(2(3\frac{1}{3}) + 2(1\frac{3}{4}))(3\frac{3}{5})$ $LA = \frac{1}{2}(2(\frac{10}{3}) + 2(\frac{7}{4}))(\frac{18}{5})$ $LA = \frac{1}{2}(\frac{20}{3} + \frac{7}{2})(\frac{18}{5})$ $LA = \frac{1}{2}(\frac{40}{6} + \frac{21}{6})(\frac{18}{5})$ $LA = \frac{1}{2}(\frac{61}{6})(\frac{18}{5}) = \frac{183}{10} = 18\frac{3}{10}$ sq. in.	$SA = 18\frac{3}{10} + (3\frac{1}{3})(1\frac{3}{4})$ $SA = \frac{183}{10} + \frac{35}{6}(\frac{7}{4})$ $SA = \frac{183}{10} + \frac{35}{6}$ $SA = \frac{549}{30} + \frac{175}{30} = \frac{1020}{30} = 34$ $SA = 34$ sq. in.
2.1 cm 2.1 cm	2.1 cm	$LA = \frac{1}{2}(4(2.1))(2.1)$ $LA = \frac{1}{2}(8.4)(2.1)$ $LA = 8.82$ cm²	$SA = 8.82 + (2.1)^2$ $SA = 8.82 + 4.41$ $SA = 13.23$ cm²
$\sqrt{13}$ 5 3 2 4	6 ft.	$LA = \frac{1}{2}(2 + 4 + 5 + \sqrt{13})(6)$ $LA = \frac{1}{2}(11 + \sqrt{13})(6)$ $LA = \frac{1}{2}(66 + 6\sqrt{13})$ $LA = 33 + 3\sqrt{13}$ sq. ft.	$SA = (33 + 3\sqrt{13}) + (\frac{1}{2}(2 + 4)(3))$ $SA = (33 + 3\sqrt{13}) + (\frac{1}{2}(6)(3))$ $SA = (33 + 3\sqrt{13}) + 9$ $SA = 42 + 3\sqrt{13}$ sq. ft.

④ Find the volume and surface area of the balls below.

Basketball radius = 4.75 in.	Baseball diameter = 3 in.	Volleyball diameter = 9 in.
$V = \frac{4}{3}\pi(4\frac{3}{4})^3$ $V = \frac{4}{3}\pi(\frac{19}{4})^3$ $V = \frac{4}{3}\pi(\frac{6859}{64})$ $V = \frac{6859\pi}{48}$ cu. in.	$V = \frac{4}{3}\pi r^3$ $V = \frac{4}{3}\pi(\frac{3}{2})^3$ $V = \frac{4}{3}\pi(\frac{27}{8})$ $V = \frac{9\pi}{2}$ cu. in.	$V = \frac{4}{3}\pi r^3$ $V = \frac{4}{3}\pi(\frac{9}{2})^3$ $V = \frac{4}{3}\pi(\frac{729}{8})$ $V = \frac{243\pi}{2}$ cu. in.
$SA = 4\pi(\frac{19}{4})^2$ $SA = 4\pi(\frac{361}{16})$ $SA = \frac{361\pi}{4}$ sq. in.	$SA = 4\pi(\frac{3}{2})^2$ $SA = 4\pi(\frac{9}{4})$ $SA = 9\pi$ sq. in.	$SA = 4\pi(\frac{9}{2})^2$ $SA = 4\pi(\frac{81}{4})$ $SA = 81\pi$ sq. in.

⑤ Complete the chart.

Velocity	Distance	Time
$v = \frac{385 \text{ miles}}{7 \text{ hours}}$ $v = 55$ miles/hour	385 miles	7 hours
48 miles per hour	$d = (48 \text{ miles/hour})(3.5 \text{ hours})$ $d = 168$ miles	3.5 hours
70 miles per hour	329 miles	$t = \frac{329 \text{ miles}}{70 \text{ miles/hour}}$ $t = 4.7$ hours

Congruent Triangles   Worksheet 78

① Mark each set of congruent sides and angles to show $\triangle ABC \cong \triangle DEF$.

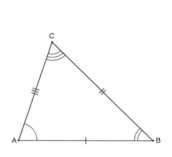 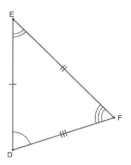

② List four congruent patterns for triangles.
SSS
SAS
ASA
AAS

③ Explain why AAA and SSA do not prove congruence in triangles.

AAA does not give any indication of the lengths of the sides. The triangles are
similar, but not necessarily congruent.
SSA allows for different angles measures between the two known sides.

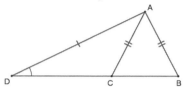

Teaching Tips, Cont.

➢ Review finding the volume and surface area of solid figures. (See Lessons 91-96.)

➢ Review congruent triangles. (See Lessons 87-89.)

➢ Have students complete Worksheet 78 in class.

➢ Review time and velocity. (See Lesson 100.)

➢ Allow students to begin working on the review exercises in class as time permits. Assist individual students as needed.

➢ Give the students the formula strip for Lesson 155 from the *Tests and Resources* book.

Assignment
• Complete Lesson 155, Activities 1-5.

Lesson 156

Concepts
- Area of plane figures
- Volume of prisms
- Volume of cones
- Surface area of cones
- Parts of a circle
- Types of angles
- Parallel lines

Learning Objectives
The student will be able to:
- Calculate the area of plane figures
- Calculate the volume of prisms having different bases
- Calculate the volume and surface area of cones
- Identify parts of a circle
- Identify angles as acute, right, obtuse, or straight
- Calculate the measure of complementary and supplementary angles
- Apply properties of parallel lines cut by a transversal to find the measure of angles

Materials Needed
- Student book, Lesson 156
- Formula strip, Lesson 156

Teaching Tips
- Review Lessons 91-107.
- Review finding the volume of solid figures. (See Lessons 91-96.)
- Review parts of a circle. (See Lesson 103.)

Review

Activities

① Find the area of each base, and the volume of a prism having the indicated height.

Base of Prism	Area of Base	Prism Height	Volume of Prism
$3\frac{1}{3}$ in. / $1\frac{3}{4}$ in.	$A = bh$ $A = (3\frac{1}{3} \text{ in.})(1\frac{3}{4} \text{ in.})$ $A = (\frac{10}{3} \text{ in.})(\frac{7}{4} \text{ in.})$ $A = \frac{35}{6} = 5\frac{5}{6}$ sq. in.	$3\frac{3}{5}$ in.	$V = Bh$ $V = (5\frac{5}{6} \text{ sq. in.})(3\frac{3}{5} \text{ in.})$ $V = (\frac{35}{6} \text{ sq. in.})(\frac{18}{5} \text{ in.})$ $V = 21$ cubic in.
2.1 cm / 2.1 cm	$A = s^2$ $A = (2.1 \text{ cm})^2$ $A = 4.41 \text{ cm}^2$	2.1 cm	$V = s^3$ $V = (2.1 \text{ cm})^3$ $V = 9.261 \text{ cm}^3$
$3\sqrt{2}$ ft. / $2\sqrt{2}$ ft. / $4\sqrt{2}$ ft.	$A = \frac{1}{2}bh$ $A = \frac{1}{2}(2\sqrt{2} \text{ ft.} + 4\sqrt{2} \text{ ft.})(3\sqrt{2} \text{ ft.})$ $A = \frac{1}{2}(6\sqrt{2} \text{ ft.})(3\sqrt{2} \text{ ft.})$ $A = (3\sqrt{2} \text{ ft.})(3\sqrt{2} \text{ ft.})$ $A = 18$ sq. ft.	$4\sqrt{3}$ ft.	$V = Bh$ $V = (18 \text{ sq. ft.})(4\sqrt{3} \text{ ft.})$ $V = 72\sqrt{3}$ cubic ft.
4.3 m / 6.1 m / 10.2 m	$A = bh$ $A = (10.2 \text{ m})(4.3 \text{ m})$ $A = 43.86 \text{ m}^2$	7.03 m	$V = Bh$ $V = (43.86 \text{ m}^2)(7.03 \text{ m})$ $V = 308.3358 \text{ m}^3$
$2\sqrt{3}$ yd. / $2\sqrt{6}$ yd. / $2\sqrt{3}$ yd. / $2\sqrt{3}$ yd. / $6\sqrt{3}$ yd. / $2\sqrt{15}$ yd.	$A = \frac{1}{2}(b_1 + b_2)h$ $A = \frac{1}{2}(2\sqrt{3} \text{ yd.} + 6\sqrt{3} \text{ yd.} + 2\sqrt{3} \text{ yd.})(2\sqrt{3} \text{ yd.})$ $A = \frac{1}{2}(10\sqrt{3} \text{ yd.})(2\sqrt{3} \text{ yd.})$ $A = (5\sqrt{3} \text{ yd.})(2\sqrt{3} \text{ yd.})$ $A = 30$ sq. yd.	$5\sqrt{2}$ yd.	$V = Bh$ $V = (30 \text{ sq. yd.})(5\sqrt{2} \text{ yd.})$ $V = 150\sqrt{2}$ cubic yd.

② Complete the chart for cones.

Radius	Height	Slant Height	Volume	Lateral Area	Surface Area
5.2 in.	1.8 in.	1.8 in.	$V = \frac{1}{3}\pi(5.2)^2(1.8)$ $V = \frac{1}{3}\pi(27.04)(1.8)$ $V = 16.224\pi$ cu. in.	$LA = \pi(5.2)(1.8)$ $LA = \pi(9.36)$ $LA = 9.36\pi$ sq. ft.	$SA = 9.36\pi + \pi(5.2)^2$ $SA = 9.36\pi + \pi(27.04)$ $SA = 9.36\pi + 27.04\pi = 36.4\pi$ sq. in.
6 m	8 m	10 m	$V = \frac{1}{3}\pi(6)^2(8)$ $V = \frac{1}{3}\pi(36^{12})(8)$ $V = 96\pi \text{ m}^3$	$LA = \pi(6)(10)$ $LA = \pi(60)$ $LA = 60\pi \text{ m}^2$	$SA = 60\pi + \pi(6)^2$ $SA = 60\pi + \pi(36)$ $SA = 60\pi + 36\pi = 96\pi \text{ m}^2$

③ Identify each item in circle A.

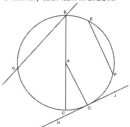

Diameter
$\overline{BC}$
Radius
$\overline{AC}$, $\overline{AB}$, or $\overline{AD}$
Chord
$\overline{BC}$, $\overline{EF}$, or $\overline{BG}$
Secant
$\overline{BG}$
Tangent
$\overline{HJ}$
Central angle
$\angle CAD$ or $\angle BAD$

④ Identify each angle as acute, right, obtuse, or straight. Find the measure of the complementary and supplementary angles, if applicable, for each given angle.

17°
Acute
Complementary angle: 90° – 17° = 73°
Supplementary angle: 180° – 17° = 163°
164°
Obtuse
Complementary angle: None
Supplementary angle: 180° – 164° = 16°
72°
Acute
Complementary angle: 90° – 72° = 18°
Supplementary angle: 180° – 72° = 108°

134°
Obtuse
Complementary angle: None
Supplementary angle: 180° – 134° = 46°
180°
Straight
Complementary angle: None
Supplementary angle: None
6°
Acute
Complementary angle: 90° – 6° = 84°
Supplementary angle: 180° – 6° = 174°

⑤ Solve.

In the diagram at the left, there are two parallel lines cut by a transversal. If $\angle 2 = 38°$, find the measure of the remaining angles.

$\angle 1 = 180° – 38° = 142°$ because adjacent angles that form a straight line are supplementary. $\angle 3 = 180° – 38° = 142°$ because adjacent angles that form a straight line are supplementary. Also, $\angle 3$ and $\angle 1$ are vertical angles. $\angle 4 = 38°$ because $\angle 4$ and $\angle 2$ are vertical angles. $\angle 5 = 142°$ because $\angle 1$ and $\angle 5$ are corresponding angles. $\angle 6 = 38°$ because $\angle 2$ and $\angle 6$ are corresponding angles. $\angle 7 = 38°$ because $\angle 4$ and $\angle 7$ are corresponding angles. $\angle 8 = 142°$ because $\angle 3$ and $\angle 8$ are corresponding angles.

Teaching Tips, Cont.

➢ Review types of angles. (See Lesson 104.)

➢ Review perpendicular lines, parallel lines, transversals, and special angles. (See Lessons 105-107.)

➢ Allow students to begin working on the review exercises in class as time permits. Assist individual students as needed.

➢ Give the students the formula strip for Lesson 156 from the *Tests and Resources* book.

Assignment

• Complete Lesson 156, Activities 1-5

Lesson 157

Concepts
- Terms and definitions
- Graphing inequalities
- Graphing functions
- Regular polygons

Learning Objectives
The student will be able to:
- Match terms and definitions
- Graph inequalities
- Graph functions of linear equations
- Calculate the sum of the interior angles of a regular polygon
- Calculate the number of degrees in each interior angle of a regular polygon
- Calculate the number of degrees in an exterior angle of a regular polygon

Materials Needed
- Student book, Lesson 157
- Graph paper
- Straightedge

Teaching Tips
- ➢ The terms and definitions reviewed in this lesson are taken from material that has already been reviewed.

- ➢ Review Lessons 105-112.

- ➢ Review two-variable equations. (See Lesson 109.)

- ➢ Review graphing equations. (See Lessons 108, 110-112.)

Review

Activities

① Matching.
Write the letter of the correct term to the left of each definition.

J. A method of writing very large and very small numbers

F. Hundredth

E. The amount the price of an item is increased

C. The fee paid for the use of money

G. The amount of money borrowed or invested

D. The percent of the principal that is paid each term

K. Interest charged on the original amount of the principal

A. The amount a sales person earns based on a percent of the price of the item sold

H. The difference between an item's selling price and the costs incurred to sell the item

I. Payment for the use of property

B. Interest earned (or paid) on the principle *and* the previously earned interest

G. The amount of money borrowed or invested

A. Commission
B. Compound interest
C. Interest
D. Interest rate
E. Mark-up
F. Percent
G. Principal
H. Profit
I. Royalties
J. Scientific notation
K. Simple interest

② Graph the following inequalities on your own graph paper.

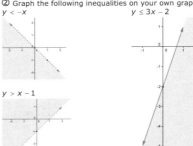

$y < -x$ $y \le 3x - 2$ 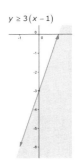 $y \ge 3(x-1)$

$y > x - 1$

③ Graph the following functions on your own graph paper.

$f(x) = x - 1$

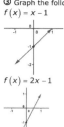

$f(x) = 2(x - 1)$

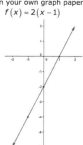

$f(x) = 3(x - 2)$

$f(x) = 2x - 1$

④ Solve.

For each regular polygon (all sides and angles are equal) in the chart below, find the sum of the interior angles, the measure of one interior angle, and the measure of one external angle.

Polygon	Sum of angles	Degrees per interior angle	Degrees per exterior angle
(triangle)	sum = $(3-2)180° =$ $1(180°) = 180°$	$180° \div 3 = 60°$	$180° - 60° = 120°$
(square)	sum = $(4-2)180° =$ $2(180°) = 360°$	$360° \div 4 = 90°$	$180° - 90° = 90°$
(pentagon)	sum = $(5-2)180° =$ $3(180°) = 540°$	$540° \div 5 = 108°$	$180° - 108° = 72°$
(hexagon)	sum = $(6-2)180° =$ $4(180°) = 720°$	$720° \div 6 = 120°$	$180° - 120° = 60°$
(octagon)	sum = $(8-2)180° =$ $6(180°) = 1080°$	$1080° \div 8 = 135°$	$180° - 135° = 45°$
(decagon)	sum = $(10-2)180° =$ $8(180°) = 1440°$	$1440° \div 10 = 144°$	$180° - 144° = 36°$

Teaching Tips, Cont.

➢ Review angles of regular polygons. (See Lessons 105-106.)

➢ Allow students to begin working on the review exercises in class as time permits. Assist individual students as needed.

Assignment

• Complete Lesson 157, Activities 1-4.

Lesson 158

Concepts
- Slope
- *y*-intercept
- Graphing linear equations
- Systems of equations
- Coordinate points
- Pythagorean formula
- Sine
- Cosine
- Tangent

Learning Objectives
The student will be able to:
- Find the slope of a line when two points are given
- Find the slope of a linear equation
- Write a linear equation when the slope and *y*-intercept are given
- Graph linear equations
- Solve systems of equations
- Use coordinate points to express the solution of a system of equations
- Use the Pythagorean formula to calculate one side of a right triangle when two sides are known
- Find the sine, cosine, and tangent of each acute angle in a right triangle

Materials Needed
- Student book, Lesson 158
- Worksheet 79

Teaching Tips
➢ Review Lessons 113-128.

➢ Review slope and y-intercept. (See Lessons 113-114.)

Review

Activities

① Find the slope of the line joining the points.

(4, 5) and (1, 3)
$m = \frac{3-5}{1-4} = \frac{-2}{-3} = \frac{2}{3}$

(-2, 1) and (-4, 4)
$m = \frac{4-1}{-4-(-2)} = \frac{3}{-2} = -\frac{3}{2}$

(5, 3) and (7, 3)
$m = \frac{3-3}{7-5} = \frac{0}{2} = 0$

(-2, 7) and (-2, 2)
$m = \frac{2-7}{-2-(-2)} = \frac{-5}{0} =$ no slope

② Find the slope of each line.

$x + y - 4 = 0$
$y = -x + 4$
$m = -1$

$2x + y - 2 = 0$
$y = -2x + 2$
$m = -2$

$-x + y - 2 = 0$
$y = x + 2$
$m = 1$

$-3x + y - 2 = 0$
$y = 3x + 2$
$m = 3$

$-2x + y + 3 = 0$
$y = 2x - 3$
$m = 2$

$3x + y - 4 = 0$
$y = -3x + 4$
$m = -3$

$2x + 2y + 1 = 0$
$2y = -2x - 1$
$y = -x - \frac{1}{2}$
$m = -1$

$x + 2y + 4 = 0$
$2y = -x - 4$
$y = -\frac{1}{2}x - 2$
$m = \frac{-1}{2}$

$3x + 2y + 6 = 0$
$2y = -3x - 6$
$y = -\frac{3}{2}x - 3$
$m = \frac{-3}{2}$

③ Write an equation having the given slope and *y*-intercept. Graph it on your own graph paper.

$m = \frac{3}{2}$
$b = -3$
$y = \frac{3}{2}x - 3$

$m = 3$
$b = -2$
$y = 3x - 2$

$m = -3$
$b = -1$
$y = -3x - 1$

$m = -\frac{1}{2}$
$b = 2$
$y = -\frac{1}{2}x + 2$

$m = -\frac{3}{2}$
$b = 1$
$y = -\frac{3}{2}x + 1$

---

④ Solve. Express the answer as a coordinate point.

$x + y = 0$
$2x + y - 1 = 0$
$y = -x$
$y = -2x + 1$
$-x = -2x + 1$
$x = 1$
$1 + y = 0$
$y = -1$
$(1, -1)$

$-3x + y + 7 = 0$
$3x - 2y - 5 = 0$
$-3x + y = -7$
$3x - 2y = 5$
$-y = -2$
$y = 2$
$-3x + 2 + 7 = 0$
$-3x = -9$
$x = 3$
$(3, 2)$

$4x - y + 4 = 0$
$-2x + y - 2 = 0$
$y = 4x + 4$
$y = 2x + 2$
$4x + 4 = 2x + 2$
$2x = -2$
$x = -1$
$4(-1) - y + 4 = 0$
$y = -4 + 4$
$y = 0$
$(-1, 0)$

$-x + 2y + 1 = 0$
$3x - 2y - 7 = 0$
$-x + 2y = -1$
$3x - 2y = 7$
$2x = 6$
$x = 3$
$-3 + 2y + 1 = 0$
$2y = 2$
$y = 1$
$(3, 1)$

$-x - 2y - 1 = 0$
$3x + 2y + 7 = 0$
$2y = -x - 1$
$2y = -3x - 7$
$-x - 1 = -3x - 7$
$2x = -6$
$x = -3$
$-(-3) - 2y - 1 = 0$
$3 - 2y - 1 = 0$
$2y = 2$
$y = 1$
$(-3, 1)$

$x - 2y - 1 = 0$
$3x - 2y - 7 = 0$
$x - 2y = 1$
$3x - 2y = 7$
$-2x = -6$
$x = 3$
$3 - 2y - 1 = 0$
$-2y = -2$
$y = 1$
$(3, 1)$

⑤ Find the length of the hypotenuse and the sine, cosine, and tangent of the marked angles.

$\sin x = \frac{8}{10} = \frac{4}{5}$
$\cos x = \frac{6}{10} = \frac{3}{5}$
$\tan x = \frac{8}{6} = \frac{4}{3}$
$\sin y = \frac{6}{10} = \frac{3}{5}$
$\cos y = \frac{8}{10} = \frac{4}{5}$
$\tan y = \frac{6}{8} = \frac{3}{4}$

$\sin x = \frac{24}{26} = \frac{12}{13}$
$\cos x = \frac{10}{26} = \frac{5}{13}$
$\tan x = \frac{24}{10} = \frac{12}{5}$
$\sin y = \frac{10}{26} = \frac{5}{13}$
$\cos y = \frac{24}{26} = \frac{12}{13}$
$\tan y = \frac{10}{24} = \frac{5}{12}$

$\sin x = \frac{6}{2\sqrt{13}} \cdot \frac{\sqrt{13}}{\sqrt{13}} = \frac{6\sqrt{13}}{26} = \frac{3\sqrt{13}}{13}$
$\cos x = \frac{4}{2\sqrt{13}} \cdot \frac{\sqrt{13}}{\sqrt{13}} = \frac{4\sqrt{13}}{26} = \frac{2\sqrt{13}}{13}$
$\tan x = \frac{6}{4} = \frac{3}{2}$
$\sin y = \frac{4}{2\sqrt{13}} \cdot \frac{\sqrt{13}}{\sqrt{13}} = \frac{4\sqrt{13}}{26} = \frac{2\sqrt{13}}{13}$
$\cos y = \frac{6}{2\sqrt{13}} \cdot \frac{\sqrt{13}}{\sqrt{13}} = \frac{6\sqrt{13}}{26} = \frac{3\sqrt{13}}{13}$
$\tan y = \frac{4}{6} = \frac{2}{3}$

Word Problems   Worksheet 79

① Solve.

The Daytona International Speedway is a 2.5-mile tri-oval track. If a race is 500 miles long, how many laps must each driver complete?

500 miles ÷ 2.5 miles/lap = 200 laps

If a driver averages 175 miles per hour, how much driving time in hours will it take to complete the race? (Ignore time for pit road, cautions, etc.) Round your answer to the nearest hundredth.

500 miles ÷ 175 miles/hour = 2.86 hours

The track is 40 feet wide with a 31° banking. How much higher is the top of the track than the bottom of the track?

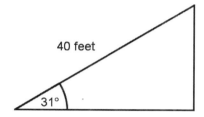

Hint: Use your calculator to find sin 31° to the nearest ten thousandth. Set up an equation to solve for the height.

$\sin 31° = 0.5150$

$\sin 31° = \dfrac{x}{40 \text{ feet}}$

$0.5150 = \dfrac{x}{40 \text{ feet}}$

$x = 20.6$ feet

Teaching Tips, Cont.

➤ Review systems of equations. (See Lessons 115-117.)

➤ Review right triangles. (See Lessons 122-124.)

➤ Review sine, cosine, and tangent. (See Lessons 125-128.)

➤ Have students complete Worksheet 79 in class.

➤ Allow students to begin working on the review exercises in class as time permits. Assist individual students as needed.

Assignment

• Complete Lesson 158, Activities 1-5.

Lesson 159

Concepts
- Terms and definitions
- English-metric conversions
- Weight
- Mass
- Reflections

Learning Objectives
The student will be able to:
- Match terms and definitions
- Convert liquid measures between English and SI units
- Convert between English measures of weight and SI measures of mass
- Graph reflections of an image

Materials Needed
- Student book, Lesson 159
- Formula strip, Lesson 159

Teaching Tips
➢ The terms and definitions reviewed in this lesson are taken from material that has already been reviewed.

➢ Review Lessons 120-121 and 140-147.

➢ Review English-metric liquid conversions. (See Lesson 120.)

➢ Review English-metric weight/mass conversions. (See Lesson 121.)

Review

Activities

① Matching.
Write the letter of the correct term to the left of each definition.

Q. Uses pictures or symbols to represent data on a graph

C. A visual representation of the percent each part is of the whole

K. The average of a set of numbers

L. The middle value when all numbers are listed in order from smallest to largest or largest to smallest

G. A table listing the number of times each value appears in a set

M. The value or values that appear the most number of times in a set

S. The difference between the largest and smallest values in a set of numbers

T. Shows groups of value frequencies within a set of data

H. A graph made from a stem-and-leaf plot

B. A graphical representation of the 5-number summary of a group of data

R. The chance or likelihood that an event will happen, when compared to all possible results

O. All the possible results, whether desired or not

A. Shows a comparison between two or more values

J. Shows trends in data over time

N. The chance or likelihood that an event will happen, when compared to all possible ways that it will not happen

P. Ordered groups of elements taken from a given set

D. Groups of elements taken from a given set where the order makes no difference

I. Event whose outcome does not depend on the outcome of a different event

E. Event whose outcome depends on the outcome of a different event

F. The weighted average of the possible outcomes

A. Bar graph
B. Box-and-whisker plot
C. Circle graph
D. Combinations
E. Dependent event
F. Expected value
G. Frequency distribution
H. Histogram
I. Independent event
J. Line graph
K. Mean
L. Median
M. Mode
N. Odds
O. Outcomes
P. Permutations
Q. Pictograph
R. Probability
S. Range
T. Stem-and-leaf plot

---

② Solve.

Convert 12 ounces to milliliters.

$$12 \text{ oz.} \times \frac{30 \text{ mL}}{1 \text{ oz.}} = 360 \text{ mL}$$

Convert 4 quarts to liters.

$$4 \text{ qt.} \times \frac{0.95 \text{ L}}{1 \text{ qt.}} = 3.8 \text{ L}$$

Convert 15 gallons to liters.

$$15 \text{ gal.} \times \frac{3.8 \text{ L}}{1 \text{ gal.}} = 57 \text{ L}$$

Convert 100 milliliters to ounces.

$$100 \text{ mL} \times \frac{0.034 \text{ oz.}}{1 \text{ mL}} = 3.4 \text{ oz.}$$

Convert 6 liters to quarts.

$$6 \text{ L} \times \frac{1.06 \text{ qt.}}{1 \text{ L}} = 6.36 \text{ qt.}$$

Convert 12 liters to gallons.

$$12 \text{ L} \times \frac{0.26 \text{ gal.}}{1 \text{ L}} = 3.12 \text{ gal.}$$

Convert 2500 milliliters to quarts.

$$2500 \text{ mL} \times \frac{1 \text{ L}}{1000 \text{ mL}} \times \frac{1.06 \text{ qt.}}{1 \text{ L}}$$
$$= 2.65 \text{ qt.}$$

Convert 100 ounces to liters.

$$100 \text{ oz.} \times \frac{30 \text{ mL}}{1 \text{ oz.}} \times \frac{1 \text{ L}}{1000 \text{ mL}}$$
$$= 3 \text{ L}$$

Convert 1500 milliliters to gallons.

$$1500 \text{ mL} \times \frac{1 \text{ L}}{1000 \text{ mL}} \times \frac{0.26 \text{ gal.}}{1 \text{ L}}$$
$$= 0.39 \text{ gal.}$$

③ Complete the chart to show conversion between the metric and English systems.

14 oz.	$14 \text{ oz.} \left(\frac{28.35 \text{ g}}{1 \text{ oz.}} \right) = 396.9$ g
42 lb.	$42 \text{ lb.} \left(\frac{0.454 \text{ kg}}{1 \text{ lb.}} \right) = 19.068$ kg
24 S. ton	$24 \text{ S. ton} \left(\frac{907 \text{ kg}}{1 \text{ S. ton}} \right) = 21{,}768$ kg
16 g	$16 \text{ g} \left(\frac{0.035 \text{ oz.}}{1 \text{ g}} \right) = 0.56$ oz.
60 kg	$60 \text{ kg} \left(\frac{2.2 \text{ lb.}}{1 \text{ kg}} \right) = 132$ lb.
8 M. ton	$8 \text{ M. ton} \left(\frac{1.1 \text{ S. ton}}{1 \text{ M. ton}} \right) = 8.8$ S. ton

④ Graph the following figures on a single Cartesian plane.
Graph the points (2, 1), (4, 1), (5, 2), (3, 3), and (2, 2) in blue. Join them to form a pentagon. Graph the reflection about the *y*-axis in red. Graph the reflection about the *x*-axis in green.

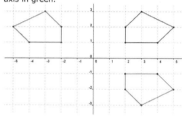

Teaching Tips, Cont.

➢ Review transformations. (See Lessons 140-147.)

➢ Allow students to begin working on the review exercises in class as time permits. Assist individual students as needed.

➢ Give the students the formula strip for Lesson 159 from the *Tests and Resources* book.

Assignment

• Complete Lesson 159, Activities 1-4.

Lesson 160

Concepts

- Temperature conversion
- Multiplying polynomials by monomials
- Dividing polynomials by binomials
- Adding polynomials
- Subtracting polynomials
- FOIL method
- Dividing polynomials by monomials

Learning Objectives

The student will be able to:

- Convert temperatures between Fahrenheit and Celsius
- Multiply polynomials by monomials
- Divide polynomials by monomials and binomials
- Add polynomials
- Subtract polynomials
- Use the FOIL method to multiply two binomials

Materials Needed

- Student book, Lesson 160
- Worksheet 80

Teaching Tips

➢ Review Lessons 118-119, 131-139, and 148.

➢ Review temperature conversions. (See Lessons 118-119.)

➢ Review adding polynomials. (See Lesson 131.)

➢ Review subtracting polynomials. (See Lesson 132.)

Review

Activities

① Solve. Round answers to the nearest tenth where appropriate.

°F	°C
0°	$°C = (0° - 32°)\left(\frac{5}{9}\right) = -17.8°$
30°	$°C = (30° - 32°)\left(\frac{5}{9}\right) = -1.1°$
50°	$°C = (50° - 32°)\left(\frac{5}{9}\right) = 10°$
75°	$°C = (75° - 32°)\left(\frac{5}{9}\right) = 23.9°$
100°	$°C = (100° - 32°)\left(\frac{5}{9}\right) = 37.8°$
125°	$°C = (125° - 32°)\left(\frac{5}{9}\right) = 51.7°$
150°	$°C(150° - 32°)\left(\frac{5}{9}\right) = 65.6°$

°C	°F
0°	$°F = (0°)\left(\frac{9}{5}\right) + 32° = 0° + 32° = 32°$
30°	$°F = (30°)\left(\frac{9}{5}\right) + 32° = 54° + 32° = 86°$
50°	$°F = (50°)\left(\frac{9}{5}\right) + 32° = 90° + 32° = 122°$
75°	$°F = (75°)\left(\frac{9}{5}\right) + 32° = 135° + 32° = 167°$
100°	$°F = (100°)\left(\frac{9}{5}\right) + 32° = 180° + 32° = 212°$
125°	$°F = (125°)\left(\frac{9}{5}\right) + 32° = 225° + 32° = 257°$
150°	$°F = (150°)\left(\frac{9}{5}\right) + 32° = 270° + 32° = 302°$

② Solve.

$3(2x + 1)$
$3(2x) + 3(1) = 6x + 3$
$5(3x - 4)$
$5(3x) + 5(-4) = 15x - 20$
$4(2x - 1)$
$4(2x) + 4(-1) = 8x - 4$

$(x^2 + 5x + 6) \div (x + 2)$

$$x + 2 \overline{)x^2 + 5x + 6} \quad \frac{x + 3}{}$$
$$\underline{x^2 + 2x}$$
$$3x + 6$$
$$\underline{3x + 6}$$

$(x^2 - x - 6) \div (x + 2)$

$$x + 2 \overline{)x^2 - x - 6} \quad \frac{x - 3}{}$$
$$\underline{x^2 + 2x}$$
$$-3x + 6$$
$$\underline{-3x + 6}$$

$4x(2x - 3)$
$4x(2x) + 4x(-3) = 8x^2 - 12x$
$9x(2x - 4)$
$9x(2x) + 9x(-4) = 18x^2 - 36x$
$2x(3x - 2)$
$2x(3x) + 2x(-2) = 6x^2 - 4x$

$(2x^2 - 5x + 2) \div (x - 2)$

$$x - 2 \overline{)2x^2 - 5x + 2} \quad \frac{2x - 1}{}$$
$$\underline{2x^2 - 4x}$$
$$-x + 2$$
$$\underline{-x + 2}$$

$(3x^2 - 4x - 4) \div (x - 2)$

$$x - 2 \overline{)3x^2 - 4x - 4} \quad \frac{3x + 2}{}$$
$$\underline{3x^2 - 6x}$$
$$2x - 4$$
$$\underline{2x - 4}$$

$6x(4x^2 + 2x - 3)$
$6x(4x^2) + 6x(2x) + 6x(-3) =$
$24x^3 + 12x^2 - 18x$
$4x(2x^2 + x - 1)$
$4x(2x^2) + 4x(x) + 4x(-1) =$
$8x^3 + 4x^2 - 4x$
$7x(2x^2 - 3x + 4)$
$7x(2x^2) + 7x(-3x) + 7x(4) =$
$14x^3 - 21x^2 + 28x$

$(6x^2 - x - 2) \div (3x - 2)$

$$3x - 2 \overline{)6x^2 - x - 2} \quad \frac{2x + 1}{}$$
$$\underline{6x^2 - 4x}$$
$$3x - 2$$
$$\underline{3x - 2}$$

$(8x^2 - 10x - 3) \div (2x - 3)$

$$2x - 3 \overline{)8x^2 - 10x - 3} \quad \frac{4x + 1}{}$$
$$\underline{8x^2 - 12x}$$
$$2x - 3$$
$$\underline{2x - 3}$$

③ Solve.

$$\begin{array}{r} 3x^2 + 6x - 5 \\ + \ 4x^2 + 3x + 1 \\ \hline 7x^2 + 9x - 4 \end{array}$$

$$\begin{array}{r} 6x^2 + 3x + 6 \\ + \ 4x^2 + 5x - 3 \\ \hline 10x^2 + 8x + 3 \end{array}$$

$$\begin{array}{r} (6x^2 + 3x + 5) \\ -(2x^2 + 2x - 1) \\ \hline 4x^2 + x + 6 \end{array}$$

$$\begin{array}{r} (3x^2 + 4x + 7) \\ -(8x^2 - 6x + 9) \\ \hline -5x^2 + 10x - 2 \end{array}$$

$$\begin{array}{r} 7x^2 + 6x + 3 \\ +2x^2 - 2x - 5 \\ \hline 9x^2 + 4x - 2 \end{array}$$

$$\begin{array}{r} 7x^2 + 3x + 5 \\ +6x^2 - 7x - 13 \\ \hline 13x^2 - 4x - 8 \end{array}$$

$$\begin{array}{r} (4x^2 - 6x + 3) \\ -(2x^2 - 8x - 5) \\ \hline 2x^2 + 2x + 8 \end{array}$$

$$\begin{array}{r} (5x^2 + 8x - 6) \\ -(8x^2 - 3x - 9) \\ \hline -3x^2 + 11x + 3 \end{array}$$

$$\begin{array}{r} 12x^2 - 6x - 8 \\ +4x^2 + 7x - 5 \\ \hline 16x^2 + x - 13 \end{array}$$

$$\begin{array}{r} 2x^2 - 3x + 2 \\ +7x^2 - 5x - 9 \\ \hline 9x^2 - 8x - 7 \end{array}$$

$$\begin{array}{r} (10x^2 - 9x - 6) \\ -(3x^2 + 3x - 3) \\ \hline 7x^2 - 12x - 3 \end{array}$$

$$\begin{array}{r} (7x^2 - 3x - 3) \\ -(2x^2 - 8x - 5) \\ \hline 5x^2 + 5x + 2 \end{array}$$

$(x + 1)(x + 4)$
$x(x) + x(4) + 1(x) + 1(4) =$
$x^2 + 4x + x + 4 = x^2 + 5x + 4$

$(x + 3)(x - 2)$
$x(x) + x(-2) + 3(x) + 3(-2) =$
$x^2 - 2x + 3x - 6 = x^2 + x - 6$

$(2x - 1)(x - 2)$
$2x(x) + 2x(-2) - 1(x) - 1(-2) =$
$2x^2 - 4x - x + 2 = 2x^2 - 5x + 2$

$(3x + 2)(x - 2)$
$3x(x) + 3x(-2) + 2(x) + 2(-2) =$
$3x^2 - 6x + 2x - 4 = 3x^2 - 4x - 4$

$(2x + 1)(3x - 2)$
$2x(3x) + 2x(-2) + 1(3x) + 1(-2) =$
$6x^2 - 4x + 3x - 2 = 6x^2 - x - 2$

$(2x - 3)(4x + 1)$
$2x(4x) + 2x(1) - 3(4x) - 3(1) =$
$8x^2 + 2x - 12x - 3 = 8x^2 - 10x - 3$

$(9x + 6) \div 3$

$$3 \overline{)9x + 6} \quad \frac{3x + 2}{}$$
$$\underline{9x}$$
$$6$$
$$\underline{6}$$

$(6x^2 - 6x + 9) \div 3$

$$3 \overline{)6x^2 - 6x + 9} \quad \frac{2x^2 - 2x + 3}{}$$
$$\underline{6x^2}$$
$$-6x$$
$$\underline{-6x}$$
$$9$$
$$\underline{9}$$

$(10x - 5) \div 5$

$$5 \overline{)10x - 5} \quad \frac{2x - 1}{}$$
$$\underline{10x}$$
$$-5$$
$$\underline{-5}$$

$(8x^2 + 6x - 4) \div 2$

$$2 \overline{)8x^2 + 6x - 4} \quad \frac{4x^2 + 3x - 2}{}$$
$$\underline{8x^2}$$
$$6x$$
$$\underline{6x}$$
$$-4$$
$$\underline{-4}$$

$(15x - 9) \div 3$

$$3 \overline{)15x - 9} \quad \frac{5x - 3}{}$$
$$\underline{15x}$$
$$-9$$
$$\underline{-9}$$

$(12x^3 + 3x^2 - 9x) \div 3x$

$$3x \overline{)12x^3 + 3x^2 - 9x} \quad \frac{4x^2 + x - 3}{}$$
$$\underline{12x^3}$$
$$3x^2$$
$$\underline{3x^2}$$
$$-9x$$
$$\underline{-9x}$$

Area of Triangles   Worksheet 80

① Solve.

A large equilateral triangle contains 9 congruent equilateral triangles. If the length of each side of the large triangle is 6 inches, what is the area of the shaded region?

An equilateral triangle divides to form two 30-60-90 triangles. This makes the area of the large triangle $A = \frac{1}{2}(6)(3\sqrt{3}) = 9\sqrt{3}$ sq. in. The shaded area is $\frac{6}{9} = \frac{2}{3}$ of the whole, making the area of the shaded region $A = \frac{2}{3}(9\sqrt{3}$ sq. in.$) = 6\sqrt{3}$ sq. in.

Teaching Tips, Cont.

- ➢ Review multiplying polynomials. (See Lessons 133, 135, and 137-138.)

- ➢ Review dividing polynomials. (See Lessons 134, 136, and 139.)

- ➢ Review finding the area of regular polygons. (See Lesson 148.)

- ➢ Allow students to begin working on the review exercises in class as time permits. Assist individual students as needed.

Assignments

- • Complete Lesson 160, Activities 1-3.
- • Worksheet 80.
- • Study for Test 16. (Lesson 148, as well as plane figures in Lessons 82-86, 155-156, and 160.)

Test 16

Testing Objectives

The student will:

- Calculate the area of plane figures
- Calculate the area of irregular shapes
- Calculate the area of regular polygons when given the length of one side and the length of the apothem

Materials Needed

- Test 16
- Formula strip, Test 16

Teaching Tips

➢ Give the students the formula strip for Test 16 from the *Tests and Resources* book.

➢ Administer Test 16, allowing the students 20-30 minutes to complete the test.

➢ When all students have finished the test, allow the students to ask questions as a final review for Exam 4.

➢ Review as necessary for Exam 4.

Assignment

- Study for Exam 4. (Lessons 118-160 if you are giving the entire test as a final cumulative exam; Lessons 118-148 if you are giving just the first two pages as a fourth-quarter exam.)

---

① Find the area of each shaded region. Label each answer with the proper units.   **18 points**

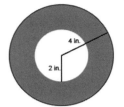

White circle:
$A = \pi(2 \text{ in.})^2 = 4\pi$ sq. in.

Gray ring:
$A = \pi(4 \text{ in.})^2 - 4\pi$ sq. in. $= 12\pi$ sq. in.

White parallelogram:
$A = (3 \text{ cm})(2 \text{ cm}) = 6 \text{ cm}^2$

Gray region:
$A = \pi(3 \text{ cm})^2 - 6 \text{ cm}^2 = 9\pi - 6 \text{ cm}^2$

Multi-colored square:
$A = (12 \text{ ft.})^2 = 144$ sq. ft.

A single black triangle:
$A = \frac{1}{2}(6 \text{ ft.})(6 \text{ ft.}) = 18$ sq. ft.

A single gray triangle:
$A = \frac{1}{2}(6 \text{ ft.})(6 \text{ ft.}) = 18$ sq. ft.

The entire gray region:
$A = 4(18 \text{ sq. ft.}) = 72$ sq. ft.

In the square above, each pair of adjacent acute angles is congruent and complementary. Each pair of angles in the center of each side is congruent and supplementary. Each side of the square is 12 feet long.

The entire black region:
$A = 4(18 \text{ sq. ft.}) = 72$ sq. ft.

---

② Find the perimeter and area of each regular polygon. Label each answer with the proper units.
    12 points

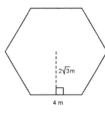

Perimeter:
$P = 5(10 \text{ yd.}) = 50$ yd.

Area:
$A = \dfrac{(6.9 \text{ yd.})(50 \text{ yd.})}{2} = 172.5$ sq. yd.

Perimeter:
$P = 6(4 \text{ m}) = 24$ m

Area:
$A = \dfrac{(2\sqrt{3} \text{ m})(24 \text{ m})}{2} = 24\sqrt{3} \text{ m}^2$

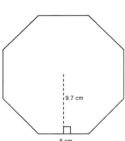

Perimeter:
$P = 8(8 \text{ cm}) = 64$ cm

Area:
$A = \dfrac{(9.7 \text{ cm})(64 \text{ cm})}{2} = 310.4 \text{ cm}^2$

30 points total

① Complete the chart to show temperature conversions. **6 points**

°F	°C		°C	°F
59°	$°C = (59° - 32°)(\frac{5}{9}) = 15°$		25°	$°F = (25°)(\frac{9}{5}) + 32° = 77°$
77°	$°C = (77° - 32°)(\frac{5}{9}) = 25°$		35°	$°F = (35°)(\frac{9}{5}) + 32° = 95°$
23°	$°C = (23° - 32°)(\frac{5}{9}) = -5°$		45°	$°F = (45°)(\frac{9}{5}) + 32° = 113°$

② Solve. **3 points**

Convert 28 ounces to milliliters.
$$28 \text{ oz.} \times \frac{30 \text{ mL}}{1 \text{ oz.}} = 840 \text{ mL}$$

Convert 10 quarts to liters.
$$10 \text{ qt.} \times \frac{0.95 \text{ L}}{1 \text{ qt.}} = 9.5 \text{ L}$$

Convert 35 gallons to liters.
$$35 \text{ gal.} \times \frac{3.8 \text{ L}}{1 \text{ gal.}} = 133 \text{ L}$$

③ Find the lengths of the missing sides. Then find the sine, cosine, and tangent of each acute angle. **8 points**

$\sin 30° = \frac{7}{14} = \frac{1}{2}$

$\cos 30° = \frac{7\sqrt{3}}{14} = \frac{\sqrt{3}}{2}$

$\tan 30° = \frac{7}{7\sqrt{3}} \cdot \frac{\sqrt{3}}{\sqrt{3}} = \frac{\sqrt{3}}{3}$

$\sin 60° = \frac{7\sqrt{3}}{14} = \frac{\sqrt{3}}{2}$

$\cos 60° = \frac{7}{14} = \frac{1}{2}$

$\tan 60° = \frac{7\sqrt{3}}{7} = \sqrt{3}$

④ Add or subtract. **6 points**

$$\begin{array}{r} 3x^2 + 5x + 8 \\ +\ 4x^2 + 3x + 6 \\ \hline 7x^2 + 8x + 14 \end{array}$$

$$\begin{array}{r} 2x^2 + 8x + 7 \\ +x^2 - 6x - 9 \\ \hline 3x^2 + 2x - 2 \end{array}$$

$$\begin{array}{r} 5x^2 - 3x + 9 \\ +4x^2 + 2x - 7 \\ \hline 9x^2 - x + 2 \end{array}$$

$$\begin{array}{r} (4x^2 + 5x + 8) \\ -(3x^2 + 3x + 6) \\ \hline x^2 + 2x + 2 \end{array}$$

$$\begin{array}{r} (4x^2 - 8x + 9) \\ -(2x^2 - 6x - 7) \\ \hline 2x^2 - 2x + 16 \end{array}$$

$$\begin{array}{r} (5x^2 - 2x - 7) \\ -(2x^2 + 3x - 9) \\ \hline 3x^2 - 5x + 2 \end{array}$$

⑤ Multiply or divide. **6 points**

$3x(8xy^2)$
$(3 \cdot 8)(x^{1+1})(y^2) = 24x^2y^2$

$18x^4y^3 \div 3xy^2$
$\frac{18x^4y^3}{3xy^2} = 6x^{4-1}y^{3-2} = 6x^3y$

$7x(3x^2 + 3x - 2)$
$7x(3x^2) + 7x(3x) + 7x(-2) =$
$21x^3 + 21x^2 - 14x$

$(24x - 8) \div 4$
$\begin{array}{r} 6x - 2 \\ 4\overline{)24x - 8} \\ \underline{24x} \\ -8 \\ \underline{-8} \end{array}$

$5x(3x^2 - 7x + 8)$
$5x(3x^2) + 5x(-7x) + 5x(8) =$
$15x^3 - 35x^2 + 40x$

$(12x + 9) \div 3$
$\begin{array}{r} 4x + 3 \\ 3\overline{)12x + 9} \\ \underline{12x} \\ 9 \\ \underline{9} \end{array}$

---

⑥ Multiply, using the FOIL method. **2 points**

$(x + 2)(x + 7)$
$x(x) + x(7) + 2(x) + 2(7) =$
$x^2 + 7x + 2x + 14 = x^2 + 9x + 14$

$(x + 4)(x - 5)$
$x(x) + x(-5) + 4(x) + 4(-5) =$
$x^2 - 5x + 4x - 20 = x^2 - x - 20$

⑦ Divide. **3 points**

$\begin{array}{r} x + 7 \\ x + 2\overline{)x^2 + 9x + 14} \\ \underline{x^2 + 2x} \\ 7x + 14 \\ \underline{7x + 14} \end{array}$

$\begin{array}{r} x + 6 \\ x - 4\overline{)x^2 + 2x - 24} \\ \underline{x^2 - 4x} \\ 6x - 24 \\ \underline{6x - 24} \end{array}$

$\begin{array}{r} 2x + 3 \\ x - 5\overline{)2x^2 - 7x - 15} \\ \underline{2x^2 - 10x} \\ 3x - 15 \\ \underline{3x - 15} \end{array}$

⑧ Graph. **18 points**

Plot the given points in blue and join them to form a polygon. Graph the reflection over the x-axis in green and the reflection over the y-axis in red.

Plot the given points in blue and join them to form a polygon. Graph the translation down 4 units in green and the translation left 3 units in red.

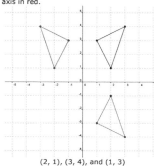

(2, 1), (3, 4), and (1, 3)

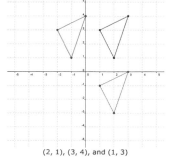

(2, 1), (3, 4), and (1, 3)

⑨ Find the area of each region. Label each answer with the proper units. **4 points**

White regular hexagon:
apothem = $\sqrt{3}$ cm

$A = \frac{12\sqrt{3}}{2} = 6\sqrt{3}$ cm^2

Gray shaded area:
$A = \pi(2 \text{ cm})^2 - 6\sqrt{3} \text{ cm}^2 = 4\pi - 6\sqrt{3} \text{ cm}^2$

Exam 4/Final Exam

Testing Objectives (first two pages)
The student will:
- Convert temperatures between Fahrenheit and Celsius
- Convert liquid measures from English to metric
- Solve 30-60-90 triangles
- Calculate the sine, cosine, and tangent of acute angles
- Add, subtract, multiply, and divide polynomials
- Draw the graphs of transformations
- Find the area of irregular shapes

Testing Objectives (last four pages)
The student will:
- Use exponents to express the factorization of numbers
- Solve one-variable equations
- Solve one-variable inequalities
- Add, subtract, multiply, and divide mixed numbers
- Calculate simple and compound interest
- Convert lengths from English to metric
- Calculate the mean, median, and mode of a set of numbers
- Calculate probability and odds of a given scenario
- Calculate permutations and combinations
- Find the lateral area, surface area, and volume of solid figures
- Identify parts of a circle
- Graph two-variable equations
- Graph two-variable inequalities
- Write equations in slope-intercept form
- Identify the slope and y-intercept of equations
- Solve systems of equations
- Calculate the measures of angles formed by intersecting parallel and perpendicular lines

Exam 4/Final Exam, Cont.

Materials Needed
- Exam 4/Final Exam
- Calculator
- Blue, red, and green colored pencils
- Graph paper
- Formula strip, Exam 4

Teaching Tips
➢ If you wish to test only material from the last quarter, administer the first two pages of Exam 4/Final Exam. For a cumulative exam covering the entire school year, administer all 6 pages.

➢ Give the students the formula strip for Exam 4 from the *Tests and Resources* book.

➢ Administer Exam 4/Final Exam, allowing 30-40 minutes if you are administering just the first two pages, and 80-90 minutes if you are administering the entire exam.

➢ Allow students to use calculators on Section 16.

➢ If you are administering just the first two pages, there are 56 total possible points.

---

⑩ Express the prime factorization of each number using exponents. **3 points**

81

$81 = 3 \times 3 \times 3 \times 3 = 3^4$

99

$99 = 3 \times 3 \times 11 = 3^2 \times 11$

125

$125 = 5 \times 5 \times 5 = 5^3$

⑪ Solve. **3 points**

$8x + 15 - 4 = 59$
$8x + 11 = 59$
$8x = 48$
$x = 6$

$\dfrac{3x}{2} + 4 + 7 = 26$
$\dfrac{3x}{2} + 11 = 26$
$\dfrac{3x}{2} = 15$
$3x = 30$
$x = 10$

$x + 2(x - 2) + 11 < 46$
$x + 2x - 4 + 11 < 46$
$3x + 7 < 46$
$3x < 39$
$x < 13$

⑫ Add, subtract, multiply, or divide as indicated. **4 points**

$1\dfrac{2}{3} + 2\dfrac{1}{4} = \dfrac{5}{3} + \dfrac{9}{4} = \dfrac{5 \times 4}{3 \times 4} + \dfrac{9 \times 3}{4 \times 3} = \dfrac{20}{12} + \dfrac{27}{12} = \dfrac{47}{12} = 3\dfrac{11}{12}$

$3\dfrac{7}{10} - 1\dfrac{2}{3} = \dfrac{37}{10} - \dfrac{5}{3} = \dfrac{37 \times 3}{10 \times 3} - \dfrac{5 \times 10}{3 \times 10} = \dfrac{111}{30} - \dfrac{50}{30} = \dfrac{61}{30} = 2\dfrac{1}{30}$

$1\dfrac{2}{3} \times 2\dfrac{1}{10} = \dfrac{\overset{1}{\cancel{5}}}{\underset{1}{\cancel{3}}} \times \dfrac{\overset{7}{\cancel{21}}}{\underset{2}{\cancel{10}}} = \dfrac{1 \times 7}{1 \times 2} = \dfrac{7}{2} = 3\dfrac{1}{2}$

$2\dfrac{1}{5} \div 1\dfrac{1}{10} = \dfrac{11}{5} \div \dfrac{11}{10} = \dfrac{\cancel{11}}{\underset{1}{\cancel{5}}} \times \dfrac{\overset{2}{\cancel{10}}}{\cancel{11}} = \dfrac{2}{1} = 2$

⑬ Solve. **3 points**

What is 65% of 80?
$x = 0.65(80)$
$x = 52$

42 is 70% of what number?
$42 = 0.7x$
$42 \div 0.7 = x$
$x = 60$

35 is what percent of 140?
$35 = 140x$
$35 \div 140 = x$
$0.25 = x$
$x = 25\%$

⑭ Complete the chart to reflect simple interest. **6 points**

Principal	Interest rate	Time, in years	Amount of interest	Total amount paid
$1500	5%	4	$i = \$1500(0.05)(4) = \$300$	$\$1500 + \$300 = \$1800$
$5000	7%	6	$i = \$5000(0.07)(6) = \$2100$	$\$5000 + \$2100 = \$7100$
$10,000	9%	8	$i = \$10,000(0.09)(8) = \$7200$	$\$10,000 + \$7200 = \$17,200$

---

⑮ Calculate the equivalent length for each given length. **6 points**

6 miles	6 miles $\left(\frac{1760 \text{ yards}}{1 \text{ mile}}\right) = 10,560$ yards
8 miles	8 miles $\left(\frac{5280 \text{ feet}}{1 \text{ mile}}\right) = 42,240$ feet
13 yards	13 yards $\left(\frac{36 \text{ inches}}{1 \text{ yards}}\right) = 468$ inches
8 inches	8 inches $\left(\frac{25.4 \text{ mm}}{1 \text{ inch}}\right) = 203.2$ mm
11 yards	11 yards $\left(\frac{0.91 \text{ meter}}{1 \text{ yard}}\right) = 10.01$ meters
7 miles	7 miles $\left(\frac{1.61 \text{ km}}{1 \text{ mile}}\right) = 11.27$ km

⑯ Use the formula $A = P(1 + r)^t$ to calculate compound interest. **4 points**

Initial principal	Interest rate	Time, in years	Total compounded annually	Total compounded quarterly
$5000	7%	6	$A = \$5000(1.07)^6$ $= \$7503.65$	$A = \$5000(1 + 0.07 \div 4)^{6 \times 4}$ $= \$7582.21$
$10,000	9%	8	$A = \$10,000(1.09)^8$ $= \$19,925.63$	$A = \$10,000(1 + 0.09 \div 4)^{8 \times 4}$ $= \$20,381.03$

⑰ Find the mean, median, and mode. **3 points**

The results of 20 rolls of a die are 2, 5, 6, 2, 3, 1, 2, 6, 1, 1, 5, 2, 3, 1, 5, 6, 2, 4, 4, 2.
Round answers to the nearest tenth where appropriate.
Mean: Sum = 63; Mean = 63 ÷ 20 = 3.2
Median: (2 + 3) ÷ 2 = 5 ÷ 2 = 2.5
Mode: 2

⑱ Complete the chart to show probability and odds. **8 points**

Scenario	Number of Possible Outcomes	Desired Event (E)	P(E)	Odds (in favor of E)	Odds (Against E)
Flip a coin once	2	Heads	$P(E) = \frac{1}{2}$	1:1	1:1
Roll a 6-sided die once	6	Odd number	$P(E) = \frac{3}{6} = \frac{1}{2}$	1:1	1:1

⑲ Calculate the permutations and combinations. **8 points**

$p(6,4) = \dfrac{6!}{(6-4)!} = \dfrac{6 \times 5 \times 4 \times 3 \times \cancel{2!}}{\cancel{2!}} = 360$

$C(8,2) = \dfrac{8!}{2!(8-2)!} = \dfrac{\overset{4}{\cancel{8}} \times 7 \times \cancel{6!}}{(\cancel{2} \times 1)(\cancel{6!})} = 28$

$p(8,3) = \dfrac{8!}{(8-3)!} = \dfrac{8 \times 7 \times 6 \times \cancel{5!}}{\cancel{5!}} = 336$

$C(5,3) = \dfrac{5!}{3!(5-3)!} = \dfrac{5 \times \overset{2}{\cancel{4}} \times \cancel{3} \times \cancel{2!}}{(\cancel{3} \times \cancel{2} \times 1)(\cancel{2!})} = 10$

Exam 4/Final Exam, Cont.

Assignment
- There is no assignment.

㉔ Find the lateral area, surface area, and volume of each solid figure. **8 points**

A prism with a height of 6 feet and a rectangular base that is 9 feet long and 3 feet wide.

$LA = PL$

$LA = 24(6) = 144$ sq. ft.

$SA = PL + 2B$

$SA = 144 + 2(27)$

$SA = 144 + 54 = 198$ sq. ft.

$V = Bh$

$V = (27)(6)$

$V = 162$ cu. ft.

A cone with a height of 8 yards, a slant height of 10 yards, and a base that has a diameter of 12 yards.

$LA = \pi rL$

$LA = \pi(6)(10)$

$LA = 60\pi$ sq. yd.

$SA = \pi rL + \pi r^2$

$SA = 60\pi + \pi(6)^2$

$SA = 60\pi + 36\pi = 96\pi$ sq. yd.

$V = \frac{1}{3}\pi r^2 h$

$V = \frac{1}{3}\pi(6)^2(8)$

$V = \pi(12)(8)$

$V = 96\pi$ cu. yd.

A sphere with a diameter of 20 cm.

A sphere has no lateral area.

$SA = 4\pi(10)^2$

$SA = 4\pi(100)$

$SA = 400\pi$ cm^2

$V = \frac{4}{3}\pi r^3$

$V = \frac{4}{3}\pi(10)^3$

$V = \frac{4}{3}\pi(1000)$

$V = \frac{4000}{3}\pi$ cm^3

㉑ Identify one of each item in circle A. Write the appropriate symbol for each figure. **6 points**

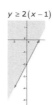

Secant
$\overline{BG}$
Diameter
$\overline{BC}$
Radius
$\overline{AB}$, $\overline{AC}$, or $\overline{AD}$

Chord
$\overline{EF}$, $\overline{BG}$, or $\overline{BC}$
Tangent
$\overline{HJ}$
Central angle
$\angle CAD$ or $\angle BAD$

㉒ Graph the following equations on your own graph paper. **3 points**

$y = x - 2$ 　　$y = -2x + 1$ 　　$y \geq 2(x - 1)$

㉓ Write each equation in slope-intercept form and identify the slope and y-intercept. **9 points**

$-3x + y - 4 = 0$	$-5x + y + 3 = 0$	$12x + y - 17 = 0$
$y = 3x + 4$	$y = 5x - 3$	$y = -12x + 17$
$m = 3$	$m = 5$	$m = -12$
$b = 4$	$b = -3$	$b = 17$

㉔ Solve. Express the answer as a coordinate point. **6 points**

$2x + 2y + 3 = 0$	$3x - 2y + 4 = 0$	$3x + y + 5 = 0$
$2x + y - 3 = 0$	$-3x + 3y - 3 = 0$	$-2x - y + 1 = 0$
$y + 6 = 0$	$y + 1 = 0$	$x + 6 = 0$
$y = -6$	$y = -1$	$x = -6$
$2x + 2(-6) + 3 = 0$	$3x + 2 + 4 = 0$	$3(-6) + y + 5 = 0$
$2x - 12 + 3 = 0$	$3x + 6 = 0$	$-18 + y + 5 = 0$
$2x = 9$	$3x = -6$	$y = 13$
$x = \frac{9}{2}$	$x = -2$	$(-6, 13)$
$\left(\frac{9}{2}, -6\right)$	$(-2, -1)$	

㉕ Find the measure of each angle in the figure below. **12 points**

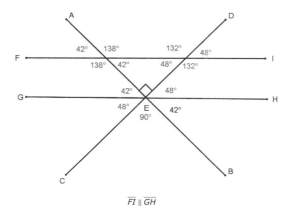

$\overline{FI} \parallel \overline{GH}$

148 points total